Grzimek's ENCYCLOPEDIA OF ECOLOGY

Grzimek's
ENCYCLOPEDIA
OF ECOLOGY

Editor-in-Chief

Dr. Dr. h.c. Bernhard Grzimek

Professor, Justus Liebig University of Giessen
Director (Retired), Frankfurt Zoological Garden, Germany
Trustee, Tanzania and Uganda National Parks, East Africa

VAN NOSTRAND REINHOLD COMPANY

New York   Cincinnati   Toronto   London   Melbourne

Van Nostrand Reinhold Company Regional Offices:
New York   Cincinnati   Atlanta   Dallas   San Francisco

Van Nostrand Reinhold Company International Offices.
London   Toronto   Melbourne

Typography by Santype International Ltd., Salisbury, Great Britain

Printed and bound in Italy by Campi Editore, Foligno, Italy

Published in the United States by Van Nostrand Reinhold Company
450 West 33rd Street, New York, N.Y. 10001

English edition first published in England by Van Nostrand
Reinhold Ltd.

15   14   13   12   11   10   9   8   7   6   5   4   3   2   1

EDITORS AND CONTRIBUTORS

Grzimek's
ENCYCLOPEDIA
OF ECOLOGY

Edited by:

BERNHARD GRZIMEK

JOACHIM ILLIES

WOLFGANG KLAUSEWITZ

ENGLISH EDITION

GENERAL EDITOR:
George M. Narita

SCIENTIFIC EDITOR:
Erich Klinghammer

TRANSLATOR:
Marguerite A. Biederman-Thorson

SCIENTIFIC CONSULTANT:
Robert H. Whittaker
D. Joseph Hagerty

ASSISTANT EDITOR:
Ruth S. Gennrich

EDITORIAL ASSISTANTS:
Rachel Davison
Karen Boikess

PRODUCTION EDITOR:
James V. Leone

INDEX:
Suzanne C. Klinghammer

CONTENTS

PART TWO:
THE ENVIRONMENT OF MAN   531

edited by Wolfgang Klausewitz

Foreword

I feel it is my duty to give warning. That is why I have suggested this volume on ecology, as a supplement to the thirteen-volume Grzimek's Animal Life Encyclopedia. In producing it I have worked with Prof. Joachim Illies, Dr. Wolfgang Klausewitz, and many other experts in the various fields concerned.

The voices demanding protection of our environment are being heard ever more clearly. The American and European people, for example, have only in this decade become really aware of what they have been doing to their rivers, their landscape—to all the features of their beloved countries —for decades past. And the danger is as great in all the "developed" countries of the world.

When new construction has been planned—whether of highways, airports, factories, resorts or railroads—or the exapansion of towns and cities contemplated, there has in the past been no legal requirement for consultation with officially appointed authorities in ecology, environmental protection, or landscape design. As a result the wishes of special-interest groups (industry, business or local communities), or even attitudes of thoughtless irresponsibility, have prevailed against considerations of the general welfare. It has been the practice to accept any sort of detriment to our natural surroundings as the price of new investment and the associated taxes obtained.

But the public outcry has now become so loud that the politicians are slowly beginning to take action. In the German parliament, as in the American Congress, there is already a majority in favor of changing the law so as to permit the passage of high-priority legislation controlling the impact of industry and technology upon the environment. Nevertheless, the opinion is still frequently heard that in other areas of conservation such action is unnecessary at a national level, since these problems can be left to the governing bodies of the individual States. But the balance of nature is not so subdivided; its intricate structure comprises a uniform whole. One cannot give top priority to the technological aspects of environment protection while relegating the other aspects of protection and conservation of nature to a subordinate level—not when it is a matter of arresting, at the last moment, the consequences of decades of errors in order to ensure our own survival.

Many of the problems and concerns of the environmentalists are not even considered in the old laws governing nature conservation. These critical factors include the progressive change in pattern of land use resulting from increased industrialization, the growing use of water and electricity, and the ever-larger population with its greater mobility by motor vehicles, its spread into the suburbs, and its increased demand for lesisure and recreation. Trends of this kind in society, technology and economy have already severely damaged the human habitat; essential parts of the countryside have in some cases been seriously endangered by unplanned and unrestricted use, and in other cases they have been destroyed.

Protection of the environment is not a regional concern, but a national and even a supranational, worldwide task. It involves not just the highly developed industrial countries but all the continents, lakes, streams, and oceans of the world, along with their envelope of air—crucial to the lives of all animals and plants as well as to man. The first part of this volume describes the physical, chemical and biological aspects of environment. By comparing it with the second part and its discussions of the ever more threatening environmental crises, we can bring home to ourselves what we human beings have done in such a short time by our blind faith in progress and our narrow views of the economy. We can see how grievously we have misused nature, and what damage this has done not only to the fauna and flora, but to ourselves.

To the two editors of the Ecology Volume, and to all who have collaborated in its preparation, I should like to express my heartfelt thanks. As with the other volumes of the Encyclopedia, the task of seeing the original German edition into print was supervised by Herbert Wendt, and the English edition by George Narita; for the many years they have spent on behalf of the Encyclopedia I am indeed grateful, as I am to the publishers who have made possible the realization of this latest project.

The battle for survival in this increasingly overpopulated and poisoned environment will become more and more intense. Our volume is intended to awaken the reader and to convince those in authority that rapid action is essential. A delay of even a few years would mean even more vandalism over large parts of the earth, bringing illness and death to many of our fellow humans. If we do not change our attitudes soon—and radically— the very next generation will have to do bitter penance for our sins.

Frankfurt/Main, Spring 1973

Part I

THE ENVIRONMENT OF ANIMALS

Edited by

JOACHIM ILLIES

Introduction
ENVIRONMENT and ADAPTATION

By J. Illies

Man's protracted interference with the balance of nature has at last opened his eyes to a fact long ignored—ignored, perhaps, because it has been too obvious: the organisms living on our earth do not exist independently and uninfluenced by their surroundings. The forces and effects of the environment, living and non-living, no longer appear as a more or less irrelevant stage-setting for the real events of life. There is a finely adjusted interplay between environmental factors and the physiological and behavioral adaptations of organisms, which the intervention of man can only too easily put out of order; it is this web of interactions that enables the coexistence of an enormous diversity of life forms and behavioral patterns. It is in fact the "sickness" to which many habitats have today succumbed—the ominous deterioration of certain environmental factors and the associated extinction of many animal species—that has made us aware of the nature of the "healthy" conditions which had previously been the norm; and for many species our awareness has come literally at the last minute.

ECOLOGY, the discipline concerned with the relationships between organisms and environment, is a very young branch of the natural sciences. Some of the great natural scientists of the 18th Century thought in "ecological" terms, but Alexander von Humboldt (1769–1859) was the first specifically to consider plants with respect to their natural surroundings—an approach which, under the name "physiognomy of plants," opened the way for a real understanding of the relationships between habitat and life form. With Charles Darwin's "Origin of Species" (1859), this new insight was triumphantly extended to zoology. The concept of "struggle for existence" introduced by Darwin is a clear expression of an ecological comprehension of nature. The most favorable or unfavorable environmental factors (climate, food supply, predators, competitors) form the framework to which not only the individual animal but the entire species must adjust its fight for life. The species as a whole can change because of the "natural selection" imposed by the environment. Adaptation to a changed environment by change of the genetic information contained in a species—that is, by survival of appropriate mutations—is recognized as a central process in evolution. At the same time, adaptation to an environment that remains unchanged is a prerequisite for the prolonged existence of a species in unaltered form. The "two great architects of species variation," as Konrad Lorenz has put it, are mutation and selection. From an ecological standpoint we can say that the present diversity of organisms, their persistence and their alteration, their Being and their Becoming, all result from the interplay of environment and adaptation.

But neither of these formulations gives us real insight into the processes, as long as the words disguise relationships we do not understand. This is of course true in all branches of science; in the theory of evolution the pitfalls are especially serious with respect to the terms "mutation," "selection," and "chance." Our first task is thus to make clear what is meant by "environment" on the one hand and "adaptation" on the other, and whether these terms are really precise scientific designations or simply the verbal expressions of our perplexity in the face of phenomena not yet comprehended.

The concept ENVIRONMENT was introduced in ecology by the biologist Jakob von Uexküll (1864–1944), to denote "those aspects of the world surrounding an organism that affect an animal's organs of sensation and action, and produce a specific behavior of the animal." He also once wrote, "Each subject spins out its relationships to certain properties of things, like the silken threads of a spider, weaving them to a firm web that supports its existence."

As the best-known example of a small, restricted environment comprising only a fraction of the external world, v. Uexküll mentioned the tick *Ixodes ricinus* which burrows into the skin of warmblooded animals and sucks in fluid until it swells to the size of a pea. This animal has three narrow sensory portals through which the outside world can enter: it can sense light and dark, but not images, with its skin; it has a sense of temperature; and it has a sense of smell capable of detecting the odor of butyric acid. These three measures are quite sufficient to enable the female tick to attain the goal of her life—a hearty meal of warm blood and thereafter a place to lay her eggs. In climbing toward the light, the animal reaches the branches and leaves of forest trees where, at a suitable height above the ground, it waits. Heat and the smell of sweat (butyric acid) announce to it that a living warm-blooded animal is passing below; the tick lets itself fall straight down and lands in the fur of its host. Now it need only crawl into the darkness and warmth—toward the smell of butyric acid—in order to reach the skin, in which it embeds itself.

In much the same way one can discover the elements that make up the particular environment of any animal species. The drawing in Fig. 0-1 shows a field of flowers from our viewpoint and from that of a honeybee.

Fig. 0-1. A field of flowers as we perceive it (above) and as it might appear to a bee (below): as the "environment" of the bee the meadow is a considerably simpler array of forms and colors than it is "in reality."

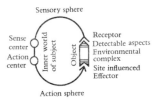

Sensory sphere

Sense center
Action center

Inner world of subject

Object

Receptor
Detectable aspects
Environmental complex
Site influenced
Effector

Action sphere

Fig. 0-2. Diagram of a "functional cycle" as devised by Jakob von Uexküll: organism and environment, subject and object, and the spheres of sensation and action are intermeshed and together comprise "reality" at any moment. The adaptation of an organism to its environment is a give and take of substances, acts, and information; events occurring in the preformed channels of the sphere of action have a reciprocal effect upon the sensory sphere of the organism.

In the latter the patterns and colors are simpler, and the background is less detailed, than as perceived by us. On the other hand, the refined sense organs of some animals, especially those for smell and hearing, detect details of the environment—such as certain odors and high tones—that we humans cannot perceive at all.

The environment concept of Jakob von Uexküll marked the beginning of experimental research into species-specific relationships of animals to their environment. Moreover, he drew a distinction between the spheres of sensation and action, and with his insight into the fact that the two spheres can interact reciprocally and cyclically (see Fig. 0-2), he laid the foundation for an approach currently designated by the term "cybernetics." The model for instinctive behavior proposed later by Niko Tinbergen is also in a sense presaged by this scheme. Finally, this approach leads to a new way of regarding the special position of the human race in nature; the goal of ecology, and indeed of all the natural sciences, is to combine existing knowledge and new research so that the limits of the environment comprehended subjectively by the individual are expanded, ultimately to coincide with those of the objective world. Only the exploratory spirit of man can follow this path. In recognizing the nature of animal environments man can, in a sense, annex them to his own. Ecology is thus insight into environments both familiar and alien.

But what is ADAPTATION, the other concept essential to the ecological way of thinking? Each animal species, by the very fact that it has existed for some time, must have evolved adequate means of surviving—to date at least—in its particular habitat. This process we call adaptation. The tick's abilities to detect brightness, warmth and sweat are key adaptations, which ensure that it survives long enough to reproduce—the criterion for species survival. Should one or more enviromental factors in its forest habitat change so as to threaten it, the species must evolve new adaptations to that situation (by survival of the animals having suitable inherited variation) or become extinct.

The adaptations of an animal cannot be interpreted except in relation to the environment with which it interacts. Among its adaptations we can distinguish two major groups (although the two are by no means sharply separated) that relate to different aspects of environment. On the one hand, the animal must be adapted to live in a particular kind of biotope, as defined by such environmental factors as temperature and moisture conditions on land, or depth and kind of bottom material in the sea. The environment of the species in this sense, as described by a kind or range of biotopes and communities in which it lives, is the species' *habitat*. On the other hand, the animal must be adapted to competition and other interactions with other species in a community in which it lives. The adaptation of the species to live in a particular way in its community—using only some fraction of the environment within the community, feeding only on certain other species, perhaps being active only at certain times—is the species' *niche*. One major rule is that the species in a community are niche specialists; in a given stable community no two species are alike in their particular use of time and resources, small-scale environments within the biotope, and way of interacting with other species (see Introduction, Section III). We can say in consequence that two species that are alike in habitat will differ in niche. We can also observe the converse: species that are closely similar in niche will have different habitats. Evolution leads to

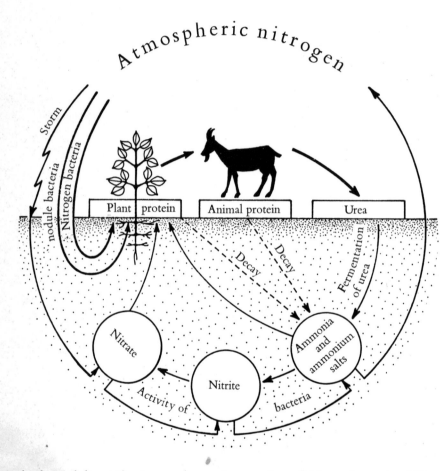

Fig. 0-3. Metabolic processes in organisms and atmospheric phenomena (here, a storm) are the stations in the circulation of a chemical element (nitrogen) contained in animal and vegetable protein and returned to inorganic substances when that protein is decomposed. The cycle involves a complicated interaction of many single factors. The cycles (in many cases with multiple pathways) of all the individual elements together comprise the "biogeocenotic" equilibrium of the ecosystem.

biological diversification, and as one expression of this, each species differs from any other in its full range of adaptations to environment, considering both its niche and its habitat.

Nevertheless, the distinction between the notion of an animal's environment on the one hand, and the adaptations which the animal makes to it on the other, is useful in that different scientific disciplines are often involved in their study. One can measure separately the nature and ranges of variation of critical environmental factors such as temperature, water availability, or oxygen concentration. The adaptations themselves, though, must be studied with reference to the animal—its anatomy, physiology, and behavior. A useful approach, the one adopted in this volume, is to begin with the environmental factors and then to use these to reveal and interpret the adaptations animals have evolved.

Ernst Haeckel, the man who paved the way for Darwinism, gave "official" status to this new "science of the relationships of the organism to the external world surrounding it"; in 1866 he defined ecology (from the Greek οἶχος, "house," and λογος, "word" or "teaching") as "the

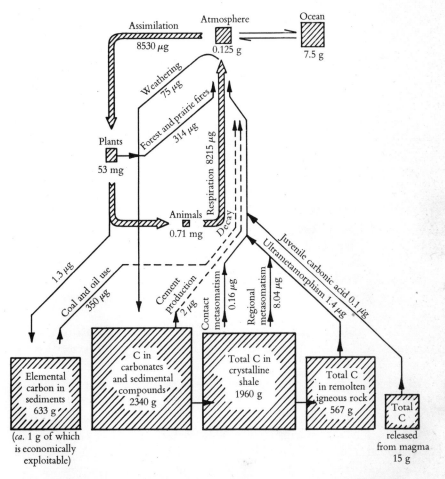

Fig. 0-4. A thorough understanding of ecological processes requires quantitative data for the various stages in the elementary cycles involved. Carbon is fundamental to all organic compounds and to all processes of respiration and synthesis, but its availability is affected by inorganic processes (weathering and volcanic eruptions). The diagram gives a detailed survey of the proportions of the total carbon on earth bound in various forms or circulating (per square centimeter of the earth's surface per year).

teaching concerned with the 'households' of organisms, which takes as objects of study the relationships of organisms to both organic and inorganic nature." The German word for household (Haushalt) goes beyond the English meaning, implying here the place where an organism is at home and the interactions of the organism with its fellow occupants, as well as the budgeting of the organism's resources and other such aspects of "home economics." The latter are not only biological, but also physical and chemical. Haeckel's description of this new branch of the life sciences was so well thought out that it is still entirely valid after more than a hundred years. In view of its wide scope, however, some ecologists (in

Germany these include particularly August Thienemann and Karl Friedrichs) have come to refer to their discipline simply as "the science of the balance of nature."

And this is quite justified. Present-day ecologists recognize that it is only by extensive consideration of all natural phenomena, and all phenomena of civilization as well, that one can come to a proper understanding of the conditions for existence of an organism in a habitat. The marine ecologist can correctly work out the nitrogen circulation involving marine algae and plankton (which is crucial for protein synthesis) only if he takes into account how much nitrogen oxide is formed by lightning in the atmosphere and brought by rains into the sea. The ecologist who wants to calculate the oxygen supplies of the earth, so as to predict how likely it is that man and animals will have enough to breathe, has to reckon with combustion by power stations, automobile engines, and jet planes as well as with the production of oxygen by plants. And the limnologist, concerned with fresh-water communities, can understand the growth of algae in a pond only if he knows how much of the sun's energy irradiates its surface.

Ecology, then, in investigating global cyclic processes and even in the study of limited habitats, is always more than just a discipline of the natural sciences. One might actually say that it is a particular attitude of the scientists concerned—that is, the conviction that only observation of *all* the effective factors in a habitat can reveal its innermost functional principles, and that therefore zoology, botany, chemistry, physics, meteorology, applied technology and even the history of civilization are simply aids, to be used as needed in fulfilling the great plan—to understand a section of nature in its entirety.

The diversity of animal life, as it has been described in the first thirteen volumes of this encyclopedia of present-day fauna, leads the zoologist to concentrate on individual species. But from an ecological point of view each species is a component of a larger web of influence and dependence, environment and adaptation, which in the last analysis encloses the entire biosphere. Figure 0-3, illustrating the circulation of nitrogen, gives an example of how problems are formulated and answered in ecology. Here the animal is one link in a chain which closes to form a circle. Here, then, one is given the opportunity of answering—with all due caution—the question, "What is the significance of a species in nature as a whole?" Ecology has a broad enough frame of reference that it can in principle draw reliable conclusions about the significance of every component to the function of the whole. Therefore it is to this branch of science that some of the most urgent of contemporary questions are directed—how far can our natural surroundings be strained before they pass the breaking point, and how much damage is in fact being done by our civilization?

Of course, useful answers to such questions are possible only as a result of intensive ecological research, in which not only the general interrelationships are revealed but the exact quantities of the materials involved and the exact extent of the various effects are determined. Such precise measurements are extraordinarily difficult—especially when one is concerned with relationships on a global scale. These represent the final and highest goal of ecological research. An example of such quantitative results is shown in Fig. 0-4, a diagram of carbon circulation in nature—on the earth's surface, in the atmosphere, and in the upper parts of the earth's crust. There we see that, while plants and animals do play a decisive role, civilization (for example, by way of the use of coal and petroleum or the production of cement) is already beginning to have a perceptible influence upon the natural cycle. The ecological approach is absolutely required to discern such relationships.

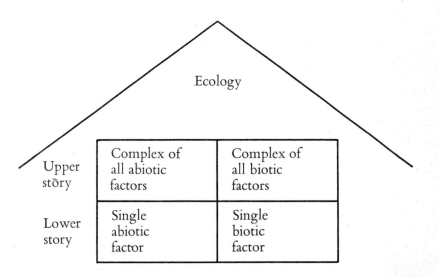

Fig. 0-5. August Thienemann has symbolized the structure of the field as a house, with "ecology" as the roof covering all the subordinate areas of study.

August Thienemann has devised a graphic representation of the way the various sciences and the different ways of viewing the world can work together to generate comprehensive ecological insights. At the same time, his diagram illustrates the organization of this book; it reflects, in a sense, both the scientific outlines of the discipline and the logic underlying the arrangement of the following chapters. The lower story of the "house" comprises the individual factors, both abiotic (non-living; e.g., temperature, humidity, light) and biotic (prey, conspecifics, competitors); upon this an upper story is built, in which the interaction of these factors is investigated. At this level, too, there is a distinction between abiotic forces as a whole (climate, habitat) and biotic complexes (communities of organisms). Scientists working in all four of these divisions must pool their results if the true "ecological" level is to be reached—where habitat and community of organisms are recognized and explained as a functional unit, the ecosystem. The chapters on habitats, ranges of distribution, and variations in fauna serve this purpose. But over and above the explanation of natural ecosystems, we must take account of the "superorganic factor," as August Thienemann has called human civilization. This topic is broached in the concluding chapters of the first part of the volume, and taken up in detail—on the basis of the preceding material—in the second part, which treats the environment of man and the ever more ominous environmental crisis.

I. ADAPTATIONS TO THE ABIOTIC ENVIRONMENT

1   The Influence of Temperature and Humidity

By H. U. Thiele

In the ice deserts of the Antarctic the temperature falls to $-88°$C; in the arid deserts of the earth it can rise as high as 58°C in the shade. Even along the hedge bordering a field in central Europe, at noon on a hot summer day, the temperature near the ground can be 40°C on the south side and only 20°C on the north. Within a given habitat one finds wide variations in temperature at different times; the range between the lowest winter and highest summer temperatures may be more than 80°C, and in the Sahara Desert there is a difference of up to 50°C between a day and the following night. In contrast, the Galapagos Islands, which are almost exactly at the equator, average 27°C each month throughout the year. All these regions of the earth will support animal life, though no single organism can endure all temperatures in this wide range—at least, not in an active state. The distribution of an animal species is limited to those habitats with temperatures to which it is adapted. Temperature also influences the annual and daily periodicity of animal activity. Wherever the temperatures are not nearly constant, as they are in the tropics, mountain streams, or caves, the temperature fluctuations during the day and the year force activity and periods of development to be limited to certain times.

Poikilothermic and homoiothermic animals

In the great majority of animal species, body temperature changes with that of the surroundings. These organisms, incapable of regulating their own temperature, are called poikilothermic. A relatively small number of species has managed, in the course of evolution, to acquire the ability to regulate body temperature actively; these are called homoiothermic. In mammals this stabilized temperature is usually between 36° and 37°C, and in the birds it can be as high as 40°C.

All animals are affected in three fundamental ways by temperature. First, there is for each species a range of temperatures which it can tolerate. Greater heat or cold are lethal, and even within the tolerance limits there is a more restricted range of optimum temperatures. This optimum range corresponds to that part of the temperature scale that a freely moving animal seeks out; it need not be the same as the species-specific optimum temperature for development.

Animals that can function well within a wide range of temperatures are called eurythermic, while those able to live only within a very narrow range are called stenothermic. Hot springs offer examples of stenothermic animals restricted to a range at the high end of the scale, which can be determined easily since the temperature of the water stays the same throughout the year. Heat as great as 85°C, which blue-green algae can withstand, is beyond the tolerance limit for animals. But larvae of the nematoceran genus *Scatella* live at 55°C in thermal springs in Iceland; the aquatic snail *Bithynia thermalis* is found at temperatures as high as 53°C. One species of the protozoan genus *Hyalodiscus* can survive in Italian hot springs at 54°C, and a small form of *Amoeba limax* is found in the same regions, where the water is nearly as hot. These species, though, set records for heat resistance among aquatic animals. Apart from these there are only a few rotifers, swimming beetles, oligochaete worms, and one kind of shrimp that can live in hot springs at temperatures above 40°C. Nor does any vertebrate seem to exceed this limit. Among the fish, only the killifish *Cyprinodon nevadensis*, a native of Death Valley, California, can endure about 42°C, in hot springs during the summer; remarkably, in winter it can be found in water at only about 3°C. Such temperature maxima are not limited to the inhabitants of hot springs; desert locusts withstand temperatures of 50–60°C. In one experiment, the cheese fly *Piophila casei* proved able to live for an hour at 52°C and for twenty-four hours at 45°C. The only animals with heat resistance outside these limits are rotifers and tardigrades in a state of almost complete desiccation. These have been shown to survive, for a few minutes, heating to 151°C and cooling to 0.008 degrees above absolute zero (that is, about −273°C).

For most poikilothermic animals, however, the lethal heat limit is far below 40°C, and thus below the temperature at which protein coagulates. It is therefore not coagulation of proteins that causes death by heat in these animals. The most important proteins in an organism are its enzymes, the molecules that determine the rate of metabolism, and the activity of enzymes depends upon temperature. Moreover, it can happen that the rates at which the various enzymes of a single organism operate change quite differently as a function of temperature. In this case there is a more or less narrow range of temperature within which the enzymes perform optimally as a system, and within which the rates of synthesis and breakdown of the various metabolites are suitably adjusted. At higher temperatures this balance is destroyed, and there may be a lethal accumulation of toxic metabolites.

When the temperature of the environment is far below the freezing point, only homoiotherms can remain active. The record is held by the emperor penguin, which breeds during the winter in Antarctica. The mean temperature in its breeding grounds is usually between −15° and

Resistance to heat

Resistance to cold

−20°C, though it can occasionally fall as low as −40°C. There is a reason for breeding at this time—it allows the young to hatch just as spring is beginning. This achievement in the face of extreme cold is possible only if reserves have been stored up in advance; these are then metabolized to maintain body temperature, for if that were to fall even as low as 15–20°C, these homoiothermic animals would die. Only animals capable of true hibernation—for example, the bats, hedgehogs, and hamsters—can change their overall physiological state so as to become temporarily poikilothermic.

Among warm-blooded animals ranging over quite different climatic regions, it is often true that the largest members of a species are found in the coldest parts of the range (Bergmann's Rule). As body size increases, the ratio of surface to volume becomes smaller and the danger of excessive cooling is less. The Siberian tiger (*Panthera tigris altaica*), native to a region famous for cold winters, is not only the largest subspecies of tiger but the largest of all the "big cats"; the Bengal tiger (*Panthera tigris tigris*) is intermediate in size, and the Java tiger (*Panthera tigris sondaica*), a tropic island form, is the smallest.

Poikilothermic animals can survive much greater cooling. Nevertheless, only a few organisms can stay active if their body temperature falls below the freezing point. The springtail *Isotoma saltans* lives on glaciers; this insect is active only during the day and is said to freeze at night. It is actually harmed by temperatures above 15°C. In an active state, it consumes just about as much oxygen at −2.5°C as closely related animals do at 20°C. In the deepest parts of the ocean, too, animals live in salt water at temperatures below 0°C.

Freezing

The body fluids of animals are of course not pure water, but a solution of proteins and salts. For this reason these fluids do not freeze at 0°C, but rather at a few degrees below the freezing point of water. Furthermore, invertebrates are able, to a greater or lesser degree, to survive actual freezing, though none of them is as resistant to freezing as some plants. Freezing of the fluid between the cells is less harmful than the formation of ice within the cells themselves. In general it can be said that animal bodies are more resistant to cold, the less water they contain and the greater the fraction of this water bound to proteins (as opposed to free water), since the bound water freezes only at −20°C or less. Many insects can reduce the water content of their bodies as winter approaches. Resistance to cold depends upon the species, the duration of the cold spell, and the rate of freezing and thawing, so that it is nearly impossible to give any general rules. An Alaskan ground beetle (*Pterostichus brevicornis*) was shown experimentally to survive −87°C for five hours. Beetles collected in winter, which were found thoroughly frozen in their winter retreats, could stand to be kept for quite long times at −35°C. When collected in summer, the same species is adapted to the warmer conditions and dies at only −6.6°C.

In the autumn, even though the temperatures are still favorable to activity, many insects respond to the signal of decreasing day length by entering a state of inactivity and suspended growth (dormancy or diapause), and thus adapt themselves to the approaching winter. Once such a resting state has been entered, certain insects can emerge from it only after chilling, whether naturally or artificially produced. In such cases, chilling is actually essential to life.

The temperature that a freely moving animal will choose can be readily determined by a device developed by Konrad Herter (see Fig. 1-1). Basically it is a long, narrow cage in the shape of a rectangle or ring, the floor of which is a strip of metal cooled at one end and heated at the other. An array of thermometers is permanently mounted in the floor so that one can measure its temperature at closely spaced intervals. A group of animals is placed in the cage and allowed to move about freely. The distributions of animals then observed are characteristic of the species. To exclude as nearly as possible any orientation to a humidity gradient, there is a moistened layer on the floor which tends to keep the humidity uniform throughout the apparatus. The German name given the device by its inventor means "temperature organ"; it was suggested by the appearance, similar to organ pipes, of a bar graph plotting temperature against position on the floor. Since the term is ambiguous in English, we shall instead refer to the "temperature-gradient apparatus."

The gradient apparatus has been used to study a great number of invertebrates, and even small vertebrates. "Preferred temperature" has proved to be a constant characteristic of individual species, influenced only slightly by the temperature to which the animals are adapted or by changes in their physiological state. Males and females of a given species respond similarly. Such variability as there is of preferred temperature is no greater than that of physical characteristics such as size or color.

Results obtained with the gradient apparatus are far more informative than observations in the field. To be sure, one can measure quantitatively the natural distribution of a species in different habitats and simultaneously determine the temperature at the same sites, but in the field there are many other factors that change along with temperature. In the gradient apparatus, on the other hand, climatic factors such as humidity and light intensity are kept as constant as possible. As a result, one can discover how the animals behave with respect to temperature alone. They may distribute themselves over a wide range of temperatures, in which case they can be ascribed to the category of eurythermic organisms. Other species become concentrated in a very narrow temperature range; these are stenothermic. Particular stenothermic animals may restrict themselves to any one part of the scale, whether warm or cold.

The point of this kind of investigation is to compare the "preferred temperatures" with those prevailing in the natural habitat at the season when the animal is active. Such an experiment may reveal that a specific

Preferred temperature

Fig. 1-1. An annular temperature-gradient apparatus seen from the side (above) and the top (below): 1. Cooling; 2. Heating; 3. Thermometers monitoring the temperature of the floor. In the ring-shaped cage there are two similar temperature gradients. The numbers of the sections where animals aggregate are recorded, and the temperature readings for these sections give the "preferred temperature" of the animals.

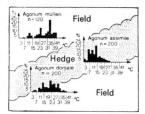

Fig. 1-2. Preferred temperature compared with habitat: Diagram of the preferred temperature of three species of the ground beetle *Agonum* found in fields and the hedges bordering them. *Agonum assimile*, a woodland animal, lives only in the hedge and has the lowest preferred temperature; *A. mülleri* is found only in fields and has a very high preferred temperature; and *A. dorsale*, the species with an intermediate preferred temperature, lives in the zone between hedge and field and moves between the two habitats according to the season.

temperature is relatively unimportant to a certain species, even though in the field this species is encountered only within a particular range of temperatures. In this case one may justifiably conclude that temperature has little or no influence on the distribution of the species, and that some other factor is responsible. But if a species displays a marked preference for a certain temperature, and this corresponds to that of its natural habitat, one may hypothesize that temperature does play a role in determining the normal range of distribution.

A number of species of ground beetle (family Carabidae), which are restricted to woods and forests, have high preferred temperatures or are eurythermic. *Carabus problematicus*, a ground beetle frequently encountered in central European woodland, shows a clear preference for 20–30°C in the temperature-gradient apparatus. The preferred temperature of a ground beetle found in fields, *Carabus auratus*, is only a little higher, 25–30°C. The difference between the two species is that *C. problematicus* prefers high humidity, which it finds only in the woods, whereas *C. auratus* chooses dry conditions. Here temperature is not the decisive factor determining the distribution of the two species, but rather humidity.

Frequently, though, experiments show that temperature is highly significant in the distribution of organisms. For example, some species of so-called "snow insects" live on the snow in winter. One of these, the snow scorpionfly *Boreus hyemalis*, has a preferred temperature lying on the average a little below 10°C. Even lower preferred temperatures, 5–6°C, are found for the springtail *Hypogastrura socialis*. The wingless *Grylloblatta*, native to the North American mountains, has the lowest preferred temperature so far found among insects—1°C. At the other end of the scale, *Adesima metallica*, a relative of the meal worm found in the North African desert, has a preferred temperature just under 50°C. Even within a group of related animals, and within a restricted area, one may find marked differences—for example, in the case of the Central European ground beetles. A typical forest species of cool, humid habitats, which becomes active early in the spring and is almost entirely nocturnal (*Agonum assimile*), chooses temperatures around 10°C. In marked contrast is the small, brightly colored ground beetle *Callistus lunatus*, which is active during the same season on dry grassland in particularly arid, warm regions of central Europe, and prefers 36–40°C.

Warm-blooded animals are less well suited for experiments in the temperature gradient apparatus, and birds are entirely unsuitable. But there are other ways of testing these animals; for example, one may measure their metabolic rate as a function of temperature. The higher the metabolic rate, the greater the rate of respiration and thus the greater the amount of carbon dioxide produced in a given time. For example, comparisons have been made of the yellowhammer and the ortolan. The yellowhammer (*Emberiza citrinella*), distributed over a large part of Eurasia, spends the whole year in its habitat, even staying over the winter in Siberia. Its breeding range overlaps with that of the closely related ortolan (*Emberiza hortulana*), though the latter extends less far to the north and further to the south. Moreover, the ortolan is a typical migratory bird. Both species prefer a range of temperatures in which their metabolism is best adjusted and its rate is lowest. At higher or lower temperatures their rate of respiration increases in response to the stress. This optimum range is 25–33°C for the yellowhammer, and 32–38°C for the ortolan. The ortolan can speed up its respiration to compensate for cooling only down to −15°C; at lower temperatures its regulatory system breaks down, and there is no further increase in rate of respiration. The yellowhammer, on the other hand, can compensate for cooling by increased respiration down to temperatures as low as −40°C. Conversely, for the yellowhammer temperatures of 33–34°C are dangerously hot, whereas the upper critical temperature for the ortolan is as high as 38–39°C. From such data one can see that the temperature requirements of a species are matched not only to its breeding grounds, but also to its behavior. The ortolan, sensitive as it is to cold, moves each year to winter quarters that offer temperatures similar to those of its breeding grounds in summer.

Such differences in range, as a function of different temperature requirements, are found not only among closely related species. The existence within a species of races with different temperature preferences has been shown in a very elegant experiment, for the fruit fly *Drosophila funebris*. At 25°C flies from all parts of the range of the species function equally well, as can be demonstrated by placing them in competition with a related species. Flies from the cooler regions of northwestern Europe are still superior to their competitors at 15°C, but at 29°C they fail to compete adequately. On the other hand, flies from the Mediterranean region function better at higher temperatures and worse when the temperature is lowered. Flies from Russia and central Asia, which are adapted to large temperature fluctuations, outperform their relatives at both high and low temperatures.

Temperature is also of great importance in the development of poikilothermic animals. As the temperature of their surroundings rises, they develop more rapidly. This temperature-dependent acceleration of development is more pronounced in some species than in others, as is the "null temperature" for development, below which the animals can continue to live but show no signs of growth. In many cases the acceleration of development follow van't Hoff's rule in chemistry which states that for every ten degrees increase in temperature, the rate doubles or triples.

In the common forest ground beetle *Pterostichus oblongopunctatus* development from egg to mature beetle takes eighty-two days at 15°C, whereas at 25°C it takes only forty-six days. A ten-degree increase in temperature, then, has almost doubled the rate of development. Its close relative *Pterostichus angustatus*, almost indistinguishable from the first

Fig. 1-3. Dependence of range upon temperature:

Range of the yellowhammer in Eurasia.

The range of the ortolan lies to the south of the yellowhammer's range.

Temperature and development

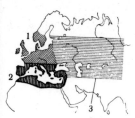

Fig. 1-4. Races of *Droso-phila funebris* adapted to different temperatures are differently distributed. 1. Northwestern European race; 2. Mediterranean race; 3. Continental Eurasian race.

Insect development

beetle in appearance, requires greater warmth and aggregates at a higher temperature in the temperature gradient apparatus. It lives in very warm sunny clearings in the forests, and is much more common in the inland parts of Europe than in the coastal regions. *P. angustatus* develops in ninety-six days at 15°C, and requires only thirty-six days at 25°C. That is, it responds to a ten-degree rise in temperature with a much greater increase in rate of development than does its forest-dwelling relative. Both species reproduce in early spring. Development of the eggs of *P. angustatus* takes twenty-one days at 15°C, while those of *P. oblongopunctatus* need eleven days. If eggs of both species are exposed to 25°C, both develop in only five to six days. In the forest, then, the development of *P. angustatus* would be greatly hampered. The strict association of this beetle with open, sunny habitats is understandable on the basis of the temperature required for development.

The effect of uniform temperature upon insect development can be different from that of fluctuating temperatures, even though the mean value is the same. If the null point for development of a species is 10°C, it will not develop at all as long as the temperature remains steady at that level. If the temperature fluctuates during the course of a day between 5°C and 15°C, however, keeping a mean of 10°C, the animals can grow in the part of the day when the temperature is above 10°C. This effect is probably the chief reason for the absence of many alpine species from the Arctic tundra. At first glance the two habitats seem very much the same, in mean temperature as well as in other respects. But during the Arctic summer the temperature is uniformly low, whereas in high mountains there is marked daily variation about a low mean value.

Temperature affects not only the rate of development but also the mortality of the various stages. By patiently working through long series of experiments it has been possible to specify these effects—particularly for destructive insects, in order to predict outbreaks in different climate regions and under different weather conditions. The data can be presented in the form of a "mortality diagram," by plotting the loci of points for a given percent mortality on a coordinate system representing temperature and humidity (Fig. 1-5). For the eggs of the pine lappet (*Dendrolimus pini*) a temperature of 20°C and humidity of 70% represent the most favorable conditions, under which the mortality is essentially zero. 30°C and 20% humidity fall beyond the 100% mortality curve; under such conditions the species cannot develop. The diagram shows that between these extremes there is a range over which some eggs can survive, depending on the balance of temperature and humidity. At 25°C, for example, mortality is complete if the humidity is 20%, but with higher humidity it is quite possible for a considerable fraction of the eggs to develop (half of them, at 60% humidity and 25°C).

Temperature is clearly a significant factor in the distribution of animals over the surface of the earth and within their habitats. But it is only one

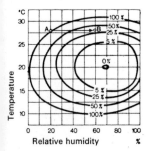

Fig. 1-5. Mortality diagram of the pine lappet, *Denerolimus pini*, in the egg stage. The lines join points representing equal percent mortality under different conditions of temperature and humidity.

of several important climatic factors. The example just discussed shows that the effects of temperature must not be considered in isolation; they can be altered by other conditions. One task of the ecologist is to determine the interaction between the many factors as they affect organisms. This can be achieved only if field observations, field experiments, and laboratory experiments are judiciously combined.

In the course of their evolution, living beings first arose in the water, and were able to conquer the land only at a much later time. An adequate supply of water has remained the foremost requirement for terrestrial life; all physiological processes are associated with aqueous solutions in the body.

It is rare for an animal body to contain less than 50% water, by weight. The "dryest" body seems to be that of the beetle *Calandra granaria*, about 46% of which is water. This beetle feeds on grain seeds, which contain very little water. Caterpillars that feed on very juicy leaves can have a water content of 85% to more than 90%. On the average, the water content of land animals (at least those not living on or in the soil) is less than that of aquatic animals. The body of the domestic cow is 52% water, that of man 64%, and that of the domestic duck 70%. In fish the water content is 75% or more; the sea anemone is almost 90% water and in some jellyfish water accounts for over 99% of the weight. Terrestrial animals lose water both by excretion and by evaporation; the lost water must be replaced by drinking or by metabolic production. Water is produced in the body by the oxidation of food molecules, and this can be a large fraction of the total supply; for example, there are rodents living in dry regions which do not drink and consume only dry food. Some animals, such as snails and amphibians, can take water in through their skins.

The amount of water an animal can lose temporarily without suffering injury varies over a wide range. Mammals can usually stand water loss amounting to only 10–15% of their body weight. The camel is an exception, being able to lose 30% of its weight; another is the house mouse, which is able to survive the loss of 40% of its weight. Its wild ancestors were desert animals, and their ability to resist desiccation has enabled the "domesticated" mouse to live in human dwellings. Some races of mouse have returned to the wild state and colonized deserts. Mice excrete very concentrated urine and dry excrement. Lizards have been found to survive a loss of water amounting to 46% of their body weight, and earthworms and snails can even recover from losses of 60–80%. Even more extreme water loss can be tolerated by certain small animals —rotifers and tardigrades—living in moss, where the danger of drying out is particularly great. They can survive loss of 99% of their weight, but only by encystment or adoption of other specially resistant forms in which their activity is entirely suspended. In such a state, with their rate of metabolism essentially zero, they can live for years; for example, a

Influence of humidity

Water content of animals

Resistance to desiccation

tardigrade of the genus *Macrobiotus* survived for six and a half years. It was even possible to bring a few rotifers and tardigrades found in a 120-year-old moss herbarium back to active life.

Among insects, it is practically impossible to find a relationship between habitat and resistance to desiccation. The greatest tolerable water loss found in twelve species of ground beetle from different habitats varied only between 25% and 34%. The greatest resistance, as might have been expected, was that of a field beetle (*Harpalus pubescens*); it died only after losing 34% of its body weight, and survived desiccation for a longer time than did the other beetles. But second place, in terms of survival time, was taken by a forest beetle (*Agonum assimile*), which died when it had lost 26% of its weight.

Protection against evaporation

The factor most important in determining an animal's ability to colonize dry habitats is usually not the water loss it can tolerate, but rather the degree to which it is protected against loss by evaporation or is capable of replacing the evaporated water. Insects of dry habitats are covered by a cuticle through which water cannot evaporate, and loss of water through the tracheae can be prevented by closure of the spiracles. Reptiles are protected by their armored skin and by the absence of sweat glands. Snails in steppe and semi-desert are characterized by particularly thick shells and often by a chalky color that reflects sunlight. During periods of drought they plug the openings of their shells with mucus, which becomes filled with calcium salts if the drought is prolonged. A record in this respect was set by the snail *Helicella striata*, from the steppe regions of the Swedish island Öland. Among some museum samples a scientist had added to his collection, under the impression that they were empty shells, living animals were found fifteen years later; they were revived and resumed full activity.

But it is not at all essential for xerophilous (dry-habitat) species to be specially protected against evaporation. Animals of the "locust type" lose large amounts of water by evaporation through their body surface, but they can adequately replenish their water stores from the juicy plants they eat. Moreover, both they and the species with protection against evaporation are frequently able to extract water from food remnants in the hindgut.

There are all sorts of transitional stages between the inhabitants of the most arid regions and the extremely hygrophilous (damp-habitat) species. Amphibia are good examples of the hygrophilous end of the scale; they have no special means of reducing evaporation, nor can they extract water from the gut contents. They must have moisture-saturated air in order to live. Whereas pythons and turtles (i.e., reptiles) lose only 0.1–0.3% of their body weight during a day in dry air at 22°C, frogs under the same conditions lose 75%.

Preferred humidity

Just as the temperature-gradient apparatus was used to determine the heat requirements of animals, a similar device can be constructed to study their requirements with respect to humidity. A round dish is divided by partitions so that it resembles a pie (Fig. 1-6), and the bottom between each pair of partitions has a lining saturated with a certain salt solution such that at a given temperature the relative humidity is different in each chamber. Above the wet lining is a floor of gauze on which the animals can walk, and there are narrow openings in the partitions through which they can move from one chamber to another. The animals thus have an opportunity to select the humidity that best suits them; this small apparatus permits a range of humidities from 100% to 40% or even lower. The arrangement is such that temperature and illumination can be kept the same in all chambers, and the behavior of the animals with respect to humidity alone can be studied.

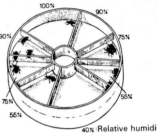

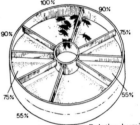

In this way, considerably more information has been obtained about the preferred humidities of various species than would have been possible from observations and measurements in the field. Although the ground beetle *Agonum assimile* normally lives only in cool, damp woodland, in the humidity apparatus it selects a dry chamber. Its resistance to desiccation (see above) is consistent with this choice. It is therefore not a requirement for moisture that determines its distribution, but rather a preference for low temperatures. In central Europe, however, moisture and coolness almost always go together. *Agonum assimile* simply tolerates the humidity prevailing in its cool habitat.

Fig. 1-6. Behavior of ten ground beetles (*Abax ovalis*) when given a choice of humidity. The chambers rage from 100% to 40% humidity.
Above: at the beginning of the experiment the beetles are distributed at random.
Below: after four hours all the beetles have gathered in the humid chambers.

Nevertheless, almost all forest-dwelling arthropods are hygrophilous, displaying a preference for moisture in the humidity apparatus. Natives of open country, on the other hand, can either endure a wide range of relative humidity (they are euryhygric) or prefer pronounced dryness (they are xerophilous). The requirement of forest arthropods for especially high humidity is also evident in other experiments. The great majority of these arthropods are nocturnal and avoid light. Their demand for high humidity is an adaptation not only to their damp habitat but also to the moist conditions associated with the hours of darkness. Ground beetles of the open field, on the other hand, are to a large extent both reistant to dryness and active during the day. Within a given species, then, there are close relationships between habitat, humidity requirements, and time of activity.

The fauna of very dry habitats—for example, that of deserts—is particularly active at night, when the temperature is low and the humidity relatively high. The mouse *Dipodomys spectabilis* builds nests in the ground of the Arizona desert in which the humidity during the day is two to five times higher than that of the outside air. Fog can also provide a small amount of moisture in the deserts along the western edge of the Americas; for example, in certain regions on the western slopes of the Peruvian Andes, where it never rains, there are periodic fogs called "garua." The Atacama Desert in northwestern Chile is near the coast, but with less than ten millimeters of precipitation annually it is the dryest region of the world. Here, too, there is frequent fog, formed above the cold Peruvian

Desert animals

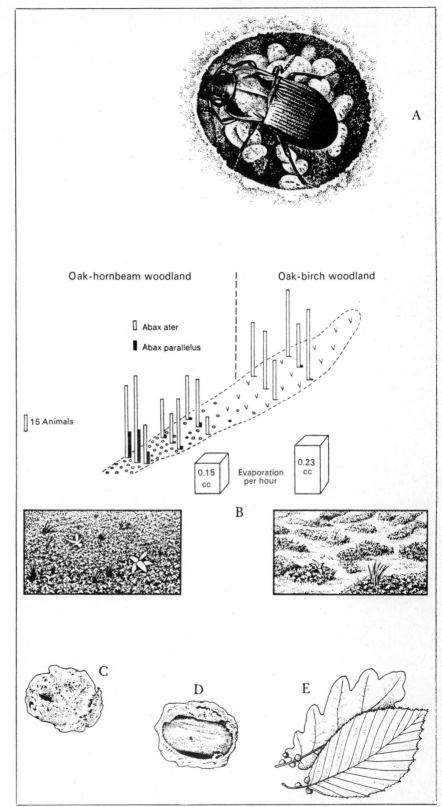

Fig. 1-7. Two species of the ground beetle *Abax*, very similar in appearance, distribute themselves quite differently among communities of forest plants varying in humidity: The diagram (B) shows the number of animals caught in automatic traps at different sites over a year. In the oak-hornbeam forest the dense growth on the floor makes the humidity uniformly high and the rate of evaporation low. It is only here that *Abax parallelus* lives; the female cares for her young by digging a nest in the ground in summer, where she spends three weeks watching over her brood of about twenty eggs (A). During this time both female and brood must be in air of high humidity. *Abax ater*, on the other hand, can also live in an oak-birch forest with open ground vegetation, high rates of evaporation, and marked fluctuations of soil moisture. After a shower of rain the female of this species encloses each of her eggs in clay (C, D) and fastens them to fallen leaves or stones (E). From then on the female pays no further attention to her brood, for the eggs are protected from desiccation by their coating of clay. (Based on investigations by Löser and Thiele.)

Oak-hornbeam woodland

Oak-birch woodland

☐ Abax ater

■ Abax parallelus

15 Animals

0.15 cc

Evaporation per hour

0.23 cc

B

C

D

E

(or Humboldt) Current off the coast. The Peruvian Current is the real reason for the existence of desert here, since the cooled air above it warms up as it moves over the continent and therefore, despite its humidity, releases hardly any rain.

Dew can enable nocturnal animals to live even in places where it is too dry during the day. The myriapod *Craspedosoma rawlinsii*, ordinarily found in wet woodland, can live in certain places along the Rhine where the waste heaps from peat-coal mines form surfaces devoid of vegetation which are exceedingly dry during the day. But the soil here is such that at night water vapor rises from deeper levels underground, and dew is formed in abundance. The appearance of a habitat seen only by day, then, can be quite deceptive.

Seasonal changes in behavior brought about by humidity can be observed most readily in climatic regions with a pronounced alternation between rainy and dry seasons. This alternation causes long-distance migrations of grass-eating animals in steppe areas, and it also determines the breeding times of the birds in such places.

Animals of the rain-forest

The tropical rainforest can satisfy the most strict demands for uniformly high humidity. In most places here the relative humidity is over 90%. As a result, the rainforest is the terrestrial home of certain members of animal groups which are otherwise entirely aquatic. Among these are the leech and large planaraians; in the soils of Indonesian rainforests one finds the polychaete worm *Lycastopsis catarractarum*, the relatives of which are exclusively marine.

Many groups of animals are found only in the ocean. These are not only obscure, apparently primitive groups with few species, but may be large phyla like the echinoderms. Other animals are restricted to fresh water. Insects of some orders (dragonflies, stoneflies, caddisflies and many others), as well as most Amphibia, repeat their ancestors' evolutionary transition from water to land ontogenetically—that is, in the development of each individual.

We are seldom aware that species in only a few animal groups have succeeded, in the course of evolution, in becoming thoroughly terrestrial. The fact that we see a large number of different animals about us is deceptive. Most of the animals we notice are vertebrates; in fact, they are almost all mammals, birds, and reptiles. These most highly developed vertebrates have conquered even arid regions. Of the many groups of segmented invertebrates, only certain arthropods—insects, myriapods, chelicerates—and a few annelids have achieved this feat, and the molluscs are represented in such habitats almost exclusively by the pulmonate gastropods. Altogether, then, only four of the many animal phyla have completely terrestrial members, and they represent only a few of the many groups within these phyla.

Soil, a humid habitat

Many animals have, so to speak, stopped halfway in their attempt to colonize the land. These, apart from the exceptional rainforest animals mentioned above, have conquered no habitats above ground but have invaded an intermediate territory: the interstices within the soil which are always saturated with moisture, or the air space just at the surface of the soil, also very humid as a rule. It is only here that the land offers a habitat for annelids like the earthworm and some enchytraeids, as well as the swarms of myriapods and—almost the only crustaceans on land— the hygrophilous isopods. One isopod of damp forest floors, *Lygidium hypnorum* dies within a few minutes at a relative humidity less than 100%. Here, too, is the realm of primitive chelicerates such as the whip scorpions, and the true scorpions as well. Wingless insects, among which the spring-tails (Collembola) comprise the most species, are also soil animals. Those protozoans, rotifers and nematodes not parasitic in the bodies of terrestrial animals can live only in the film of water covering the particles of soil. It is thus particularly the members of lower phyla that have made an incomplete transition to land.

The development of reproductive behavior among terrestrial animals still shows traces of their slow adaptation to life on land. Aquatic animals usually shed their eggs and sperm into the water, leaving the sperm threads to drift into contact with the eggs. The direct copulation of sexual partners on land may seem the only alternative to this, but it is not. Recently mechanisms of "indirect copulation," often rather bizarre, of soil animals have been discovered.

Male soil mites and springtails deposit a sperm holder (in these cases a simple drop of sperm on a stalk); later, when a female appears on the scene, she picks the droplet up with her genital opening. The females of the primitive myriapod *Scutigerella* take the sperm into pockets in their mouths, seize an egg in their mouthparts as it is laid and fertilize it, and then fasten it to a substrate. Another primitive myriapod, *Polyxenus*, makes a web, deposits a sperm droplet on it, and spins out a thread to signal its presence. Females stumbling across this thread can find their way along it to the sperm long after the male has disappeared.

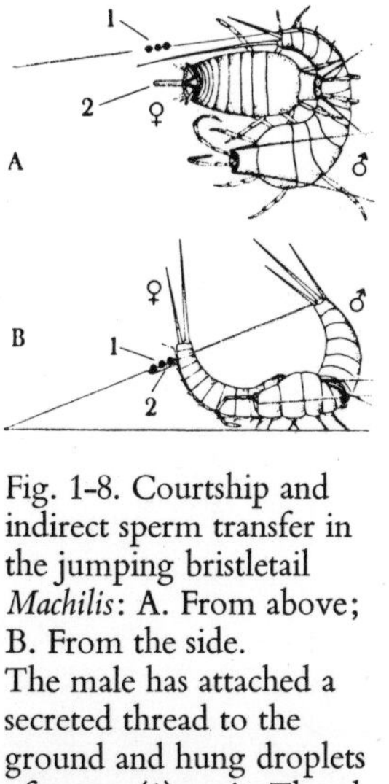

Among the primitive insects the jumping bristletail (*Machilis*) has an even more advanced mating behavior—it includes a courtship ceremony. Having found and made preliminary overtures to a female, he spins a thread out from the end of his body and deposits a sperm drop upon it. Then the male holds the thread up with his hindlegs so that the sperm is not soaked up by the soil, and simultaneously steers the female into a suitable position so that she can take up the sperm drop.

All these remarkable patterns of behavior have one thing in common: they are possible only in air saturated with moisture, and this is found on or in the soil. In the dryer air even a short distance above the ground, sperm drops would dry up before their purpose was fulfilled. Even in those animals that copulate directly, the development of real copulatory organs is a terminal stage of evolution reached within only a few phyla. The males of some myriapods of the subclass Diplopoda, as well as many

Special aspects of reproduction in soil animals: traces of the "route onto land"

Fig. 1-8. Courtship and indirect sperm transfer in the jumping bristletail *Machilis*: A. From above; B. From the side. The male has attached a secreted thread to the ground and hung droplets of sperm (1) on it. Then he steers the female so that the can take up the sperm droplets with the ovipositor apparatus at the hind end of her body.

chelicerates, use modified legs to assist copulation. The trip from water to land, begun hundreds of millions of years ago, was long and filled with detours. Only a very few groups of animals have managed to complete it. It is no wonder, then, that humidity has remained, even for these, one of the most important determinants of their distribution in terrestrial habitats.

2   Light

By W. Tobias

Fig. 2-1. Light is electromagnetic radiation, only a certain part of which we perceive as color. The diagram shows the different parts of the spectrum seen by man and by the bee.

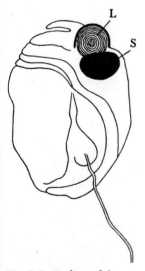

Fig. 2-2. Outline of the flagellate *Pouchetia cornuta*, showing the "eyespot." L, "lens"; S, stigma.

The biologist August Thienemann once spoke of the "cosmic meshwork" of factors to which all living beings were subordinate. Indeed, the origin and existence of living matter on the earth is to a great extent dependent upon an abiotic factor arising in outer space—the light of the sun. It is not surprising, then, that in human history the sun has always been revered as the source of life, and often has been given divine status. Powerful, highly developed cultures like those of ancient Egypt and the Incas were based on a sun cult, and even today this star plays a central role in the religion of many primitive peoples.

From the point of view of physics, light is a form of electromagnetic radiation released by sources such as the sun, other stars, light bulbs, and flames. The light we perceive with our eyes represents only a limited range of the whole spectrum of wavelengths; this visible range extends approximately from wavelengths of 0.75 to 0.40 μm (1μm = one-thousandth of a millimeter). We perceive infrared radiation, which includes the wave-lengths above 0.75 μm, only as heat; the short-wave-length ultraviolet radiation, on the other hand, is not directly perceived by humans. Other organisms, such as lower invertebrates and insects, have photoreceptors quite capable of detecting infrared or ultraviolet waves invisible to man.

The light emitted by a source is in certain cases part of the thermal radiation (or incandescence) associated with its own temperature; other kinds of sources emit "cold light" (or luminescence). The two differ both in the spectral composition of the radiation and in its origin. Heat radiation has a spectrum characteristic of the temperature of a radiating body and independent of its atomic structure. Luminescence, on the other hand, is restricted to certain ranges of wavelength, depending on the nature of the light source and the material of which it is composed. Light emission here can be excited in different ways—for example, by chemical reactions or electrical gas discharge in fluorescent tubes. Fluorescence is the emission of light at a specific wavelength during excitation; another form of luminescence, phosphorescence, is similar except that light emission begins with some delay after the phosphor is excited, and continues after the excitation has been turned off.

A light source is characterized both by the energy in each light quantum produced and by the total rate at which energy is emitted. The first of these determines wavelength, which in the visible range is perceived as color. Proceeding from the long-wavelength end of the range, the spectral colors are red, orange, yellow, green, blue, and violet; the mixture of these gives white light.

Although the color, or spectral composition, of light is certainly of biological significance, it is usual in ecology to measure only the intensity (strictly, "illuminance")—that is, the total luminous energy impinging on a given area in a given time. This quantity is usually measured in terms of lux. An illuminance of one lux is defined as one lumen per square meter, The lumen, in turn, is the rate of emission of luminous energy in a solid angle of one steradian ($\frac{1}{2}\pi$ of a full sphere) from a point source of one "candela." The candela is the new internationally agreed unit of luminous emittance, defined in terms of a certain area of blackbody at the temperature of freezing platinum.

Two other aspects of optics important in biology, especially for aquatic organisms, are refraction and absorption. According to the rules governing refraction and reflection, a ray of light striking an interface between two transparent objects is divided into two rays, one of which is reflected while the other is bent toward or away from the perpendicular as it enters the second object; only if the ray strikes the interface perpendicularly does it pass straight through without being bent. One consequence of this is that not all the light illuminating a body of water actually enters the water; some fraction of it, depending on the angle of incidence of the rays (i.e., the height of the sun), is reflected back into space. It follows that the "day" is shorter for organisms living in water than for land organisms, and the "night" is longer.

The second of these important effects, absorption, is very much dependent upon wavelength. In the ocean the red wavelengths are completely absorbed by the water very near the surface; at deeper levels the shorter wavelengths progressively become completely absorbed, and just above the depth where darkness is complete, only blue-green light penetrates.

Because of the great distance between sun and earth, sunlight arrives in nearly parallel rays. This directional property is important to many lower animals in that they orient themselves by reference to it (see below). Finally, one further property of light which is detected by some animals is polarization; the direction of partial polarization of reflected sunlight is a key factor in the well-known "light-compass orientation" of arthropods, in particular hymenopterans such as bees.

In order to respond to light stimuli, animals must have special body

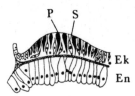

Fig. 2-3. Flat ocellus of the medusa *Catablema eurystoma*. P, pigment cells; S, sense cell; Ek, ectoderm; En, endoderm.

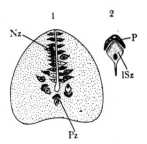

Fig. 2-4. Pigment-cup ocelli of the lancelet *Branchiostoma lanceolatum*: 1. Cross section through the notochord; 2. Single pigment-cup ocellus. 1Sz, light-sensitive sense cell; Nz, nerve cell; P, pigment cell; Pz, pigment-cup ocellus.

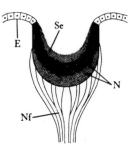

Fig. 2-5. Pit eye of the limpet *Patella*. E, epidermis Se, secreted layer; N, visual and intermediate cells; Nf. nerve fibers.

Fig. 2-6. Vesicular and lenticular eyes:

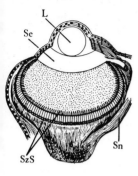

Eye of the polychaete *Vanadis.*
L, lens; Se, secretion; Sn, optic nerve; SzS, sense cells with rods.

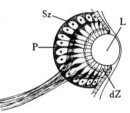

Eye of a spider.
L, lens; dZ, transparent cells; Sz, sense cells; P, pigment.

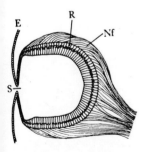

Eye of the cephalopod *Nautilus.*
S, pupil; E, epidermis; R, retina; Nf, nerve fibers.

structures that can absorb light in its various forms and if necessary transmit or modify it. The light receptors found at the different levels of animal organization are often very complicated physico-chemical systems involving reversible photochemical processes. On the other hand, some protozoans, hydrozoans and sponges—and even certain species among higher groups such as clams, crustaceans and insects of caves—lack special light receptors, although these animals do respond to light. The situation is similar in the lower worm phyla and in the gastropods and amphibia, members of which still show responses to light after their photoreceptors have been removed. Such responses are also found in numerous species living in caves or in the ground water. Responses to general illumination of the skin are explained on the basis of sensitivity of the cell plasma to light, especially at short wavelengths.

Light sense organs or photoreceptors—generally called eyes, as long as they exist of more than a single sensory cell—may have devices to adjust the amount of light entering, and lens systems to refract the light, but the fundamental element in light absorption is the visual pigment of the retina. Each pigment absorbs light most strongly in a certain range of wavelengths. The most familiar animal pigment is the rhodopsin of vertebrate eyes, so called because of its reddish color in the dark. When illuminated it is chemically altered (bleached), and the products of this chemical reaction cause excitation of the optic nerves, which leads to the sensation of brightness. Bleached pigment is continually being reconverted to its original state so that it can respond to new stimuli.

The biochemical processes in the illuminated eye are closely coupled to adaptation of the receptor to the prevailing light intensity. Depending on the brightness of the light, the pupil through which light enters the eye constricts or expands; this pupil reflex is thus an additional mechanism regulating vision.

The variations in structure and function of animal light-sensing organs are many; here we shall mention only a few representative types in protozoans and multicellular animals:

1. Red "eyespots" (stigmata); in front of these there may be light-refracting amylum granules that probably serve as lenses. Eyespots are found among the protozoa in certain flagellates (Fig. 2-2).

2. Flat ocelli, in which light-sensitive cells are usually closely packed to form a flat surface, sometimes shielded on one side by pigment, are found in jellyfish, certain worms, and sea stars (Fig. 2-3).

3. Pigment-cup ocelli; here visual cells are surrounded by a "cup" consisting of one or more pigment cells; these are found in turbellarians and lancelets (Amphioxi; see Fig. 2-4).

4. Pit eyes; these represent a more advanced stage of development, with the upper layer of the skin (the epithelium), including visual and pigment cells, indented and thus better protected. Pit-type eyes are found in gastropods (Fig. 2-5).

5. Spherical or vesicular eyes, with our without lenses, as found in poly-chaetes, mollusks, arthropods and vertebrates; these are the most highly developed light sensors in the animal kingdom. The retina in this type of eye can contain visual cells differentiated into rods and cones so as to per-mit color and form vision as well as intensity discrimination (Figs. 2-6 and 2-7).

6. Compound eyes, also called facet eyes, as found chiefly in the arthro-pods; these are composed of many single "eyes" (ommatidia) in a close-packed array (Fig. 2-8). There is an important functional distinction between two anatomical types. The most common type, found in insects active by day such as the bee, is called the "apposition" type. Here the ommatidia are well shielded from one another by opaque pigments—each ommatidium forms a tiny inverted image of a small region of the surrounding environment. In the other type, called the "superposition eye," little pigment is present between adjacent ommatidia and it has long been suggested that many ommatidia can cooperate (act as an extended lens) in producing a sharp, erect image near the base of the ommatidia (Fig. 2-10). Such an arrangement, in a sense, has more light-gathering power and has been thought to be advantageous to nocturnal animals. It has recently been shown that the eye of the nocturnal moth *Ephestia* is of the superposition type. Remarkably, a third type of com-pound-eye organization has recently been demonstrated by K. Kirschfeld, in the eye of the housefly. Here each ommatidium has its several receptors spread out in space in such a way that several nearby ommatidia have receptors "looking" in the same direction; in the nervous system, the signals from just these sets of receptors are combined into one signal!

There are many examples of a direct influence of light upon the ex-ternal appearance of animals, and such effects have been demonstrated experimentally. Morphological adaptations to this aspect of the environ-ment are especially familiar among those species which, in the course of evolution, have come to live in habitats with little or no light. Animals constantly exposed to sunlight have pigments in the skin to shield them from harmful radiation. By contrast, a great number of animals living in ground water, caves, and the soil, as well as wood-burrowing insect larvae and parasites within the bodies of other animals, are known to have lost their skin pigments and undergone regression of the eyes.

True ground-water organisms (stygobionts) are as a rule completely blind, colored a translucent white, and very unwilling to stay in the light. Chief among these animals are small crustacea, most probably descended from ancestors that once lived above ground and must have had eyes. In this case blindness and loss of pigmentation are secondary develop-ments. This interpretation is corroborated by examples among their contemporary relatives which display successive stages in regression of the eyes according to habitat; all parts of the eye may be involved in this regression—muscles, cornea, iris, lens, and the layers of pigment and

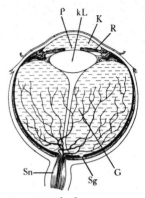

Fig. 2-7. The human eye. P, pupil; kL, lens; K, aqueous humor; R, iris; G, vitreous humor; Sg, fovea; Sn, optic nerve.

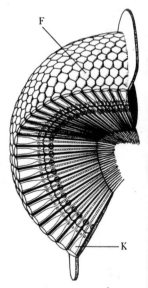

Fig. 2-8. Compound eye of a butterfly, with a wedge-shaped section removed. F, facets; K, crystalline cone.

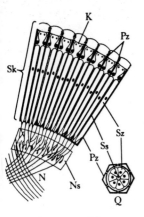

Fig. 2-9. Some of the ommatidia forming a compound eye.
K, crystalline cone; N, nerve fibers; Ns, nerve-cell layer; Pz, pigment cells; Q, cross section of an ommatidium; Sk, longitudinal section of the ommatidia; Ss, rhabdome (visual pigment); Sz, retinula (sense) cells.

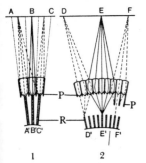

Fig. 2-10. Diagram of the paths of light rays in an apposition eye (1) and a superposition eye (2).
P, pigment; R, rhabdome; A-F, points on an object; A'-F', rhabdomes receiving light from these points.

Controllable reduction of pigmentation

visual cells. Regression of the light-sensing organs can be so complete that only the optic nerve remains. However, the various stages of regression found in ground-water animals do not fit into a single general arrangement; they are found to different degrees in different species (Fig. 2-11).

One well-known eyeless ground-water animal is *Niphargus*, a crustacean widespread in central and southern Europe. Of the two most common species, *Niphargus aquilex* inhabits slowly flowing streams of ground water in the plains of central and western Europe, while the larger *Niphargus puteanus* lives in the water in clefts of the central mountains. Both are found frequently in springs and because of their white coloration can easily be distinguished from the related brook-dwelling crustacean *Rivulogammarus pulex*. Instead of eyes, *Niphargus* has only a small spot composed of a clump of nuclei surrounded by cytoplasm; this is associated with a nerve ganglion. There are no pigments in the skin at all.

A series of investigations has shown that the habitat of the subspecies *N. aquilex schellenbergi* is not entirely restricted to the lightless ground water, but extends to connected bodies of water above ground. Ground water is known to be poor in nutrients, and all animals living there which are not entirely carnivorous must depend upon plant food washed down from the surface. The scarcity of food in the ground water often drives the vegetarian *Niphargus* up to a point where the water emerges from the ground; in such springs, or sometimes even at some distance, it finds food in the form of dead leaves and the like. But since it avoids light, it must wait until darkness falls in the evening to begin foraging, and with the approach of dawn it returns to its subterranean refuge. Kureck's observations have shown that this small eyeless crustacean responds with undirected "startle reactions" when illuminated with diffuse light of more than 3.5 lux; it finds its way back to the darkness of its home by moving against the current of water.

Lack of pigmentation is an inherited characteristic of many stygobiotic Crustacea and cave isopods. There are scotophilous species (with a preference for darkness) in which loss of color is a short-term, reversible adaptation under physiological control. The turbellarian *Crenobia montenegrina*, a species frequently encountered in Balkan mountain streams, is colored greenish to grey-black; it occasionally wanders into caves, and then it loses all its color and becomes pure white. A similar loss of color occurs in the brook crustacean *Rivulogammarus pulex*, the brownish-yellow exoskeleton of which becomes almost colorless when the animal leaves the water above ground to live in a cave. The reverse of this process can be demonstrated experimentally with the colorless cave salamander *Proteus anguinus*; when exposed for some time to weak illumination, its whitish-yellow skin turns a dark gray as a result of pigment formation.

Another example of gradation of skin color associated with the light available in the habitat is given by the different species of the fish

Chologaster (family Amblyopsidae, a native of the southern U.S.A. *Chologaster cornutus* lives in the open water of large swamps and is dark brown with gray on the underside; the skin of the spring-dwelling *C. papilliferus* is distinctly paler, and *C. agassizii*, which lives in subterranean rivers where any coloration would be invisible, may lack skin pigments altogether. In parallel with this stepwise regression of skin pigmentation, these three species also show a progressive diminution of the size of the eyeball.

Many inhabitants of caves, where light of course has no ecological significance, are completely blind. Such animals often compensate for the loss of vision by an enormous development of the senses of touch and smell. In a dimly lit environment, on the other hand, there is often an emphasis on development of the organs of sight. For example, think of the large eyes of deep-sea fish, owls, and some lemurs.

Studies of the eyes of benthic fish have shown that the pupil and lens may be disproportionately enlarged, independent of any increase in the diameter of the eyeball. Moreover, the retinas of such fish rarely contain cones, the visual cells that enable color vision and the sharpest image formation. In their place are between 100,000 and twenty million long rods per square millimeter of retina; these allow the fish to detect extremely low light intensities.

Such eyes, highly sensitive under twilight conditions, are presumably important in feeding, since predatory deep-sea fish can thus detect passing prey, perhaps directly or at least by way of its shadow. But they also participate to some extent in the search for a sexual partner. In angler fish of the genus *Ceratias* (family Ceratiidae) the eyes of the females are greatly regressed, whereas those of the males are enlarged. The females, on the other hand, have luminescent organs, by the light of which the males can locate them in the darkness of the deep sea. The fish share this habitat with a variety of organisms, from many different animal groups, which also are equipped with luminescent organs. One would expect, then, that the female angler fish must glow or wink in a particular way if she is to attract a male of her own species; additional stimuli, chemical or tactile, are certainly involved as well. There is a great deal still to be learned about the ecological relationships between light production and the development of light-sensitive organs in benthic animals.

Apart from the influence of weak or absent light upon the formation of visual organs and upon skin color in dim habitats, light is also effective in producing color change in diurnal animals. Such color changes may be either physiological or morphological. In both cases the light stimuli —more precisely, certain changes in illumination—are detected either by the eyes or special sensors in the skin, and elicit nerve impulses which directly or indirectly affect the color of the body surface.

In physiological color change, no new pigments are formed as a result of the light stimulus; color change is brought about by shifting of the

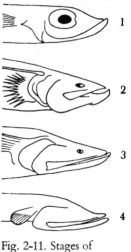

Fig. 2-11. Stages of regression of the eyes in benthic fish:
1. *Chlorophthalmus productus* from depth of 575 m;
2. *Bathypterois dubius*, 800-1000 m;
3. *Benthosaurus grallator*, 3000 m;
4. *Bathymicrops regis*, 5000 m.

Physiological color change

Fig. 2-12. An insect approaches a light source along a spiral path. This behavior presumably results from light-compass orientation.

pigment granules already present in the skin. In some cases pigment cells may expand or contract, forming local patterns which can change the overall coloration of the animals. Physiological color change is often controlled by the change in light intensity during the day; for example, springtails (order Collembola), stick insects like *Carausius morosus*, the larvae of the axolotl (*Amblystoma mexicanum*), and the fish *Stenostomus chrysops* usually change color very rapidly as night falls or the sun rises. Color changes in adaptation to the color of the surroundings proceed considerably more slowly and are independent of the daily light rhythm. The best-known example here is probably the color change by which many bottom fish—like rays and flounders—match themselves to the background; even the occasional dark spots in an otherwise uniformly light sea floor are faithfully imitated in the pattern of the fish's skin.

Physiological color changes have several functions. On the one hand, they can protect the animal from the effects of harmful radiation such as ultraviolet light, if it is absorbed by the pigment, and they may also serve in temperature regulation. On the other hand, they provide protection in the form of camouflage, and can help to disguise a predator as it lies in wait for its prey. A special case is the play of color and pattern in the skin of cephalopods, which can change in a fraction of a second and probably acts to frighten off attackers.

Morphological color change

In the case of morphological color change, pigments are not rearranged but broken down or synthesized. Accordingly, the effects of a light stimulus require a much longer time to become apparent. To this category belong the darkening in light of *Proteus anguinus*, mentioned above, and the destruction of pigments in animals that have evolved into cave dwellers.

It has been found by H. J. Müller that light can affect the color and pattern of the wings of a great number of butterflies. Depending on whether the larvae are exposed to short or long periods of light each day during development, the butterflies emerging from the pupae are differently colored and patterned. This phenomenon is called seasonal dimorphism; it has been the cause of some mistakes in classification. For example, the brush-footed butterfly *Araschnia levana* is orange-yellow flecked with black if it develops in the spring, when the days are short, and also has a dark brown, white-spotted summer form. At first, because of their dissimilar appearance, the two forms were described as separate species.

Some birds such as the ptarmigan, as well as mammals like the alpine hare or weasel, change their coats of feathers or fur at the onset of winter, turning white. Recently it has been shown in the case of a certain subspecies of hamster (*Phadopus sungorus sungorus*) that the color change was not—as had been thought—elicited by the falling autumn temperatures; the sole cause was the shortening of the periods of daylight.

Light and orientation

Light also has a strong influence upon the orientation behavior of animals. Practically everyone has observed its attracting effect on flying insects, which gather around light sources like street lamps, show windows and automobile headlights. The movement of an animal directly toward a light stimulus is called a positive phototactic reaction; if it goes away from light, it is showing negative phototaxis. Phototactic orientation can be observed even in relatively primitive animals. Fresh-water coelenterates of the genus *Hydra* in a glass aquarium, illuminated from one side only, move toward the light source, whereas the turbellarian *Dugesia* shows a negative photic reaction, turning away from the light and searching out dark corners of the observation tank.

Some animals adopt a certain angle to a light source, rather than moving toward it or away. Movement in a direction at a specific angle to the sun has been studied especially in hymenopterans, but orientation at an angle to light has also been observed in caddisflies and butterflies; such behavior requires a certain capacity for memory. Nest-dwelling hymenopterans such as the workers in ant colonies find their way through familiar territory, when foraging for food and bringing it back to the nest, by noting the angle of their route to the parallel rays of the sun. If black garden ants (*Lasius niger*), following a path at a certain angle to the sun, are covered with a light-tight box and kept there for several hours, after the box is removed they resume movement at the same angle and thus diverge from the original path.

Sometimes flying animals—for example, Mayflies—approach an object emitting light by following a spiral path. This is presumably also a form of light-compass orientation; the animal eventually flies into the light if the angle between the light rays and the illuminated side of its body is less than 90° (Fig. 2-12). With an angle greater than 90°, its flight path will follow a spiral that takes it further from the light. It has been suggested that this behavior is more closely comparable to the dorsal and ventral light reflexes of aquatic animals; these reflexes function to keep the upper or lower side of the body turned toward the light source. The back-swimmer *Notonecta glauca*, for example, always moves about on its back, whereas leeches, the larvae of water beetles, and diving odonatans keep their backs toward the water surface.

Positive and negative orientations are not the only forms of behavior influenced by light; level and type of activity may also be affected. Decreasing light intensity draws nocturnal moths, owls, bats and many small mammals out of their hiding places, and the twilight before sunrise drives them back again. Their place is taken then by day-active animals that respond to light in just the reverse manner. In both cases daylight exerts a general control over their behavior, imposing a rhythm of sleep and wakefulness.

Light-dependent changes of activity during both the day and the year have been studied in detail. Not only variations in intensity are effective; an even more crucial aspect for development of the locomotor, feeding and sexual behavior of animals is the duration of the photoperiod in the

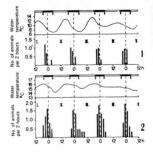

Fig. 2-13. Daily periodicity in the emergence of caddisfly populations (genus *Potamophylax*) under natural conditions in the field on five successive days (I-V). 1. *Potamophylax cingulatus*; 2. *P. luctuosus*. Black horizontal bars: dark period between sunset and sunrise. Vertical bars: number of animals emerging in two hours; the grouping shows that emergence is concentrated during the night. The wavy line above the bars gives the water temperature in °C.

Light-dependent change in activity

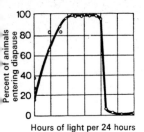

Fig. 2-14. Influence of photoperiod upon the onset of diapause in the caterpillar of *Apatele rumicis*.

daily alternation between light and darkness. The fact that numerous species of insect interrupt the development of the young stages in summer —despite the apparently favorable high temperatures and abundance of food—and enter a resting phase (diapause) can definitely be ascribed to the influence of light. The light sets in motion certain hormonal regulatory mechanisms evolved in association with the climatic or other peculiarities of an animal's environment; during the resulting diapause, seasons unfavorable to development and reproduction are skipped over.

Diapause may be elicited directly by light, but in some cases it is "pre-programmed," in the sense that light conditions to which early developmental stages, such as larvae still within the egg, are exposed induce diapause indirectly later on, in the pupal stage. For example, if caterpillars of *Apatele rumicis* are exposed to short periods of daylight, less than fifteen hours, all the pupae that develop enter diapause; but if the light period is increased to more than sixteen hours the pupae omit the resting phase.

Georges Cuvier, as early as 1817, described diurnal changes in the movement of planktonic animals, which rise to the surface of the water at night and by day move into deeper zones. But it was not until this century that this vertical migration of plankton in lakes and in the ocean was shown to depend upon light, even in the case of benthic crustacea at such depths that the daily oscillation of light intensity can barely be detected. From observations of the daily and annual periodicity of certain biological phenomena there has developed a separate branch of the natural sciences called chronobiology. It is concerned with discovering the influence of regulatory factors upon biological rhythmicity. And probably the most important abiotic regulatory mechanism in eliciting biological rhythms—as we have seen in these examples—is light.

3 Currents and Oxygen

Currents of air and water are predominant features of many animal habitats, and they are among the environmental factors that determine the distribution of animals. Their effects can be classified in two groups: currents transport matter and energy to and from the animals (for example, they may supply food or affect temperature by heat convection); second, currents transport the animals themselves.

By M. P. D. Meijering

The open air is rarely free of currents; periods of quiet are only local and of short duration. Air movement is the rule—as wind, if the flow is horizontal over the earth's surface, or as thermal updrafts. Winds can reach hurricane velocities; these may be as high as 100 meters per second. Wind velocities of 40–60 meters per second are frequently measured during storms. At any given place wind direction can vary considerably, but there are often prevailing winds; for example, west winds are so common on the shores of the Deutsche Bucht (northern Germany and western Denmark) that they affect the angle at which trees lean along the roads, and the trade winds of the tropics blow toward the equator all the year round.

Air currents

Winds of course have long-lasting effects upon flying animals; insects and even birds can be swept over great distances during prolonged storms. The Parry expedition in 1827 found the spruce aphid *Cinaripsis piceae* on snowdrifts in northern Spitzbergen, ten degrees of latitude away from the northern timberline in Scandinavia. The aphids had drifted with the air currents in great numbers, over more than a thousand kilometers. Dispersal so far from the normal range is disastrous from the viewpoint of species survival; therefore insects on windy islands often develop adaptations limiting their ability to fly, and by remaining on the ground escape being blown out to sea. More than half of the insect species living on subantarctic islands have regressed wings or none at all. Their habitats are small and the climate is extremely stormy, so that it is essential for the animals to keep to the ground. The effects of storms on insects not so adapted can be seen in summer on the coast of the North Sea, when the wind is blowing from the land; thousands of white cabbage butterflies (*Pieris brassicae*) are carried offshore, and their bodies drift back and pile up on the beach at high tide.

But there are other species that turn the air currents to their own advantage. Larvae of the black arches (*Lymantria monacha*) have many very long hairs that help them become dispersed by drifting through the air. Some species lacking special flight structures make such devices for themselves; caterpillars of *Cacoecia murinana* and the spider *Teragnatha extensa* spin threads on which they drift for great distances—a striking phenomenon which can be observed in late summer.

Moving masses of air assist many species in orientation by transporting odor substances. Scents carried by air currents announce the location of enemies, prey, or sexual partners. Male gypsy moths (*Lymantria dispar*) can detect sexual attractant substances produced by the females and wafted to them over the remarkable distance of three or four kilometers.

Vertical air movements (convection currents) are used by gulls and many birds of prey as they rise effortlessly to great heights. A master of this technique is the arctic fulmar (*Fulmarus glacialis*), which glides close to the surface of the sea for great distances without beating its wings, using the winds that rise above the slopes of the waves. When the air is still, this bird finds it difficult to take off from the water. But in severe storms, when most sea birds stay on the ground or water, the arctic fulmar flies as nimbly as ever, without concern for the wind.

The most pronounced ecological effects are those of large-scale air movements, involving warmed masses of air from lower latitudes flowing toward the poles. In northwestern Europe the onset of spring is often associated with the displacement of the cold air over the continent by warm air masses moving in from the Atlantic. The temperature of a region is largely dependent upon the direction from which its prevailing winds come. Moreover, such winds transport clouds, and the degree of cloud cover affects the water balance of an area. The distribution of all terrestrial animal species is influenced by such indirect effects of air currents.

Ocean currents

In water, too, there are significant currents, though their velocities are a good deal lower than those of air currents. The highest values are reached in waterfalls, where the water can travel at as much as six meters per second. The largest-scale movements of water masses are found in the oceans, where warm currents and the associated cold currents flow over thousands of kilometers. In warm currents velocities of more than two meters per second have been measured. The ecological significance of these streams lies chiefly in their long-distance heat transport; in this respect they are comparable to the massive air currents. In the Atlantic, the north equatorial current flows into the region of the Caribbean. From there the main pattern of circulation is represented by the Gulf Stream, which turns to the northeast and crosses the Atlantic toward the European coast. The outermost offshoots of the Gulf Stream wash up on the western coasts of Spitzbergen, where even in winter, at 78° latitude, there are fiords free of ice. At the same time the cold Labrador Current carries drift ice from the polar sea down to the coast of Nova Scotia, at 45° latitude. Whereas the northern timberline in Norway is at 70° latitude, in Labrador the forests reach only as far north as 52°. There, at the same latitude as Berlin, tundra begins. The spatial distribution of the climate, vegetation and faunal belts in the Atlantic region is due to combined effects of ocean and air currents. An analogous system is found in the northern Pacific.

Tidal currents, by comparison, are of only local significance, but they can often be very strong. Near coasts the regular fluctuations of water level produce regularly reversing currents. Upon the flood and ebb tides are superimposed the more rapid changes in water level caused by the surf (see Color plate, p. 53). Animals adapted to tidal currents live in zones forming belts parallel to the coast. In order to stay in this zone, and not be thrown ashore by the currents, numerous species of the tidal zone have adopted a sessile way of life. As sessile animals with adequate attachment mechanisms, they are safe from being washed away, but they have other problems—they may quickly exhaust the food supply within reach. To this end, the currents prove beneficial; the water flowing past continually renews the supply of food and oxygen, and carries away the waste products of the animal's metabolism. The flowing water is a substitute for locomotor activity of the animal, which would otherwise be required to find food.

Life in the tidal zone has considerable advantages, as one may infer from the density of the animal populations there. The sea water near the coast is particularly rich in floating organic matter, the special food supply of filter-feeders. Very high densities of individual organisms are found in mussel colonies (*Mytilus edulis*), in "fields" of the tube worm *Lanice conchilega*, and on rocks and pilings covered with the barnacle *Balanus balanoides*. The great fertility of the animals on such surfaces is due to the abundant supply of nutrients. These populations are comparable in a sense to the herds of animals that can be kept in barns when there is sufficient cultivated land outside to provide fodder.

The water in the surf zone is rich in oxygen. When the water is churned into froth by the waves its surface area is greatly increased and there is more opportunity for oxygen to become dissolved. A sufficient supply of oxygen is another requirement for high fertility in aquatic animals, and in flowing waters conditions are excellent for respiration.

Animals colonizing the tidal zones encounter difficulties when the flowing water shifts the soil or sand. Where the beach is being washed away large numbers of animals normally buried may become exposed; the long-necked clam, *Mya arenaria*, dies and leaves its empty shell projecting from the ground. And where the current slows, the materials carried by the water are deposited, so that the animals there must somehow save themselves from being buried. The tube worm *Lanice conchilega* under such conditions must repeatedly work its way to the surface and build a new

Tidal currents

▷
Breakers occur when waves formed by winds on the high seas (swells) hit shallows or coasts. Water in these regions is especially rich in oxygen.

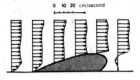

Fig. 3-1. Current velocity in an artificial channel having an obstruction on its floor.

Flowing waters

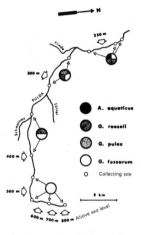

Fig. 3-2. Distribution of three species of the amphipod *Gammarus* and of the isopod *Asellus aquaticus* in the upper Fulda River.

◁

Left, top to bottom: Large boulders in a brook high in the South American Andes; high-mountain brook in eastern New Guinea carrying a suspension of yellow clay; stream from a glacier near Ny Ålesund (northwestern Spitzbergen), carrying red clay.
Right: Casts of the mud-flat worm *Arenicola marina*.

tube. If large amounts of substrate are displaced, sessile animals can be torn from their moorings and flung onto the beach. In warm tide pools and in the wrack left as the tide recedes one can find, among the torn-up seaweed, dying clams, sea anemones, other polyps and marine worms. Swarms of jellyfish can be caught in landward currents and stranded on the beach. Cabbage butterflies over the ocean, aphids on Arctic snow fields, and jellyfish on beaches are all victims of currents which for one reason or another they could not avoid. It becomes as no surprise, then, when we find that in habitats characterized by currents only a highly adapted fauna can survive.

Particularly good examples of such habitats are found in fresh-water streams. The special property of these currents is that they are fairly steady and always move in one direction. In most cases these habitats are extra-ordinarily long in comparison with their width, and the current velocity is related to the terrain, being highest just below the source. Further down-stream the velocity falls, rapidly at first and then more slowly. Often, though, the distribution of current velocity along a watercourse differs from this model. If one considers a cross-section of a river, the current becomes stronger from the banks to the middle of the stream, but it fre-quently happens that the point of highest velocity is shifted toward one of the banks. Finally, the current of course becomes progressively weaker as one makes a series of measurements from the surface down to the stream bed and in the spaces between stones there.

Free-moving animals are subjected to the most rapid changes in current velocity—for example, when they move from the sheltered lee of a stone onto its upper surface. But even sessile animals experience gradual changes in current strength if the water level fluctuates. Life in flowing water thus requires adaptation to variations in current.

As the water flows it carries heat energy, oxygen, nitrogen, carbon dioxide, salts, suspended clay particles (see Color plate, p. 54) and organic compounds for long distances. Whereas in standing waters these sub-stances form layers, in streams they are mixed so that over large regions the conditions of life are relatively uniform. Changes in the ecological situation appear only gradually, so that flowing-water animals that drift along with the current are transported initially into regions similar to those they have left. Only after drifting for some time do they find themselves in unsuitable zones.

A flowing-water (lotic) habitat may be classified as rhithral (brooks) or potamal (rivers). Rhithral habitats are characterized by strong currents and a bed covered by large stones or boulders (see Color plate, p. 54). The finer particles are suspended in the fast-flowing water and carried into the potamal region, where the current slows and they fall as sediment to the river bed. The dividing line between the two regions in a system of streams is taken as the place where the amplitude of the water temperature fluctuation during a year (that is, the range between minimum and maximum temperatures) is 20°C; near the source the amplitude is very small, and it gradually increases at points further downstream. In the Fulda river, for example, the boundary between rhithral and potamal regions coincides roughly with the place where it is joined by the Fliede. The distribution of certain crustaceans in the upper reaches of the Fulda makes clear the extent to which individual species are adapted to the different current conditions. The upper subsection (epirhithral region) of the Fulda is colonized only by the highly adapted amphipod *Gammarus fossarum*; this species is joined in the middle subsection by *Gammarus pulex*, which can actually withstand strong current equally well but is kept out of the upper region by the low winter temperatures. This limitation was demonstrated in experiments with *G. pulex*, in which the animals were left to cope as best they could for an hour in a five-meter long artificial stream. At moderate temperatures the great majority remained in the upper stream, near the inlet, whereas at low winter temperatures most of them drifted down toward the sieve at the outlet (Fig. 3-3). Correspondingly, in natural conditions, *G. pulex* expands its range by upstream migration in summer, but in winter it loses the ground it has gained. This, then, is a case in which the effects of current and temperature upon an animal species interact. In the lower (hypothithral) subsection of the brook region of the Fulda there is a third species, *Gammarus roeseli* (Fig. 3-2), that can maintain itself only in weak currents. And in the upper river (epipotamal) region begins the range of the water isopod *Asellus aquaticus*.

The distribution of *Gammarus* species described here for the Fulda is repeated in comparable river systems of central Europe. Moreover, a similar zonation has been found for other flowing-water animals, such as fish and insect larvae. Fisheries biologists call the epirhithral in these rivers the "upper trout region" and the epipotamal, the "barbel region."

In swiftly flowing waters bottom-dwelling organisms are at an advantage. They have a direct hold on the substrate and their bodies are in a thin layer of slower current produced by frictional resistance of the stream bed (Fig. 3-1). Many rhithral animals are very much flattened, so that they can move about without encountering the stronger currents. Plankton is very sparse in the rhithral region, since any organisms moved passively by the open water are carried downstream. Only in the lower river regions is there an appreciable plankton population.

Even small bottom animals with low-slung bodies occasionally stray into the fast-moving water; nets hung across a stream catch a variety of drifting organisms that have lost their hold on the bottom and have been carried some distance downstream. Such drifting animals try to return to the stream bed as quickly as possible, where they can find new shelter from the current, behind stones or in tangled vegetation. Nevertheless, the total distance covered repeatedly by drifting bottom animals is considerable, and one may well ask what compensates for this downstream shift of the population. There are two mechanisms operating, though

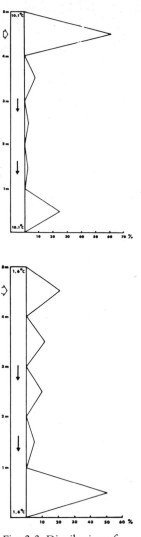

Fig. 3-3. Distribution of *Gammarus pulex* one hour after the animals were placed in a stream of water at the position of the white arrow; the temperature was 10.1°C (above) or 1.6°C (below). Black arrows indicate the current direction.

Drift and upstream migration

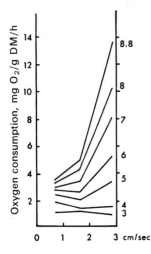

Fig. 3-4. Oxygen consumption (mg per g dry matter per hour) of larvae of the caddisfly *Rhyacophila nubila*, as a function of oxygen content and current velocity.

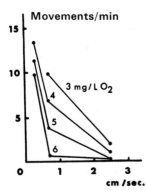

Fig. 3-5. Frequency of respiratory movements of larvae of the caddisfly *Hydropsyche angustipennis*, as a function of oxygen content and current velocity.

Oxygen

their relative share in negating the effects of drift is not exactly known. One of them is simply the balance between mortality and reproduction; the removal of some animals leaves more room for the animals that remain, and this becomes filled with their progeny. The other process is upstream migration; many species, some of them amphipods, do this at certain seasons of the year. Reproduction and migration together must make good the losses by drift, since the communities in running water do manage to maintain themselves over long periods.

The upstream migrations make evident that many animals have a "current sense," which allows them to orient themselves with respect to the flowing water. Fish detect water movements with the lateral lines. In insect larvae, current-sensitive groups of bristles have been demonstrated. The capacity to detect direction and strength of current gives a rhithral animal the opportunity to seek out habitats where the current is most suitable. Many species have been observed to show a definite preference for certain currents; this suggests that in the natural habitat currents offer physiological advantages which can be exploited by properly adapted animals.

For example, it has been shown that larvae of the caddisfly *Rhyacophila nubila* take up more oxygen in fast than in slower currents. Larvae of the caddisffly *Hydropsyche angustipennis*, which live in streams, increase their rates of respiration when the current slows as well as when the oxygen tension falls. Both observations indicate that a given oxygen concentration can be better utilized in flowing than in standing water. In fact, this is the heart of the problem encountered by animals—particularly sessile animals—living in standing waters; their respiratory activity withdraws oxygen from the water, and they must expend energy (derived from respiration) in locomotion in order to exchange the depleted water in their immediate vicinity for fresh water. Animals in streams have both water and food delivered to their doors.

Currents of all sorts, then, bring a number of advantages to the habitats where they exist. But these are available only to a suitably adapted fauna, with effective protective mechanisms against involuntary deportation.

Oxygen plays a central role in the metabolism of most organisms. It participates in respiration—a chain of chemical reactions related to combustion, from which energy is obtained for other physiological processes. Energy-rich molecules such as carbohydrates are broken down in oxygen-consuming reactions to form low-molecular-weight compounds with little energy; carbon dioxide and water are given off in these reactions, and energy is liberated. The process of respiration can be summarized in terms of its initial and end products, as follows:

$$C_6H_{-2}O_6 + 6\,O_2 \rightarrow 6\,CO_2 + 6\,H_2O + 674 \text{ kilocalories (kcal)};$$

in terms of weight, to burn up 180 grams (1 mole, or gram-molecular weight) of glucose 192 grams of oxygen are required, and 264 grams carbon dioxide and 108 grams of water are produced.

Respiration steadily consumes oxygen and produces another gas, carbon dioxide, at the same rate. To maintain a supply of energy the organism depends upon a continual replenishment of oxygen and removal of carbon dioxide. This regular gas exchange with the environment is crucial for animals, since they are incapable of storing any appreciable amount of oxygen. If the environment runs out of oxygen, respiratory stress develops and death is imminent.

Balancing this constant oxygen consumption and carbon dioxide production of almost all animals is the assimilation of carbon dioxide by the green tissues of plants (photosynthesis), summarized as follows:

$$6 \; CO_2 + 12 \; H_2O + \text{sunlight energy} \rightarrow C_6H_{12}O_6 + 6 \; O_2 + 6 \; H_2O.$$

The energy consumed in this combination of carbon dioxide and water to form glucose is provided by the sun. Photosynthesis produces oxygen at the same rate as it consumes carbon dioxide; an overall equilibrium is established in nature between the processes of respiration and photosynthesis.

But observation of specific plant and animal habitats reveals that the circulation of oxygen and carbon dioxide by no means always functions to maintain equilibrium. There can be local accumulations or deficiencies of gases, and these affect the limits of distribution of organisms. An animal must leave any site where the oxygen is depleted; that is, at such sites oxygen content becomes the limiting environmental factor.

In small animals most of the cells are near the surface of the body, and gases are exchanged directly through the skin. As body size and metabolism increase, breathing through the skin is no longer sufficient. Additional exchange surfaces are developed and elaborated into special respiratory organs. Land animals, by invagination of the body surface, have evolved complicated systems of cavities with enormous surface area, over which the exchange of oxygen and carbon dioxide can take place; for example, the tracheae of insects conduct air from outside the animal to the sites of respiratory metabolism in the tissues. Land vertebrates developed lungs with many tiny vesicles, the alveoli; the total alveolar surface can be many times as great as that of the body. The gills of aquatic animals also serve to enlarge the respiratory surface, in this case by evagination of tissues which protrude into the surrounding water. With lungs and gills, transport of the gases to the site of metabolism and back is accomplished by the circulation of blood.

The blood of an adult human contains about one liter of oxygen, bound to the red pigment hemoglobin; oxygen is withdrawn from the hemoglobin as it is required for metabolism. Exchange of oxygen occurs whenever there is a concentration difference between the oxygen in equilibrium with that bound to hemoglobin and the oxygen in its surroundings—that is, oxygen is freed if the oxygen tension in the tissues is less than that in the blood. The same principle applies in reverse in the respiratory organs; the partial pressure of oxygen in the air is relatively high as com-

Oxygen production

Oxygen uptake

Oxygen transport

pared with the oxygen concentration in the blood, and hemoglobin takes up oxygen. The exchange of carbon dioxide proceeds similarly, except that carbon dioxide is to a great extent dissolved in the blood plasma itself, only a fraction of it being carried in the red corpuscles in the form of sodium or potassium bicarbonate. The capacity of hemoglobin to bind oxygen depends not only on the oxygen concentration but on other factors as well, such as the concentration of carbon dioxide in the vicinity. This means that as the carbon dioxide concentration in the air or water at the respiratory organ increases, so must that of oxygen, if the rate of oxygen uptake is to remain constant.

Oxygen in the air

For terrestrial animals, the air is the source of oxygen and the sink for carbon dioxide. The air has a mean oxygen concentration of 21% by volume, far above that of water, which never exceeds 1%. These numbers in themselves suggest that changes in oxygen concentration will have greater ecological effects in water than on the land. The atmosphere forms a continuous envelope surrounding the earth, within which large-scale air movements ensure thorough mixing. As a result, the concentrations of oxygen and carbon dioxide are relatively constant. The only permanent oxygen gradient occurs at great altitudes and parallels the air-pressure gradient. The extent to which lack of oxygen in the high mountains acts to limit animal distribution is difficult to determine, in view of the large number of other conditions that are also changed at these altitudes. But it is a familiar fact that mountain climbers require an artificial oxygen supply in order to stay at great heights.

Even at lower and intermediate altitudes there can be short-term changes in the oxygen/carbon-dioxide ratio. For example, in the herbaceous layer of open woods during a night when the air is still, the respiration of animals and plants (which also respire) can raise the carbon dioxide content of the air tenfold; during the day it falls again because of photosynthesis by the plants. Here again there are no aspects of animal distribution obviously related to the pattern of oxygen and carbon dioxide content. Ecologists in general emphasize that oxygen plays no appreciable role in the distribution of terrestrial animal species living above ground.

But recent developments make it doubtful that this will always be so. The increase of air pollution in densely populated or industrialized areas has stimulated more intensive study of the gaseous components of the environment; it has been found that on windless days in large cities the atmospheric carbon dioxide, usually around 0.03% by volume, can increase by a factor of ten. This carbon dioxide is one of several end products of the combustion of coal and petroleum. Of the industrial CO_2 about 36% is assimilated by plants in the overall habitat, 14% is dissolved in the oceans, and about 50% remains in the atmosphere, the carbon-dioxide content of which thus steadily increases.

In the course of this century atmospheric carbon dioxide has increased by 15%, and calculations based on the rate of rise in the last few years indicate that by the end of the century the carbon dioxide concentration in the atmosphere may have doubled. And we must keep in mind that processes of combustion also use up oxygen. The burning of 100 liters of gasoline consumes as much oxygen as a man would breathe in a year. According to the most recent calculations, one hectare of pine forest produces about thirty metric tons of oxygen annually, which corresponds to the annual consumption of ninety people; one hectare of deciduous forest yields about sixteen tons, and the same area of land under cultivation gives three to ten tons of oxygen per year. By 1980 Germany will lose an estimated 500,000 hectares of green country, which at present are providing enough oxygen for more than ten million people. The CO_2/O_2 ratio in the air we breathe is undergoing long-term if not permanent changes, and we are well on the way to making gaseous compounds the limiting factors in our environment. This is a trend that man, as a member of the terrestrial community, must no longer ignore.

Another major continental habitat is the soil. Gas exchange here is determined by its porosity; fine gaps and spaces in soil provide for the exchange of air, slow though it may be, with the outside atmosphere. If the inhabitants of the soil are respiring vigorously there may develop oxygen deficiencies and accumulations of carbon dioxide. Depending on the nature of the soil, the concentrations of oxygen and carbon dioxide can vary widely. In humus soils, for example, where there is a great deal of organic matter being decomposed and thus a high rate of respiration of the soil organisms, the carbon dioxide concentration may amount to more than 5% by weight. The local fauna must be adapted to such conditions. It has been shown that springtails (insects of the order Collembola) living near the surface of the soil (*Orchesella villosa* and *Tomocerus vulgaris*) are injured if the carbon dioxide content of the air rises to one or two percent, whereas the deep-soil form *Onychiurus armatus* can withstand a CO_2 content of up to 35%. The earthworm *Lumbricus terrestris* can also survive high carbon dioxide concentrations for considerable periods, though after heavy rain, when water displaces the air from the soil, it temporarily moves to other soil layers or even up to the surface. The amount of oxygen required and consumed by the different soil-dwelling species thus varies widely, and we find a zonation of the soil fauna which corresponds in part to differences in respiratory physiology.

Some soils, like those of the coast and alluvial flats, are conspicuously low in oxygen. Here the decomposition of organic matter and the reduction of sulfates by the metabolism of bacteria causes the production of hydrogen sulfide and a smell familiar to anyone who has dug in the blue-black silt of such regions. But it is surprising how thickly populated these soils are. The problems of survival here have been dealt with in a great variety of ways. A good example of a tidal mud-flat animal is the polychaete worm *Arenicola marina*. It shields itself from the toxic gases in the soil by lining the wall of its tube with sand from the surface; these sand

Oxygen in the soil

Oxygen in mud flats

Fig. 3-6. Oxygen in inland waters:

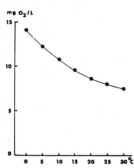

Solubility of oxygen in water, as a function of temperature, at a pressure of about 1 atm.

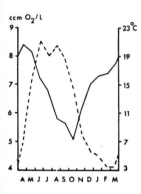

Annual variation of oxygen content (dashed line) and temperature (solid line) in Lake Zurich.

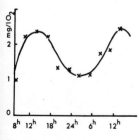

Fig. 3-7. Daily variation of oxygen content in a pond.

grains may be quite different from the surrounding material so that the tube, particularly in blue-black silt, stands out as a light gray. Within its tube, the worm has no contact with its immediate surroundings. It gets all its oxygen from the surface; water flows through the U-shaped tube in a "air conditioning" process comparable to those used in mines. While the worm's oxygen requirements are met by the water of the open sea, it is protected by the slimy soil and can take advantage of the sand as a food filter. To renew the water in the tube, *Arenicola* extends the hind end of its body, decreasing its diameter so that fresh water can flow in around it through the back opening of the tube. Then the worm thickens the posterior segments so as to trap the water inside, and pumps it forward by a series of contractions of the body musculature. The gills are everted and washed by the fresh, aerated water. For about ten minutes the water is moved back and forth in this way, until the blood is charged with oxygen. Then there is a pause of up to fifteen minutes before the "air conditioning" is turned on again. In case of oxygen deficiency the rate of water circulation through the tube can be considerably increased. If the deficiency should persist, the animal leaves its tube—a typical ultimate recourse for inhabitants of such structures (see Color plate, p. 54).

In inland waters oxygen plays a crucial ecological role. The comparatively small amount of oxygen that can dissolve in water depends upon air pressure, temperature and other conditions. The oxygen concentration at which water is saturated can vary by a factor of almost two over the normal range of temperatures (Fig. 3-6); this effect is particularly important in small bodies of water. The change of oxygen content in the upper layer (the epilimnion) of Lake Zurich in the course of a year is shown in the lower graph of Fig. 3-6. Comparison of the curve for oxygen content with that for temperature makes clear the relation between the two. The apparent time lag—the minimum and maximum oxygen content occurring later than the maximum and minimum, respectively, of temperature—indicates other, biotic influences affecting oxygen balance in the lake. For example, vigorous growth of plant plankton in spring enhances the increase in oxygen concentration. In the course of the summer these reserves are steadily used by up the respiration of animals and bacteria, and this process continues after the temperature begins to fall, until the autumn minimum of oxygen is reached. During the winter the combination of low temperature and reduced metabolic activity of the organisms encourages the building up of dissolved oxygen stores, and this is accelerated again in spring when photosynthesis by plankton increases. Hence there is a regular annual oscillation in oxygen content. Fluctuations of oxygen content during the course of a day are also ecologically significant. During algal "blooms" the nighttime respiration of plants and animals can deplete the oxygen reserves of a pond so severely that the fish begin to die, even though the photosynthesis of the algae raises the oxygen content again during the day. Oxygen fluctuations due to biotic causes, then, can under some circumstances predominate over those due to temperature.

Near the surface of a lake (in the limnetic zone) the water may be well illuminated, so that photosynthesis by the plankton proceeds vigorously and oxygen is produced, but in deep lakes the water near the bottom is dark. Here, in the profundal zone, oxygen is only consumed, in the respiratory processes of animals and bacteria that decompose the organic matter sinking to the bottom. This is the case especially in eutrophic lakes, rich in nutrients. If water can circulate to the very bottom of such lakes, the masses of cooling water that sink in autumn from the surface to the depths suffice to replenish the lowest layer with oxygen. This circulation takes place twice a year in some lakes, and in others only once. Lakes with complete circulation are called "holomictic"; there are also "meromictic" lakes in which the water never circulates all the way to the bottom, so that there is a permanent oxygen-free zone in the depths where no organisms that require oxygen can live. In these deep zones hydrogen sulfide may take the place of oxygen. If light can penetrate to the H_2S-containing layers, specialized microorganisms such as the red sulfur bacteria of the genus *Chromatium* carry out photosynthesis without oxygen, combining hydrogen sulfide and carbon dioxide to produce carbohydrate, sulfur and water. *Chromatium* lives in the upper H_2S region of a lake, which is sharply delimited above by the oxygen-containing zone and is bounded below by the gradual decrease in light intensity. There are organisms, then, that can live entirely without oxygen—for these organisms, in fact, oxygen is a poison. Most of them are bacteria.

Many of the animals living in standing waters respond to lack of oxygen by migration. In densely populated ponds, for example, there may be an oxygen deficiency at midday when the temperature is high; then water fleas rise toward the surface in such numbers that the surface water can turn a brownish red. Movements of this sort are based on a positive phototaxis, which in the water flea becomes apparent only when respiration is hampered. This light reaction leads them toward the surface and ceases to operate when the oxygen content of the water allows normal respiration.

There is no layering of oxygen in flowing waters. The movement of the water provides continual mixing and distributes the oxygen uniformly; most of the dissolved oxygen comes from the atmosphere, through the turbulent water surface. Oxygen uptake occurs particularly rapidly when the concentration in the water is reduced; as in standing waters; this happens primarily during the night, when both plants and animals are consuming oxygen in respiration. During the day algae and mosses attached to the stones on the riverbed, as well as submerged higher plants, contribute oxygen to the water. The overall pattern of oxygen concentration in streams amounts to an increase continuing until the afternoon, followed by a decrease lasting until the early morning.

The distribution of animals in ground water is critically dependent

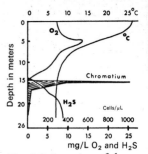

Fig. 3-8. Layering of the sulfur bacteria *Chromatium* in a lake, in relation to the distribution of temperature, oxygen, and hydrogen sulfide.

▷
Upper left: Natives catching the Samoan palolo worm *Eunice viridis* at night on the coral reef Pago Pago.
Upper right: Bowls containing the posterior ends of the palolo worm.
Center: Anterior part of a palolo worm in its coral shelter.
Below: Palolo worm, showing the transition to the sexually mature posterior part (the epitoke).

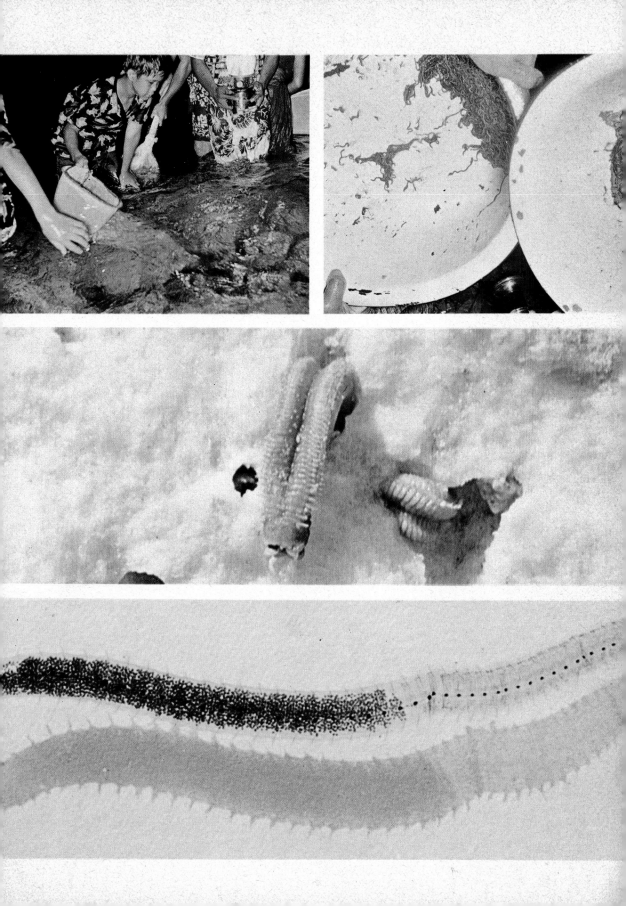

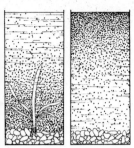

Fig. 3-9. The water-flea
(*Daphnia magna*) in
oxygen-rich water (left)
and in water deficient in
oxygen (right); from a
photograph.

◁

Above: Declining "bloom"
of blue-green algae (the
Titisee in the Black Forest,
August, 1969). In nutrient-
rich waters certain
planktonic algal species
tend to undergo occasional
massive increases (blooms),
often the cause of fish
mortality. When they die
off all at once, the bacterial
decomposition of their
remains uses up all the
oxygen dissolved in the
water.
Below: Pool in a highland
moor with wool grass and
peat moss in September
(Schwarzes Moor in the
Rhön). The peat mosses
and humic substances give
the moor waters a low pH;
they take up the traces of
metal ions dissolved in the
water and give off corresponding amounts of
hydrogen ions (ion
exchange).
(See Chapter 5.)

upon the presence of oxygen. Layers of ground water rich in oxygen contain a well developed fauna, and animals are scarce where the oxygen
reserves are low. In the upper layers of the soil near the beds of streams the
oxygen concentration is minimal owing to the high rate of bacterial respiration, especially when the water is rich in organic waste. At lower levels
the oxygen content increases, probably as a result of horizontal diffusion
through the soil, and here one again finds the characteristic interstitial soil
fauna. Thus the population density of ground-water animals does not, as
one might expect, decrease steadily from higher to lower levels, but passes
through distinct fluctuations that can often be associated with the measured
variations in oxygen availability. Figure 3-10 shows such an oxygen plot
for the upper forty centimeters of a ground-water system.

Habitats in which the salt concentration varies—for example, brackish
water in estuaries—often also vary, in a complicated way, with respect to
the oxygen concentration. Here the oxygen concentration depends not
only on temperature, but on the salt content of the water as well. As the
latter rises, the oxygen-saturation point falls. In a number of animal
species from brackish water, which are able to withstand wide fluctuations
in salt content, it was found that respiratory activity increased after the salt
concentration was reduced; this was ascribed to the change in turgidity
of the tissues due to osmotic effects. Results of this kind were obtained, for
example, with the tidal-zone crab *Carcinus maenas*. Moreover, there are
indications that closely related species from habits differing in salinity very
markedly in oxygen consumption; for example, the marine amphipod
Gammarus marinus consumes 562 cubic centimeters of oxygen per hour,
whereas the hourly oxygen consumption of a brackish-water species of
the same genus, *G. chevreuxi*, is 648 cc, and that of the fresh-water species
G. pulex is 1098 cc. Species restricted to a narrow range of salinity (steno-
haline species) usually respond with decreased respiratory activity to either
increase or decrease of salt content; here decreased respiratory rate is a sign
of injury.

Sometimes parts of the sea become essentially cut off from water exchange with the open ocean, as has happened with the Baltic Sea. In such
cases brackish seas can be formed, characterized by vertical layering of salt
content. The Black Sea is a very impressive example. The salt concentration in the deep water is so high, as compared to that of the surface water,
that its density prevents its displacement by oxygen-rich water from
above. The layering on the basis of specific gravity persists throughout the
year. The sinking of organic substances from the upper water brings
about a complete disappearance of oxygen in the depths, so that there has
developed a deep-water zone in which there are no animals, oxygen is
absent, and hydrogen sulfide is present in concentrations which rise near
the floor of the sea. The situation here is similar to that in the meromictic
lakes discussed above. In the Black Sea the zone inhabited by animals extends to depths of only about 180 meters, where the boundary between

oxygen and hydrogen sulfide is encountered. The lifeless region below reaches to the bottom, as deep as 2246 meters; the hydrogen-sulfide zone covers 77% of the bottom of the Black Sea—about 325,000 square kilometers on which no animals can live.

The oceans, too, are divided into regions of differing oxygen content. At the surface the water is generally saturated with oxygen, owing both to the thorough exchange with the atmosphere and the photosynthetic activity of the marine plankton. From the light-permeated upper layers, which in some parts of the sea at low latitudes can reach to depths of 100 m or more, there falls a steady rain of organic detritus. In the decomposition of this detritus, oxygen is consumed. Thus at depths between 300 and 1000 meters there is an oxygen minimum, but at still greater depths the oxygen content rises again. Because of this layer there exists a benthic fauna of oxygen utilising organisms. In the darkness of this realm no oxygen is produced by plants, and the reserves must be replenished by large scale water circulation patterns; these effects are now the subject of extensive research programs. In any case, the earlier assumption that the deep sea was without oxygen and therefore without life has proved incorrect.

Another question as yet unanswered is whether the difference in oxygen content known to exist at higher levels in the ocean have pronounced effects on the distribution of the animals. So far no unambiguous variations in population density have been found that correspond entirely to the relative amounts of oxygen; if found, such a correlation would point to oxygen as a limiting factor. On the evidence, it seems likely that the influence of oxygen in the huge mass of sea water is relatively small, as it is in the open air. Extremes with respect to oxygen supply are in most cases local phenomena, appearing only in restricted habitats.

In conclusion, we shall mention the special habitat provided by animals themselves, when they are hosts to parasites. Many species have succeeded in colonizing this habitat, among them the maw worm, *Ascaris lumbricoides*. The maw-worm spends most of its life as a parasite in the human small intestine, where essentially no oxygen is available. *Ascaris* has evolved the ability to break down carbohydrates in the absence of oxygen, by converting sugar to carbon dioxide and lactic acid. This incomplete breakdown frees less energy than does complete oxidation. But it provides enough for the worm to grow and produce an enormous number of eggs. The eggs can develop, however, only in the presence of oxygen. They leave the host's body in the excrement and proceed to develop in the open. After the eggs have reentered a host, usually along with food, their shells dissolve and the little worms hatch out in the gut, where at first they cannot live because of the low oxygen supply. The young maw-worm burrows through the gut wall and makes its way into the bloodstream; here, with an abundance of oxygen, it can metabolize food completely. The energy thus provided enables it to grow rapidly during the first few days. Gradually the worm makes its way through lungs,

Oxygen content of the ocean

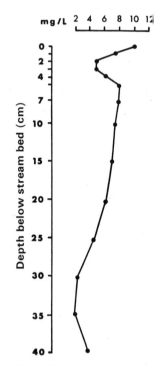

Fig. 3-10. Oxygen content of the ground water in the gravel bed of a slightly polluted brook.

Oxygen in host animals

trachea, esophagus and stomach, and after three weeks or a little longer it arrives back in the small intestine. There it shifts to the incomplete, anaerobic metabolism of the adult maw-worm. One can see, then, that the maw-worm has only partly succeeded in solving the difficult problem of living without oxygen. Its developmental stages require the presence of oxygen, and to ensure this it has had to evolve a complicated pattern of migration.

For most animals, though, oxygen is entirely indispensable. Because its availability is limited in certain habitats, it is yet another environmental factor that affects the evolution and distribution of animals.

4 The Influence of the Moon

By G. Jens

Since ancient times people have believed that the moon, with its 29.5-day cycle of changing phases, is associated with fertility, reproductive processes and growth in man, animals and plants. But the matter is still in debate, and it has not yet been established, for example, whether the female menstrual cycle is related directly or indirectly to the lunar period. People still argue, without sufficient proof on either side, whether during rising tide the number of births to humans and domestic animals in the coastal regions is greater than when the tide is falling. And the same is true of the theory defended by many anglers, that fish are particularly eager to bite at certain times, depending on both the sun and the moon.

For a hundred years now, the natural sciences have been producing critical interpretations to set against popular superstitions about the effects of the moon and tides on living beings. The first clarifying observations on the relationship between the moon and reproduction in the palolo worm in the South Seas (see below) were made shortly before the turn of the century, but it was only about twenty-five years ago that the study of periodicity attained the status of a special branch of biology. Research in this area is concerned with the connection between periodically recurring abiotic phenomena and the biological annual, daily and lunar rhythms.

At first glance annual and daily rhythms would seem easiest to explain, since the changing seasons—like the alternation between day and night—present periodic stimuli to which organisms can simply respond. In fact, though, at least from the viewpoint of the organisms, things are much more complicated. Whereas it formerly seemed reasonable to separate endogenous rhythms, originating within organisms themselves, from exogenous (induced by external factors) rhythms, it is now accepted that there is an endogenous periodicity underlying most biological rhythms. That is, if the external cues are eliminated the endogenous rhythm carries on, though not with perfect accuracy. This situation is rather like that in which a clock movement, which is not quite accurate, is continually adjusted by external timing signals. Since the internal clock, when made to run free, is only approximately right, one speaks of rhythms that correspond "about" to a day (circadian) or to the tides (circatidal).

The timing signals with which the internal clocks are observed to be synchronized are the tides themselves, or the crossing of a certain light threshold in the morning or a temperature threshold in the spring. Of course, we must bear in mind that this experimental linking of endogenous and induced rhythmicity does not necessarily bring us any closer to an understanding of the actual mechanisms affecting the animals. In the case of rhythms corresponding to the phases of the moon, the physical nature of the direct causative factors is still a mystery. But it is just because we know next to nothing about them that the lunar biorhythms, the source of many popular beliefs, are so interesting to the scientist.

But we do know one very important environmental factor associated with a lunar rhythm of shorter period than that of the moon's revolution. This factor—the tides—is not at all mysterious.

The mantle of ocean water clothing 71% of the earth's surface is—like all other parts of the earth—subjected to the gravitational attraction of the moon. Ignoring the sun for the moment, the earth-moon system is in equilibrium because the centrifugal forces due to rotation, as a whole, are just balanced by the sum of all the gravitational forces of attraction. Because of the large size of the earth, however, these forces at different points (at different distances from the moon) are not all equal, so that strains are set up, and these produce the tides. The whole earth itself is distorted slightly by these strains—sensitive seismometers can measure this "tidal creaking" of the earth. The oceans, being fluid, can change shape, much more than can the earth's core and crust, in response to these unbalanced forces. As a result, two slight bulges, two to three feet high when measured in the open ocean, appear (as shown in Fig. 4-5) in association with the gravitational attraction of the moon. One of these is approximately on the side of the earth facing the moon and the other is on the side away from the moon. The basic reason for these two bulges (Fig. 4-1) is easy to see; the water nearest the moon is attracted more strongly by the moon than the average for all of the earth (and bulges toward the moon), whereas the water on the far side is attracted less strongly than average (and bulges away from the moon). Many other forces due to gravitation and rotation are of course keeping the system, as a whole, in equilibrium.

For precisely the same reasons, there are two smaller bulges oriented with respect to the sun. Whenever the sun and the moon, as viewed by an observer on earth, are exactly opposite one another or exactly superimposed (in conjunction), their gravitational effects add and a "moon bulge" coincides with a "sun bulge" of water. Under these conditions

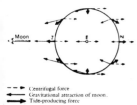

- - - Centrifugal force
— Gravitational attraction of moon.
➡ Tide-producing force

Fig. 4-1. The system of forces producing tides on the earth's surface: A section through the plane of the equator shows the gravitational pull of the moon (thin arrows), greater on the side of the earth toward the moon than on the opposite side. Counteracting the moon's attraction is the centrifugal force (dashed arrows), which is the same at every point. Only in the center of the planet are the two forces in equilibrium; at all other points the resultant of the two vectors is a net pull in a direction indicated by the thick arrows, drawing the ocean (and to a lesser extent, the earth itself) into tidal bulges. Z, moon in zenith; N, moon in nadir; E, Earth.

of "spring tide" the difference between high tide (the crest of the tidal bulge) and low tide (between the two bulges) is greatest. In a little over a day the bulges are swept around the planet, as the earth rotates. As the moon revolves about the earth it pulls its component of the tidal bulge after it, and when the solar and lunar bulges are furthest apart the range between high and low tide is smallest (neap tide).

The tides are of course much more complex than this explanation suggests. Because of the varying depths of the oceans, the frictional drag of the ocean beds (by way of which the tides are actually slowing down the earth's rotation) and other factors, high tide rarely occurs when the moon is at zenith. At coasts, of course, the timing and heights of the tides are further altered by local factors. Usually only a few feet separate high and low tide, whereas in the Bay of Fundy the change may amount to fifty or sixty feet.

Marine animals display countless adaptations to this phenomenon, in which the ebb and flood of the tide alternately leave dry and inundate broad coastal areas. An effect of the moon on organisms is therefore not only to be sought in events occurring at specific lunar phases or happening once or twice a month. The apparent movement of the moon as the earth rotates in the course of a day has clearly modified life on earth.

Most animals living in the tidal zone restrict their activity when the habitat is left dry and resume it when they are flooded once again. But a few, like the turbellarian *Convoluta*, behave in the opposite way. This turbellarian, which at high tide buries itself in the coastal sand of Brittany and England and emerges at low tide, is responding not only to the water level; it continues this rhythm of activity even in a marine aquarium where there are no tides. Oysters, which open their shells at high tide and close them at low, also persist in this behavior in a tideless aquarium, even "changing beat" when they are moved, in the aquarium, to another meridian. Initially they keep up the old tidal rhythm, but eventually they come into phase with the local rhythm, without direct exposure to tides. Their endogenous rhythm, then, has been shifted by the local "lunar timing signal." Such phenomena are only with reservations considered as moon-dependent rhythms, even though one might justifiably regard them as such if the periodicity were shown to correspond not to the day/night alternation but to that of the tides.

According to popular belief, the influence of the moon is greatest when it is new or full (i.e., in conjunction or opposition; the two points collectively are termed the "syzygies"). In fact, there are various lunar biorhythms for which this is true. But the most impressive phenomena appear at another phase, at the waxing or waning half-moon.

About twelve species of polychaete worms, native to various parts of the world, have been found to reproduce periodically at times coinciding with the syzygies. These animals are ordinarily sessile, but they swarm upward to copulate; they go all the way to the water surface,

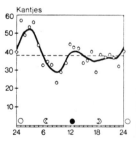

Fig. 4-2. Average daily catch (in barrels per ship) of the German herring fleet in the course of a lunar month (1953).

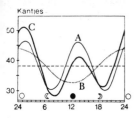

Fig. 4-3. Harmonic analysis of the curve in Fig. 4-2: A curve like that for the herring catch (C) can result from the addition of two sinusoidal oscillations, one with a half-month period and delayed some-what in phase (curve A) and the other with the lunar period (curve B).

where the native fishermen in the South Seas, knowing when they can be expected to swarm, wait to catch them. The polychaete family Nereidae is distinguished by the division of the body into a front section and a reproductive section. The anterior part is, as it were, the living and feeding animal, and the posterior part is the reproductive animal, which when mature releases itself from the front end, makes its way to the surface, and there releases the gametes into the water where fertilization takes place.

Near the Bermuda Islands one finds the crab *Anchistoides antiguensis*, which reproduces in swarms on the surface at night, always in the time just preceding new and full moon. The sea urchin *Centrechinus setosus* in the Suez region releases its gametes at full moon in summer, until September. Such animals have proved to be filled with the greatest numbers of ripe reproductive cells when examined just prior to full moon.

Three widespread species of marine bivalves, the blue mussel *Mytilus edulis*, the Baltic tellin *Macoma baltica*, and the long-necked clam (*Mya arenaria*), spawn primarily at full moon on the Atlantic coast of Canada. The larvae of the Mediterranean *Teredo pedicellata*, a bivalve that bores in wood, appear between October and March, often a few hours or at most one or two days before the full moon.

The investigators making these observations could in many cases show that neither the tides nor the moonlight could be the direct inducer of spawning. But a several-year program of experiments on the inconspicuous midge *Clunio marinus* produced different results. In the rocky shallows around Helgoland, the *Clunio* larvae live at the lower edge of the tidal zone; the emergence of the mature insect must be timed so as to coincide with the lowest water level, the spring ebb tide, which recurs about every fifteen days. The insects do not emerge in zones that are completely dry, since they can free themselves more easily from the pupal case while it is still submerged. The winged males have only two hours in which to find and mate with a wingless female. The female dies shortly after the fertilized eggs have been laid, before the rising water sweeps her away. It is remarkable that pupation takes place only a few days before emergence, regardless of the duration of the preceding larval stage. Evidently, then, it is not emergence by itself but the preceding pupation as well (or exclusively) that is controlled by a fifteen-day periodicity. This endogenous "syzygic" rhythm, as far as one can judge from the experiments on this point, is synchronized by the changing moonlight. The time of day at which the animals hatch, on the days when the moon is full or new, is controlled by a circadian rhythm. The animal not only takes advantage of the spring tides to reproduce when the water level is optimal; synchronization also increases the probability that the short-lived insects will be able to find partners.

The lunar periodicity of a familiar fish, the herring, is transitional between the preceding semilunar or syzygic rhythms and the true lunar

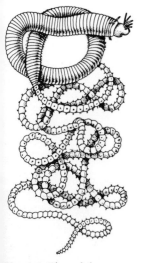

Fig. 4-4. The palolo worm (*Eunice viridis*).

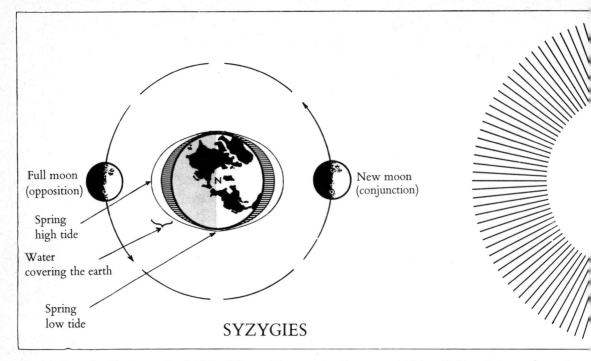

SYZYGIES

Fig. 4-5. How the tides are produced: 71% of the earth is covered with water, which is pulled into bulges at four points by various physical forces, chief among them the gravitational attraction of moon and sun. The larger pair of bulges is approximately at the part of the earth nearest the moon and the part directly opposite, and the smaller pair is similarly oriented with respect to the sun. When the forces of sun and moon act in parallel (conjunction and opposition, left

rhythms with a period of about 29.5 days (the lunar or synodic month). The habits of edible animals have always been attentively observed by humans, since one can catch them most successfully by using methods that exploit these habits. Then if the same method is used over a period of time with variable results, one suspects that the associated behavior of the animals may have changed. For example, the size of the catch of herring in nets can give information about the number and distribution of schools of the fish in a certain area, about their size, their density, and their mobility. Fluctuations in the intensity of certain herring behavior patterns, as indicated by the success of the fishermen, have for centuries been believed by the inhabitants of the North Sea coasts to be rhythmic in nature and to depend upon the phases of the moon.

Over the last fifty years there has been no lack of experiments designed to track down the supposed connection between large catches of herring and the full moon. But it was only twenty years ago that the first statistical evidence implicating the moon was obtained. The evaluation of the entire year's catch of the German fleet of herring luggers showed that mobility and swarming behavior of the herring in the North Sea is in fact dependent on the lunar periodicity. Fig. 4-2 summarizes the data for 10,374 catch-nights as a function of time of the lunar month;

Herring behavior and the phases of the moon

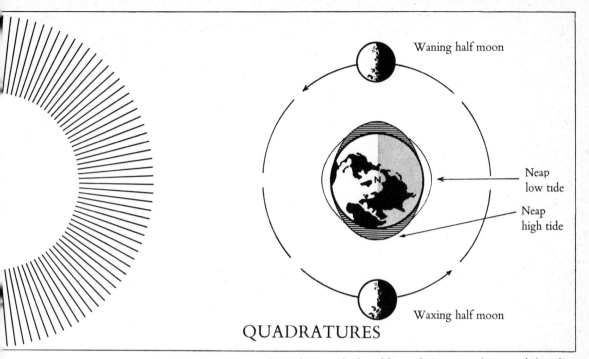

Waning half moon

Neap
low tide

Neap
high tide

Waxing half moon

QUADRATURES

diagram) the bulges add and the amplitude of the oscillation between high and low tide is greatest (spring tides). When the moon and sun are at an angle of 90° (the moon in its first and third quarters) the bulges are similarly displaced and the tidal oscillation is lowest (neap tides).

it is quite clear that in the period after full moon the catches—measured in kantjes (barrels)—were largest. There appears to be another, smaller peak around the time of new moon. Evidently a monthly and a semi-monthly rhythm are superimposed.

Harmonic analysis of this oscillation (Fig. 4-3) confirms this first impression; the monthly curve is composed of a lunar and a syzygic or semilunar rhythm—the latter, as we know, corresponding to a tidal rhythm. Barely fifteen days (to be precise, 14.765 days) separate the spring and neap tides. The peak herring catches are two days after full and new moon, and these are also the times of spring tides in the North Sea. The troughs in the curve correspond to the neap tides. The harmonic analysis also shows that the semilunar rhythm is more pronounced than the lunar rhythm, though the latter is distinctly present.

In terms of the current theoretical framework, then, the herring has an endogenous rhythmicity corresponding both to the syzygic period and to the lunar period, the timing signal for which is the moon.

As mentioned above, many nereids spawn at the syzygies, but one of the best-known nereid reproductive cycles is synchronized to another phase of the moon. The first description of the classical example of a lunar rhythm in a living being, the palolo worm (*Eunice viridis*), was given by Collin in the year 1897. He described the palolo worm as an inhabitant of the coral reefs around Samoa, Fiji, Tonga, and Gilbert Islands, rising to the surface only twice a year, in October and November, to release its eggs and sperm. The worms arose in such vast swarms that the sea appeared more solid than liquid. The natives, as he wrote, regarded the palolo swarming as a festive occasion; people of all ages rowed out at dawn to scoop up this gift of nature with sieves, baskets, and even with their hands. Part of the mass of worms was eaten immediately, raw, and the rest was wrapped in bread-fruit leaves and baked over an open fire. The hind section of the worm that rises to the surface, filled with gametes, is up to fifty centimeters long, but gradually breaks into smaller and smaller parts as it releases the sperm and eggs (see Color plate, p. 63).

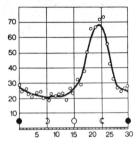

Fig. 4-6. Mean eel catch (number of eels per net per day) during a period in which the moon passes through all its phases (upper Rhine).

As early as the turn of the century researchers gave unqualified confirmation to a fact long known to the natives—the appearance of the palolo worm occurs at the time of the waning half moon. It was this circumstance that made it possible for the natives to prepare for their feast even before the first worms appeared, which at first astonished the European observers. Now it is known that no less than twenty species of polychaetes, of different families and living in different parts of the world, have a similar reproductive rhythm; it is usually synchronized to the third quarter of the moon, but in some cases to the first.

The turbellarian *Convoluta*, mentioned previously, lays its eggs even in an aquarium at neap tide—that is, at the quadratures of the moon. Among the mollusks, the North American snail *Chaetopleura apiculata* spawns at the waning half moon. Off the coast of Holland, larvae of the oyster (*Ostrea edulis*) have been observed to swarm at the same phase of the moon. This fact has as much practical significance to the oyster farmer as does knowledge of the swarming times of the palolo worm for the South Sea islander, or the timing of eel migration to the European river fisherman.

So far we have spoken only of animals that spend most or all of their lives in the tidal movements of the sea. The migration of the European eel to its spawning grounds in the Sargasso Sea begins in fresh water, and even here it has a very pronounced lunar rhythmicity. The revolution of the moon can thus also regulate the activity of animals spending much of their lives in fresh water.

When the two-year-old, transparent "glass eel" migrates back into the mouths of western and central European rivers, it has completed a considerable journey from west to east across the Atlantic. It spends five to seven years in the rivers, growing through the "yellow eel" stage to the adult form; the appearance of the adult is attained before sexual maturity, and for some time males and females can hardly be told apart. But it is in this stage that the eels begin their downstream spawning migration, toward their own birthplace in the Atlantic. During this

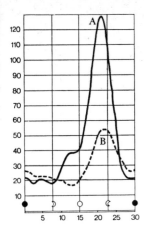

Fig. 4-7. Catch (and migratory) rhythm of the eels in the upper Rhine when the water level is falling (A) and rising (B).

migration it is caught, in large sacklike nets up to thirty meters long and with an opening, pointed upstream, covering seventy square meters. Since the migration proceeds in spurts, the catch is also intermittent, and follows a rhythmic pattern.

As in the case of the herring, the rhythm of the eel catch is a direct indication of the migratory rhythm. This is related to the lunar cycle both in the rivers and in the Baltic Sea. The migratory drive reaches a peak when the moon is in its third quarter (Fig. 4-6) and a minimum near the first quarter. At new moon and full moon, equal numbers of eels are migrating. Most of the eels make their journey in the autumn, but those that happen to start out in summer follow the same lunar rhythm. The maximum catch comes at the same phase of the moon whether the water level is high (when migration is most intensive) or low (Fig. 4-7). Even when the moon is obscured by clouds the rhythm is just as distinct. Of course, this does not necessarily exclude the possibility that moonlight is the effective timing signal for the endogenous lunar rhythm of these long-distance travellers, and that the clear nights suffice to maintain synchronization. But in this case, as in almost every other moon-related biological rhythm, the actual physical nature of the "moon signal" has not been demonstrated.

In conclusion, it seems to be true that the moon affects only those aspects in the life cycles of entirely or partially marine animals that have to do with reproduction—the shedding of gametes, the emergence from the pupa, the swarming of animals ready to mate, or the spawning migration. The popular belief that the moon is associated with reproduction is thus no superstition, but has a real scientific foundation. As far as the scientific results go, however, it must be said that lunar rhythmicity has been demonstrated only in aquatic animals.

5 Acidity and Salinity

The single most important biological substance, carbon dioxide, comprises on the average 0.03% of the volume of the air. As mentioned in Chapter 3, there is evidence that the carbon dioxide content of the air has recently become appreciably greater, but direct effects upon the earth's fauna are not yet to be expected. A more immediate and rapidly increasing danger, especially in areas where industry is concentrated, is pollution of the air with sulfur dioxide, which can be converted into acid forms. Acidity is measured in terms of pH, which indicates on a scale from 0 to 14 the negative of the log of the concentration of hydrogen ions in a solution; that is, a solution with a pH of less than 7 is acidic and one with pH greater than 7 is basic or alkaline. Pure water, because of the dissociation properties of H^+ and OH^-, has a pH of just 7.

Under natural conditions there are only trace amounts of free acids and bases in the atmosphere. It is said, however, that in Scandinavia precipitation containing large amounts of sulfuric acid, at pH values as low as 3.3 to 3.7, has eradicated the fish in thousands of lakes and streams.

Other acids in the atmosphere have more beneficial effects. Certain unstable organic acids secreted by organisms can act as "signals" for animal orientation, despite their extremely low concentration in the air. Mammals with a good sense of smell are frequently able to detect their conspecifics or enemies at great distances, by means of the scent of the characteristic mixture of fatty acids in the secretions of their skin glands (for example, the scent and sweat glands).

In open bodies of water and in the soil, acids and bases, in both the qualitative and the quantitative senses, are environmental factors crucial to the animal world. Even under natural conditions pH varies over the wide range of nearly 0 to 11, both extremes of which are inimical to life. Waste water from certain industrial establishments can raise the pH even above 11.

The pH of natural bodies of water is determined by a complex interplay of biochemical, chemical and physical processes. Water can be

By J. Brehm

Acids and bases in soils and open water

categorized—somewhat arbitrarily, since the boundaries between the divisions are not distinct—in terms of the substances most important in setting the pH, as follows (the numbers in parentheses are extreme values):

I. Calcium- (more precisely, calcium carbonate- and calcium bicarbonate-) containing water:
1. High calcium concentration (hard water)   pH 11–9 (6)
2. Intermediate calcium concentration   pH 9–6 (5)
3. Low calcium concentration (soft water)   pH 8–5 (4)

II. Calcium-free water:
4. Water containing organic (humic) acids   pH 4–3
5. Water containing inorganic acids   pH 4–3 (0)

The carbonic-acid carbonate system

At pH 8 in calcium-rich surface waters (in the presence of atmospheric carbon dioxide and calcareous soil or rock), the dissolved substances are present in a number of interconvertible forms. The relative amounts of these are determined by a system of equilibria including the following:

1) gaseous $CO_2 \rightleftarrows$ dissolved CO_2 (CO_2 solution equilibrium)
2) dissolved $CO_2 + H_2O \rightleftarrows H_2CO_3$ (carbonic acid formation eq.)
3) $H_2CO_3 \rightleftarrows H^+ + HCO_3^-$ (first stage eq. for carbonic acid dissociation)
4) $HCO_3^- + H_2O \rightleftarrows H_2CO_3 + OH^-$ (hydrolysis eq. for hydrogen carbonate)
5) $HCO_3^- \rightleftarrows H^+ + CO_3^{2-}$ (second stage eq. for carbonic acid dissociation)
6) $CO_3^{2-} + H_2O \rightleftarrows HCO_3^- + OH^-$ (hydrolysis eq. for carbonate)
7) $CO_3^{2-} + Ca^{2+} \rightleftarrows CaCO_3$ (calcium solution eq.)
     crystalline

As the pH of the water rises, when carbon dioxide escapes as a result of increased temperature, or when carbon dioxide and hydrogen carbonate are taken up by water plants in the process of photosynthesis, the balance is shifted in favor of carbonate formation and the relatively insoluble calcium carbonate precipitates readily:

8) $CO_2 \leftarrow CO_2 \xleftarrow{\;-H_2O\;} H_2CO_3$
    gas   dissolved

$$\leftarrow 2HCO_3^- \rightarrow CO_3^{2-} \underset{-Ca^{2+}}{\overset{+Ca^{2+}}{\rightleftarrows}} CaCO_3$$
                                              crystalline

Precipitation and solution of calcium carbonate

That is, when carbon dioxide is withdrawn from the carbonic-acid/carbonate equilibrium system, hydrogen carbonate is broken down into carbonate, carbon dioxide, and water. In nature this process can be associated with an increase in pH to values as high as 11. This degree of alkalinity is immediately lethal to fish.

If, on the other hand, carbon dioxide is supplied to the system (by the respiration of organisms, particularly in soils and the deeper layers of standing waters, from which excess carbon dioxide escapes only slowly into the atmosphere), the equilibria shift in favor of hydrogen carbonate formation. In this process, the calcium carbonate can be completely dissolved and the carbonate can be converted to hydrogen carbonate:

9) $CO_2 \rightleftarrows CO_2 \quad \xrightleftharpoons[-H_2O]{+H_2O} \quad H_2CO_3 \rightleftarrows 2HCO_3^-$

    gas   dissolved

$$\leftarrow CO_3^{2-} \quad \xleftarrow{-Ca^{2+}} \quad CaCO_3$$

    crystalline

The excess carbon dioxide, in the form of carbonic acid, dissolves carbonate as hydrogen carbonate. It is for this reason that there are no calcium deposits in the deep regions of the sea, as there are in the more shallow regions. Calcareous remains of dead animals of the surface waters which sink to the depths are dissolved, and the benthic organisms are incapable of forming calcareous exoskeletons or shells.

When water rich in carbonic acid and hydrogen carbonate emerge to the earth's surface in springs, carbon dioxide escapes into the atmosphere until the characteristic solution equilibrium (Equilibrium 1, above) is established. Then, again, Equilibrium (8) obtains; carbonate ions are formed and eventually combine with calcium ions to precipitate as calcium carbonate. In the "Karst" regions of the Alps, where limestone formations are heavily leached, these processes are particularly striking.

When pH and water temperature increase together, the solubility of calcium carbonate is reduced. Under these conditions it is evidently easier for water animals to take up Ca^{2+} and HCO_3^-/CO_3^{2-} ions and convert them to calcium-carbonate deposits, for animals of the warm regions of the ocean in general form larger, thicker-walled shells and tubes than do related forms or species in cooler regions. It is only in the shallow waters of the warm seas that corals find conditions suitable for the construction of their massive reefs.

The carbonic-acid/carbonate system of calcium-containing waters determines not only the pH but also, as a function of both pH and overall concentration of solutes, their buffering capacity with respect to introduced ions—especially hydrogen and hydroxyl ions. The pH-buffering capacity is greatest near the neutral point and is completely lost outside the pH range lying between 4 and 13. The most important buffer substance is hydrogen carbonate, which can neutralize both acids and bases:

10) $HCO_3^- + H \rightleftarrows H_2CO_3$ (equivalent to Equilibrium 3)
11) $HCO_3^- + OH^- \rightleftarrows CO_3^{2-} + H_2O$ (equivalent to Equilibrium 6)

That is, hydrogen carbonate buffers by binding a larger or smaller fraction of the introduced hydrogen or hydroxyl ions, so that the pH of the solution changes only slightly; pH is thus stabilized by the carbonic-acid/carbonate equilibrium system. Sea water, being well buffered, in general has a pH between 7 and 8.5—it is weakly alkaline. In fresh water

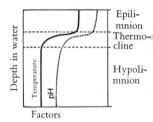

Fig. 5-1. In the deeper parts of standing surface waters in the warmer seasons there appear vertical gradients in certain factors, including temperature and pH. Lakes are divided into three layers with respect to temperature: the epilimnion (warm, with plentiful light, oxygen, and nutrients and good mixing of water), the thermocline (sharp decrease in temperature with depth, frequently paralleled by the other factors), and the hypolimnion (cool, with poor mixing of water, low light intensity, and predominance of animals and bacteria over plants).

the pH varies comparatively widely according to the type of lake or stream, the depth of the water, the time of day or year, and other factors. Weakly buffered waters are very sensitive to the addition of electrolytes. For example, the pH of brooks with water low in calcium carbonate can fall from 7 to 4 or less when sudden showers or thaws wash in acids (humic acids) from plant debris. The fish mortality from such causes is sometimes considerable. In waters rich in nutrients, fairly large gradients of pH, in space and time, can appear in spite of the increased calcium carbonate concentration; these are associated with the fact that the carbon dioxide balance, a function of the photosynthesis of the abundant plants and thus of daylight, combined with the constant respiration of all organisms, varies continually with depth and with the hour and season.

Differences in acidity of surface waters

Such spatial and temporal differences in acidity of bodies of water make it even more clear how inadequate any attempt at strict categorization of water types must be. But with an organization like that given above, in terms of descending calcium carbonate content, we can discern the following trends: (i) shift of the carbonic-acid/carbonate equilibrium system in favor of hydrogen carbonate and carbon-dioxide/carbonic-acid, (ii) decrease of the capacity to buffer hydroxyl ions, and (iii) loss of the H^+-buffering capacity.

Calcium carbonate concentration

Waters rich in calcium carbonate are of course inhabited by animals adapted so as to tolerate or even depend upon this compound. In brooks of this type, the larvae of the chironomid *Lithotanytarsus emarginatus* build calcareous tubules, sometimes so densely packed that they resemble the porous limestone called tufa. Mollusks with shells also live primarily in calcareous waters. A noteworthy and apparently unique exception is a pearl-forming bivalve (*Margaritana margaritifera*) found in streams low in calcium carbonate.

The pH of pure carbon-dioxide/carbonic-acid solutions cannot be less than 4, because of the slight tendency of carbonic acid to dissociate. This limiting value is nearly reached in some springs in calcium-poor variegated sandstone regions. If the pH is decreased by the addition of hydrogen ions, the concentration of carbonate and bicarbonate ions is negligible, since the reaction is driven in the direction of association by the extra H^+:

$$12)\ CO_2 \rightleftarrows CO_2 \xrightleftharpoons[-H_2O]{+H_2O} H_2CO_3 \xleftarrow{+H^+} HCO_3^-$$
$$\text{gas}\quad\text{dissolved}$$
$$\xleftarrow{+H^+} CO_3^{2-} \xleftarrow{-Ca^{2+}} CaCO_3$$
$$\text{crystalline}$$

In nature the required hydrogen ions can be provided by acids from organic detritus and other cation exchangers (cations are positively charged ions, which move to the cathode in electrolysis), as well as by free sulfuric acid produced by bacterial oxidation of hydrogen sulfide and other sulfur compounds (chiefly pyrite).

In the characteristically humus-rich waters—dark-brown pools on moors, yellow to brown lakes in cool, humid climates, and the black waters of the tropical rainforests—cation-exchanging humic acids and related organic substances supply the surplus active hydrogen ions. The pH values in these waters can approach 3. Ion exchange takes place at the surfaces of high-molecular-weight, predominantly undissolved organic acids; these substances take up dissolved cations such as calcium ions and release into the water corresponding (in terms of electrical charge) amounts of hydrogen ions. Particularly well known as ion exchangers are the cell walls of peat mosses, which retain this capacity even after the plants have died.

Humus-rich waters

The low pH of waters containing inorganic acids is due to their content of free sulfuric acid. In some flooded open lignite mines and clay pits H_2SO_4 can bring the pH down to about 3. In a very few extraordinarily acid crater lakes the pH can even fall to zero.

Sulfuric-acid waters

Such extremely acid waters are devoid of animal life. A few species appear in the less acid waters of, for example, the high moors, which are inhabited characteristically by amoebas with siliceous cases. The insects are represented by a number of specialized species, whereas the mollusks are entirely absent and the vertebrates, nearly so. The degree to which individual animal species of acid waters require or can tolerate acid is, in most cases, not yet known. The number of species colonizing bodies of water increases rapidly for higher pH values, by far the most abundant fauna being found in the neutral to weakly alkaline range. From about pH 9 upward, the number of animal species falls again, and above pH 10 only a few species are permanent inhabitants.

pH requirements of animals

Even closely related species can vary widely in the water or soil pH they require, with respect both to absolute value and to range. The ciliate *Colpidium campylum*, for example, can withstand pH values ranging from 4.5 to 9, whereas the related *Spriostomum ambiguum* can carry out all its vital functions only at pH 7.4–7.6. Soil animals are often particularly well adapted to, or at least tolerant of, low pH. Earthworms can live in weakly acid soil; in this case, the animal "neutralizes" the soil acids by excretion of calcium carbonate.

It is not often possible to be certain of the specific influence upon animals of changes in pH, since these are frequently accompanied by changes in other factors. We have already seen that in the carbonic-acid/carbonate equilibrium system there are readjustments in all the equilibria involved whenever the concentration of one component is altered, and this is not the only example. The wide variation in pH found in nature is produced by a considerable variety of substances, and for that reason alone—even at a given pH—one would expect animals to be differently affected. The high concentrations of sulfuric acid, not in itself a toxic substance, in the very acid crater lakes and of carbonic acid in some soils and springs, prohibit animal life. The humic acids in brown and black

Effects of certain acids and bases on animals

waters severely restrict it. Hydrogen sulfide and its salts are very poisonous. These substances are produced anaerobically (in the absence of molecular oxygen) by bacteria, and to a lesser extent by the decomposition of organic matter. Therefore they appear primarily in the deep parts of standing, layered surface waters and in stagnant soil water.

Finally, free ammonia can also appear in toxic concentrations where the environment is alkaline. It is occasionally formed in large quantities when masses ("blooms") of algae, having used up the available nutrients, die off and are decomposed by bacteria (see Color plate, p. 64). Where the water is neutral or acid, on the other hand, ammonia takes the form of the harmless ammonium ion.

Among the associated factors that can limit animal distribution under natural circumstances are lack of oxygen (especially in the carbonic-acid-containing springs), high electrolyte concentrations, and increased temperatures in the extremely acid crater lakes.

Salts in the atmosphere and in soils

The air in general has such a low salt content that animals are not detectably affected. In the soil, on the other hand, salts can occur as solutes in all sorts of concentrations, and as solids as well. The chemistry of soil salts is so complicated that we shall pass over it here and consider instead the simpler relationships in the open waters above ground.

Salts in open water

In open water salts are always present, almost entirely in the dissolved state. The chief components of the mixed salt solution (Fig. 5-2) are the cations of the metals sodium (Na^+), potassium (K^+), calcium (Ca^{2+}) and magnesium (Mg^{2+}) and the nonmetallic anions of chlorine (Cl^-, chloride), sulfur (SO_4^{2-}, sulfate) and carbon (HCO_3^-, bicarbonate, and CO_3^{2-}, carbonate). Among the important minor components are the ions of iron (Fe^{2+}, Fe^{3+}) and manganese (Mn^{2+}). The percentages of other heavy-metal and nonmetallic ions are negligibly small. Organic salts are formed by the free amino acids, though these are represented in very low concentrations. Moreover, atoms of metals (in particular heavy metals) are bound to form complexes. Such minor components are almost never present in greater than trace amounts; their concentrations rarely exceed a few milligrams per liter of water. In the least saline waters, such as the blackwaters of the tropical rainforests, even the chief components are dissolved only in trace amounts.

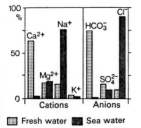

Fig. 5-2. The proportions (in equivalent %) of the salts dissolved in fresh and sea water: Whereas in most fresh waters the calcium and bicarbonate ions predominate, in sea water the sodium and chloride ions contribute by far the greater proportion of the total salt content.

Although the percentages of the chief ions can vary widely from one body of water to another, characteristic patterns of distribution are discernible. In sea water, as well as in sea water made brackish by dilution with rain, melted snow, and fresh-water streams, the sodium and chloride concentrations are by far the greatest. The relative percentages of the other chief ionic species in these waters are so similar that determination of one—for example, the chloride concentration—suffices to permit accurate estimates of the concentrations of the other components. In fresh water the relative concentrations of the different ions vary much more widely. But on the average over the world the proportions of calcium, hydrogen carbonate and carbonate ions are greatest. In inland brackish and salt waters, as in sea water, estuaries, and tide pools, sodium and chloride ions frequently predominate. At the same time, in some of these inland waters, sulfate (Caspian and Aral Seas) or carbonate/bicarbonate (the Van Sea in Anatolia) are more strongly concentrated. In other fairly saline waters the concentration of chloride ions may even be exceeded by those of sulfate ions (in the oases of Tunisia) or carbonate and bicarbonate ions (alkali lakes such as the Neusiedler See in Austria and the Kurusch-Göl in Iran).

On the basis of total salt content we can distinguish four water types (salt concentration is given in parts per thousand):

1) Fresh water (limnetic bodies of water)   up to 0.5
2) Brackish water (mixohaline)   0.5 to 30 (40)
3) Sea water (euhaline)   30–40
4) Salt water (hyperhaline)   40 or more

Since the composition in terms of ions species varies widely between the saline inland waters and sea water and its derivatives, a further distinction can be made between marine and inland brackish water (with 0.5–30 and 0.5–40 parts per thousand of salt, respectively) on the one hand, and hyperhaline sea water and inland waters on the other.

The body fluids of fresh-water animals as a rule have a higher osmotic pressure (a measure of the concentration of solutes which cannot pass biological membranes, and hence a measure of the tendency to take up water by diffusion) than does the surrounding water. Water thus tends to enter their bodies and must be continually excreted. In protozoa this is accomplished by the pulsating excretory vacuoles, and in metazoans it is the task of kidneys and functionally similar organs. Only a very few of the many fresh-water animal species can survive an increase of the salt concentration in the surrounding water (i.e., brackish-water conditions); those that can are called euryhaline animals. The three-spined stickleback (*Gasterosteus aculeatus*) can live even in sea water; it is thus said to be a "holeuryhaline" species.

Brackish-water animals are adapted to their habitats in different ways; depending on species, subspecies or form, as well as on the relative amounts of solutes in the water, the osmotic pressure of the animal fluids may be higher, the same, or lower than that of the outside water. Moreover, the salt content fluctuates rather widely, particularly in estuarine habitats—in space and even more in time, as a result of the regular movement of the tide and the unpredictable dilution or concentration resulting from rainfall or evaporation. The animals must be adapted to such fluctuations. Only a few species have accomplished this, so that the fauna of brackish water is relatively undifferentiated. Estuarine animals belong primarily to the lower vertebrates. In brackish inland seas of the Ponto-Caspian region (southeastern Europe and the Near East), on the other hand, there

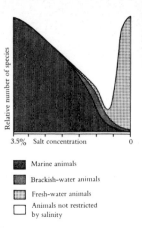

Fig. 5-3. In fresh water and in sea water there are many species, whereas in brackish water the number is strikingly reduced. Most brackish-water species are immigrants from the ocean, with only a few endemic or originally fresh-water species. Very few species can adapt to the whole range of salt concentrations between those of fresh and sea water.

Fig. 5-4. The spawning area of the European river eel (*Anguilla anguilla*) is in the Sargasso Sea, a vast region between the West Indies and the Azores, full of drifting seaweed. The eel requires about three years to cross the Atlantic.

are, by comparison, many more highly developed species. Among the fish the gobies (family Gobiidae), originally marine animals which in the Ponto-Caspian region are relicts of the Tertiary, are represented there by more than twenty species. Some of these species, and even genera, are found only in this region (i.e., they are endemic). Salt-tolerant immigrants from fresh water can often stand salt concentrations only up to eight parts per thousand, though the river perch can survive up to fifteen parts per thousand. One well-known immigrant from the ocean is the flounder *Platichthys flesus*; its adaptation is incomplete, however, since it must return to the ocean to spawn.

Marine animals have the same or a lower osmotic pressure than their sea-water environment; they are often strictly limited to the specific salinity of the ocean. The teleosts, characterized by a low osmotic pressure, lose water to their surroundings and must replace it by drinking sea water; the excess salt consumed in the process is excreted. Low osmotic pressure is also the rule among the other higher marine vertebrates. By contrast, the more primitive cartilaginous fish (sharks, rays, and chimaeras) have body fluids of the same osmotic pressure as the surrounding sea water. Poikilosmotic marine animals, which are not harmed by change in their own osmotic pressure, are at an advantage in the colonization of brackish water; the common starfish *Asterias rubens* is found in such conditions in the Baltic Sea, and the shore crab *Carcinus maenas* is similarly adapted. The Chinese crab *Eriocheir sinensis*, introduced to European waters from China, can live even in fresh water and moves considerable distances inland along the rivers; it has migrated from the Elbe along the Moldau as far as Prague. But it is only in the ocean that it becomes sexually mature.

Very few animal species are holeuryhaline—capable of living in fresh, brackish and sea water. The most familiar example of such an animal is the three-spined stickleback, which has evolved a form or subspecies for each of these habitats. The three forms differ in appearance as well; for example, in fresh water the length of this fish is six centimeters, in the eastern Baltic Sea eight, and in the North Sea eleven. A comparable increase in body size with increased salt content of the habitat is observable in the cod, the herring, and other animals in the brackish water of the Baltic and the sea water of the North Sea.

Certain fish spend part of their lives in the ocean and part in fresh water, without changing their own osmotic pressure appreciably. The European river eel (*Anguilla anguilla*) spawns in the ocean (Fig. 5-4). The young eels migrate up the rivers, where they grow to their full size, and when ready to spawn they return to the ocean. The sea trout and the salmon behave in just the opposite way, spawning in fresh water and growing to maturity in the ocean. It is characteristic that all the relatives of the eel are purely marine animals, whereas those of the salmon and trout (order Salmoniformes) are in general restricted to fresh water; the

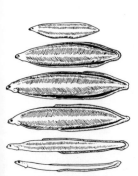

Fig. 5-5. Development of the river eel: the leaf-shaped marine larva eventually turns into the "glass eel" (lowest picture), which migrates upriver.

migratory species reflect, in their sites of spawning, the evolutionary history of their respective families.

Hyperhaline waters have fauna with few species, most of which are found only in such habitats. In salt works there are often masses of the crustacean brine shrimp *Artemia salina*, which can withstand salt concentrations from 40 to 230 parts per thousand; this animal is not found in the ocean. Inland hyperhaline waters, like inland brackish lakes and seas, because of their isolated situation are the home of endemic species as well as widely distributed species such as the larvae of flying insects. Very saline waters with concentrations approaching that of a saturated sodium chloride solution (330 parts per thousand) do not in general support animal life. The only organisms capable of reproducing in these waters are a few species of blue-green algae and flagellates, and certain groups of bacteria. The deeper parts of the Dead Sea and, when the water level is low, those of the Great Salt Lake in Utah reach such extreme concentrations.

Whereas most environmental factors tend to be characterized by just one optimum range in which conditions favor animal life, in the case of salinity there are two distinct ranges favorable to life—these represent fresh water and sea water. They delimit three separate unfavorable ranges—the fresh waters lowest in electrolytes, brackish waters, and concentrated salt solutions. It is particularly striking that the number of species in brackish waters is reduced; this is due not only to the variable salt concentration in such habitats, but certainly also to changes in the relative concentrations of the chief ionic species—particularly with respect to the calcium/sodium and bicarbonate/chloride ratios.

The salt content of water can also have an indirect effect upon animal life. As salt concentration increases, the solubility of molecular oxygen in water falls. This is unlikely to be a limiting factor. On the other hand, in standing surface waters there can appear fairly sharp vertical gradients in salt concentration. These may lead to a stable layering of the whole body of water; the greater the salt concentration, the higher the specific gravity, so that more concentrated water accumulates in the depths. This happens, for example, in brackish lakes into which fresh-water streams flow. In the dark depths of such lakes, far from contact with the air, the dissolved molecular oxygen is gradually used up by respiring organisms. The oxygen deficiency that results can very easily lead to the appearance of sulfur bacteria, which release hydrogen sulfide into the water and suppress animal life completely. This has happened extensively in the Black Sea.

Chemistry, like the other abiotic factors, links animals and their environment at many points. Each habitat is characterized by a particular combination of these factors, to which its fauna is adapted. The organisms in a habitat also show an array of other adaptations—to each other; these will be the subject of the chapters in the following section.

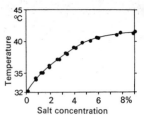

Fig. 5-6. Salt tolerance of the crab *Tigriopus fulvus* increases with water temperature. This capacity is advantageous, since in the coastal pools near the high-tide mark where it lives, temperature and salt concentration generally change together over a wide range. This example also shows how greatly one environmental factor can change the effect of another on an organism.

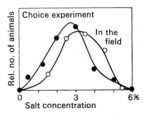

Fig. 5-7. The beetle *Bledius spectabilis* prefers substrates with salt concentration of about 3%, both in nature (the sea coast) and in an experiment with soils differing in salt content. The slight difference between the curves suggests that, in the natural habitat, additional environmental factors operate, such as the competitive and predatory effects of other species with similar salt requirements.

II. ADAPTATIONS TO THE BIOTIC ENVIRONMENT

6 Food and Relationships with Other Species

By D. Matthes

Every animal must have the capacity to find and consume food. In its evolution, the earth's fauna has developed a great diversity of structures and behavior patterns, so that full advantage can be taken of the abundant and varied food supply in nature. By specializing in one sort of food, an animal can limit the competition it must face. Specialization has reached its peak in the case of the parasites, some of which show quite astonishing adaptations to their unusual way of life.

Close to the roots of the tree of animal evolution, one finds animals that take up food by very simple means. Within the class Rhizopoda, the naked amoebas (order Amoebida) send out pseudopods to engulf food objects. Rhizopods of the order Heliozoa approach the problem differently; from their spherical cell body they send out fine "rays," each reinforced by a central axial thread. The rigid axis is covered with fluid protoplasm, to which small organisms become stuck and are transported, as though on a conveyor belt, to the body of the heliozoan.

Ciliate feeding
mechanisms

There is much greater variety in organs for food intake among the ciliates (class Ciliata). Some engulf their food, while others sweep it in with a current of water produced by the cilia; members of the order Suctoria feed by sucking through fine tubules. The most primitive ciliates are those that hunt and ingest the food. The "mouth" of the cell is capable of wide expansion and usually is reinforced by a rim around the edge. *Didinium nasutum* feeds only on slipper-shaped ciliates like *Paramecium*, first attaching its proboscis to the prey and then paralyzing it by poisonous threads resembling trichocysts.

Paramecium is one of the ciliates that generate a water current to sweep bacteria and algae into the mouth. It very often happens, among metazoans as well, that this sort of water-current feeding is associated with a sessile habit. Another group of ciliates, the order Peritricha, offers examples of this specialization. The peritrichs are attached to the substrate by a stalk, and they bear cilia only on the feeding apparatus at the anterior end. The cilia surround a retactable disk, forming a counterclockwise spiral with one or more turns. There is an inner double circlet of cilia which undulates constantly; food is swept toward an outer circlet, in which the cilia adhere to form a membrane near the mouth, and thus guide it into the mouth. Ciliates enclose the food, and the water taken in along with it, in a vacuole, where the prey is killed and digested.

As a rule, members of the order Suctoria are also sessile. Mature animals have no cilia and no mouth opening; instead, they extend fine tentacles into the surrounding water and suck the contents of prey animals through the tentacular canal. Their ancestors are thought to have had a mouth, with small tentacles surrounding it as an accessory structure to seize prey and push it into the mouth. These tentacles were the fore-runners of the closed suction tubules of the present-day suctorians. Only after functional suction tentacles had been completely evolved did the cell mouth disappear. There are still suctorians—for example, *Ephelota gemmipara*—which, in addition to the suction tentacles, have "prehensile" tentacles. Among the present-day protozoans there is also a typical case of feeding by pushing prey into the mouth; *Spelaeophrya* lives attached to the antennae of fresh-water shrimps and has a mouth opening surrounded by grasping tentacles.

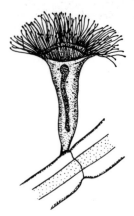

Fig. 6-1. The protozoan *Spelaeophrya*, its mouth surrounded by grasping tentacles.

But the most impressive suction arrangement is that of *Choanophrya infundibulifera*. This suctorian has tentacles that can be extended for rela-tively great distances and have a broad, trumpetlike expansion at the end. *Choanophrya* attaches to the mouthparts of small crustaceans (genus *Cyclops*) and participates as a commensal in the feeding of its host, using its tentacles like an underwater vacuum cleaner.

Among the Metazoa, some feed on particles and others take larger food. The particle feeders are aquatic animals, consuming primarily bac-teria or planktonic organisms. Some of these sweep their food in with water currents, like the ciliates. Tube worms feed in this way; for example, the polychaete *Spirographis* has, at either side of its mouth, a structure bearing thirty tentacles. When the worm spreads out its tentacles, after extending its anterior end from its tube, they form a funnel in front of the mouth. Each tentacle bears two rows of feathery appendages (pinnules) covered with cilia. The cilia send a stream of water into the funnel, and the plankton in this stream are caught on a band of cilia that transports them along a groove in the tentacle. Here the particles are sorted and distributed according to size among an outer, a middle, and an inner band. The large particles are discarded, the medium-sized ones are used for con-struction of the tube, and only the small particles are conveyed to the mouth. A very similar feeding mechanism is found in the crinoid echinoderms.

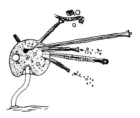

Fig. 6-2. The suctorian *Choanophrya* attaches to the mouthparts of small crustacea and sucks up part of its host's meal.

The clams also feed in this way. They push their anterior ends into the soft bottom underwater and produce a current with the cilia which are present on gills, mantle, and the lobes around the mouth. The stream of water flows in and out again through two separate openings at the pos-

How clams feed

terior end of the animal. From this water, the clam obtains both food and oxygen. Food uptake has been studied in detail in clams—one can cut a window in the shell and observe the process directly. The outer gill surface was found to be covered with a curtain of mucus, through which the water must pass before it can flow out again; the nutrient particles that are not too small stick to this sheet of mucus. In a ciliated groove along the lower edge of the gills, the mucus sheet is continually rolled up, like a carpet, and moved forward. Two ciliated lobes transfer the mucus-coated food to the mouth or separate out inedible particles. Clams, then, feed both by generating water currents and by filtration. It has been calculated that an eight-centimeter-long mussel passes between 1.8 and 5 liters of water through its siphon in an hour.

The simply constructed sponges, too, are filter feeders and can pump water through at an impressive rate. The inside of the sponge is lined with flagellate collar cells; these generate a current of water, entering through fine pores in the body wall and leaving by way of a larger opening, the osculum. The food particles carried along with the water are taken up either by the collar cells themselves or by special amoebocytes. It is claimed that a sponge about the size of a man's head can set up such a strong current that no less than two liters of water pass through it per minute; this would amount to about 760 gallons per day.

The branchial gut It is characteristic of the Chordata (the phylum to which the vertebrates belong) that the gut has an anterior "branchial" region with the side walls interrupted by slits through which water can emerge from the gut to the exterior. In the lancelet (genus *Branchiostoma*, subphylum Cephalochordata), it is in the branchial region that food is taken from the water current. The lancelets are up to 7.4 cm in length; usually they bury themselves in the sand of the ocean, with only the anterior end and the mouth showing. The respiratory water current generated by cilia on the gills contains small organisms which, as in the case of the clams, stick to bands of mucus. The mucus, enriched with food, moves into a ciliated groove and is transferred into the esophagus.

Legs as feeding organs Water-fleas, the familiar food of aquarium fish, have five pairs of legs but move about by means of their antennae, which are developed into a pair of powerful oars. The rowing motion of these propels the animal in a series of "hops"—a movement that has given these crustaceans their name. Not required for locomotion, the legs function in respiration and feeding; they move constantly, waving back and forth two to three hundred times a minute. Their activity creates a current of water that flows into the carapace in front and leaves it at the rear. Long, dense combs of bristles on the third and fourth leg pairs retain the tiny plants and animal organisms in the water that flows past. The food thus filtered out is conducted into a ventral groove between the legs, in which it passes to the mouth; swallowing movements move it into the esophagus.

Filter-feeding fish Some fish—for example, herring, sardines, and whitefish—are plankton feeders, filtering suspended organisms from the water that enters the mouth and passes out through the gill slits. Long, thin processes on the gill arches cover the gill slits and catch the plankton like a net. The food that accumulates on these processes is pushed toward the gullet and swallowed by the fish.

Even among the sharks, so famed for their predatory behavior, there are plankton feeders. The basking shark (genus *Cetorhinus*), which can grow to a length of 14 m, and the whale shark (genus *Rhincodon*), up to 21 m in length, swim with mouth wide open. The basking shark catches its food, primarily small crustaceans, with "gill rakers" formed by the modification of dermal teeth. At the most "economical" swimming speed, four kilometers per hour, 2000 cubic meters of water are filtered by the gill system in an hour. In the whale shark, the gill processes form a dense network projecting into the gullet. Other gigantic filter feeders are the manta rays, which have two fleshy "horns" protruding forward, one at either side of the large mouth. These extensions of the pectoral fins help to drive plankton into the mouth.

The largest plankton catchers and filter feeders are the whales, one of which, the blue whale (*Balaenoptera musculus*), is the most enormous animal known to have existed on earth. It can reach a weight of 135,000 kg—the weight of twenty-five elephants or 16000 humans. Blue whales and other whalebone whales feed primarily on shrimplike crustacea, about six centimeters long, of the genus *Euphausia*, which often appear in the surface water of the Antarctic Ocean in such dense swarms that the water seems like a thick soup. The apparatus used by the giant whales to catch these crustacea consists of plates hanging down from the roof of the mouth and made of a horny material called whalebone or baleen. The inner edge of each plate forms a sort of fringe.

At first one might think it strange that it is the largest animals which feed on such small organisms. Part of the explanation is that only the minute animals, in either the plant or the animal kingdom, can reproduce rapidly enough to be available in such masses. It has been calculated that a large whale consumes about 1500 kg of *Euphausia* every day.

"Fishing" with a net is a special form of filter feeding. Certain species of caddis-fly larvae, living in standing and flowing waters, have evolved such behavior. Many of these are predators, and others build nets in which they wait for prey. The sievelike net of *Neureclipsis* is often longer than a human hand. The "tailed" tunicate *Oikopleura* (class Larvacea) surrounds itself with a gelatinous case having a built-in filter mechanism that retains the plankton in the respiratory stream of water. The mesh here is so fine that even protozoans—which slip through the finest manmade plankton nets—are caught.

A most peculiar form of feeding is found in the wormlike gastropods of the family Vermetidae. These marine mollusks live in calcareous tubes very like those of sessile polychaetes. From their well-developed

▷
Above: Brightly colored coral fish of the genera *Amphiprion* and *Premnas* flee when threatened, into the tentacles of giant sea anemones. Remarkably, the fish are not stung by the anemone.
Center: The crab *Dromia* covers its back with a red tunicate colony.
Below: Between the podia of a starfish—the picture shows the underside of one of its arms—the polychaete worm *Acholoe* lives as a commensal.

Whales that catch plankton

Net-fishing

Left, top to bottom:
Parasitic mites on an
aphid; a ladybug
(*Coccinella septempunctata*)
with parasitic mites;
aphid excreting a drop of
sweet liquid.
Right: A pavement ant
vibrating an aphid with its
antennae. The successful
result—a shiny droplet at
the anal opening of the
"dairy cow"—is already
visible.

pedal glands they extrude threads of mucus into the water, to which small organisms adhere. After a while, the thread or web of mucus is drawn in and eaten, along with the prey.

No less remarkable is the method of feeding employed by the freshwater oligochaete *Ripistes*. This worm extends the anterior end, with its long bristles, from its tube and sways it back and forth. Small organisms stick in the mucus coating the bristles, and from time to time the bristles are drawn through the mouth and licked off. *Ripistes* is so thoroughly adapted to this form of feeding that it is unable simply to take food through the mouth as other oligochaetes do.

A similar approach has been adopted by sea cucumbers of the genus *Cucumaria* and certain other forms. Their tentacles, branched like a tree, are stretched far out to catch drifting organisms and cleaned off in a regular sequence. There is also a squid (genus *Chiroteuthis*) which "fishes" in a way most unusual for a cephalopod, using its extraordinarily long tentacles like flypaper, to catch plankton.

The algal growth on stones and plants in the sea and in fresh water offers a meal consisting of both plant and animal organisms. This coating of algae is eaten by the grazing gastropods after they have scraped it off with the filelike radula. Mud and humus also contain nutrients. These are the foods of mud-dwelling tube worms and earthworms.

An animal that can manage larger bits of food handles them in one of two ways—swallowing it directly or reducing it to smaller pieces first. Whereas the "gulpers" all eat other animals, the "chewers" can take plant or animal food or both. There are also animals which subsist entirely upon liquid food; they suck up plant juices or blood with a muscular gullet. We shall encounter such blood-suckers later in the discussion of external parasitism. The animals living on plant nectar are described in the chapter on flower biology (see Chapter 7).

Food is swallowed whole by some invertebrates, the cnidaria and certain leeches. But the most remarkable adaptations to this gulping habit are found among fishes. In the bottom-dwelling anglerfish (order Lophiiformes) the anterior ray of the dorsal fin has been modified into a lure. This "fishing rod" is mounted on a ball joint far ahead of the eyes; it has a movable attachment at the end that looks like either a worm or a small crustacean. The anglerfish itself is superbly camouflaged by its coloration and outgrowths of skin, with the appearance of algae. As soon as a prey fish approaches, the anglerfish begins to wave the bait vigorously back and forth. When the prey has been attracted close enough, the anglerfish suddenly opens its mouth, creating a powerful suction that sweeps in the nearby water and the prey with it. The only anglers with teeth that can grasp prey are those of the deep sea, which, in the permanent darkness of their home, attract prey with a luminescent organ.

Among benthic fish, gigantic mouths and greatly expandable stomachs are adaptations to the scarcity of food in their habitat. There, an animal

Blood-suckers

Anglers and big-
mouthed fish

Fig. 6-3. The oligochaete
Ripistes with its sticky
bristles extended to
catch prey.

simply cannot afford to ignore any potential prey, however large. The black swallower (family Chiasmodontidae) lives in the Atlantic at depths down to 2500 m and swallows animals a good deal larger than itself. Having swallowed such prey, it looks like no more than an appendage of its enormous stomach. Another group of benthic fishes, the suborder Stomiatoidei, can overcome very large animals by opening their mouths to an astonishing extent. They have taken advantage of the fact that the upper jaw of fishes is connected to the cranium only at its anterior end, the joint between upper and lower jaws being loose. They have evolved a jaw that is much elongated posteriorly and can therefore be opened very wide. Their prey is often quite large and does not let itself be swallowed without a struggle; there is thus considerable strain on the connection between head and body. To deal with this problem, a remarkable adaptation has been evolved; the anterior end of the vertebral column in these fish is not ossified, but remains cartilaginous and therefore elastic. In one genus the end of the spine is even curved into an S, so as to act as a still better spring.

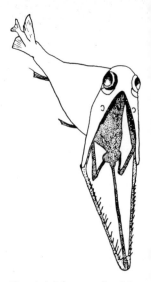

Fig. 6-4. The mouth of the deepsea loosejaw *Malacosteus* lacks both floor and back wall, so that the water resistance that would hamper prey capture is eliminated.

The deepsea "loosejaws" of the genus *Malacosteus* are particularly wierd in apperance, having lost both the floor and the upper walls of the mouth (Fig. 6-4). As a result, the mouth cavity is open below and at the back, and there is a great reduction in the water resistance to be overcome when the lower jaw is flung forward to grasp prey. Smaller prey, of course, can escape—they simply fall through the jaw.

The most familiar swallowers in the animal kingdom are without doubt the snakes. Again, the structure of the skull permits them to swallow prey of remarkable size. The lower jaw is very long and flexibly attached; in addition, the bones of the upper jaw and the two halves of the lower jaw can be pushed outward. All the grasping teeth point backward, so that if the prey makes efforts to escape it drives the teeth still further in. If the jaw is pushed forward, the teeth slide out of the prey. In the act of swallowing, the movable parts of the jaw are pushed forward in alternation, and alternately grip with the teeth. In this way the snake laboriously pulls itself step by step over its prey, until the whole piece is inside and the esophageal musculature can take over the rest of the work. A python about eight meters long, with a head so small that a man's hand can almost enclose it, can manage prey animals a meter and a half in circumference.

In India and Africa, snakes of the subfamily Dasypeltinae subsist entirely upon eggs; they can even swallow very large eggs whole, because of the stretchable mouth and esophagus. The curious thing about these snakes is the apparatus with which they cut through the eggshells. On a number of vertebrae there are ventral processes covered with a hard substance like enamel; these extend into the esophagus through its dorsal wall. The eggshell is slit open with these vertebral "teeth." The content of the egg then flows into the stomach, and the snake regurgitates the shell, now a compressed lump. A circular muscle in the

Vertebrates that gulp their food

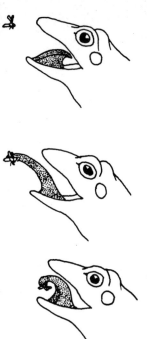

Fig. 6-5. A frog catching a fly.

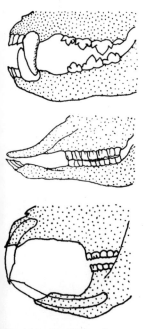

Fig. 6-6. Dentition of predator, ruminant, and rodent.

posterior part of the esophagus ensures that no bits of the shell get into the stomach.

Frogs also gulp down the food they have captured on their tongues. The tongue is attached to the floor of the mouth only at the front, just behind the jaw. The movable part is laid back at rest, and shot forward when a prey animal comes within reach; the animal sticks to the tongue and is grasped by inrolling of the tongue until it can be swallowed.

Birds may either swallow their food whole or break it up with the horny beak, the shape of which is adapted to the manner in which each species eats. In many birds there is an evagination of the esophagus, the crop, where food can be stored temporarily. In the hoatzins of the Amazon jungles the crop has actually taken over the role of the gizzard.

Even the toothed whales (Odontoceti) usually swallow their food whole rather than chewing it. The dolphin's two hundred or so teeth serve only to grasp the fish it eats. The large delphinid *Orcinus orca*, which feeds primarily on birds and marine mammals, is the only odontocete that tears pieces out of its victims, when they are too large to be swallowed whole.

In mammals the teeth are the most important tools for feeding, and one can tell with little difficulty by examining them what type of food an animal eats. There are four basic groups of mammalian teeth: incisors, canines, premolars and molars. The incisors, as their name implies, are for cutting food. The canines are often larger than the incisors and have a more conical shape; predatory animals use these teeth to kill their prey. Among males of the Old World monkeys and the great apes, well-developed canines often serve as weapons in rivalry battles. The last premolar in the upper jaw and the first molar in the lower jaw are used by predatory mammals to bite pieces out of large chunks of meat and to break up bones; by twisting the head they can tear out bites with these teeth. To make this maneuver more effective, the joint of the jaws is so constructed that the lower jaw cannot move sideways. The omnivorous bears are better equipped with molars, and the lower jaw is hung in such a way that it can move from side to side.

The rodents are distinguished by their two pairs of large, and continually growing, gnawing teeth, the incisors. Gnawing requires that the jaw move in an antero-posterior direction, for as the lower gnawing teeth slide along the angled hind surface of the upper teeth, the lower teeth and the lower jaw are pushed backward. Even when chewing, rodents move the jaws back and forth rather than sideways.

The various orders of hoofed mammals are adapted quite differently to feeding on plants. The incisors are relatively less prominent and the molars play a special role. In the ruminants (the camels, the horned ungulates, and the chevrotains) the incisors are usually present only in the lower jaw; they point forward and, together with the canines, operate like knives to cut off parts of plants. Premolars and molars are used to crush food. In the process of "chewing the cud," the lower jaw is pressed strongly against the upper jaw and moved from one side to the other; the joints are arranged to permit such movement.

In the course of evolution, the dentition is occasionally adapted to a certain type of food by becoming regressed or even disappearing entirely. Animals that eat ants and termites all have an elongated oral cavity and a long, sticky tongue. They have either teeth without enamel or no teeth at all, as in the pangolins and scaly anteaters. In these, chewing is performed by an array of horny teeth in the stomach.

A muscular stomach, the gizzard, is also used by birds for chewing. Birds that eat plants and seeds take little stones into the gizzard which help to grind the food. Many birds also retain indigestible items in the gizzard and eventually regurgitate them as a mass of fibers. The chewing stomach of the higher crustaceans—for example, that of the crayfish—contains chitinous teeth moved by the musculature so as to cut and knead the food. Among the insects, the cockroaches, crickets and grasshoppers have a toothed chewing stomach that continues the work begun by the biting/chewing mouthparts.

Spiders differ from the other arthropods in the manner of eating. A spider siezes its prey with two pincerlike chelicerae, at the tips of which there open poison glands. The victim, usually an insect, is killed by the injection of poison and then kneaded between the basal segments of the chelicerae and drenched with digestive juice secreted in the midgut. The spider's food, then, is largely digested before it enters the mouth and can be sucked in bit by bit. When the meal is over, only the empty exoskeleton of the prey remains. In insects, on the other hand, external digestion is rare; it is found, for example, in the aquatic larva of the great water beetle, which can consume only fluid food by sucking through the channels in the mandibles and through minute lateral mouth openings. To liquefy the food, the larva squirts digestive secretions from the midgut into the victim through the mandibular channels. A different approach to external digestion is found in certain starfish, which evert their stomachs and envelope their prey.

The insects have been remarkably successful in exploiting the food supplies in their habitats. This is reflected in the diversity of their mouthparts. The primitive biting/chewing type has been modified into the licking/sucking mouthparts of the adult hymenopterans and lepidopterans, the piercing/sucking proboscises of the bugs and mosquitoes, and the sponging proboscis of the fly. In some cases specialization for a certain type of food has gone so far that the insect must form an association with a lower plant (for example, fungi or bacteria) to obtain essential nutrients lacking in the basic food source. Since the plant partner also benefits from such associations, they are classified as symbioses. Symbioses can also occur between animals of different species, and the relative advantages to the two partners may differ widely. For example there is mutualism in which both species benefit. Mutualisms range from permanent associations in which the two species essentially form one organism together (as in lichens) to looser and more temporary relationships. Commensalism occurs when one species benefits, and the relation is largely neutral for the other. The benefited species may use the other as a surface of attachment, or as a means of transportation; the benefited species may live on, or in the other, or it may live in its burrow or dwelling, and so forth. When one species benefits, and the relation is clearly to the detriment of the other, it is called parasitism. Parasites include endoparasites that live within the host, and ectoparasites that live and feed on the surface of the host, and may not have a permanent association with a given host.

A prime example of symbiosis is the association between the hermit crab *Eupagurus prideauxi* and the sea anemone *Adamsia palliata*. The well-armed anemone protects the crab and in return shares its food (that is, the two animals are mutualists). The two are so dependent upon one another that often neither can live alone. Another sea aenemone, *Calliactis parasitica*, can live without a crab, but there are four different species of hermit crab eager to possess one or more of these anemones. If the snail shell in which the crab lives is large enough, it may carry on its surface as many as seven or eight anemones. It has been reported that the anemone can attach itself to the shell without the crab's assistance, but the crab frequently initiates the relationship. There are films showing very clearly how the hermit crab releases a selected coelenterate from its substrate by stroking and tapping, and sets it in place upon its shell.

The crab *Lybia tesselata*, which lives on the corals in the Indian Ocean, also makes use of the stinging sea anemone as a weapon of defense. It carries an anemone in each of its claws, and holds them out when confronted by an enemy. Little teeth on the inner surfaces of the claws keep the anemone firmly in place, and the anemone must find it easier to obtain food when the crab carries it about. It has been stated that anemones are picked up only when danger threatens, but I regard this as unlikely.

The almost spherical, sponge crab *Dromia*, found in the Mediterranean at depths from ten to thirty meters, behaves as though it had a compulsive urge to cover its back with some kind of camouflage. It uses sponges or the red colonies of the sea squirt *Amaroucium*, cutting a piece to size with its claws. Having been pushed onto the crab's back, the covering continues to live and grow, molding itself to fit the contours of the crab's body (see Color plate, p. 89, and Fig. 6-8). It is held in place by the last two leg pairs, which are displaced dorsally and equipped with large claws. If one puts a large piece of cardboard into an aquarium with one of these crabs, it will cut out a suitable section. Two crabs in an aquarium, one of which is camouflaged, will fight over the piece of camouflage so that it continually changes ownership. Whether the sponge or the tunicate colony gain anything from being carried about is not yet known. But since they are filter feeders, one can assume that they profit by the regular change of location.

Fig. 6-7. The crab *Lybia tesselata* with an anemone in each claw.

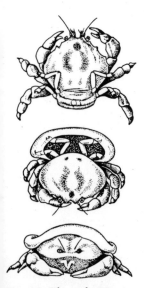

Fig. 6-8. The crab *Dromia vulgaris* holds its camouflaging sponge in place with the modified posterior leg pairs.

A special form of symbiosis to be discussed in more detail in Chapter 9 was discovered only recently. These are the cleaning symbioses. In the "barbershops" of the cleaner fish *Labroides dimidiatus* the "customers" can have parasites and bits of dead tissue removed from their bodies. Even the insides of the mouths of large fish are cleaned. To find out the significance of this cleaning behavior, an enterprising experiment was done in the Bahamas, with highly informative results. All the *Labroides* were removed from two reefs, and it was not long until a large number of the other native fish had left the area as well. The few that remained showed distinct skin injuries after two weeks without the usual body-care service.

There are also two species of shrimp that use their claws to clean fish. *Periclimenes petersoni* even invades the mouths of its clients. Since there are no cleaner fish in undersea caves, their place is taken there by the shrimp *Stenops*. But the customers in this barbershop must enter swimming backwards; a fish approaching head on evidently reminds the shrimp that it can also be eaten by such an animal.

Aphids pierce plants with their proboscises and suck up the starch- and protein-containing juice. Then they digest the proteins in the midgut, while the starches are converted to sugar by a salivary enzyme. The excretion eventually emerging from the anal opening is thus a sweet-tasting fluid. Other insects which suck plant juices—for example, scale insects, psyllids, and cicadellids—also produce sweet excretions; sometimes these are simply squirted out, and the leaves of the plants on which the juice-suckers are feeding extensively become covered with the sticky "honey-dew." It is quite understandable that insects fond of sweet food do not let this go to waste. Ants, in fact, go right to the source of the sweet juice; if one looks more closely at a plant attacked by aphids one will also discover ants in their vicinity.

Aphids as "ant cows"

An observer using a lens will very soon see one of the ants position itself behind an aphid and proceed to stroke and tap the aphid's back with its antennae. Then the aphid raises its abdomen, and there emerges from its anus a clear, golden yellow drop which the ant immediately licks up. The aphid is essentially being milked; some species even have a wreath of hairs around the anal opening which holds the sweet drop and serves it to the ant as though in a bowl. Ants may tap juice from the same aphid several times in succession. When one aphid has been milked dry, it is the turn of the next. Finally, with its abdomen distinctly distended, the ant returns to its nest and distributes the sweet contents of its crop.

All this has been going on since ancient times. A piece of amber from the Tertiary has been found which encloses thirteen ants and their herd of aphids. The relationships between aphid and ant are not as one-sided as it at first appears, for the ants protect and guard their "cows" and sometimes even their eggs. It has been discovered that aphid colonies visited by ants eat more and produce more offspring. This then is a true, mutualistic symbiosis, of a type sometimes called trophobiosis.

Ants can go to even greater lengths in caring for their herds. There is one species of ant, *Lasius brunneus*, provided with sugar-water by the aphid *Stomachis*, which feeds on willow and poplar trunks. To protect their precious cosymbionts from enemies and bad weather, the ants roof over cracks in the bark with rotten wood, building little rounded shelters where they can milk the aphids in peace. Should one destroy one of these shelters, the ants will carry the aphids into another that is still intact. Endangered aphids which do not succeed in pulling their proboscises out of the wood rapidly enough are helped out of their difficulty by the ants. *Stomachis*, by the way, is never found without ants.

Ideal partners for ants with underground nests are the soil-dwelling aphids and scale insects that suck the juices from roots. The ants have developed especially close relationships with them. By its protection of a scale insect, an ant (*Acropyga*) in Surinam shares the responsibility for the severe damage this insect (*Pseudorhizoecus coffeae*) does to the roots of coffee trees. The ants are so accustomed to their domestic animals that when a female takes off on her nuptial flight, preparatory to founding a new colony, she carries an inseminated female scale-insect between her jaws. The new colony is thus assured of its dairy herd.

Guests in anthills

A similar taste for sweetness is evidently also the basis for the symbiosis between ants and the beetles; the latter, as real guests of the ants, enjoy shelter and protection in their nests. These "ant-loving" (myrmecophilous) beetles belong to a variety of families but have one trait in common—at some place on their body they produce secretions which are eagerly consumed by the ants. To put it anthropomorphically, they are paying rent not only for room but for board as well, for they are fed by the ants. Some of the beetles or their larvae even eat the young of their landlords, in which case the appearance of mutual benefit is decidedly deceptive. However, since both species benefit, it is a commensal relationship. Termites, too, share their nests with beetles and dipterans. The termite flies known to live in the nests of African and Indian termites are hermaphrodites, with separate male and female genital apertures.

One-sided exploitation

Other insects are tolerated as guests by ants even though they have no delicacies to offer, either because they look like ants or because the ants cannot catch them. For example, their exoskeletons may be so hard and smooth that the ants are unable to get a good grip. In such cases there can be no question of mutual benefit; the advantage is entirely on the side of the guest, even though the ant may suffer no harm. This sort of one-sided, harmless exploitation has been called "carposis." If an animal is found in the nest of another, with no other evidence of a relationship between the two, the stranger is called a synoekete. Such shared housing is a common form of commensalism.

In the nests of ants of the genus *Lasius* there lives a small mite, *Antennophorus*. The mite clings to the underside of an ant's head with its three posterior pairs of legs, holding the much elongated anterior legs out in

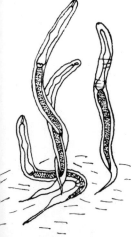

Fig. 6-9. Waving their heads in the air, nematode larvae search for a beetle to fly them away.

front like antennae. In this position it waits until its ant gives a droplet of food to another ant, or receives one; then the mite helps itself. The mites are not only thieves, but "confidence men" as well, for they can beg like an ant by tapping their forelegs against the labium of the ant carrying them. Deceived, the ant regurgitates a drop of food, and the mite has it all to itself. Ordinarily there are several of these pests on a single ant. While they are climbing on, the ant tries to rid itself of them, but when the mites have settled into symmetrical positions the ant's balance is restored and it is evidently no longer bothered.

Fig. 6-10. Nematode larvae "stowing away" under the elytra of a beetle.

Indeed, the mites go to considerable trouble to distribute themselves symmetrically over the ant. If there are two mites, they place themselves one at each side of either the head or the abdomen; if at the head, the mites face forward, whereas on the abdomen they face backward. With three mites, one occupies a central position beneath the head and the others take the places, clearly less desirable, on the abdomen. Groups of four sit at the sides of the head and of the abdomen. Although the position at the underside of the head is the most favorable for *Antennophorus*, those at the sides of the head also permit access to the food drops. The mites riding on the abdomen must be satisfied to obtain food by begging from other ants that come within reach, and that is why they are turned backward. Presumably every mite sometimes has the good fortune to attach to the underside of the head, directly at the food source.

Even in the ocean there are animals that share the food of others without an invitation. Most sea stars of the genus *Astropecten* carry between their rows of tube feet a polychaete worm, *Acholoe astericola*, which obtains part of the echinoderm's food. A related worm genus, *Nereilepas fucata*, has a similar relationship with the hermit crab *Eupagurus bernhardus*, sharing the snail shell in which it lives. To study the symbiosis between these two quite different partners, one zoologist had the ingenious idea of providing them with a snail shell of glass. He could then observe that the polychaete usually stayed far back in the common dwelling, but as soon as the crab began to eat, the worm emerged far enough that its head reached the mouthparts of the crab and it could share in the meal. This curious commensal behavior has recently been captured on film.

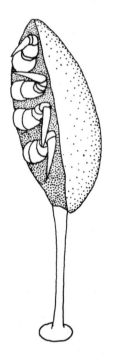

Ant nests are not the only insect establishments to attract visitors. In the nests of bumblebees it is not uncommon to find beetle larvae feeding on the bee's young. These beetles emerge from their eggs in the bee's nest. In order to enter the nest and deposit her eggs, a female *Antherophagus* waits on a flower until a bumblebee comes to suck the nectar; then she bites firmly into its proboscis or antennae. The startled bee takes flight and returns to the nest, where the passenger debarks and proceeds to lay. Such use of one animal by another for purposes of transport is called phoresy.

Of those animals living in dung and carrion, nematodes and mites have a special problem regarding air transport. Their habitats consists of

Fig. 6-11. The larva of the mite *Uropoda* attaches itself to a beetle by a stalk of hardened secretion for its trip through the air.

decomposable organic substances which, as anyone who has walked through cow pastures is aware, gradually lose their initial steaming freshness and then rot. But it is only in the fresh material that these animals find conditions suitable for life. As soon as decay begins they must move on to a new home. For carrion and dung beetles this is no problem; they simply fly away, and are guided by their sense of smell to fresh food. Nematodes and mites cannot fly, and they are not especially proficient at walking, so they use the beetles as taxis. It is only in certain stages (as juveniles or deutonymphs) that the worms and mites can be so transported; having left the beetle in the mass of fresh food, they become sexually mature and reproduce. In some cases the prospective passengers have evolved a behavior that makes it easier for them to find transport. The juvenile nematodes raise themselves vertically and wave their anterior ends about in search movements (Fig. 6-9), and the mite nymphs stand on the back pairs of legs and wave their forelegs. In either case, as soon as contact is made with a beetle, the passenger climbs aboard.

Mite larvae of the family Uropodidae have developed a special procedure to keep themselves from falling off the beetle. As soon as they have mounted, they produce from the anal opening an excretion that hardens to form a stalk. When the beetle flies away, the "stalked mites" travel along in a state of suspended animation, with legs clamped close to the body. Only after they have landed in fresh dung do they become active again. The moisture in their new home softens the stalk so that it bends over and the mite can take hold of the beetle with its feet. By pulling and twisting it tears the now useless stalk away from its body. Recent investigations have shown that a quite specific beetle odor is required to make the mite climb on.

Among the animals that ride on other animals, some are permanent passengers. These are sessile protozoans, many of the orders Peritricha and Suctoria, which spend all their lives, apart from a brief free-swimming phase, firmly attached to other aquatic animals. This is another form of harmless exploitation, which has been called "symphorism." All the benefit accrues to the protozoan, which is continually moved to new territory. The carriers of these microscopic animals, usually beetles, bugs or crustaceans, do not notice that they are there. It is surprising that some species of protozoans have become so specialized that they choose not only a particular species but sometimes one particular spot to attach. An example of such an extraordinary degree of specialization is given by the suctorian *Discophrya stammeri*, which lives only on the water beetle *Helochares lividus* and is found nowhere else but on the inside of the legs near the joint between femur and tibia.

Some peritrichs have even managed to invade the body cavities of their carriers. Again, the protozoan confers no known advantage to the larger animal; by analogy with the synecetes described above one may call these internal passengers entecetes. Two closely related species of the

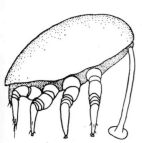

Fig. 6-12. *Uropoda* in the process of secreting its stalk.

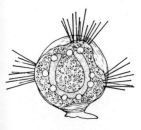

Fig. 6-13. The suctorian *Discophrya stammeri* attaches only to the legs of the water beetle *Helochares lividus*.

genus *Orbopercularia* live in the oral cavity of whirligig beetles; *Operculariella parasitica* lives in the esophagus of predaceous diving beetles, and *Termitophrya* lives in the endgut of termites.

Even multicellular animals can be entoeketes; a famous example is the pearlfish *Carapus acus*. This slender, delicate teleost makes its home in the sea cucumbers that lie sluggishly on the bottom of the ocean. It pays for the protection of this shelter with its independence, for without the sea cucumber it cannot survive. The newly hatched larval fish swims freely for some time. Eventually it pushes into a sea cucumber, head first. It does not move into the gut, as one sometimes reads, but into the respiratory tree. There it enters a second larval stage and remains in the sea cucumber until it has developed into a juvenile fish. Only as a juvenile can it leave the echinoderm; at this stage the fish reenters its shelter head first. The juvenile fish differs greatly from the preceding larval form: its tail is shortened and the anus is not at the hind end but has migrated forward to lie anterior to the pectoral fins. An adult pearlfish always enters its sea cucumber tail first. It recognizes the cloacal opening of the sea cucumber by the flow of respiratory water in and out. The opening may be constricted so that the door is closed, but as soon as the sea cucumber opens it the fish pushes in the front part of its head and, with an elegant twisting movement, reverses its orientation: the tip of the tail is pushed past the head and into the cloaca. Entrance is rapid, and when the fish is in place nothing can be seen of it but the head. At night it leaves its refuge occasionally in search of food; to release its feces it need only push the head out a little distance, since the anus lies under the throat.

The boundary between harmless exploitation and harmful parasitism is often rather vague. Even the pearlfish is not such a well-mannered tenant as was once supposed. Full-grown pearlfish do not remain in the respiratory tree, but break through it and live in the body cavity of the echinoderm, feeding on the gonads. It may be that even the second larval stage, which never leaves the sea cucumber, also has such destructive habits.

In so doing, *Carapus* becomes an entoekete which does undeniable harm to its partner. Animals which damage others by feeding on their bodies are called parasites. A parasite is usually smaller than its host, to which it has an obligatory relationship during some part of its life. It is clearly in the parasite's interest to limit the injury it does so as to maintain the host's life—and its own supply of food. Almost all animal groups are known to contain species that have evolved from the free-living to the parasitic habit. There are even whole classes of invertebrates, such as the tapeworms (class Cestoda), in which there are no longer any free-living forms; the animals are so thoroughly adapted to parasitism that they cannot live outside their hosts.

A fundamental distinction is made between external (ectoparasites) and internal (endoparasites) forms of parasitism. Ectoparasites may live

Fig. 6-14. The peritrich *Orbopercularia gnathophila* lives in the oral cavities of whirligig beetles.

Ectoparasites

permanently on the surface of the host, as do lice, or they may simply visit it occasionally to feed, like mosquitoes or bedbugs. In either case, they display appropriate adaptations. Lice, for example, have a flattened body so as to keep in close contact with the host, whereas fleas are laterally compressed and can thus move with no difficulty through the forest of hairs covering the furry animals on which they feed. For these permanent guests it is an advantage to be able to cling tightly to the host. Lice have legs modified so that they can anchor themselves to hairs, and even the eggs are attached to the hairs, glued by a sticky secretion.

Trematode worms, faced with the problem of fastening themselves to the smooth skin of fish, have evolved at the hind end of the body an attachment organ consisting of hooks and suckers. On the other hand, ectoparasitism renders certain organs superfluous, and these become regressed or disappear completely. For example, permanent parasites like the true lice lack wings, though these are among the basic structures of higher insects. The biting lice (suborder Mallophaga), which feed on keratinous substances among the feathers of birds and are also found in mammalian hair, are wingless and in some cases have even matched their color to that of the host. Since birds use their eyes to search for these parasites, such coloration is a useful camouflage. The lice in the feathers of white gulls are usually light in color, whereas those of the dark-colored skuas are dark.

Endoparasites

The most extreme modifications are those evolved by internal parasites. In the blackness of the vertebrate gut the endoparasite encounters an environment offering almost no oxygen, a number of toxic byproducts of the host's metabolism, and in warm-blooded animals a sustained high temperature, about 37°C. On the other hand, there is an abundant and easily accessible food supply. In the predigested mass of food filling the small intestine, tapeworms need have no digestive apparatus themselves and can simply absorb nutrients through the body surface. Such sedentary animals are under little mechanical stress, and there has been nothing to prevent an increase in size and in the production of eggs. Of course, the worms must be able to find a host in the first place, and many endoparasites must go through a complicated life cycle involving intermediate hosts. The mortality resulting from these difficulties is compensated by an extraordinarily large number of eggs or by reproduction in the larval stage. A female *Ascaris* lays 200,000 eggs a day, or about 70 million in the course of a year. The cattle tapeworm sheds twelve to fifteen segments every day, each of which contains 100,000 eggs. That amounts to about 500 million eggs a year, and since the worm can easily live for twenty years its production of eggs cells is immense.

But how is it possible for free-living animals to evolve into parasites and make themselves at home in—and utterly dependent upon—the unusual conditions in the gut of a host? There is in fact one group of animals living today that can serve as a model, illustrating the conditions under which the endoparasitic habit can be adopted. This is the class Nematoda which includes a vast number of free-living forms distributed in all conceivable habitats, as well as a great many parasitic species. A large fraction of the parasitic nematodes are related to those groups previously described as inhabitants of dung and carrion, environments in which conditions are very like those in the gut of a warm-blooded host. In a cow pat or a compost heap there is a lack of oxygen, poisonous products of the decomposition of organic matter are formed, and it is very warm. The nematodes living there are so well adapted to these conditions that when the situation becomes more "normal" they take the first opportunity to move out.

The ability to make contact with another animal, necessary if the worm is to be transported, is also very useful to an internal parasite. Altogether, then, the nematodes that live in decaying matter are practically "predesigned" for the role of endoparasites. And it was a very similar type of worm which, millions of years ago, succeeded in making the step—not as large as it might first appear—from external to internal parasitism.

7   Flowers and Insects

By F. Schremmer

The ecological study of flowers is a recent chapter in a story that began long ago—the gradual realization that plants have two sexes, which must interact in reproduction and seed formation. Sexuality in plants was much harder to recognize than it was in animals. Plants, after all, display no obvious mating behavior, and the morphological differentiation is subtle; the two sexes may be combined in the same plant or in a single flower. Even in the rare cases in which the male and female gametes are produced by different individuals, "male" and "female" hardly ever differ in any conspicuous way—i.e., sexual dimorphism is uncommon.

Nebuchadnezzar and the date palms

In ancient Mesopotamia the Assyrians and Babylonians had noticed that in order for the date palm, one of their most important cultivated plants, to produce ripe fruit the cooperation of two palm trees was necessary. Plants like the date palm, with the sexes housed in two separate individuals, are called "dioecious." The female palm trees bear the fruit, while the male trees produce a great deal of pollen in their flowers. The pollen from the male flowers is carried to the flowers of the female trees by the wind. People learned by bitter experience that when the unfruitful, apparently useless trees were cut down, the trees which had been bearing fruit ceased to do so. Once the situation was understood, it became the custom to cut off the inflorescences of male palms in the flowering season and hang them in the crowns of the female trees. One of the many ordinances of Nebuchadnezzar specifies that his subjects must deliver a certain number of flowering branches of male date palms to the royal palace. The fact that the cooperation of two sexes is necessary for the production of ripe fruit was thus an empirical discovery resulting from the cultivation of fruit trees.

Rudolf Jakob Camerarius' castration experiments on monoecious plants

The title of founder of the study of plant sexuality can be given to Rudolf Jakob Camerarius. In his paper "De sexu plantarum" (Tübingen, 1694) he drew the correct distinctions between plants with hermaphrodite flowers, those with flowers of different sexes borne on the same shoot (monoecious plants), and those with male and female flowers borne on different individuals (dioecious plants). His castration experiments led him to the insight that two flower structures must always work together in producing fertile seeds, the stamen, which bears the pollen, and the pistil. About the latter he wrote, "As the stamens are the workshops creating the male gametes, the pistil with its little stalk or style represents the female organ of a plant."

In the next century attention was aroused by the so-called "Berlin Experiment" performed by the botanist Gleditsch. In Berlin, in 1749, he cultivated a female dwarf palm of the genus *Chamaerops* which had never borne fruit. Somehow he learned that there was a male palm of the same genus growing in the Botanical Garden in Leipzig. He obtained a flowering branch of this male tree and dusted the female flowers of his own tree in Berlin. He was lucky; the pollen had not been entirely spoiled during the nine-day coach journey, and the experiment succeeded. About seven months later his Berlin plant produced ripe fruits with seeds capable of germinating.

Gleditsch and the "Berlin experiment"

An enormous step forward was marked by the "botanical mules" of the researcher Joseph Gottlieb Kölreuter. In his "Preliminary Report of Certain Experiments and Observations Concerning the Sex of Plants," published in 1761, and in three subsequent papers appearing from 1763 to 1766, he described an extensive series of experiments on hybridization. Among other things, he bred the first "botanical mule" to be studied in detail, from *Nicotiana rustica* and *Nicotiana paniculata*. This hybrid demonstrated that plants descended from two natural species have properties intermediate to those of the parent plants. This was an irrefutable proof of the sexuality of plants, since the intermediate characteristics of the hybrid clearly displayed the influence of both the male and the female parent.

The "botanical mules" of Joseph Gottlieb Kölreuter

Only a few sentences about pollination by insects, written by Kölreuter in connection with the various devices by which pollination was accomplished, will be cited (in essence and in part verbatim): "Experience has taught me that what has long been observed in fig plants is also true of many other plants, some very common. In all the Curcurbitaceae (cucumbers, melons etc.), in the irises, and in many Malvaceae (mallows) pollination of the female flowers or parts of flowers (stigmata) is done by insects alone." The iris he described quite correctly as having the special structure associated with pollination by bumblebees: "In short, all aspects of the arrangement of the parts of the flower (*Iris*), their shape and other properties show clearly that the pollen can neither reach the flowers of its own accord nor can it be carried by the wind; rather, in this case, there are certain species of bumblebees which bring the pollen to the stigmata." Kölreuter, then, was already distinguishing self-pollination from cross-pollination brought about by the wind or by insects, though he did not make these ideas explicit.

In 1793 Christian Konrad Sprengel published a work which did not become famous until much later, but which retains its fascination even

Christian Konrad
Sprengel and the
"Secret of Nature
Discovered"

today; its title was "The Secret of Nature Discovered in the Structure and Fertilization of Flowers." He investigated in the greatest detail an incredible number of flowers (488 species). His description were accompanied by 1076 pictures, and in addition he related his observations of the activity of the insects that visit these flowers. The nectaries (glands secreting a sweet substance) of different flowers were particular objects of study. With his "nectar-marker" theory he added much insight into the already recognized interrelationships between flowers and insects, putting the evidence into a consistent theoretical framework. Sprengel, a child of his time, regarded objects entirely from the viewpoint of teleological utilitarianism. This approach found clear expression in the introductory sentences of his classical work. In the investigation of nectar in a species of stork's bill (Geraniaceae), the trend of his thoughts is evident:

"Convinced that the wise creator of nature brought not one single hair into being without specific intent, I reflected upon what the purpose of these hairs might be." His hypothesis concerning nectar-marking functions led him to the proper interpretation of the colors of flowers: "For I saw that flowers, the corollas of which at one spot are colored differently from the overall coloration, always have these spots, figures, lines or speckling of a special color just where the entrance to the nectary is located. Then I made the step from the particular to the general. If, I thought, the corolla is colored in a special way at a special spot on account of the insects, its overall coloration is on account of the insects." The nectar-markers help the insect find the way to the nectar, and the coloration of the corolla as a whole serves to attract the insects from a distance.

Not until one hundred years later was Sprengel's great achievement recognized and emphasized by Friedrich Hildebrand and Charles Darwin. Here we shall mention just one of the many insights obtained from great numbers of experiments on flowers, the Knight-Darwin Rule. This says, in effect, that nature did not evolve hermaphrodite flowers to be fertilized by their own pollen.

Flower ecology

The main problem of flower ecology, as demonstrated extensively about a hundred years ago by Darwin, Delpino, Hildebrand, Hermann and Fritz Müller, is associated with the fact—for which there is much evidence—that numerous peculiarities of structure and physiology of flowers are obviously related to certain morphological and physiological properties of the animals (practically all of them insects, as far as was then known) that pollinate them. This reciprocal relationship between flowers and their visitors had been pointed out earlier by Kölreuter and Sprengel —for example, in the case of the iris and the bumblebee. It was illustrated once again by Hildebrand; the lever mechanism of the two stamens in a flower of Salvia pratensis is unthinkable without a bumblebee or another organism of a certain size and strength which can operate this mechanism while searching for food in the flowers. This so-called "flower theory" is still being developed and expanded by modern ecologists.

The question as to how evolution could have brought about these intimate and remarkable relationships has been answered in very different ways. From a strictly causal standpoint, in which no teleological (i.e., in terms of "purpose") interpretations are admissible, the answer is based on a purely accidental matching established by natural selection. Since the modifications of the different characteristics in the course of evolution appear to have followed clearly defined lines (orthogenesis), others defend the notion of a guiding principle; they see in the world not only measurable quantities, but also qualities which cannot be encompassed by physicochemical rules alone. Perhaps both views ultimately are statements of faith, but preference among scientists lies with the interpretation based on natural selection.

In terms of geological and evolutionary history, pollination became a special problem after the development of flowering plants capable of living out of water. These plants, firmly rooted in the ground and surrounded by air, could evolve only by solving the problem of transferring pollen from one individual to another—pollination, of course, being the prerequisite for fertilization, seed formation, and maintenance of a species. As soon as the terrestrial flowering plants grew taller than the mosses and prothalli of ferns, raising their reproductive organs (the flowers) higher in the air, it became necessary to protect the male gametes from drying out. They remained enclosed in the microspores, which in flowering plants are called pollen grains. These pollen grains actually contain an entire special intervening generation—the "microsporophyte" can, in a sense, be considered a whole plant, though greatly reduced or dwarfed. It is this microsporophyte that produces the male gametes, usually two of them, and forms a pollen tube through which the sperm move to the egg. The sperm, then, are no longer set free and need not, as in the case of the mosses and fern prothalli, swim actively to the egg through the film of water covering these lower plants.

If the sperm of flowering plants, themselves incapable of motion, are to reach the female organs and the eggs they contain, the spatial separation between the egg-containing organs (pistils) of one plant and the pollen-producing organs (stamens) of another must be bridged by some means of pollen transport. Flowering plants have solved this problem in three ways: 1. the pollen is carried by the wind (anemogamy); 2. it is carried by moving water (hydrogamy); 3. it is carried by flying animals such as insects, birds, and bats (zoidogamy).

The key to the understanding of the flower theory is provided by making clear what is meant by "flower." The word as it is commonly used does not always designate a flower in the botanical sense, which is defined as an appendage of an angiosperm plant specialized for reproduction. In the Calla lily, for example, the flowers are inconspicuous structures on the central spike, while the showy part surrounding the spike is really a leaf. A grouping of flowers, set apart from the foliage, is called an

The flower theory

inflorescence. Often an inflorescence is taken to be a single flower; for example, in the sunflower (a typical member of the family Compositae) the disk surrounded by yellow petals is an inflorescence containing as many as several hundred single flowers of two different types, the ray flowers at the edge having large fused petals and the disk flowers having petals so small that they are not ordinarily noticed. The everyday use of "flower," to designate a structure that is noticeable, reflects a basic tendency of evolution in the flowering plants: where the flowers themselves are inconspicuous, the inflorescence is so shaped or colored as to stand out from the surrounding foliage or grass. But this competition for attention is not directed to humans; it serves to attract animals with a sense of sight and often of color as well.

Anemogams

Of course, plants which disseminate pollen by air currents can dispense with such elaborate devices; the flowers of beech trees, stinging nettles, and grasses are small and inconspicuous, with no striking accessory structures.

Zoidogams

For zoidogams to advertise their presence is not enough; in order that pollen-carrying animals continue to be attracted, there must be some reward associated with this behavior. Therefore many flowers not only have developed a visual display, often enhanced by an attractant odor, but have become sources of nectar as well.

Nectar is a sweet juice, rich in carbohydrates, secreted by special glandular organs and eagerly sought as food by animals. "Pollen flowers," such as the poppy, lack nectar but offer the animals an extra amount—more than is required for fertilization—of protein-rich pollen, also a valuable food. In either case, of course, the food offered by a single flower is small with respect to the animal's needs; an insect must visit many flowers in succession, spreading pollen as it goes. Sprengel's flower theory actually began with his discovery of the nectaries in the flowers and his realization that the nectar was being provided for insects. Proceeding from this fundamental insight, he recognized the significance of the nectar-marking devices of many flowers. His conclusion that many, if not all, aspects of flowers were associated with pollination by animals was correct.

Present-day research on the biology of flowers has been much affected by the discovery of these relationships underlying pollination. Analyses of functional morphology and experiments in sensory physiology are combined, in hopes of understanding the relationships in detail—not only for insect-attracting flowers but for those pollinated by birds and bats as well. Large size, bright color, and the presence of nectar are not the only indications of zoidogamy. Other aspects deserve more consideration—for example, the structure of the pollen of zoidogams as compared with anemogams. It is immediately apparent that the pollen of anemogams must be small, smooth, dry and powdery, since it must be blown out of the flowers and carried as far as possible. In contrast, the pollen of zoidogams must remain in the anthers despite the wind, and stick to the hairs or feathers of the visiting animals.

Zoidogam pollen is thus, as a rule, coated with a thin sticky film and the surface of the grain is sculptured with ridges, knobs, or spines. Such pollen grains not only have a greater tendency to stick together, but they adhere better to other surfaces such as the anthers and the bodies of animals. In most of the Orchidaceae and Asclepiadaceae (milkweeds, etc.) the pollen in each anther lobe sticks together as a single clublike mass, the pollinium, with a slender stalk ending in a sticky mass. The pollinium sticks directly to the body of the visiting animal.

In summary, then, the flowers of zoidogams are usually large and visually striking in themselves or are arranged in conspicuous inflorescences; in many cases they produce a scent, usually (in about 90% of the species) nectar is formed, and the pollen in general is sticky rather than dusty. The stigma (the part of the pistil which receives the pollen) is relatively small, and its surface is bumpy and in the mature state damp and sticky. Anemogam flowers, on the other hand, are small, inconspicuous, often greenish in color, and produce no nectar; their pollen is abundant, dry and powdery. Anemogam stigmata are feathery or brushlike, to provide a greater surface area on which the drifting pollen grains can be caught. Often these flowers are exposed to the wind (male flowers of the hazel, for example, are on long, flexible inflorescences called "catkins"); the stalks of the flowers may be long and sway in the air, or the anthers may be suspended on long threads so that the slighest air current shakes out the pollen and carries it away.

The classical flower theory remained rather one-sided and contained many gaps until the beginning of this century. For historical and geographical reasons botanists studying flowers limited themselves to those pollinated by insects. Their chief interest was directed toward the variety of structures associated with pollination, which even in hermaphrodite flowers were evidently designed to prevent permanent self-pollination. The morphological adaptations of the insects were also observed, in particular the development of proboscises of different length for sucking nectar. But in ignorance of the sensory physiology of insects, these scientists tended to interpret their behavior anthromorphically, treating the insects as little intelligent beings with an appreciation of color and even —in the case of hoverflies, for example—a certain sense of beauty. Charles Darwin himself considered the "theft of nectar" by bumblebees as an intelligent act; he expressed the opinion that they bite holes in the tube of the corolla to "save themselves work."

In any case, it was already recognized that flowers are structures for display, and that they attract animals. The colors of flowers are matched to the spectral sensitivity of the eyes of their visitors. In the northern temperate zone of the Old World, many flowers are pollinated by insects but none by birds, and these insects, except for the pierid butter-

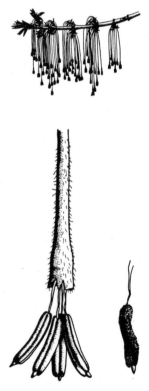

Fig. 7-1. The ash-leaved maple, *Acer negundo*. Above: a twig with many male flowers hanging on thin stalks. Below: single flower (enlarged) with four stamens, and to the right a single stamen that has burst open.

flies (e.g., the brimstone; see Color plate, p. 117), are red-blind. Accordingly, the flora of that region includes only a few purely red flowers. The apparent exception to this rule, the red flower of the corn-poppy (*Papaver rhoeas*), to the bees, looks not red but rather ultraviolet—a color (wavelength) that the human eye cannot perceive.

By contrast, the birds that visit flowers—the American hummingbirds, the nectar birds of Africa and other groups—see red quite well, and many (though by no means all) species of the flowers they visit are colored scarlet or glowing orange. The bats which assist pollination are color-blind, and many of the flowers they visit are open only at night; here color plays no role, but the flowers tend to be very light, whitish, yellowish-green, or a dull muddy color. The birds in this region which do not visit flowers are also sensitive to red, a fact indicated not only by experiments but by the red color of the fruits of many berry bushes.

Patterning as well as color is adapted to the sensory capacities of the animal pollinators. The often-seen spots, lines, or dotted markings of flowers (see Color plate, p. 117) actually show insects the way to the nectar, as the experiments of F. Knoll demonstrated and as Sprengel had suggested earlier in discussing "nectar-markers." We now know that many flowers have nectar-markers invisible to our eyes, which we can see only if we employ ultraviolet photography. Patterning of this sort depends on increased ultraviolet absorption in certain parts of the petals, which ordinarily are highly reflective in ultraviolet light. It is a remarkable fact that the honeybee, when crossing the boundary between the ultraviolet-reflecting and the ultraviolet-absorbing inner part of a petal, automatically extends its proboscis, as if it "knew" that it was now next to the source of nectar.

Honeybees can be trained to approach certain colors, and this is one of the reasons that we know as much about their sense of color as about our own. Color-mixture phenomena exist for the honeybee as well as for ourselves, at least in terms of the way the various color-sensitive receptors are stimulated. A flower which to us looks yellow and also reflects ultraviolet light, appears to a bee not yellow but "bee purple"—a color quite beyond our powers of imagination. On the other hand, a flower we see as white is presumably white to the honeybee only if it reflects ultraviolet; otherwise the honeybee sees it as the complementary color to ultraviolet, blue-green. Strictly speaking, then, we should use the terms "bee blue-green," "bee yellow," and so on in this context. There are many white (to us) flowers, in fact, which reflect little or no ultraviolet and would appear blue-green to the honeybee; among them are the blossoms of fruit trees and the ray flower of the daisy *Bellis perennis*. When a honeybee flies over a field of blooming daisies, blue-green spots shine up at it from a yellow-green background.

The relationships between flower and animals are similar with respect to the scents the flowers produce. Flower-visiting birds, like most other

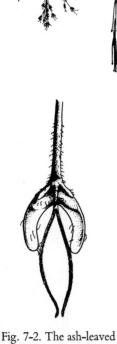

Fig. 7-2. The ash-leaved maple, *Acer negundo*. Above: a twig with female flowers. Below: single female floret (enlarged).

birds, have a poor sense of smell, and the flowers that depend upon birds for pollination have no scent. In contrast, flowers pollinated by insects with a preference for carrion produce a stench reminiscent of rotting meat or other organic substances in the process of decomposition. Some flowers (*Stapelia*, *Rafflesia* and others) manage such deceptive imitations of rotting meat, in both scent and color, that carrion flies lay their eggs in the flowers. The ecologist H. Kugler, interested in knowing whether the dull, dirty colors of many flowers smelling of carrion were particularly attractive to carrion flies, experimented by offering the carrion flies model flowers of different colors—yellow, white, and dark-red flesh colors. The flies paid no attention whatever to the dark flesh-colored models. But the situation changed instantly when the smell of dung was introduced to the experimental cage. Not until they had detected this aroma did the flies begin to take a lively interest in the dull colors.

Fig. 7-3. The bee *Euglossa cordata* (male).

Scents may also act as nectar-markers; in such flowers there is a change in quality or quantity of the scent emitted near the nectary. The flowers visited by bats send out a musty, acid or cabbagy smell unknown among those flowers that attract insects. The bats which evolved from the Microchiroptera to become flower-visitors fed upon fruit, and it is notable that the flowers they visit not uncommonly smell like fermenting, overripe fruit.

There are a few flowers, among them the insect-traps, which lure insects deceptively and actually have nothing to offer, but most zoidogams feed their visitors with nectar or pollen. Only about ten percent of the insect-pollinated flowers offer only pollen as a reward. These pollen flowers ordinarily have numerous stamens and a simple construction offering easy access to them. Familiar examples are the wood anemone (*Anemone nemorosa*), the corn-poppy (*Papaver rhoeas*), and the wild rose (genus *Rosa*). Less familiar, and thus the more interesting, are a number of Papilionaceae with ingenious pollination mechanisms which manufacture no nectar; among these are the common garden lupines (genus *Lupinus*; see Color plate, p. 117), broom (*Sarothamnus scoparius*), and spiny rest-harrow (*Ononis spinosa*). These plants are visited by the honeybee and other insects, entirely for the sake of their pollen. Experienced foraging bees hold on to the flower in such a way that the carine (the two petals surrounding the stamens) is between the tarsal segments of the hind legs; in this position they can take up the pollen that emerges directly with the collecting brushes on the insides of the last pair of legs, and store it in the "pollen basket" on the hind tibiae (see Color plate, p. 117). Occasionally one can observe bees just beginning their season as collectors, which have not yet learned how to cope with the rest-harrow flowers; then the pollen emerging from the tip of the carina is smeared onto the ventral surface or the flanks of the body.

Orchidaceous flowers without nectar cannot be described as pollen

What the flowers offer in return for pollination

Fig. 7-4. The South American hawkmoth *Cocythius antaeus*; the proboscis is twice the length of the body.

Orchids and male bees

flowers; far too little pollen is produced and the pollinia are not usable as food for larvae. Therefore biologists spent considerable time looking for something in these flowers that could serve as food, for flowers offering nothing to their visitors would soon cease to receive visits. As early as a hundred years ago Crüger reported that the flowers of species of *Catasetum* are visited only by the males of the honeybee tribe Euglossini; as Darwin did later, he assumed that they were attracted by a food tissue lining the inner wall of the flower. The assumption that food was involved was accepted until very recently.

In the last decade, finally, there appeared in rapid succession several papers by different researchers which clarified the matter in a surprising way: the nectarless orchidaceans in the subfamilies Catasetineae and Gongorinae, as well as certain other groups, are visited and pollinated exclusively by euglossinine males. Color and shape of the flowers have practically no attractive effect; it is only the strong odor that draws the bees. In fact, the bees collect the aromatic oil secreted by the flowers (see Color plate, p. 118). Once the behavior of the bees was carefully observed, it was evident that the supposed food tissue in the flowers was not being taken up by the mouthparts, but was simply stroked with the forelegs in alternation. The tissue turned out to be the source of the odor substance, which was collected in a particularly interesting way.

The male bees have tufts of hairs on the tarsi of the anterior legs, with which they wipe the microscopic droplets of aromatic oil from the surface of the gland. Then, in flight, they pass the droplets on to brushes of hairs on the middle legs, and these pass them to the hindleg tibiae. The hind tibiae of these bees are both widened and thickened, so that they look as though they had been blown up. Along the posterior edge of the tibia (see Fig. 7-3) is a furrow within which is an opening into the actual collecting vessel for the odor substance. This is not simply a hollow space it is filled with a very fine, spongy arrangement of chitinous rods.

Some orchidaceous species can be pollinated only by certain species of bees, which they attract by a species-specific odor or mixture of odors. In some cases only a single bee species responds to this stimulus. In Panama, for example, only the male *Euglossa cyanura* visit the orchid *Gongora tricolor*, whereas another *Gongora* species in the same area attracts five different *Euglossa* species. The orchids pollinated by euglossinine bees have exceedingly complicated pollinating mechanisms. Some orchird flowers are cleverly designed so that, while collecting the perfume, the males slip and fall backwards out of the flower; as they fall they pass strategically projecting clumps of pollen which stick to the precise spot on the body that will touch the stigma when the bee falls from another orchid flower of the same species. At the tip of the labellum (the most prominent petal) in the orchid genus *Coryanthes* there is a little depression that catches the water secreted by and dropping from a gland (the process of guttation). Just above this water basin, directly next to the odor-

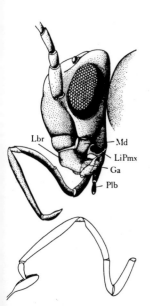

Fig. 7-5. Diagram of the head of the primitive moth *Micropteryx* sp. Below, the elongated maxillary palp is shown scraping out the contents of an anther. Ga, galea of the left maxilla; Lbr, labrum; LiPmx, base of the left maxillary palp, which has been removed; Md, mandible; Plb, labial palp.

Lbr
Md
LiPmx
Ga
Plb

producing part, is the slippery zone, so that when the male bee slides he falls into the basin. To get out of it, the bee must take a route passing the stigma and the stamens, so that pollen can be removed by the former and replaced by the latter.

Only very recently, the botanist and flower ecologist St. Vogel made another discovery that excited great interest among biologists: he found flowers which offer a liquid oil as food, instead of nectar. These South American and South African oil flowers belong to a wide variety of plant families. About 500 species are already known to fall into this category. One example is the slipperwort (genus *Calceolaria*), in which the oil is secreted at the surface of glandular organs resembling nectaries. These are protected from rain, arranged in pairs in the flowers, and consist of columnar cells or of dense cushions of glandular hairs. Such flowers are visited exclusively by females of two subfamilies of potter flower bees (Anthophorinae and their relatives). The oil is not collected like nectar, which is sucked up with the proboscis and carried in the crop, but rather is carried like pollen on the legs and is used as food for the larvae. The bees take up the oil with spoonlike bristles and other fine collecting devices on the tarsi of the forelegs; not until they are in flight do they pass it back to the middle and then to the hindlegs. It is then retained in the long hairs of the hindlegs until the bees reach the brood cells. The food eventually given to the larvae is a mixture of oil and pollen, apparently without nectar. The mature bees feed quite normally on nectar, which of course they must obtain from other flowers. It is not known which animals exploit the South African oil flowers, but presumably they, too, are solitary insects with brood-care behavior.

Flowers offering oil

Besides pollen, nectar, perfume, and nutritious oil, flowers offer still other products to their visitors. There are many orchiadceous flowers without nectar—for example, species of *Maxillaria*—which present a nutrient-rich powdery mass called pseudopollen on the labellum. Pseudopollen is considered to be a substitute for the more common food offerings, but bees have so far only rarely been observed collecting it. In the flowers of several species of the orchidaceous genus *Ornithidium* wax is secreted, and this is used by some solitary bees to build their nests. The Javanese euphorbiaceous plant *Dalechampaeia bidentata* actually produces resin in its flowers; this is gathered by a stingless bee of the genus *Trigona* and used in nestbuilding.

Other foods offered

Flowers and the animals that pollinate them, in many cases, display such intimate and complex relationships between form and function that the experienced investigator confronted by one partner can usually predict the existence and nature of the other. The best-known example of this inference is perhaps the Madagascan white orchid *Angraecum sesquipedale*, the nectar of which is hidden in a tubular flower 20–34 cm in length. As early as 1862 Charles Darwin predicted that there must be some lepidopteran, probably a hawkmoth, which was capable of reaching the nectar of this flower with a long proboscis. Alfred Russell Wallace repeated this prediction somewhat later. Not until forty years after Darwin's suggestion, in 1903, was a moth with a 225-mm-long proboscis actually discovered on Madagascar. This moth could feed upon and pollinate *Angraecum* flowers, but despite repeated efforts no one has yet seen it doing so. It is a subspecies of the hawkmoth *Xanthopan morgani*, found on the neighboring African mainland, and it was given the name *X. morgani praedicta*.

Partnerships

The ecologist O. Porsch was able to select from a large number of tropical flowers—the structural peculiarities of which he knew only from collections, pictures, or verbal descriptions—those that must be pollinated by birds or by bats. In the great majority of cases, his predictions were accurate.

Such predictions, however, do not work equally well in both directions. From the structure and life history of a flower one can make inferences about the animal pollinator, but one cannot conclude from the unusually long proboscis of a hawkmoth, or any other animal characteristic, that there is a flower in which the nectar is hidden at a certain depth. There is a South American hawkmoth species, *Cocythius cluentius*, with a proboscis 250 mm long; but no South American plant has ever been discovered with such a long flower enclosing its nectar.

Fig. 7-6. The carpenter bee *Xylocopa leucothorax* (male) sucking nectar from a flower of the tropical asclepiadaceous plant *Calotropis procera*.

Two other findings may shed some light on this situation. The European hummingbird hawkmoth (*Macroglossum stellatarum*) is active by day, frequently using its *ca.* 35-mm-long proboscis to suck nectar from all sorts of flowers, including those in which the nectar could be reached just as well with a proboscis only 10–15 mm long. The hummingbird hawkmoth is something of a thief, since it does not pollinate the flower in which the corolla is short. And there are other, similar cases among the diurnal lepidopterans. For example, the silver-washed fritillary (*Argynnis paphia*) frequently visits the inflorescences of wild angelica (*Archangelica silvestris*), hemp agrimony (*Eupatorium cannabinum*), and the thistle *Cirsium oleraceum* to suck their nectar. For none of these flowers do the butterflies need their long proboscis. Yet the longer the proboscis of a fly, bee, or butterfly, the better adapted they "appear" to be for obtaining more deeply hidden nectar.

The hawkmoth with a long proboscis

Is this the case with our South American moth with the extraordinarily long proboscis? The question arises whether evolution has here gone beyond what is required; but it cannot be answered at our present level of knowledge. Our time is too short to observe and fully understand evolutionary processes; in comparison with the history of the earth and its fauna, our lifespan is rather like the flash of a camera bulb. We could regard the extra long proboscis as a "preadaptation" and surmise that even though it is of no use to the hawkmoth now, it may be just what it needed in the distant future, when a flower with a corella 20–30 mm long happens to evolve and by chance becomes established in the range of this moth.

Then the advantage to this moth would be great, since the nectar of the new flower would be inaccessible to all the other moths. In this sense, the moth's special ecological niche would not exist until this imagined flower appeared.

Conversely, flowers bearing nectaries within a deep corolla could only evolve and survive if suitable insects with long proboscises were available to suck the nectar and pollinate the flowers. Otherwise the mutant flowers would not be pollinated regularly and would die out. In this respect insects and other animal pollinators can be regarded as setting the pace in the development of reciprocal relationships between flower and animal. One might say that insects and birds are the breeders of flowers; O. Porsch and other researchers have considered the nectar-sucking birds as the creators of the lively variety of flowers that they visit. In our example, of course, one must be prepared to accept that the long proboscis of the South American hawkmoth remains unchanged during the wait for the appearance of a suitable flower—that neither the moth nor its caterpillar evolves in a way that affects this aspect of its morphology or habits.

Fig. 7-7. Head and proboscis of the tropical nectar-sucking midge *Toxorhynchites splendens* (family Megarrhinidae).

The matching of flower and pollinator is also clearly evident in the correspondence of their ranges, with respect both to geographical location and to altitude. An example is offered by the monkshood (genus *Aconitum*), a flower characteristically visited by bumblebees and found nowhere outside the range of these bees; wherever one sees monkshood, there must be bumblebees with long proboscises. But the reverse conclusion, that bumblebees live only where monkshood is growing, by no means follows, for bumblebees are found far away from the limits of monkshood distribution.

Correspondence in range of flower and pollinator

It is worth mentioning in this connection that in regions where no bumblebees live—for example, in all of Africa south of the Sahara—carpenter bees (genus *Xylocopa*) take over their role. There is a similar correspondence between the distributions of flower-visiting birds and of the flowers they visit. In Europe neither are found, though the occurrence of birds as flower-pollinators is by no means limited to the tropics. Certain species of hummingbirds are migratory, travelling over North America in summer as far as the Alaskan border, and even in the far north they find a number of North American flowers specialized for pollination by hummingbirds. The flowering season of these plants is synchronized with the summer appearance of the birds.

Of the African nectar-sucking sunbirds (Nectariniidae) only one species, *Cynniris osea*, travels as far to the north as the Dead Sea in Palestine; following the bird, the plant *Loranthus acaciae*, with its long, tubular, red flowers, has extended its range northward.

Sunbirds and hummingbirds

In the southern hemisphere, flower-hummingbird associations are found far beyond the temperate zone, down to the southern tree line in Tierra del Fuego, where *Fucshia coccinea* is pollinated by the giant hummingbird *Patagonas gigas*. In the Australian region, on the islands south of

New Zealand, there are two species of honey-eaters (Meliphagidae) which prefer to visit the flowers of *Metrosideros lucida*; the ranges of the plant and the birds coincide even in terms of altitude. Certain species of hummingbird, and the particular flowers they visit, are found in the Andes at altitudes of over 5000 meters, up to the snow line. The same is true in the tropical African mountains; on Kilimanjaro two species of sunbirds and the lobelias they pollinate are found as high as 4000 meters.

Flowers pollinated by bats

Describing his investigations on the flowers pollinated by bats in Central and South America, St. Vogel in 1969 reported that the geographical distribution of partner species matched to a considerable degree. The northern limit of such associations is about 33° north latitude, in Texas and Arizona, where cacti (Pachycereae) and agaves in particular are pollinated by two species of bat (*Leptonycteris nivalis* and *Choeronycteris mexicana*). Like the hummingbirds, the bats come to these northern regions only as summer visitors, when the flowers are in bloom. In the southern hemisphere flowers are visited by bats as far south as northern Argentina (about 28–30° south latitude); examples of such flowers are *Nicotiana otophora* and *Vriesea joghii*, which are pollinated by *Glossophaga soricina*. In southern Asia, too, the ranges of bats and the flowers they pollinate coincide. Trees of the genus *Kigelia*, among the first plants known to be pollinated by bats, were planted in Hawaii but proved to be infertile there, since there are no nectar-sucking bats in Hawaii.

Nectar-sucking organs

The most striking adaptations of many flower-visiting animals are in the mouthparts, which usually have been modified into a more or less elongated nectar-sucking organ. Only in certain insects have the mouthparts been adapted for pollen-eating. Flower-visiting birds, especially the hummingbirds, developed long forcepslike beaks and a tongue that in most cases can be extended a long way, is slit at the tip to form a sort of brush, and is tubular in form—both sides being rolled inward. The modifications of the bats are similar; they have a more or less sharp snout and an extensible tongue with fine horny protrusions at the tip, pointing back toward the mouth. There is an especially great variety in the proboscises of nectar-sucking insects, which belong to quite different orders.

Of all the known Lepidoptera, only the primitive moths (family Micropterygidae) have retained chewing mouthparts and feed upon pollen. These little moths, most of them with a dark metallic sheen, tend to congregate in buttercups and other *Ranunculus* species, sitting on the yellow flowers with wings laid together like a roof over the back, and eating the abundant pollen (see Color plate, p. 118). Their mouthparts serve neither for holding nor biting, but only for chewing. To gather pollen they use the conspicuously elongated and very flexible palps. The terminal palp segment is sharp and slightly bent into a claw shape; with it, they scrape the pollen directly out of the opened anthers and with quick movements of left and right palps in alternation carry it to the mouth, where it is crushed and then swallowed.

Fig. 7-8. The horsefly *Corizoneura longirostris*; the proboscis is 5 cm long.

These moths are not restricted to the pollen of buttercups and marsh-marigolds; I have also seen numbers of them eating pollen on the male inflorescences of a species of sedge. It follows that specialization of the mouthparts for feeding on pollen by no means always implies association with insect-pollinated flowers. Honeybees, especially in spring, often collect a great deal of pollen from anemogams—for example, from poplars and ashes, from the sedge *Carex verna*, and in some cases even from grasses like *Dactylis glomerata*.

Lepidoptera other than the Micropterygidae have entirely regressed chewing mouthparts; only the galea of the maxilla remains on either side, and these two structures are laid together and interlock to form a tube through which liquid food is sucked up. When not in use, this proboscis is rolled up like a watchspring on the underside of the head. Butterflies and moths can also suck nectar or other fluids such as water up from moist sandy ground. The longest proboscises known among insects are those evolved by the hawkmoths (family Sphingidae). It is easy to imagine that these moths would find it difficult to unroll their proboscises when they are perched on a flower; they usually feed while hovering over the corollas (which are often quite deep) of the flowers they visit. Correspondingly, flowers specialized for pollination by hawkmoths have no particular structures on which the moths can land or sit, nor do most of the flowers pollinated by hummingbirds. Certain owlet moths (family Noctuidae) have evolved a proboscis capable of boring into juicy fruits, and one species, as Bänzinger discovered, even sucks the blood of mammals.

Species of Hymenoptera display all sorts of transitional forms between the short, broad-lobed licking proboscis of many wasps and some primitive bees, and the sucking proboscis of the euglossinine bees, which is longer than the body (Fig. 7-3). The proboscis is formed from the maxilla and labium; its middle section, which consists of the fused glossa of the labium, is covered with fine hairs and can be pushed up and down in the tube of the proboscis. In the honeybee and the bumblebees with long proboscises, the resting position of the proboscis is folded up against the back of the head, while in the euglossinine bees it is stretched out against the ventral surface—in some cases extending beyond the end of the abdomen. The carpenter bees, usually thick-bodied, powerful insects, have a proboscis that can be used for piercing as well as sucking. The maxillary components are broadened near the base, very hard, and joined to form a rigid wedge. This structure enables the bees to open firmly closed nectaries and even to reach the nectaries by piercing through the corolla and slitting it open.

A nectar-sucking proboscis has clearly been evolved several times independently by the Diptera. Some of the midges and their relatives (suborder Nematocera) visit flowers; examples are the March flies (family Bibionidae), seen in horse-chestnut flowers in the spring, and male mosquitoes (family Culicidae). The female mosquitoes are well known as

Lepidoptera as nectar-suckers

▷
Above: A brimstone (*Gonepteryx rhamni*) sucking from the flower *Dianthus carthusianorum*.
Lower left: The hemp-nettle *Galeopsis speciosa*, a labiate flower with markings on the lip to indicate the presence of nectar.
Lower right: A honeybee collecting pollen from the nectarless flower of a lupine (*Lupinus polyphyllus*). Note the masses of pollen carried on the hind legs!

Fig. 7-9. The South African nemestrinid fly *Megistorhynchus longirostris* hovers while sucking nectar from the long corolla of an iridaceous flower.

◁

Upper left: A hairy euglossinine bee (*Eulema cingulata*) as large as a bumblebee collecting odor substance from an orchid (*Catasetum* sp.).
Upper right: Primitive moths (*Micropteryx* sp.). eating pollen in a buttercup (*Ranunculus* sp.).
Lower left: A hover fly (*Eristalis*) on ivy flowers.
Lower right: The beetle *Leptura cordigera* on a flower of *Chrysanthemum segetum*.

blood-suckers, and the structure of their proboscises differs correspondingly from that of the males. The latter, with no need to pierce animal skin, have stylets which are shorter or which may have regressed completely. A similar regression is found in the tropical mosquitoes of the family Megarrhinidae, but here it has occurred in both sexes. Their proboscises are quite unsuited to piercing and blood-sucking; the stylets have become short, hairlike, nonfunctional threads. This proboscis can easily be regognized as specialized for the sucking of nectar, by the characteristic downward bend at its tip.

Even among those compactly built Diptera with short antennae, commonly called flies (suborder Brachycera), certain blood-suckers have switched to nectar as food. Female horseflies (family Tabanidae) suck blood, whereas the males visit flowers. But in certain tropical and subtropical species of the genus *Pangonia*, the females have long nectar-sucking proboscises. In recent years the horsefly *Corizoneura longirostris* has been studied in some detail; in this species both male and female have proboscises five centimeters long; with these they suck nectar from a variety of flowers, usually those with nectaries at the bases of narrow tubes. The sucking tube, longer than the normal horsefly proboscis, is formed by the labium alone. It is quite remarkable that the females of this species have not given up the blood-sucking habit, even though the long proboscis is incapable of piercing skin. To suck blood, the female simply folds the proboscis at its base, pressing it against the ventral surface and exposing the tips of the short stylets; it is these which are stuck into the victim. Males have never been observed to suck blood. Probably they cannot do so, since their stylets have disappeared entirely and the rodlike mouthparts are not, as they are in the female, covered with fine teeth.

Among the Diptera that feed exclusively upon flowers are the Nemestrinidae of South Africa, the proboscis of which is the longest found in the order (up to 7 cm). Like all insects with extremely long proboscises, they suck nectar while hovering; when they are directly above a long tubular flower, they thread the proboscis delicately into it, letting the body slowly sink through the air and then rising again. When not in use the proboscis is laid close to the ventral surface, sticking out beyond the end of the body like a tail. The hairy European bee flies (family Bombyliidae), which carry the long proboscis pointing straight ahead, also hover when sucking nectar, but receive additional support from the delicate legs (see Color plate, p. 123). The species with long proboscises feed not only upon nectar, but consume pollen just as eagerly. The labella at the tip of the labium are elongated but study, and participate actively when the fly is eating pollen.

All the species of hover flies (family Syrphidae) visit flowers, showing an equal interest in the nectar and the pollen. Species of the genus *Rhingia* have a proboscis as long as that of the honeybee, so that they can successfully draw nectar from some labiate flowers such as the bugleweed (*Ajuga*). The shape of the head, with its snoutlike projection (Fig. 7-11), is evidently associated with the elongation of the proboscis. The other hover flies have sponging proboscises and can take up nectar only if it is exposed, as in umbellifers or ivy flowers (see Color plate, p. 118), but they can obtain pollen directly from the anthers of a great variety of flowers. Thick-headed flies (family Conopidae) and some Larvivoridae (*Prosena* and other genera) also have considerably elongated proboscises. And there are a number or other flies, among them many larvivorids and the muscid sub-family Anthomyinae, which play a very significant role as pollinators in many communities.

Finally, let us consider the beetles. These are without doubt among the original flower pollinators, for their evolutionary history goes back to the time when flowering plants were evolving. But it is striking how few beetles have specialized in flowers as food. A number of long-horned beetle species are commonly found on flowers (see Color plate, p. 118); with the tufts of hairs on the maxillae they sweep up pollen and eat it, and they can also lick up nectar. Some species, such as those of the genus *Strangalia*, even have head and prothorax so narrow that they can obtain nectar from inside the corolla, if it is not too deep and narrow. Among the typical pollen-eaters are the European rose-chafer species (genus *Cetonia*). The biting mouthparts ordinarily found in beetles have here lost their holding and gnawing functions and are used only to crush pollen.

In many other beetle families, too, there are regular visitors of flowers, some with mouthparts evidently adapted to pollen-eating. Only in a few species of two genera of blister beetles (family Meloidae) do we find pro-boscises clearly specialized for sucking nectar. These can be as long as the body or longer (Fig. 7-10). Remarkably, the proboscis is formed from different elements of the mouthparts in these two related genera. In *Nemognatha* the galeae of the maxillae are more or less elongated, and their inner sides, with a dense covering of hairs, together form the proboscis; in *Leptopalpus* the proboscis consists of the elongated palps of the maxillae.

And there are a great many more species of beetles, mostly rather small animals, of different families that are regularly found on flowers and could act as pollinators, but only a few flowers are clearly specialized to attract beetles. The only characteristic these "beetle flowers" have in common is their scent. Many of the flowers visited by beetles are extremely primitive —for example, the magnolias and certain shrubs with aromatic bark in the family Calycanthaceae. The flowers of *Calycanthus* species offer the visiting beetles neither nectar nor pollen, but special little lumps of food located at the tips of modified stamens (staminoids).

Whereas there is a reciprocal relationship in the morphology of polli-nator and flower with respect to the length of sucking device in the animal and the depth of the nectar in the flower, there is no correspondence be-tween flower structure and the various devices by which bees collect and transport pollen. Only bees and wasps of the family Apidae collect pollen in order to carry it home as food for their larvae. Since they require such

Fig. 7-10. The beetle *Nemognatha bicolor* with a proboscis longer than its body.

Fig. 7-11. Head of the hover fly *Rhingia rostrata*, at three stages during folding of the proboscis.

large supplies, the bees are among the most industrious visitors of flowers and thus the most important pollinators. The more primitive bees, usually with a body that is smooth rather than hairy, collect pollen with their mouthparts, either directly from the anthers or after it has been pulled out by the legs; they swallow it and carry it home in their crops. All other bees carry the collected pollen on the surface of the body, either in the hairs on the legs or between the bristles of a brush on the abdomen, and often the same flower is visited by bees that carry the pollen in different places. The way the pollen is stored in the flowers is purely a matter of what is most advantageous to the plant; the structures are entirely designed to ensure successful pollination of the flowers.

Many animals that visit flowers have learned to "outwit" these devices, stealing nectar and pollen without performing the reciprocal service of pollination. In fact, it is the flowers of more complicated structure that are most frequently victims of such theft. But there is no known case in which the theft of nectar has actually threatened the continued existence of a plant.

Mechanisms for attraction and deception

The means evolved by zoidogams to attract their visitors are based on the most important drives in the lives of the animals, those associated with feeding and reproduction. With colors like decaying flesh and with the smell of carrion they lure hungry carrion insects; with sexual odors they deceive males eager to mate with a conspecific female. And they even set traps for their pollinators. There are flowers into which insects slide and are kept until pollination is completed, by a clever trick: the insects tend to flee toward the light, but the flowers have walls with light, transparent spots like windows, which divert the insect from the real exit in a darker part of the flower.

It has already been mentioned that various orchidaceous flowers are so constructed that the bees gathering aromatic substances slip and fall; other plants cause a sort of intoxication in the bees which brings about a loss of coordination. As the insects fall, the pollinia become glued or caught on the surface of the body, just where they will contact the stigma of the next flower of the same species that they visit. Other orchidaceous species imitate a female bee, with remarkable success. Kullenberg has analyzed in great detail such a deceptive mechanism in the flowers of *Ophrys*, which are pollinated by the males of some hymenopteran species. *Ophrys* sends out an odor strongly resembling the attractant substance of the females of certain species of thread-waisted wasps or bees; related flowers imitate ichneumons. These odors attract the appropriate male insect which, after landing on the flower, is actually stimulated by the hairy surface of the labellum to make copulatory movements. In this case the female is imitated by olfactory and tactile signals, but other orchids achieve the same thing with visual signals. A groove in the stigma so resembles the open genital aperture with which females of certain larvivorid flies induce the males to copulate, that the males fling themselves onto the flowers to mate

Fig. 7-12. Head of the beetle *Nemognatha chrysomelina*.

with them. The attempt is given up after only a moment, but this is enough for the orchid to attach the pollinium which will be left on the stigma of the next flower with which the bee tries to mate.

The territorial behavior of males of the tropical bee genus *Centris* is turned to advantage by orchids of the genus *Oncidium*. In shape, and even more in the way they vibrate when set in slight motion, an *Oncidium* flower imitates a flying insect so deceptively that a *Centris* male patrolling his territory takes it for an intruder. The bee mounts a frontal attack and tries to drive the stranger away. In so doing, it sometimes strikes the center of the flower so precisely that the pollinia may become attached to its head, between the eyes. This defensive drive is so strong that male bees will attack every flower in their territory that happens to be moving, one after another.

The relationship between the yucca flower (*Yucca filamentosa*) and the moth *Pronuba yucasella* is so close that it qualifies as symbiosis. Certain figs depend upon a highly complicated procedure of pollination by a gall wasp, *Blastophaga grossorum*. Some species of *Ophrys*, as well as certain tropical orchids, attract and are pollinated by only one species of insect. And there are orchids of the temperate zones, such as the soldier and green-winged orchids (*Orchis militaris* and *Orchis morio*), which attract few visitors and are pollinated only rarely, for they have neither nectar nor other offerings to repay such attention.

Fig. 7-13. The thread-waisted wasp *Gorytes mystaceus* trying to copulate with an orchid (*Ophrys insectifera*).

▷
Above: The bee fly *Bombylius major* hovering just in front of a flower of the purple gromwell (*Lithospermum purpureocoeruleum*).
Lower left: Flower of the orchid *Ophrys tenthredinifera*.
Lower right: Male of the bee *Eucera nigrilabris*; the four pollinia stuck to its head came from orchids like those in the left-hand picture.

8   Other Interactions of Animals and Plants

By F. Schremmer

All animals depend, directly or indirectly upon plants for food. But other special relationships have also been evolved between animals and plants; in most of these, the benefit obtained by the plants is associated with the ability of the animals to move about. One example was described in the preceding chapter—the pollination of flowers by insects, birds and bats. The dispersal of seeds also often requires the participation of wind, water or animals. Plants with seeds or fruits distributed by animals are called zoochores—"endozoochores" if the seeds are taken into the animal's body as food and pass out (still capable of germinating) with the excrement, and "epizoochores" if the seeds or fruits are transported on the surface of the body.

Ants are notable agents of seed dispersal; the number of plants (myrmecochores) which depend on ants to carry their seed is astonishing. The seeds are distinguished by a peculiar appendage, a surface growth called the caruncle which is rich in protein, fats and oils and is prized as food by the ants. When an ant finds such a seed it takes the caruncle between its jaws and drags the seed toward its nest. During the journey the caruncle may break loose, or the ant may eat it, so that the seed is left by the wayside at a point that may be many meters away from the mother plant. Sometimes the seeds are taken all the way to the nest and thrown out after the caruncle has been eaten. In either case, the goal of dispersal has been attained.

It is striking that all the temperate-zone myrmecochores are plants of the lower herbaceous stratum; no shrubs or trees have seeds distributed by ants. The undergrowth of European oak and beech woods includes many myrmecochores. Some of the most familiar are *Corydalis*, cow wheat (*Melampyrum*), ivy speedwell (*Veronica hederaefolia*), and sandwort (*Moehringia*). The restriction of myrmecochores to the shady strata, especially in woodland, is explained by the fact that there is little wind there; in the tree canopy, by contrast, air movement is considerable and the plants are more likely to be anemochores (seeds dispersed by wind). In the shrub

◁
Upper left: A twig and part of the trunk of *Acacia cornigera*. Beneath this: Belt's corpuscles at the tips of the leaflets of this acacia. Upper right: Open fruit of the greater celandine (*Chelidonium majus*). Beneath it: A myrmicine ant (*Myrmica laevinodis*) has seized a celandine seed by the caruncle in order to drag it away.
Lower left: Gall of the spruce gall aphid *Sacciphantes abietis*. The chambers in the gall have just opened, and the aphids have emerged and are molting on the adjacent needles to produce winged animals.
Lower right: A beech-leaf gall cut in half. The minute larva of the gall midge *Mikiola fagi*, which produced this gall, can be seen in the chamber.

stratum berry bushes frequently predominate, and their seeds are dispersed by birds.

The seeds of the greater celandine (*Chelidonium majus*; see Color plate, p. 124) ripen throughout the summer. This plant thrives in hedges and near rubbish dumps, where ants—often myrmecines (e.g., *Myrmica laevinodis*), which prefer humid habitats—are almost always present as well. When the seeds fall to the ground, they are soon found and carried off by the ants, always being grasped by the caruncle (see Color plate, p. 124) since the rest of the seed is too hard and smooth to offer a secure hold. Celandine also tends to grow in the crevices of loose stone walls, where the seeds would be most unlikely to arrive unless brought there by the ants.

Another myrmecine ant genus, *Messor*, is found north of the Alps only in a few very warm, dry places, but it is one of the commonest forms in the Mediterranean region. *Messor* collects essentially every sort of small, dry fruit or seed that it can reach and carries it to its nest; sometimes it gathers grain to such an extent that it does real damage. Within the nest the ants remove the seeds from their fruits or husks, which are taken out and piled around the nest entrance; the seeds themselves are stored in special chambers and form the chief food of the nest inhabitants and their brood. Although most of the seeds are destroyed in this way, it does occasionally happen that an ant will lose a seed en route and thus contribute to the dispersal of the plant. Apart from such accidents, the advantage in this relationship is entirely on the side of the ants.

Many plants in the herb and shrub strata have evolved fruits (generally called burs) with hookline devices designed to catch in the fur of passing mammals. They usually become detached from the plant quite easily and are carried away; these plants are thus epizoochores. An example that comes immediately to mind is the burdock *Arctium lappa*, in which the bracts enclosing the flower heads are hooked spines. The club-shaped fruits of the common enchanter's nightshade (*Circaea lutetiana*) are covered in tiny hooked bristles, as are the fruits of goosegrass (*Galium aparine*). When fruits of *Geum* ripen the pistil becomes a hooked spine, and in the agrimony *Agrimonia procera* there is a wreath of hooked spines surrounding the edge of the bell-shaped fruit. The achene-type fruits of the bur-marigold (genus *Bidens*) bear two or four sturdy spines with recurved hooklets by means of which they cling tenaciously to clothing as well as to the fur of mammals; in either case, they are often carried for long distances before they come loose and fall to the ground.

Another sort of relationship between animal and plant is exemplified by the flowers which harbor ants. There are many tropical species of these; ants are commonly found living in the higher parts of the trunks of certain *Cecropia* trees, in the stems and twigs of *Triplaris americana*, and in the thickened hollow thorns of various species of *Acacia*. Once it was realized that each of these plant species is inhabited only by ants of a certain species, which do not leave their home even to forage for food, it became clear

Fig. 8-1. Burs transported by mammals:

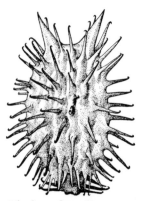

The bur of *Xanthium strumarium*, an achene-type fruit with hooked spines.

The fruits of the common enchanter's nightshade (*Circaea lutetiana*) caught in the hairs of an animal.

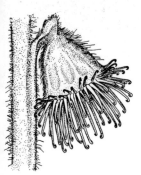

Fig. 8-2. Bur of an
agrimony (*Agrimonia
procera*).

Myrmecophytes

that the plants themselves must offer a food supply. On the leaves or
petioles of some of these "ant plants" were discovered small, easily de-
tachable structures of high nutrient value; it seemed evident that these
must be the suspected food source and in fact they are collected regularly
by the ants. These plants, then, not only offer shelter to their guests but
feed them as well.

Of course, one would not expect a plant to do this unless there were
some advantage to be gained. Indeed, these ants proved to be particularly
aggressive and capable of biting even humans quite painfully. If one tears
a leaf from such a plant, or even shakes it by tapping on the trunk, hundreds of animals hurl themselves out of their dwellings as though in response to an alarm signal and rush over the whole tree, ready to attack any
intruder. An insect or grazing animal that touches the tree is met with the
same deterrent response. One could justifiably conclude that the plant's
advantage consists in its being defended from foliage-eating animals—
caterpillars, for example, or the dreaded leaf-cutter ants. The ants, of course,
are simply defending their home and food supply, the benefit to the plant
being a byproduct of their behavior.

Plants ordinarily associated with ants in this way may be called "myrmecophytes." It is interesting to consider whether this form of symbiosis
is absolutely necessary to both partners. An ant for which the association is
"obligate" cannot survive without its plant, but the myrmecophyte can
continue to live without the ants. The apparent demonstration that the
plant is healthier since it is protected from damage by herbivores has been
much disputed by scientists—especially when generalized to all plants that
attract ants by nectaries of some sort—and it is still sometimes questioned.
Occasional observations made during a visit to the tropics, even if they are
well planned, are naturally insufficient to clarify matters completely. For
this reason, the American biologist D. H. Janzen spent several years during
the 1960's in Mexico, making extensive and meticulous control observations and experiments on *Acacia cornigera*, which harbors the ant *Pseudomyrmex ferruginea*. He came to the following conclusion:

The ant *P. ferruginea* is dependent on *A. cornigera* for its survival, and the
acacia is just as dependent upon the ant for its normal development. When
all colonies of *P. ferruginea* (and another species of the same ant genus, *P.
nigrocincta*) disappeared from the region he investigated, there was a
marked decrease in the number and density of stands of the acacia. Only a
few little stems and shoots were able to survive, in isolated locations where
conditions were abnormal. Surprisingly, Janzen determined that the main
effect of the ants was not so much to repel herbivorous insects and mammals as to prevent the young acacias from becoming overgrown by climbing and twining plants. On former grazing land which has become densely
overgrown, the young acacias and new shoots are in great danger of being
choked by the creepers and climbers before they grow above the shrub
stratum. The shade of the entwining plants slows the growth of the

acacias to such an extent that they soon die. It was unquestionably demonstrated that the ants chew off all parts of the climbing plants that come into contact with their acacias, thus preserving their food source and dwelling place.

Of course, this result cannot automatically be extended to all the other myrmecophytes. But it is quite possible, and even probable, that the ants of the genus *Azeteca*, which live in *Cecropia* trees, also protect their home—especially against defoliation by leaf-cutter ants and/or caterpillars.

As one of the best-known myrmecophytes, *Acacia cornigera* deserves more detailed description. Saplings are colonized by the ant *Pseudomyrmex* when they are only 25–30 cm high and consist of just a stem, a few leaves and one pair of thorns, united at the base (see Color plate, p. 124). The thorns are swollen and hollow, each pair forming a single cavity which is used as a dwelling by the ants. There is only one entrance to each chamber, usually chewed out just behind the tip of one thorn on the side away from the rain. The ants in each acacia form a single colony; eggs are laid and the young are raised entirely in the chambers within the thorns. In addition to a sheltered place to live, the acacia offers its ants two kinds of food, nectar and the so-called Belt's corpuscles. The nectar comes from nectaries on the pinnate leaves; one to three, or occasionally four, are arranged in a row on the upper side of the slightly broadened rachis. They are green, flat mounds with a crater or bowllike depression in the middle. The nectar, rich in carbohydrates, accumulates in these depressions and is collected by the ants at frequent intervals.

The second form of food is much richer in protein. Belt's corpuscles are small growths, round or oval, at the tips of the leaflets (see Color plate, p. 124). Since there is an orderly division of labor in the ant colony, the corpuscles are harvested by certain workers only; they are brought to the chambers to feed the larvae and are never eaten on the spot by the ants. Chemical analyses have shown that there is a greater concentration of nutritious material in these corpuscles than in any other part of the leaf. They are often tested by the ants repeatedly before being harvested; they require five or six days to ripen. The corpuscles do not grow back after removal, and hence are to be found only on young leaves. It has been observed that the corpuscles on a new shoot, growing in the shade from the base of an acacia and not yet colonized by ants, were yellow and relatively long and pointed, whereas those on a tree three to four meters tall standing only twenty meters away in the sun had a more bluish-gray color.

Other myrmecophytes, such as species of *Cecropia*, offer their ants similar nutrient-rich food bodies; these "Müller's corpuscles" grow between closely packed hairs at the thickened base of the petiole. The *Azeteca* ants living on the trees find no nectar as a second food source, but they have found a substitute. Within the stem, where they live, they keep "herds" of scale insects and feed upon the honeydew these insects produce.

Many plants display structural modifications or deformations resulting

Fig. 8-3. Achene of the bur-marigold (genus *Bidens*); each single fruit bears two or four spines covered with recurved hooks.

Plant galls

from the stimulatory influence of an animal, or, less commonly, of bacteria or fungi. These are called galls (or cecidia); those produced by animals are sometimes called zoocecidia. They are produced by increased growth—hypertrophy of cells or more rapid cell division—and thus resemble tumors. The animals causing plant galls belong to quite different systematic groups, and include not only insects but, for example, nematodes and mites as well. But there can be no doubt that the insects take first place, in terms of numbers of species and variety of forms of the galls. The most important gall insects are aphids (suborder Aphidina), gall wasps (superfamily Cynipoidea), and gall midges (family Cecidomydae), but there are also gall-producers among the beetles, sawflies, Lepidoptera and other insect groups.

Experiments have shown that gall formation is elicited by a growth substance (a phytohormone similar to auxin) given off by the animal. Only sawflies of the genus *Pontania*, which produce galls on willow leaves, have been demonstrated to produce such a substance as an adult, introducing it into the plant at the same time as the egg is deposited. In the other cases, growth of a gall does not begin until after the larva has left the egg; it is the larva which produces the active substance, either through its skin (as does the gall midge *Mikiola fagi*) or at a later stage in its saliva while it is eating (see Color plate, p. 124).

One aspect that has received much attention is the great variety of galls which can be produced in a single plant by different species of gall insects. On the three European species of oak there occur about 200 different sorts of gall. These are characterized not only by shape but by the site of formation; often they are limited to specific plant organs or parts of organs. Familiar examples are the spherical "oak apples," yellowish at first and later red, which are found only along the veins on the underside of the leaf. Neither at other places on the leaf nor in any other organ can this species of gall wasp induce gall formation. But quite different galls may be produced in other parts of the same leaf, by different insects.

For this reason many students of the subject accept that gall-producers release substances peculiar to their own species, and that these determine growth and form of the gall. But others defend the opposite view; that is, that the growth substance released depends upon the species, but its effect depends upon the instinctive behavior of the larva producing it and upon capacities for growth and differentiation inherent in the plant which are simply activated and regulated by the gall-producer. The biochemistry of gall induction involves problems difficult even to formulate, and their solution remains obscure.

Gall-inducing substances

Nevertheless, it has been demonstrated that the saliva of the aphidine genus *Phylloxera* contains a great variety of substances that accelerate or inhibit growth, among them the amino acids: lysine, histidine, tryptophane, glutamic acid and valine. Gall formation thus seems also to depend on the relative amounts of the effective substances present. In general, a plant forms a gall only if the growth regulator contacts young cells or tissues still capable of cell division. Only in exceptional cases can galls be produced in full-grown organs such as old rose leaves. When this happens, it must be that under the influence of the gall-producer certain circumscribed parts of the tissue return to a state in which division is possible.

A gall, then, usually grows along with its inducer. It seems justified to assume that the inducer has a continuing effect upon the plant, for if a young larva is removed from the forming gall it frequently fails to develop further. In summary, a gall arises by the combined action of gall-inducer and host plant; and it is obvious that the plant has a great deal more to do in the process than does the inducer.

The fundamental "gall problem" is most clearly exemplified by galls like those produced on oaks by cynipid gall wasps; these galls are usually well formed, with a distinct "functional" internal structure. In the center of an oak gall is the larval chamber, a small rounded cavity lined with a layer of nutrient-rich cells with fragile cell walls. This layer serves as food for the larva; its cells are not only nutritious but often much enlarged, and they begin to regenerate as soon as the larva has eaten them. The nutrient layer is often surrounded by a hard layer of more or less lignified cells, usually considered to be a protective structure. The outside of the gall is covered by a thick coating of parenchymal tissue, frequently containing large amounts of tannin.

Such a gall appears to be built entirely for the benefit of its inhabitant, especially in view of the fact that the cells of the nutrient layer are continually renewed. The harder woody layer and the thick coat of tannin-rich tissue protect the larva in the gall from predators such as ichneumons. But problems still remain, for experience shows that gall-inducers are attacked by ichneumons with unusual frequency. Remarkably, some galls are so well designed that they open automatically at the proper time to let their fully developed inhabitants escape. Galls induced by gall wasps, curculionid beetles, and other insects with biting mouthparts do not open in this way, but the animals can free themselves by biting holes in the galls.

Aphids usually develop in galls of simpler structure, such as pockets or sacks on the leaves of poplars and elms which open of their own accord by shrinking and tearing of the wall. An aphid, with its sucking proboscis, would never be able to make an opening for itself. There are other galls which open automatically by the loosening of a preformed circular lid or stopper; the gall enclosing the lepidopteran *Cecidoses eremita* is an example. The most striking aspect in all such cases is the timing, by which the gall opens just when the insect is fully developed and ready to emerge.

All the above facts, taken together, gave rise to the theory that aspects of the function of one organism can be entirely designed for the benefit of another; such a view appealed to the natural philosophers, but was rejected by scientists committed to causal analysis. It seems more consistent with our general understanding of biology, as well as with human value

Structure of the galls

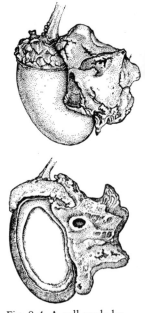

Fig. 8-4. A gall made by the wasp *Andricus quercuscalicis* on an acorn of the oak *Quercus robur* (above). The lower drawing shows a longitudinal section through the gall and the centrally located larval chamber.

Is gall-formation altruistic?

judgments and considerations of expediency, to consider the view that the plant itself derives some benefit from gall formation, in that it is thus protected from worse damage. That is, it would be better for the plant to encapsulate the pest and provide it with food than to have it wandering freely about and destroying the plant tissue at arbitrary places. Gall formation limits pest attacks not only in space (to one leaf or bud) but also in time. In this sense, gall formation can be understood as a protective or defensive measure evolved by the plant.

An acorn-gall wasp

These relationships may be further illustrated by a description of the life cycles of certain gall insects. The gall wasp *Andricus quercuscalicis* customarily makes its galls on the acorns of the English oak (*Quercus robur*). These are large tumorous growths, irregular in shape on the outside and bearing thick, rounded projections (see Fig. 8-4), but with a precise internal structure. A section through the gall and the acorn shows that it arises from the base of the cupule, causing some deformation of the acorn, and that the larval chamber is a rounded cavity within the gall. The light area surrounding the chamber in the figure represents the woody protective layer; the lining of nutritive cells is not shown, since it had already been eaten by the yellowish wasp larva when this gall was investigated. By the end of the summer the gall-wasp larva is fully grown. After the acorn, with its gall, has fallen from the tree in September the larva pupates; sometimes it hatches as early as November, but the winged wasp spends the winter in its protective house. Sometimes two or even three winters are passed, but when the wasp does leave the gall it is early in the spring, in February or March. All the wasps emerging from the acorn galls are female, and they produce fertile eggs by parthenogenesis. When the Turkey oak (*Quercus cerris*) is in bloom these female wasps go to the catkins and deposit eggs in the male flowers. One gall develops per stamen; the galls are small, one to two millimeters long, and pointed at one end. From these galls both males and females emerge. The females of this bisexual generation are inseminated by the males, and to lay their eggs they fly back to the young fruits of the English oak. Altogether, it is rather complicated cycle, involving alternation of both generations and hosts. Such alternations are not at all uncommon, and apart from the gall wasps are particularly prevalent among aphids.

Fig. 8-5. Pupa of the gall midge *Giraudiella inclusa*; at the upper end are the boring spines used to break through the outer part of the reed stalk that was left to close off the exit tunnel.

Several different kinds of gall occur on the common reed (*Phragmites communis*). The cigar-shaped galls of the fly *Lipara lucens* are a familiar sight; less conspicuous but still worthy of note are those of the gall midge *Giraudiella inclusa*. Gall midges are minute, fragile Diptera. *Giraudiella* galls cannot be discerned externally on a reed stalk, for they are located around the inner wall of the hollow stem; they are hard-walled lumps the size of a grain of wheat, and are often present in great numbers. How do these delicate midges free themselves from the hard gall, which has no automatic opening mechanism? The larva has actually prepared a way out; before its metamorphosis into a pupa it makes a channel into the outer wall of the reed stalk, tunneling almost up to the leaf that surrounds the stem but not quite breaking through to make an opening. In the fall the reed dies, and the gall-midge larvae spend the winter safe in their shelters, which they have lined with a firm mat of silk. In spring the larvae pupate. The pupa has no legs but is nevertheless able to move about slowly; with a snakelike wriggling movement it pulls itself through the prepared escape channel until it reaches the still-closed end. The head of the pupa is equipped with tools for breaking through the reed wall, two or four hard, sharp spines projecting straight forward (see Fig. 8-5). By pressing these against the wall and moving vigorously back and forth, the pupa bursts through the obstruction. Only the front half is pushed out; the hind end is anchored in the chamber (see Fig. 8-6). Soon afterward, the pupal cases are broken and the midges emerge, leaving behind the dry reed stalk with empty cases sticking out of it in all directions.

The spruce *Picea abies* bears quite conspicuous "pineapple galls" consisting of several chambers; these are induced by aphids of the family Adelgidae, which live only on conifers. After the aphids have emerged the galls become woody and turn brown, and they can remain for years, even on dead twigs that have lost their needles. Galls of this sort occur on the spruce in two different sizes. The small galls are about the size of a hazelnut or smaller; they are located at the tips of the shoots and are produced by *Adelges laricis*. The other galls may be over 3.5 cm in length. These are made at the base of the May shoots by the aphid *Sacchiphantes abietis*. In both species the life cycle is a complicated process covering two years and involving alternation of generations and hosts. We shall describe only one of these galls, that produced by *Sacchiphantes* on the spruce (see Color plate, p. 124).

The initial gall-inducer is an aphid larva at the base of a May shoot; in the preceding summer or autumn it took up its position and sank its threadlike sucking proboscis deep into the tissue of the tree (Fig. 8-7). Enveloped in woolly fibers of wax, it spends the winter without moving from the spot. When the sap begins to rise in the spring, the larva begins to suck and grows into the wingless egg-laying form (the fundatrix) molting twice in the process. While it is sucking it injects saliva into the plant tissue, and in the saliva are growth regulators that cause growth and division of the plant cells. The axis of the shoot and the lower parts of the attached needles gradually become thicker. Since the gall often develops more on one side of the twig than the other, the tip of the shoot becomes curved or sharply bent. A longitudinal section (Fig. 8-7) through a developing gall reveals that the swelling of the needles is not uniform around the base, but rather produces a depression and broadening on the side toward the shoot axis. Finally, the needles at the thickened base of the shoot become so closely apposed that the space between them and the axis is divided into pocketlike cavities, accessible only temporarily from outside the gall, by way of fine slits.

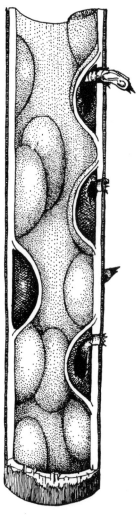

Fig. 8-6. The stem of a reed, cut open to show the ridge galls and the empty pupal cases.

Fig. 8-7. Longitudinal section through a developing spruce gall. The aphid "fundatrix" is shown at lower left with its proboscis piercing the shoot.

By this time the larvae have hatched from the 100–150 eggs laid by the fundatrix. These make haste to enter the pockets; then further swelling of the gall closes up the chambers completely. The edges of the closed entrance slit are thickened like lips and not uncommonly are reddened. Within the gall chambers, the enclosed larvae suck sap from the phloem of the plant and grow into a winged stage. But before the molt that liberates the winged insect, the larva is released from the gall chambers; the molt then takes place immediately on one of the adjacent needles or directly on the outside of the gall (see Color plate, p. 124).

Once again, the synchronization of gall opening with insect development is remarkable. The substances put into the plant by the mother aphid can certainly induce growth, and probably regulate the shape of the structure according to a certain program; but whether they can produce special effects later, long after the death of the fundatrix, so as to bring about the opening of the galls at the right time, is quite questionable. A much more attractive interpretation is that the sucking of the larvae causes shrinking of the gall wall so that the chambers open; but we do not yet know what really happens. In any case, the winged gall aphids that emerge generally fly to larch trees, and on this secondary host subsequent generations of aphids develop.

9 Mimicry and Camouflage

By W. Wickler

In 1862 the English naturalist Henry Walter Bates (1825–1892) published a discovery that has been the subject of fierce argument ever since. As one result of the eleven years he spent collecting animals in the Amazon region, Bates realized that butterflies of the families Heliconiidae and Ithomiidae, which insect-eating birds find inedible, are imitated by other more palatable butterflies (for example, the pierid genus *Leptalis*), both in appearance and in the way they fly. Before long it had been demonstrated that the striking coloration and patterning of the heliconids is repeated in many other lepidopteran families. Similarly, the equally unpalatable danaids, the caterpillars of which feed chiefly upon poisonous asclepadaceous plants (milkweeds), are imitated by swallowtails, brush-footed butterflies, and others. Bates was the first to express the notion that the departure of these imitative butterflies from the norm set by their relatives must have improved their chances of survival.

Batesian mimicry

When animals that do not "taste good" are strikingly colored and thus easy to recognize, their coloration must serve to warn off potential predators which, on another occasion, have experienced their unpalatability. In fact, it has been demonstrated that having once tried such an unpleasant mouthful, a predator will not snap at others of the same sort. It follows that it will also be fooled into avoiding animals with an acceptable flavor if their coloration matches closely enough the warning coloration of the unpalatable species. Such a disguise, a misleading warning coloration, represents one form of mimicry. Since Bates was the first to call the phenomenon to our attention, this type of mimicry is called Batesian in his honor. Other forms of mimicry will be discussed later. Another kind of protective coloration, camouflage, is distinguished from mimicry by the fact that camouflage causes an organism to resemble a background of no interest to the observer, whereas mimicry is a resemblance to an object in which the observer is potentially interested.

The key figure in all cases of mimicry is the animal which the process is meant to deceive. Those aspects of the appearance of objects that are

Fig. 9-1. The caterpillar of *Euchelia jacobaea* is avoided by birds that have tasted it a few times. Its conspicuous coloration serves to warn away predators and at the same time tends to conceal the caterpillar; when the animal is in an inflorescence in full bloom it cannot be detected from above.

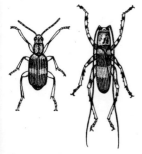

Fig. 9-2. The acid-spraying bombardier beetle *Pheropsophus agnatus* (left) with its conspicuous warning coloration is mimicked by the harmless orthopteran *Gryllacris* (right).

noticed by an organism are called "signals," and the organism detecting the signals may be called the receiver. Since human beings orient primarily by means of their eyes, the scientists studying mimicry were first impressed by the visual signals of animals—warning, camouflaging, and other sorts of protective coloration. But many animals depend more upon their senses of smell or hearing, and we now know that there are also olfactory and auditory signals which serve for warning, camouflage, and so forth.

Most of the examples of Batesian mimicry involve insects. There are many insects that look like wasps and thus enjoy immunity from attack even though they are themselves defenseless. In the Philippines there are species of cockroach (genus *Prosoplecta*) which mimic the local lady beetles, unpalatable to insectivores. The bombardier beetle *Pheropsophus agnathus*, which expels a pungent glandular secretion when disturbed and has a conspicuous warning coloration, is the model for the almost identically colored but harmless grasshopper *Gryllacris*; another grasshopper, *Condylodera tricondyloides*, walks in a manner so closely resembling that of a tiger beetle of the genus *Tricondyla* that it is easily mistaken for a tiger beetle. The larva of the mantid *Hymenopus bicornis* looks just like a bad-tasting assassin bug, whereas the adult mantid deceives the observer by its resemblance to a flower. Another mantid larva mimics an ant in both appearance and behavior; it does not lie quietly in wait, as is customary for mantids, but scurries about like an ant.

In other words, then, Batesian mimicry is a warning coloration or behavior which is not backed up by a real deterrent. Among lepidopterans it is often found only in females; for example, in various species of swallowtail, brush-footed, and white butterflies only the females look like the members of other butterfly families. One of the most astonishing cases is the African swallowtail *Papilio dardanus*. Females of the many subspecies look quite different from one another, whereas the males all have the characteristic "tail" on the hindwings that one expects in a swallowtail. Some of the females also have the "tail," but others look like Danaidae and can be identified as swallowtails only after careful examination. Within one and the same subspecies these swallowtail females mimic a variety of danaids—that is, the females are polymorphous. In breeding experiments, crosses and back-crosses have actually produced more female morphotypes than are known to exist in nature. Mimicry in this butterfly thus is not based on a single mutation, the effects of which have remained unchanged; rather, there have been additional genetic modifications that regulate the effect of the genes responsible for the patterning of the animals. Mimics, of course, do not ordinarily evolve their final appearance at one step. Only after a chance mutation in an "unprotected" species gives it a slight resemblance to a protected species does the mutated gene become distributed more widely in the population, since it is associated with increased survival. The effects of the gene are gradually modified, and as a result the similarity to the model can slowly increase.

Camouflage has a great deal in common with mimicry. Camouflage colorations vary according to an animal's normal background. Animals living in the polar fields of snow and ice—polar bears, foxes, hares, and birds such as the ptarmigan—are white; geometrid caterpillars resemble the twigs on which they live; the mollusk *Neomenia corallophila*, one of the wormlike solenogasters, is patterned in red and white like the branches of precious coral among which it hides. The very names of the phasmids—stick insect, leaf insect, etc.—reflect their imitation of parts of plants, and there is a butterfly, *Kallima*, which is indistinguishable, to the casual observer, from a faded leaf.

In eastern Africa there is a plant that appears to have unusually pretty flowers, rather like those of broom but arranged like lupine flowers on a vertical stem. Even experienced botanists have been known to pick this flower spike and find themselves holding a bare stem from which the flowers had flown away—the "flowers" were cicadids, either the yellow *Ityraea gregoryi* or the whitish *Oyarina nigritarsus*. A single animal sitting on a stem by itself is sufficiently flowerlike to deceive the observer. *Ityraea nigrocincta* has two morphotypes, a green and a yellow, in each sex, and they often arrange themselves on vertical stems so that the green insects are near the tip and yellow, below them. This enhances the resemblance to a natural flower spike. But no one knows just which animal is deceived by this strategy.

The "eyespots" on the wings of butterflies and moths, the bodies of caterpillars, and the feathers of peacocks are among the best known types of patterning in the animal kingdom. Here the eyes of birds may be the model that is simulated; birds are probably most often the predators that are scared away, at least in the case of the insects with eyespots. In 1957 the zoologist Blest did the following experiment: he raised yellowhammers by hand, so that he knew they had had no experience of lepidopterans patterned with eyespots, and then he confronted them with such insects. The birds were uniformly frightened off when they threatened a butterfly (for example, the peacock, *Nymphalis io*) and it suddenly spread its wings to display the eyespots. But if the colored scales were removed from the butterflies' wings, the birds showed no fear of the "eyeless" insects and devoured them. Similar results have been obtained with other insects—for example, with caterpillars bearing eyespots. Blest also did experiments with "dummies," presenting yellowhammers, chaffinches and tits with a plate of mealworms and projecting various artificial patterns to the right and left of the mealworms just as the birds were about to eat. All the birds were deterred more by circular figures than by crosses or parallel lines, and the most marked avoidance was produced by the patterns most like eyespots. Other studies have shown that when birds recognize and escape a predator, its eyes are crucial stimuli; one could thus infer that the eyespots of insects scare away a bird because of their resemblance to the bird's own enemy.

Fig. 9-3. The harmless grasshopper *Condylodera tricondyloides* (left) mimics the predatory, well-armed ground beetle *Tricondyla gibba* (right).

▷
Above: the tropical hairstreak *Protographium aristeus* appears to have a head at the hind end of its body.
Lower left: Its false warning coloration, which resembles that of a stinging hornet, protects the tasty hornet moth.
Lower right: A camouflaged predator, the spider *Misomena vatia*, lies in wait for a bee on a flower of its own color.

Let us return to the question of camouflage, and consider the problem encountered by an animal that moves about over considerable areas. To maintain the camouflage, its coloration must continue to correspond to the background. This can be achieved in two ways; either the coloration could be adapted to a new background, or the animal in each new location could seek out the background it matches most closely. In fact, the ability to change coloration is found quite commonly among animals. It is extraordinarily well developed among flatfish. The skin of these fish contains several systems of cells with variously colored pigments in the cytoplasm. These can be expanded over a large area so that the colors are displayed, or contracted into a very small area so that the colors effectively disappear. The whole system is under nervous control; complicated neuronal interconnections ensure that the patterning of the fish matches approximately that of any background on which it finds itself. The animal first observes the background with its eyes, but it does not, as one might imagine, then proceed to compare it with its own coloration and adjust the latter until the two match. The process is more automatic, and can be compared with typing into a computer a request for a body pattern like that the fish sees in its surroundings. This can be demonstrated by making it impossible for the fish to have any visual information about the state of the camouflage; flatfish covered with sand so that only the eyes are exposed can still match the color of their bodies, which they cannot see, correctly to that of the background.

In exceptional cases animals match the background to themselves. For example, certain South American caterpillars cut pieces out of leaves of exactly their own size and hang them on threads in the vicinity. There are spiders that powder their nests with brown, rotten wood, so as to camouflage themselves; others spin the remnants of animals they have eaten into little piles, hang them up in the nest, and surround them with special threads so that it is not at all easy to decide which of the objects is the actual spider.

It more often happens that an animal simply rests on places with background corresponding to its own color. Leaf-green animals rest on leaves, bark-colored ones on bark, and sand-colored ones in sand. This matching becomes particularly striking when the animal, as it ages, changes both its color and its resting place. The larva of the hawkmoth *Hyloicus pinastri* is blue-green when young, with six thin white stripes along its body; during the day it rests on pine needles, parallel with the long axis, and because of its coloring it can scarcely be detected. But after the last molt the caterpillar is brown, with irregular white and black spots, and in this stage it rests on the brown shoot that bears the needles. It has been demonstrated that in such cases the camouflage not only deceives people, but makes it difficult for the birds to find the caterpillars as well.

In this industrial age a new form of camouflage has developed; industrial melanism. Melanin is a black pigment common in the animal king-

Fig. 9-4. The peacock butterfly with its startling eyespots exposed (above) and hidden when the animal is at rest (below).

◁
Camouflage:
Upper left: flatfish change the color and patterning of their bodies according to the ground on which they are lying.
Upper right: Industrial melanism: the relative numbers of light and dark peppered moths (*Biston betularia*) depend upon the degree to which trees in industrial areas are blackened by smoke and thus are an indicator of pollution.
Below: Geometrid caterpillars, imitating dry twigs in color, shape and posture, are superbly matched to their surroundings.

dom; the term "industrial melanism" refers to the prevalence of dark colorations of animals in industrial areas. A famous recent example is the peppered moth (*Biston betularia*; see Color plate, p.138), which, like the birch trees on which it is commonly found, is usually white with dark dots and stripes—or was. Again and again there appeared melanistic, or unusually dark, animals which differed from the ordinary form in only one dominant gene. These dark mutants rested in the same places as the normal moths, where of course they were very conspicuous. This was the case in England around 1850. But by 1895 dark moths were no longer a rarity; in fact, near the industrial city of Manchester, 95% of all peppered moths were of the dark form. Since the peppered moth has only one generation per year it could be calculated that the dark form must have a selective advantage of 30% over the normal form, in order to increase their relative numbers so greatly in fifty years. It seemed almost certain that this advantage must lie in a different degree of vulnerability to predators.

In fact, toward the end of the 19th Century increasing industrialization had more or less blackened everything in the industrial areas, because of the soot being poured into the air, and the white trunks of the birches had also been darkened. Now, when both light and dark moths were sitting on the dark trunks, the lighter moths were the more conspicuous and were eaten. This, at least, was the simplest explanation. Very recently, however, it has turned out that the light form not only suffers more from predation, but its caterpillars eat more rapidly and pupate sooner than those of the dark form. Probably the "light" caterpillars make use of the young foliage before it has become dirty, whereas the "dark" ones must spend much time excreting the toxic substances consumed along with the darker foliage. Apparently as a result of this exposure, from the turn of the century until the present, the hardiness of the black form has increased; originally it was inferior to that of the white moths, but now it is somewhat greater. Moreover, the dark form of a hundred years ago was not as intensely black as the present-day form. The genetic basis of the melanism has thus probably also been altered.

The industrial melanism of moths is one of the most impressive examples of the effect of certain selective factors upon the continued evolution of animals—in this case, upon the adaptation of coloration for greater protection. Of 780 English lepidopteran species, seventy are now on the way to industrial melanism, and in some even the caterpillars are melanistic.

"Most remarkable," said the English zoologists, on discovering that since the government passed laws against air pollution in the 1950's the peppered moth in some regions of England has begun to grow lighter in color. That this reversal of the direction of adaptation is really due to natural selection in the sense of Darwin was shown by the British researcher H. B. D. Kettlewell, in several experiments in the field. Of 477 black and 137 white moths that he released in the vicinity of the industrial city of

Fig. 9-5. In the midst of all these different shapes, the circle attracts the eye with an almost magical power. In nature such circles, called eyespots, have a very special function.

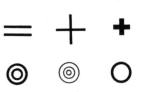

Fig. 9-6. The deterrent effect of these figures was tested experimentally by the zoologist Blest; the animals were repelled more strongly by the circles than by the other patterns.

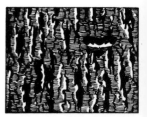

Fig. 9-7. The same pattern can make an animal either show up against, or blend with, a background (there are two moths with transverse markings in the picture).

Birmingham, 40% of the dark and only 19% of the white form withstood the selective pressure exerted by the birds that hunt them. Then, in an area of Dorset that had not been dirtied by soot, he released 473 black and 496 light moths; he recaptured only 6% of the dark moths but 12% of the light ones. Here, then, the light form had a clear selective advantage.

Henry Walter Bates himself had noted that there is sometimes an extremely close resemblance between two lepidopteran species which are not at all closely related—but that both are unpalatable. An explanation of this situation was suggested soon afterward, in 1878, by the German zoologist Fritz Müller; like Bates, he observed and captured Lepidoptera in Brazil. Müller, too, started with the assumption that animals must learn by experience—if other animals are not able to pass the knowledge on—which prey does not "taste good." Now, if different unpalatable species look the same, so that the predator cannot distinguish them, he learns to know them as one type, regardless of the species he happens to encounter, taste, and "learn" from. If he has learned to avoid a type from his experiences with individuals of only one species, the other species of similar appearance can enjoy protection with no loss of life. Thus the total number of individuals that must be sacrificed in order to make the warning coloration effective is shared among as many species as are members of the "warning-coloration society." The more species that operate with the same warning signal, the smaller the losses of each species. Many such mimicry groups have been discovered. Of course, a Müllerian mimicry group can also be associated with instances of Batesian mimicry; the more species there are in a Müllerian group, the greater the number of models for Batesian mimicry.

Models of this sort are found among the different species of net-winged beetles (family Lycidae). Their coloration is striking, usually orange and black or orange and blue, and their shape is unusual (the elytra are broader at the end than at the base). They often sit in the open on flowers, and they fly slowly, but when danger threatens they exude an evil-smelling white juice from the hind femora; as a result, they are avoided by birds as well as by insectivorous mammals, and even sun-spiders, mantids, ants and polistine wasps will not attack them. The protective juice does not come out like blood from a wound, but is actively exuded by the intact animals. A similar protective mechanism is found in other beetle families, among them the soldier beetles (Cantharidae). In Borneo there are several quite different insects that look like a soldier beetle; among them are the bug *Serinetha abdominalis*, which is itself unpalatable, the lepidopteran *Phauda limbata*, which can be found sitting quietly on plant stems near the above bugs, and the long-horned beetle *Erythrus rotundicollis*.

Interestingly enough there is a parallel situation in South Africa involving just the same groups of insects, but of different genera. Here, again, there is a soldier beetle, a bug, a lepidopteran, and a long-horned beetle, and there is yet another insect of similar appearance, a spider wasp,

Müllerian mimicry

Fig. 9-8. Pigment cell of a fish. On the left the pigment is spread out and on the right, concentrated in the center of the cell. The nucleus is shown in black.

Fig. 9-9. Within the family Papilionidae in Malaysia there are both edible and inedible species. Butterflies of the genus *Atrophanura* (left half of each picture) are unpalatable and serve as models for the unprotected *Papilio memnon* (right half). Females of *Papilio memnon* can imitate either tailless (above) or tailed (below) species, whereas all the males have tails.

which itself is protected. In the southern United States one finds corresponding mimicry groups. One of these consists of two species of net-winged beetles, three species of lepidoptera, and one long-horned beetle; another comprises two net-winged beetles, two lepidopterans, and a long-horned beetle. Long-horned beetles in general are well known as mimics; they can look like wasps, bees, ants, or unpalatable beetles of other groups. In some cases the most closely related long-horned beetles differ greatly in

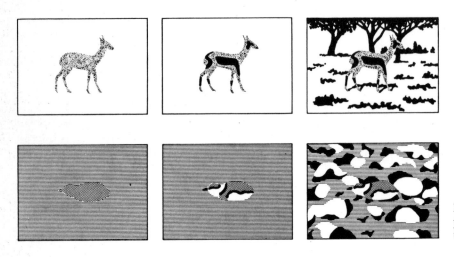

Fig. 9-10. Examples of patterning that obscures the shape of the body.

size, color and shape; they are mimicking very different models. Such examples offer especially compelling evidence of mimicry.

A remarkable discovery was made in a meadow at a research station in Arizona. Here were found, side by side, the net-winged beetles *Lycus loripes* and *Lycus fernandezi*, which are considered inedible, and the edible long-horned beetles *Elytroleptus ignitus* and *Elytroletpus apicalis*. The long-horned beetles are much rarer than the net-winged beetles. There is an astonishingly exact resemblance between the members of each long-horned beetle/net-winged beetle pair: *Lycus loripes* and *Elytroleptus ignitus* are a uniform, glowing orange, whereas the elytra of the two other beetles in addition have black tips. In both cases the mimic, which most insectivores would find edible, has been observed to approach the otherwise inedible model and nibble at its elytra or limbs, sometimes even hollowing out the whole thorax. These long-horned beetles—presumably the only predatory members of their family—attack not only the net-winged beetles they resemble, but also the other species of net-winged beetle. This cannot be a case of aggressive mimicry (Peckhamian mimicry, of which we shall hear later), for it is unlikely that the victim has time to inspect the predator and decide that it is harmless. The behavior of the long-horned beetles while they are eating their models resembles the behavior preceding copulation with a female long-horned beetle; on the other hand, various male lycid beetles release special secretions on the elytra, which the females

▷
Upper left: Threat (or bluff) behavior of *Idolum diabolicum*, an African mantid.
Upper right: Genuine warning coloration in the unpalatable burnet *Zygaena*.
Below: The tongue appendage of the alligator turtle (*Macroclemys temminckii*) looks like prey to the fish which the turtle is waiting to catch.

MIMICRY AND CAMOUFLAGE 145

Fig. 9-11. The young caterpillar of the hawkmoth *Hyloicus pinastri.*

Fig. 9-12. The caterpillar of *Hyloicus pinastri* after the last molt.

◁

Left, top to bottom:
The larva of *Lilioceris* camouflages itself by piling its own excrement on its back; if one removes the excrement (next picture) the conspicuous red coloration is revealed. The male of the African mouth-brooding *Haplochromis burtoni* has on the anal fin colored spots resembling eggs, which attract the female (see text).
The male hamadryas baboon (middle animal) imitates on its hindquarters the estrous swellings of the females (left and right animals); see discussion in text.
Right: mimicry of a twig by a tropical stick insect.

nibble prior to copulation. It cannot be excluded, therefore, that the relationship between these long-horned and net-winged beetles involves certain misunderstood or misused elements of courtship behavior.

Among the favorite models for many mimics are stinging insects like wasps, bumblebees, and bees. The hover flies which resemble bees also mimic their models acoustically. In experiments in which bees and hover flies were offered as food to toads; it became evident that hover flies from which the wings had been removed so that they did not buzz were eaten more frequently than those that did buzz. Bumblebees also produce a threatening buzz when they have spent the night outdoors and in the morning are rendered incapable of flight by the dew; when in danger, they let themselves fall onto their backs, make stinging movements, and release a fluid from the anus. In 1965 a married research team, the Bowers, performed experiments on toads which were offered either bumblebees or other bees, together with the flies that resembled them. The toads very quickly learned to avoid both kinds of bees; after only a few experiences, they stopped snapping at the bees at all, and from then on they usually left the flies alone as well. Some toads will continue to avoid such prey, even after a lapse of three months without practice. When the toads were fed bees from which the sting had been removed, they learned nothing, but continued to eat them uninhibitedly. Another observation in these experiments was that the bumblebees, with more poisonous or at any rate more unpleasant stings than the other bees, were more effective models, even though the degree of resemblance was closer in the case of the flies imitating the other bees.

A great number of insects and spiders look like ants, which long ago gave rise to the notion of "ant mimicry." This similarity can extend to size, coloration, body structure, and even behavior. With respect to coloration, it is particularly noticeable that the thin stalk connecting thorax and abdomen in ants, which is absent in other insects, is often imitated in the patterning of the mimics. Spiders, on the other hand, deceive the observer by their behavior. They have eight legs while the ants, like all insects, have only six; but the spiders imitating ants run on only six legs, waving their forelegs in front of them just as ants wave their antennae. They are often found on shrubs, running about among the ants.

There is still no answer to the question, "whom does the resemblance to ants deceive?" Some of the mimics actually live among ants or are parasitic in their nests, in which case it is advantageous to look like an ant; but there are also insects and spiders that mimic ants but are not associated with them. Moreover, many insects living in ant nests have no resemblance to their hosts. But one can easily make mistakes by looking at things only from the human viewpoint. Staphylinid larvae of the genus *Atemeles,* which live in ant nests but do not look like the ants, secrete a substance that causes them to be accepted as ant larvae. The ants feed the beetle larvae—which also eat the larvae of the ants—because the beetle larvae beg for food in the same way as the ant larvae, but even more urgently. These, then, are extraordinarily good mimics of ant larvae.

The importance of the characteristics and reactions of the signal receiver, the object of the deception, is shown by the example of the aphids, which from our point of view have no resemblance to ants. Aphids digest only the protein in the plant juices, excreting the sugar as honeydew. Because of these sweet excretions, they serve as a food source for the ants. But the relationship between ant and aphid is really based on a misunderstanding. Ants beg from one another with extreme frequency, and the ant which is so approached will feed the begging ant with a drop of fluid food from the so-called crop. Now, when travelling their ordinary routes the ants occasionally encounter the hind end of an aphid, which they evidently take to be the head of an ant and, accordingly, greet it and tap it with their antennae. This beating upon the aphid's back elicits defensive behavior: the aphid raises the hind legs and makes stamping movements. The ant regards this as the expected response of a con-specific, a reciprocation of the antennal vibration. When the aphid so greeted eventually excretes a drop of honeydew, the illusion is complete—the ant has been "fed."

It actually happens that ants attempt the reverse behavior; if they are full of food, they may try to pass some on to the hind end of an aphid, naturally without success. This confirms the view that the ants take the aphid abdomen and its appendages for the head of a conspecific. This theory also explains the fact that ants defend their aphids from lady-beetle larvae and other predators. The extent to which ants have modified their social behavior, originally directed only to conspecifics, in the direction of aphid care is unknown, but attention to the aphids is clearly worth-while; aphids visited by ants produce considerably more honeydew than those not so visited. The ants' "error" brings them a reward.

As we have seen, striking coloration often warns other animals that the bearer is either inedible or well-armed. Particularly noteworthy examples of the latter are the so-called coral snakes of the tropical and subtropical zones of America. There are about eighteen genera and seventy-five species of these snakes, all ringed in red, yellow, and black but not related systematically to one another. "True" coral snakes are members of the family Elapidae, genera such as *Micrurus*, *Micruroides* and *Lepto-micrurus*; they are highly venomous, though ordinarily reluctant to bite. The "false" coral snakes belong to four different subfamilies of the Colubridae and include quite nonvenomous species of the genera *Atractus*, *Lampropeltis* and *Simophis* as well as moderately venomous but very aggressive snakes such as *Erythrolamprus*, *Pseudoboa* and *Rhinobothryum*.

Opponents of the motion of mimicry have regarded these different sorts of coral snakes as supporting their view that there is no real mimicry, for a supposed signal receiver can hardly acquire experience from an encounter with a true coral snake—its bite is almost always lethal. In

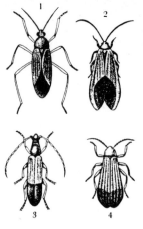

Fig. 9-13. A mimicry group from Borneo: the bug *Serinetha abdominalis* (1), the lepidopteran *Phauda limbata* (2), and the beetles *Erythrus rotundicollis* (3) and *Lycostomus gestroi* (4).

Mertensian mimicry

Fig. 9-14. The long-horned beetle *Elytroleptus ignitus* nibbles at the elytra of the net-winged beetle *Lycus loripes*.

fact, however, the real models in this mimicry group are not the very venomous elapid species, nor are they the nonvenomous, defenseless species. Animals representing both these extremes must be considered as mimics, deriving protection from their resemblance to the "false" coral snakes with an intermediately poisonous bite. It is probably "worthwhile" both for venomous animals not inclined to bite and for animals which are not venomous, if they mimic the snakes with both a poisonous bite and a willingness to use it; both the elapids and the harmless colubrids benefit from their similarity to the moderately venomous colubrids. This particular case of deceptive coloration has been called Mertensian mimicry, after the German herpteologist Robert Mertens.

Peckhamian mimicry

A very old parable concerns a wolf in sheep's clothing. It is thought that certain hover flies, like that wolf, use their similarity to bees to gain admittance to the nests of the bees and leave their predaceous larvae there. This brings us to another form of mimicry: mimicry which disguises an attack, called Peckhamian mimicry after the researcher E. G. Peckham.

An example is the phenomenon, widespread in the animal kingdom, of angling for prey with the aid of deceptive signals. There is even an order of fish (the Lophiiformes) bearing the name angler fish. Most of these are bottom-dwellers; they have a special dorsal fin, the anterior rays of which are not joined by membranes. The most anterior ray, often almost transparent, is seated in a ball joint far in front of the eyes, at the upper margin of the upper lip, and at its tip it bears a fleshy skin appendage. In the genus *Phrynelox* the appendage looks like a pink worm, and it can even twist and roll up. The angler fish waits, motionless, until a prey fish becomes interested in the "bait," and then waves it vigorously back and forth, up and down, in front of the mouth. When the prey has approached close enough to snap at it, the angler fish opens its mouth and sucks in the prey and the water surrounding it. The appendages that serve as lures can vary widely in shape, depending on the prey concerned. Fish with worm-shaped lures catch only victims which feed on worms. Sometimes the lure resembles a bundle of algae; deep-sea anglers of the family Ceratilidae have luminescent lures in various colors, some of them on extraordinarily long "fishing rods" (Fig. 9-16).

Other fish not closely related to the angler fish, star gazers of the genus *Uranoscopus*, attract prey in a similar manner. They dig themselves into the bottom until only eyes and gaping mouth are visible. All of a sudden there emerges slowly from the mouth a structure one to two centimeters long that looks and moves like one of the annelid worms living in the mud. This apparent worm is a continuation of the membrane formed by the oral mucosa inside the lower jaw, which in fish is located at the front of the mouth and prevents the respiratory water from flowing back out of the mouth. Another angling technique has been evolved by the catfish *Chaca chaca* (Fig. 9-16). When hungry, this catfish does not

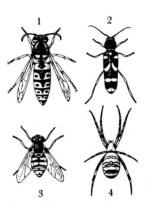

Fig. 9-15. A wasp (1) and its mimics, a long-horned beetle (2), a hover fly (3), and a spider (4).

simply spread out the barbels at the corners of its mouth, but it rolls them up with a wormlike motion and stretches them out again. When small fish tug at these "false worms," the catfish gulps them down with a powerful snap.

The alligator turtle (*Macroclemys temminckii*) catches its prey in the same way. When it is hungry, it opens the mouth wide. Near the end of the blackish tongue is a double process spotted with red; muscles twist this appendage back and forth. Fish hunting prey of similar appearance and approaching close enough to nibble at the appendage have already placed the front ends of their bodies in the mouth of the turtle, which then shaps shut its strong hooked jaws (see Color plate, p. 143).

The animals we have discussed so far disguise themselves either in order to be inconspicuous or to be so conspicuous that they warn or frighten predators away. But there are also parasites which have adopted a conspicuous appearance in order to be eaten. As unreasonable as that may sound at first, the mouth is a direct route of entry for internal parasites which are not digested but turn the tables on the predator that has eaten them, attacking it from within. That is, this is a rather unusual case of Peckhamian mimicry.

The class Trematoda is a large group of parasitic worms which is related to the tapeworms and the turbellarians. Their life cycle includes many intermediate forms in different hosts; among parasitologists it has become almost a sport to guess from all conceivable signs what should be the next (intermediate or final) host of a newly found trematode stage. Such information is important since many of these intestinal worms are dangerous parasites; but they can often be combatted with relative ease in a certain intermediate host, if this host is known. In this sense, research into mimicry can actually be of value to medicine.

A well-known example is the trematode *Leucochloridium macrostomum*, which lives in the intestines of songbirds. Its eggs leave the bird with the exrement and are taken up by the snail *Succinea*. Inside the snail there hatches the first form, the miracidium larva, which develops into a sporocyst with rootlike branchings. This forms several sacks, each about a centimeter long, in which are packed cercariae—another reproductive generation. The sporocyst sacks are colored green and yellow-brown, so that they resemble caterpillars. One such sack pushes itself into each of the snail's tentacles and there begins to contract and expand vigorously. The snail, which ordinarily avoids light, when so infested goes into the light; there it is soon found by a songbird which regards its conspicuous tentacles as a delicacy and either eats them itself or feeds them to its young. In the gut of the bird, finally, the cercariae turn into the parasitic worms.

Some cercariae escape from an intermediate host into the open water; there they search for their next host. The behavior of these cercariae is so similar to that of insect larvae or small crustaceans that the fish mistake

Fig. 9-16. Examples of animals that attract prey with special body appendages: the angler fish *Phrynelox scaber* (1), the catfish *Chaca chaca* (2), and the alligator turtle (*Macroclemys temminckii*, 3).

Fig. 9-17. Ants are famous for "milking" aphids. But this behavior is based on a misunderstanding: the ant takes the hind end of the aphid (left) for the head of another ant (right), and greets it with vibration of the antennae.

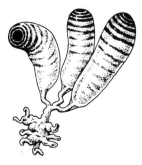

Fig. 9-18. The snail *Succinea* is an intermediate host of the trematode *Leucochloridium macrosto-mum*. The trematode's sporocyst (below) develops in the snail, and the sacks migrate into the snail's tentacles, which are eaten by birds. In the gut of the bird the parasites continue their development.

The "bluff" of the mantids

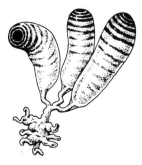

Fig. 9-19. A mantid from the Congo.

them for these animals and swallow them; in the stomachs of the fish the cercariae continue their development. Such a fish may be in effect an intermediate host, if it is eaten by a larger fish; then the parasite stays in the gut of the predator.

The life cycle of certain North American unionid mussels is not very different. The young develop in a brood pocket which they leave as larvae; the larvae attach to fish by hooks on their shells, and live there for some time as parasites. The larvae (glochidia) of another genus, *Lampsilis*, parasitize fish even though they have no hooks on their shells; they live in the gills, feeding on tissues and blood. They are brought into contact with the fish's gills by an ingenious trick. The female mussel bearing young develops a mantle appendage that makes twitching movements. In certain *Lampsilis* species this appendage is practically indistinguishable from a fish; the "front" end looks like a head, with eyespots, and the other end has a fishy tail. The regular movements of these appendages attract fish. As soon as the shadow of a fish falls upon the mussel, she expels a white ball of glochidia with such force that it rises several centimeters above the mussel. It is highly probable that the open mouth of the fish that cast the shadow will be just in that position; if so, the fish becomes the host of the mussel larvae. In this case, then, a lure has been evolved not for feeding purposes but for the benefit of the next generation.

Among the most remarkable insects are the mantids (suborder Mantida). The "praying mantises" are so named because of the customary position in which they hold their forelegs. The tibia of the foreleg can be folded tightly back against the femur, and both parts have toothed edges; the legs are used to capture insects. The mantids wait quietly on plants for an insect to pass, and catch it when it comes in striking range. The coloration of most mantid species serves as camouflage—that is, those found among leaves are green, those on bark are spotted gray and brown, and so on. This camouflage is surely not to hide the mantids from their prey, which would be as likely to approach uncamouflaged objects, but rather from their own enemies.

But other mantids are very brightly colored, and these are found in flowers. An example is *Hymenopus coronatus* of Malaysia, which sits in the red flower of an orchid. Close examination is required to tell where flower stops and insect begins. The resemblance to the orchid is so close that insects go to the mantid in search of nectar, and pay for their mistake with their lives.

In fact, flower-shaped mantids can actually manage without real flowers. The African mantid *Idolum diabolicum* (see Color plate, p. 143) is famous for its likeness to a flower; it hangs from trees and shrubs displaying its thorax and anterior femora, which are much broadened and magnificently colored. Observations in the field indicate that flies and sometimes lepidopterans do visit this supposed flower; to catch them, the mantid would simply need to clap its forelegs shut. One might imagine such flower mimicry evolving from the protectively camouflaged mantids sitting on bark and leaves to the brightly colored mantids in flowers and finally to mantids that did not depend on any particular background for camouflage. But their behavior argues against this interpretation. Both the "ordinary" mantids and the brightly-colored mantids that sit in flowers hold their prehensile legs folded while waiting for prey. The prey-catching movements of *Idolum diabolicum* have not been studied, but if it used the same posture as the other mantids, its flower coloration would not be apparent.

Fig. 9-20. The African mantid *Idolum diabolicum* in defensive posture.

Now, the posture in which the flower mimicry of *Idolum* is displayed is adopted by many mantids in a quite different situation—when they are in danger. This sudden display of striking patterns of color is pure bluff, for they have no means of harming an enemy; this is not, then, an instance of warning coloration. Nevertheless, it proves to be an effective defense. The unexpected change in its intended prey confuses the predator sufficiently that it gives up the attack. One could call this an instance of "surprise coloration." Accordingly, it is unlikely that *Idolum diabolicum* uses the threat posture to catch prey.

One of the most fascinating relationships between different animal species is that in which one cleans the other, removing external parasites, bits of injured tissue, and so forth. Such cleaning symbioses are found particularly often in warm oceans. The cleaner frees its "customer" of undesirable and sometimes harmful things, which the cleaner eats. The cleaner fish *Labroides dimidiatus*, a wrasse (family Labridae) of the Indo-pacific region, swims in a "dancing" motion; moving slowly forward,

Cleaner-mimicry

Fig. 9-21. The predatory blenny *Aspidontus taeniatus* (below) mimics the dance of the harmless cleaner fish *Labroides dimidiatus* (above) and, under the protection of this disguise, attacks larger fish.

it repeatedly swings the hind end of its body upward, tailfin spread out, and then returns to the horizontal position. This calls the cleaner fish to the attention of other fish, which approach and let themselves be cleaned. Other species of wrasse, and fish of other families, also act as cleaners. The fish they clean belong to a great variety of species; most of them are nonterritorial species that happen to be passing, but there are also "local customers," occupants of territories near the cleaner fish, which come to be cleaned with astonishing regularity. Even large carnivorous fish let themselves be cleaned, and when the little cleaners have finished their work they come safely out of the mouth of the predator; they are protected.

The mimics of the cleaner fish turn this situation to their own advantage. In areas where the cleaner fish is active one finds fish of another family (a blenny, family Blenniidae) which is scarcely distinguishable in external appearance. This blenny, *Aspidontus taeniatus*, is the same size and color as the cleaner fish and even swims with a similar dancing movement. Fish familiar with the cleaner fish unsuspectingly allow *Aspidontus* to approach, and receive a nasty surprise; the mimic carefully steers up to its target, then bites a semicircular piece out of one of its fins and eats it. Because of its disguise, the "false cleaner" remains unharmed.

At the first encounter most fish cannot tell a real cleaner fish from its mimic, but in the course of time they do learn the difference. There is a simple distinction: the mimic always attacks from the rear, directing its bites chiefly to the tailfin. The cleaner, by contrast, can approach its clients from the front. Accordingly, the client fish need only turn their heads toward any fish they think is a cleaner. Some species actually do this in an aquarium, but we do not yet know whether it also happens in the natural habitat. In any case, satisfactory encounters must predominate, since there are fewer mimics than cleaners. The most successful mimic is the one that manages to bite many fish as often as possible, and success thus depends to a great extent on the lack of experience of young fish. We can conclude that a selection pressure is still operating to enhance the resemblance of *Aspidontus* to *Labroides*, but only in certain characteristics, so that it will remain possible for the other fish to learn to discriminate.

The cuckoo egg

Sometimes the signal receiver (the animal deceived) is also the model; the mimic benefits from appearing to be a conspecific. For example, the cuckoo (*Cuculus canorus*) lays its eggs in the nests of various birds. The involuntary foster parents hatch out the eggs and care for the young cuckoo until it grows up. Cuckoo eggs have been found in the nests of about 180 species, though in some of these they are a rarity. To be suitable for a cuckoo egg a nest must not only be occupied by a breeding pair of birds; it must also already contain some eggs of the host birds.

Several notable aspects of disguise are involved. The cuckoo lays eggs that are amazingly small as compared with its own size, but they require no longer to develop than those of the host birds. Moreover, the cuckoo eggs correspond in color and patterning with those of the host birds. Mistakes do happen from time to time; many birds throw an egg that looks different out of the nest. Therefore, a female cuckoo which regularly lays her eggs in the "wrong" nests has no offspring. It can, easily be calculated that a cuckoo which lays its eggs in any nest it finds and leaves it up to chance whether the eggs fit those of the host birds or not, is unlikely to have any descendants. Since in most cases the cuckoo eggs do match the hosts' eggs closely, the cuckoo must be somehow responsible.

It is known that every cuckoo female lays the same sort of egg throughout her life, and always in the nest of a certain species of bird. In a sense, then, the cuckoo must recognize its host. There is nothing remarkable in this, since of course it grew up with birds of this species. The coloration of cuckoo eggs is hereditary. Each female cuckoo that has been raised by a certain host species must have come from an egg acceptable to that species, and if she lays her eggs in a nest of the same species it should match as well. But what about the male cuckoos? If the male genes also affected the appearance of the egg, the system would work only if cuckoos mated exclusively with other cuckoos that had been raised by the same host species. This is most unlikely; the adult cuckoos have no way of knowing where their potential partners grew up. We must assume, then, that the female genes are primarily responsible for size, color and patterning of the eggs.

The situation is probably similar in other cases of "brood parasitism" among birds. It appears that originally all members of a species were associated with a single host species. The variability that has developed in the European cuckoo—different females being associated with different hosts—is most likely a higher level of specialization. Brood parasitism occurs in a number of different groups of birds. In some cases the young parasite does not throw its step-siblings out of the nest, but rather resembles them and grows up with them. This happens among the whydahs (subfamily Viduinae), the hosts of which are weaverfinches (family Estrildidae); each species of whydah is associated with a particular weaverfinch species.

As a rule, the female whydah does not destroy any of the eggs of the host finch, and she lays only one egg in each host nest. But it sometimes happens that several whydahs choose the same finch nest, so that the nest contains more than one whydah egg. According to the observations of Jürgen Nicolai, in such cases the whydah female may destroy some of the eggs; then she chooses for destruction not one of the other whydah eggs, but an egg of the finch. The parasite seems able to distinguish among the eggs more accurately than the host.

Of all the passeriform birds, the weaverfinches have a unique method of feeding the young; they sink their beaks into those of the nestlings and pump a large part of the crop contents into the crops of the young birds. The whydah nestlings are the only other birds adapted to being fed in this way. In contrast to the young cuckoo, the young whydah does no harm to its fellow nestlings. In this case, then, the host species suffers hardly at all from the relationship; the weaverfinches simply have one more hungry mouth to feed. The whydahs get their full share, for they have conspicuous patterning in the mouth just like that of the host species. This correspondence is entirely equivalent to that between the egg of the cuckoo and that of its hosts. The weaverfinch parents also respond to other signals— the begging sounds, begging movements of the head, and the plumage color of their young. In the young whydah, mouth patterning, begging sounds, juvenile plumage, and digestive apparatus must all be matched to those of the particular host species.

Fig. 9-22. Phases of spawning in the mouth-brooding *Haplochromis burtoni*: the female (right in top picture) lays her eggs; she gathers them in her mouth for brooding (middle picture); the male discharges sperm onto the bottom while the female tries to pick up the "dummy eggs" on the male's anal fin (bottom picture); thus the sperm cells reach the eggs in the mouth of the female.

There is no room to go into all the many other cases of mimicry, but one more category must be mentioned—mimicry within a single species. It can happen that not just two but all three of the members of a mimicry system (model, mimic, and signal receiver) belong to the same species. Among the cichlid fishes (family Cichlidae), all of which care for their young, females of the genus *Haplochromis* take their eggs into their mouths as soon as they are laid, and there the eggs develop. To ensure that the eggs are fertilized the male, whose job it is to defend the spawning area, holds his anal fin spread out when shedding the sperm. On the fin are round colored spots that look like eggs (see Color plate, p. 144) and which affect the female accordingly. She repeatedly searches for eggs that she may have missed, and time and again she attempts to take the "dummy eggs" on the male's fin into her mouth. Since the spots are close by the male genital opening, this action automatically brings sperm cells into the mouth and into contact with the eggs.

Another example of intraspecific mimicry is found in ground-dwelling Old World apes such as the hamadryas baboon (see Color plate, p. 144). The ischial callosities on the hind end of the male baboon are a glowing red; they are "presented" to other baboons as a form of greeting. The females in such species develop pronounced swellings of the genital and anal regions when they are in estrus, which resemble very closely the red callosities of the males. In this case, the males have imitated female sexual characteristics. Presenting of the hind end with the tail raised or bent to one side—the characteristic way in which a female induces a male to copulate—inhibits aggressiveness and is especially important when the male is much stronger than the female and of higher social rank. Presenting is also used to appease aggressive members of the same group, and in this case sex is irrelevant; even low-ranking males present to females higher in rank. Presenting in a less pronounced form (comparable to our doffing of hats) can serve as a greeting when a baboon meets a higher-ranking baboon. The degree of protection this behavior offers is indicated by incidents like the following: One baboon threatens another with furious screeches, and this brings the dominant male to the scene. If the animal expressing the threat simultaneously presents to the dominant male, the latter walks around the aggressor and drives away the other baboon. The animal that caused all the trouble escapes punishment. Here the mimicry signifies something different from the model behavior; males never, of course, use their "imitation estrous swelling" to induce copulation, but rather simply as a means of appeasement within the group.

Opponents of the mimicry theory, as one of their arguments, refer to examples in which the imitation must have existed before the model. It has been claimed that the similarity of many orthopterans to leaves (found in its most perfect form in the genus *Phyllium*) could not be mimicry of a leaf since insect fossils resembling leaves date back to the Upper Jurassic, when there were as yet no foliage plants. To this one can

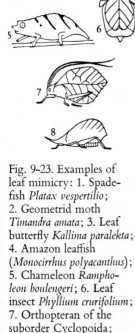

Fig. 9-23. Examples of leaf mimicry: 1. Spadefish *Platax vespertilio*; 2. Geometrid moth *Timandra amata*; 3. Leaf butterfly *Kallima paralekta*; 4. Amazon leaffish (*Monocirrhus polyacanthus*); 5. Chameleon *Rampholeon boulengeri*; 6. Leaf insect *Phyllium crurifolium*; 7. Orthopteran of the suborder Cyclopoida; 8. Leaflike southeastern Asian acridid grasshopper (*Systella rafflesi*).

reply that characteristics lending an animal a resemblance to something else appear repeatedly, even if the "model" is in quite another place or unknown at the time. Let us assume that for some reason grasshoppers that looked like leaves were living in a region where there were no such leaves. If plants with suitable leaves did eventually appear in this region, and the grasshoppers thereupon fell victim less often to their predators, then a characteristic which until that time had had no biological relevance would have become a true camouflage, contributing to the preservation of the species.

Remember that mimicry serves to deceive a signal receiver. As a rule such deceptions can be considered successful if they work at least once, and the more often they work the better it is for the mimic. The ability of the signal receiver to learn plays a quite different role in different cases Some receivers have no chance to learn since they are eaten instantly (for example, by an angler fish); others, like the clients of the cleaner fish, have ample opportunity and as a result are the agents of selection pressure toward more exact imitation. Warning coloration often depends upon the receiver's learning as quickly as possible, and this is true of many other warning signals as well. But any given warning or punishing stimulus affects only certain specific enemies. The stink of bugs is of little avail against birds; the defensive secretion sprayed out by the South American stick insect *Anisomorpha* works against ants, ground beetles, mice and jays but not against the opossum. There is no complete protection.

All the examples of mimicry discussed here have one thing in common; the signal receiver is fooled by a false signal that has a quite specific significance for that animal. This is true of intraspecific mimicry as well; the individual animal is deceived, though the deception is for the good of the species as a whole. An important question is whether the meaning of the signal to the receiver is inborn or learned. The study of appropriate cases of mimicry provides deep insights into the evolution of signals, crucial elements in all animal behavior.

▷
Defoliation during an outbreak of caterpillars: Left, top to bottom: Processionary caterpillars (*Thaumatopoea processionea*); larvae of the pine sawfly (*Diprion pini*); caterpillars of the owlet moth *Perigrapha cincta*.
Right: The crown of an oak, completely stripped of its leaves by a mass outbreak of oak-twist caterpillars (*Tortrix viridana*).

10 Competition within a Species

By W. Altenkirch

Part of the biotic environment of an animal consists of the other animals of its own species; they form a biotic environmental factor that is easily overlooked but is of considerable importance in many ways. Its effects may be beneficial or harmful, and it may effect a single animal or group of animals, or even the whole species.

We shall focus our attention primarily not upon the individual animal but upon the group of animals of a single species (the population) living in a specific area. The branch of ecology involved with questions at this level is called population ecology; it is concerned with the relationships between animal populations and their environment, and the latter is of course considered to include conspecific animals. Population ecology marks a transition from the study of the individual to the study of communities, in which various species participate.

The concept of an animal population is a useful one, even though in the field a population must usually be rather arbitrarily delimited. The complex of interactions of a population, the individual, and the environment was summarized in a simple diagram by the Dutch zoologist Bakker in 1964 (Fig. 10-1); we shall refer to this diagram in the discussion that follows.

The population consists of the individuals of a species, with all their morphological, physiological, and behavioral characteristics. But in addition, a population has its own distinguishing characteristics. It has a particular composition of individuals of different sexes, ages, and vitality. It is characterized by its size, its density, and its distribution in space. Moreover, it undergoes changes in its composition; rate of reproduction and mortality are also characteristics of a population.

A population is embedded in its biotic and abiotic environment. First, there is the local habitat with all its properties and components, three of which are of most direct significance to the population:

1. Food and other factors absolutely required for survival of the population but present only in limited amounts; these include places to shelter, lay eggs, and raise offspring.

◁
Upper left: young tit nestlings preparing to receive food when the parents approach. The parents give preference to the oldest and strongest nestlings, which stretch their gaping mouths up the furthest (yellow throats).
Upper right: caterpillars of the ermine moth *Yponomeuta padella.*
Below: hedge infested with ermine-moth caterpillars and completely covered with silk.

2. Antagonists: all the agents of disease, parasites, or predators found in the natural environment.

3. Other species sharing the habitat, apart from the antagonists, to the extent that they affect the population; these may be competitors for food and shelter, alternative prey for the predators, or alternative or intermediate hosts for the parasites.

Superimposed on all of this is the weather. It influences all the other components of the system, but is of course not ordinarily influenced by them in return. At the other levels, however, the relationships are reciprocal; effects can be exerted in either direction. For example, the prevalence of food or prey is influenced by the consumers and it in turn affects their condition and numbers.

The relationships between conspecifics can take many forms. These range from simple coexistence to the highly complicated interactions in societies of insects. Large numbers of animals of the same species can live side by side in a small space without showing any sign of interaction. This happens, for example, in many species of leaf-eating insects; caterpillars feed wherever the butterfly laid her eggs. But here, as well as in the case of asocial animals that avoid their conspecifics, like certain field rodents, the individual must at least occasionally seek out and tolerate interaction —with a sexual partner, and perhaps with its offspring. Sexual relationships and care of the young are the simplest and most widespread forms of social behavior within a species. Additional communal relationships may develop—more or less extensive, temporary or permanent, and serving a variety of functions. Familiar examples are herds of ungulates, flocks of birds, and schools of fish. Sometimes these associations are based on family groups, but not necessarily so. In a herd, the individual enjoys greater protection from predators by joint defensive action, the benefits of communal food-finding, and other advantages. Some groups involve one of these factors in particular; animals may band together specifically for hunting, migrating, sleeping, hibernating, building and occupying a dwelling, or breeding.

A prerequisite for such associations is the "social drive" of the individual. Added to this is the drive to imitate, which can forge out of individual animals a community capable of well-directed cooperative effort. Such cooperation, at one extreme, is simple simultaneous movement (for example, in fleeing together from danger); higher levels of organization include long-distance migration and the division of labor among members of a community. The high point in this line of development is reached by the communities of social insects. The basis of most of these is a family group; in the simplest case, as in wasps and bees, the groups are renewed annually. The more highly developed societies of ants, bees, and termites are maintained for years or even decades. Here division of labor is associated with morphological differentiation (polymorphism). "Castes" are formed, ranging from the simple distinction

Levels of socialization

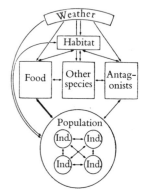

Fig. 10-1. Diagram of the network of relationships between an animal population, the individual animals, and the environmental factors; designed by the Dutch zoologist Bakker. (Ind. = individual)

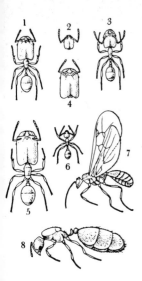

Fig. 10-2. Polymorphism among ants: soldier (1), intermediate forms (2-5), typical worker (6), male (7), female after loss of the wings (8).

between reproductive animals and workers to the development of various specialists—for example, different types of "soldiers." Finally, the task of a given individual may change; the worker bee performs different duties in a fixed sequence, starting with brood care, continuing with comb construction, keeping guard, and finally making foraging excursions.

If individuals are separated from an insect society, they live for an appreciably shorter time than their conspecifics that have remained in the group. A similar effect has been observed in many insects, and in fish, birds, rodents and apes as well; one finds a measurable increase in the performance of an individual when it is in a group of its conspecifics. The French scientists who first described this phenomenon called it the "group effect." Increased performance can be measured in several respects; the rate of metabolism rises, the animals take more food and are more active, their growth is accelerated, and their lifespan is prolonged.

A special form of this group effect is the so-called "phase phenomenon." This term was first used by the Russian researcher Uvarov in 1921, when he discovered that migratory locusts of a single species can form two different types of individual. Later it was found that such phases occur not only among the migratory species of acridids but in other insects as well, including certain lepidopteran and coleopteran species.

A good deal is known about the phases of migratory locust and how they arise. The solitary, nonmigrating animals differ from their social, migratory conspecifics not only in behavior and level of activity, but also in color and details of body shape such as the form of the prothorax and the length of the wings and legs. It is possible to show experimentally that the transformation from the social to the gregarious phase is brought about entirely by tactile stimuli associated with contact between animals of the same species. Animals in the gregarious phase show certain characteristics of the group effect; they eat more and develop more rapidly. Two animals are enough to produce this change.

One feature of the group effect is that it does play a role in fairly sparse populations. But the migratory locusts happen to be a prime example of a species that, at least occasionally, occurs in enormous numbers. Since ancient times these mass outbreaks have aroused attention; not least because man is usually affected directly. Hordes of insects or rodents appearing within a confined space ordinarily cause considerable harm to crops. The migratory locust is one of the animals with the longest history of destructive activity; as early as 2500 B.C. they were mentioned in ancient Egypt. Since then a large number of species—most of them insects but also species of nematodes, mites and vertebrates—have been added to the list of pests which occasionally or regularly appear in masses and can do formidable damage to cultivated plants or to stored food and other human goods.

What happens in a population when it undergoes this sort of mass outbreak? The least complicated case is found in certain leaf- or needle-eating lepidopteran caterpillars and sawfly larvae. Oaks are frequently infested by such caterpillars in the spring and may be completely defoliated. Here the culprit most often involved is the pea-green oak twist (*Tortrix viridana*). Its caterpillars feed side by side in the crown of the oak, with no sign of interaction. Feeding continues until no more foliage is available. This is the factor that limits the number of caterpillars; in favorable years, when the caterpillar population is very large, the foliage is insufficient. The caterpillars must compete with one another for food. The tree is bare (see Color plate, p. 155) and many caterpillars die. Some of them may find just enough food or be satisfied with less than the optimum amount, so that they can at least complete their development. The shortage may also affect other species using the same food source (interspecific competition); oak-twist caterpillars can take food away from caterpillars of other species or from June beetles.

Competition for food can bring about the death of all the oak-twist caterpillars making up the "subpopulation" in a given oak. But since other oaks are usually growing in the vicinity which have not lost so much of their foliage, some subpopulations survive; the total population, and thus the species, need not be threatened with extinction. In such cases intraspecific competition acts as a brake, preventing the mass outbreak of a population which would otherwise occur.

Competition commonly involves food, but it can arise over anything which is important to the species and not abundantly available. Frequently animals compete for territories, shelters, hiding-places, or nests for their young. Competition becomes more intense as the number of competitors increases.

Most simply stated, two contestants (for present purposes, animals of the same species) dispute possession of a third thing. The dispute may come to a catastrophic end. However, other interactions between conspecifics under crowded conditions can also end in catastrophe, and these are not always easily distinguishable from competition in the strict sense. These direct interactions between members of an animal population have been studied particularly closely in rodents.

The field mouse *Microtus arvalis* has been observed to change its behavior when the population density increases. A mouse is stimulated by the continual close presence of another mouse, and as a result it becomes not only more active, but more aggressive. If the situation is maintained, it eventually leads to physiological changes that can result in the death of the affected animal. The operation of this "crowding factor" has similar effects among the various birds and mammals that have been investigated—including humans under unusually crowded conditions. In 1936 the physician Hans Selye described this "stress syndrome." Striking aspects of the syndrome are the enlarged adrenal cortex and the changes in the gastrointestinal system of all stressed animals. There is an associated increase in adrenalin production, as a result of

Competition and other interactions

Fig. 10-3. Caterpillar and imago of the pea-green oak twist (*Tortrix viridana*), with partially eaten and twisted oak leaves.

The crowding factor

which reserve substances in the body (glycogen) are broken down. The blood-sugar level falls; death occurs with the symptoms of shock from excessive reduction of blood sugar. Moreover, there is an increased vulnerability to all sorts of unfavorable external influences—for example, bad weather. Whether the collapse of mass outbreaks of rodents in nature is actually brought about by the consequences of stress is still in debate; but this phenomenon has at least been observed in field mice under experimental conditions.

Similar interactions have been observed in insects. For example, cater-pillars of the bordered white moth (*Bupalus piniarius*) subjected to slight disturbances by their conspecifics lose appreciable weight, and as a result the fertility of the female moths is reduced. Even a brief encounter between two caterpillars can elicit such a response if one animal ejects its stomach juices onto the other.

Mass migrations resulting from increased density

Disturbance by conspecifics also plays a role in the phase change of the migratory locust. The locust responds to this stress by entering the migratory phase. Mass migrations offer one possibility of avoiding the consequences of increased density, competition, and other unfavorable interactions. A vertebrate famous for such behavior is the lemming. Many lemmings undertake migrations, but usually they cover only small distances. The true lemmings include the mountain species *Lemmus lemmus*, well known for its travels in Scandinavia. Among the true lemmings, migrations recur regularly as the animals move between the tundra and their winter quarters in spring and autumn. From time to time—in the so-called "lemming years"—conditions for reproduction in summer are so good that especially large numbers of lemmings are produced. Under the pressure of competition for food in late summer, the activity and unrest of the animals increases. Long distance migrations start from the winter quarters. Again, the symptoms of stress are evident; the animals, in any case not very peaceable, become especially irritable and aggressive. Even on the long migrations they make every effort to avoid their neigh-bors, but all proceed in exactly the same direction.

None of these wanderers returns to the starting point. Most of them die, in many cases falling prey to the numerous carnivores that follow the line of march, on the ground and in the air, to enjoy this unusually abun-dant food supply. The number of lemmings remaining in the area from which the migration began is so much reduced that competition is no longer a critical factor; the mass migration acts as a pressure-release valve.

Bird invasions

The migrations of certain birds are also dependent upon population density. Among the birds best known for such invasions of unusual areas are the Siberian nutcracker (*Nucifraga caryocatactes macrorhynchos*) and the Bohemian waxwing (*Bombycilla garrulus*). In certain species, like the Siberian nutcracker, with quite specialized feeding habits, lack of food is probably the critical factor eliciting longdistance migration. In other bird species, however, crowding evidently plays the central role. In the case of the great tit (*Parus major*), for example, we know that fluctuations in population density are compensated by migrations; such fluctuations are brought about chiefly because the survival of young birds in the nest and immediately after leaving it (and hence the number of adults) is determined to a great extent by weather conditions and their effect upon the food supply. In the fall of an abundant year most of the young birds and some "surplus" older ones leave the breeding area, so that the local population is kept within bounds. But unlike the lemmings, these wanderers do return in the spring, and can compensate for winter mortality among the local population.

There are further mechanisms operating within populations that alleviate the overall consequences just described. These make possible an "organized competition" in which a part of the population does not suffer from such effects.

Organized competition

One way in which the danger to the population as a whole is reduced has been mentioned above with respect to the oak-twist caterpillars—that is, the risk may be shared among subpopulations so that, for the population as a whole, local catastrophes do not amount to disasters.

The unpleasant consequences of competition can be avoided if the animals in a population "automatically" retard their rate of reproduction as population density increases. This happens in diverse groups of animals. An example from the class Nematoda is the root worm *Heterodera schachtii*, the numbers of which decline when a certain density has been reached. When pests in food stores, which live in the food they eat, become too numerous, the fertility of the females and the potency of the males are reduced as a result of the accumulation of the excrement. This has been shown to occur, for example, in flour beetles of the genus *Tribolium*. As the population density of mice increases, the number of young in each litter decreases, though the animals' readiness to mate is unchanged.

Limits to reproduction

Behavioral mechanisms regulating competition are particularly interesting. These include rank-ordering among the members of a population, and territoriality. Both result in the partial or complete suppression of competition for commodities in limited supply; some of the animals are forced to leave the area or die, while the rest are amply served by the available supplies. Part of the population is assured of survival and another part is sacrificed. The sacrificed fraction frequently consists of the weaker members of the community.

The young of the great tit (see Color plate, p. 156) die as nestlings in numbers corresponding to the food situation at the time. The parents do not distribute the food evenly among all the young in the nest, but pay most attention to the beaks that gape the widest. As a rule, these are the strongest and oldest nestlings. Their younger and weaker siblings receive adequate food only if there is an abundant supply; in case of a food shortage, they are the first victims of the competition. The young birds cease to die when a balance is reached between the amount of food the parents can bring and the number of consumers in the nest. Similarly, tadpoles living under too-crowded conditions secrete growth-inhibiting substances, and it is the weakest animals that are most affected by these.

Social stress

Rank-ordering within a community usually serves to minimize disputes among the members and thus to conserve their strength and time. But in cases of overpopulation such as observed in mice and lemmings, the subordinate animals suffer more than those of higher rank. The stress syndrome (e.g., enlargement of the adrenals) is pronounced in the subordinate animals, and the higher an animal's rank, the less evident are the physiological consequences of crowding. Measurement of the statistical distribution of adrenal weight in a community makes this tendency quite clear; as the extremes of the distribution move farther apart, the part of the population at one end is condemned to death, and that at the other has increased chances of survival.

Territorial behavior

Territorial behavior, from the ecological viewpoint, is a property of a population by means of which the members in a given area become distributed as uniformly as possible; it sets an upper limit on the density of the population. A few examples will illustrate the possibilities and limitations of this mechanism.

First, we return to the great tit; this bird has territorial behavior, but it is evident only in the period just preceding the spring breeding season. Later other birds are allowed to infiltrate the breeding population, as long as nesting places (holes) are available. In this case, then, territorial behavior is limited; nevertheless, it brings about a well-adjusted distribution of the birds. Overpopulation of the preferred areas—for example, leafy woods with ample supplies of food—is prevented. The left-over birds are crowded out into less desirable places, such as coniferous woods. These marginal regions constitute a reserve of birds which are always ready to close any gaps in the main nesting area.

Under such conditions, the animals cannot reproduce to excess. How, then, can catastrophic increases in population arise among field mice, which are also known to hold territories? The territorial behavior of these mice adapts itself to the population density; rather than counteract an increase in density, it actually contributes to a further increase. The basis for this is the enormous reproductive capacity of the animals; females can mate when only thirteen days old, and from then on can bear young at intervals of twenty days, even in winter if conditions are right.

Initially, each female mouse has her own territory, and the males wander about with no affiliation to any particular one. There are rivalry battles between the males, and these become more frequent as the population increases. As a result, at the height of a population explosion there can be three times as many females as males. As the density of animals rises, the females move closer together, eventually occupying family and even community nests in which several females cooperate in caring for a large number of young. There is no mechanism for crowding out surplus mice as they appear; their numbers increase until the stress is intolerable, and the "crash" of the population that follows is as impressive as was the rapid buildup.

Almost all the animal species we have described play a significant role in human life. This is no accident; our knowledge of a species is often directly related to its practical importance. The European wild rabbit (*Oryctolagus cuniculus*) was transported to Australia, where it became a pest throughout the country. Consequently, much of what we know about this species has been discovered by Australian zoologists. Usually it is major pests that arouse special interest. On the other hand, certain species such as the tits are the object of special study because they can assist in the battle against such pests.

Efforts to understand mass outbreaks of animals and thus to be able to plan methods of counteracting them have, in recent decades, led to the rapid development of population ecology. The potential role of this field in the future of mankind can hardly be overestimated. These studies are not confined to the struggle against pests, though this is the starting point and the area in which the need is currently most pressing; population ecologists also work out the scientific bases for conservation of endangered species, and make specific contributions to the planning of the human future. Our tendency to overexploit, and eventually destroy, our environment is well exemplified by the irresponsible whaling and fishing that has led to the extinction of certain species and the endangering of others. Prevention of such disasters is one goal of research in population ecology.

Animal populations in the field are the focal point of such research. The first step is to discover the state of the population; here statistical methods are a fundamental tool, for as a rule it is necessary to infer the state of the overall population from small samples. Moreover, each population is in a state of constant flux, changing its organization to some extent in both space and time. We have encountered spatial changes (dispersion dynamics) in the examples of migration discussed above. Changes in time (abundance dynamics) are most apparent in the fluctuations in population size in the course of years or generations. Mass outbreaks are the extremes in a continual process of more or less cyclic change, found to some extent in all animal species. Real mass outbreaks occur only among certain species, in certain places and under certain conditions which can be revealed only after laborious research. Such investigations involve drawing up "balance sheets" for a population, in which its size is measured at selected intervals and compared with the environmental influences prevailing at these times. The results over many years, finally, are analyzed in the hope of discovering whether one or more key factors are responsible for the fluctuations.

When inquiring about the causes of population fluctuations, then, one is asking what influences are exerted upon a population from without and from within. The statistical analysis of field observations must be

Tasks, goals and methods of population ecology

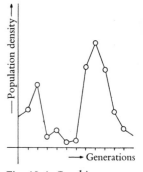

Fig. 10-4. Graphic representation of the fluctuation in size of a population in successive generations.

Causes of fluctuation in populations

supplemented by experimental study of the relationships between animal populations and specific environmental factors. The crux of such controlled experiments, of course, is that all factors other than the one under study are eliminated or kept constant.

In the ideal case, population fluctuations would be clearly ascribable to certain distinct effects, but in practice this rarely happens. The best result ordinarily obtainable is the mathematical formulation of the basic relationships—the construction of a model that represents the variations in the population as faithfully as possible. Such a model can be useful in predicting how the population will change under certain circumstances, which is of great practical significance in identifying potential pest outbreaks and taking suitable and timely preventive action. Modern population ecologists are making increasing use of methods and techniques derived from other areas. The problems are so complex, involving an enormous number of separate factors, that systems analysis and computer simulations are required to clarify even approximately the network of interactions. And all the tools at present available may still not suffice; many attempted analyses get no further than the initial stages. Above all, the ecologist must make the effort necessary to learn new approaches. The most "biological" of the biological sciences, ecology, increasingly demands knowledge of mathematics and systems technology as well as mastery of computer techniques and languages.

Present interpretations of the origin of population fluctuations are based on the notion that there is never a perfect equilibrium among reproductive capacity, mortality and migration (both into and away from the population). The capacity for reproduction in species displaying pronounced fluctuations is usually very large. Ordinarily this is balanced by a correspondingly high mortality, which may have many causes such as weather conditions, predators, and hunger. Under special conditions, however, mortality is decreased—for example, at times when the weather is especially good or the food unusually abundant. The latter situation is often created by man, when he plants large areas with single crops; man can also bring about a sudden reduction in the number of predators affecting a species, with a corresponding reduction in mortality. In laboratory experiments in Hungary, a single pair of field mice produced a total of 2557 progeny (in three generations) in a year. Of the 128 first-generation offspring, 126 would have to die if the population were to remain constant. Should four survive, the population will have doubled in a single generation.

One wonders, in view of the many factors permitting inconstancy of population size, why populations tend in general to stay within certain limits. The upper limit is the most interesting from a practical point of view—that is, is the population in question regulated at an upper limit, and does this limit lie above or below a tolerable level with respect to the animal's destructive potential?

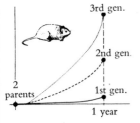

Fig. 10-5. Graph showing the reproductive capacity of an animal species, using the field mouse as an example. Within a year, a single pair of field mice produced 2557 progeny (in three generations).

Regulation of population density

Current theoretical formulations of population dynamics allow one to distinguish different roles of the various factors that may limit or regulate population density. Of special importance are the factors which themselves change in effectiveness as a direct result of the changes in population density. These can include the numbers of predators and intra- and interspecific competition. In calculating the effects of these in terms of systems theory, one recognizes that stabilization by "negative feedback" is involved—that is, the greater the population density, the greater the stabilizing effect. By contrast, factors which do not "respond" to population density—such as weather conditions—have entirely different kinds of effects and not exert "fine control" on the population density. This is not to say that weather conditions are unimportant; the above feedback mechanisms themselves are subject to weather, and periodic weather fluctuations can of course affect or limit population density drastically. But the system-theory formulation underlines the special role of competition among conspecifics as a central and reliable regulatory mechanism—it will always act to keep a population from growing without limit. Naturally, the point at which this mechanism becomes effective may be only at very high population densities. In such cases it acts rather like an "emergency brake," and the population in question may long before have become larger than humans consider desirable or tolerable.

A population, the density of which is affected by such factors, may be in a state of dynamic equilibrium. Either sudden or long-term changes in the environment can upset the balance; the population can enter a period of explosive growth, it can die out in a certain area, or equilibrium may be restored at a new level. Thinking in these terms, one arrives at certain generalizations that are of considerable practical significance.

To begin with, one can identify specific factors which compensate or replace one another. An example involves the great tit in Holland. The rate of reproduction was lowered by artificial means and as a result the rate of survival of the birds in the following winter increased greatly. In controlling man's exploitation of animals (for example, in fishing) the goal is to achieve a situation in which the losses due to man simply replace other, natural causes of mortality so that the animal population is maintained at a desired level. Ideally, controlled exploitation should decrease the influence of intraspecific competition such that the population as a whole is actually benefited.

Compensation among factors

Another example of compensation is offered by the oak-twist caterpillar. A large number of birds had been introduced into an area with a view to reducing the defoliation of trees by caterpillars. But the losses suffered by the caterpillar population at the end of the leaf-eating season proved to be just the same as in an adjacent area not specially protected by birds. It was found that the mortality of the caterpillars caused by the birds was about the same as the mortality in the second area due to competition among the caterpillars for food. Whenever humans try to manipulate nature they can expect to encounter effects of this kind, but they are difficult to predict in advance. There have been cases in which parasites introduced to a region, as a method of biological control of non-indigenous pests, interfered with one another so as to be completely ineffective. In other cases, insectivorous birds fed selectively upon prey that was sick or weakened by parasites, so that their usefulness in population control was diminished.

It is particularly important to consider possible compensating mechanisms when chemical pest control is attempted. Chemical controls are relatively indiscriminate, and disturb the entire biological system. There are many examples in which the end effect has been just the opposite of what was intended. If interspecific competition is reduced by chemical means, "overcompensation" can occur, and the population can grow more rapidly than it would have done without interference. The "natural enemies" of pests—disease pathogens, parasites, and predators—are, as we have seen, collectively termed "antagonists." It often happens that the antagonists of a pest are affected more severely than the pest itself, and take longer to recover. Moreover, there are compensatory effects by which a previously insignificant animal suddenly takes the place of a pest that has been successfully controlled, and in turn becomes a pest. Accordingly, before undertaking any sort of interference with nature, one ought to know as much as possible about the relationships in the natural system; only when armed with such knowledge can one act responsibly.

Diversity within a population

We have already pointed out that natural populations are not homogeneous; individual animals differ, and their relative numbers can vary in space and time. There is a tendency for the sharing of the risk to a whole population among the largest possible number of subpopulations. In the

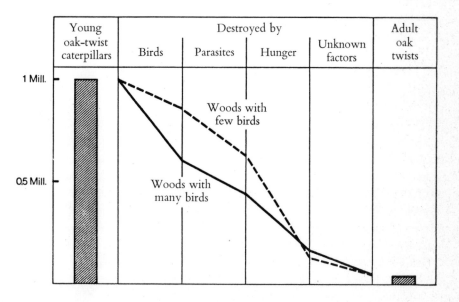

Fig. 10-6. Different factors substitute for one another to produce the same final mortality in two caterpillar populations.

extreme case one can even imagine that there are special regulatory processes based entirely upon these differences among subpopulations, the interactions of which vary with their respective requirements and habits.

In mice, it was observed that average viability decreased with increasing population density. There was thus a general deterioration in the quality of the overall population. But it could be shown that certain genetically determined groups within the population respond to overcrowding with special aggressiveness, while others tend to migrate away. The same result has been observed in insects. For example, American tent caterpillars (*Malacosoma pluviale*) could be divided into two groups, an "active" type and a "sluggish" type. They were distinguished not only by the activity level of caterpillar and mature insect, but also by their reactions to light and their behavior in foraging and nest-building. When population density is increasing, the "active" caterpillar type is in the majority. When the peak population is reached, the "sluggish" type begins to predominate, and it continues to do so during the subsequent decline in density. A similar finding was reported by Swiss entomologists studying the moth *Zeiraphera griseana*. This serious pest on larch trees also has two sorts of caterpillars, a dark type and a light type. The dark type is sensitive to stress, whether caused by crowding, competition for food, weather or insecticides. When the population is increasing rapidly it is progressively crowded out by the more resistant light type, which eventually predominates, like the sluggish tent caterpillar, in the declining phase. Other studies could be described, but all of them suggest that an increase of population density is accompanied by the increased prevalence of a particular subpopulation.

Whether this sort of interaction of genetically distinct parts of a population is by itself sufficient to account for density fluctuations between certain limits is still a matter of debate. In any case, the various situations we have noted in the course of the normal fluctuation of a species can contribute to the development of genetic diversity. Intraspecific competition plays a special role here; it becomes more intense, the more alike the competitors are with respect to their characteristics and requirements. Accordingly, intraspecific competition is ordinarily more intense than that between species.

The reason a drastic outcome of competition is not more common is that competition can be reduced within a species by the development of subpopulations differing slightly in habits or needs, and distributed differently in space. This sort of adaptation undoubtedly plays a central role in evolution. The so-called "struggle for existence" is sometimes thought of as a physical confrontation, although Charles Darwin never regarded it in that way; in fact, it seldom occurs in this form, especially among vertebrates, owing to adaptations by which aggressive tendencies are modified.

When population ecology turns to man himself, it departs from the present context, to the extent that many other factors are involved. Never-

Human population
ecology

theless, it is tempting to indicate the extent to which the rules we have found to apply to animals are also applicable to man.

We shall consider primarily the findings related to intraspecific competition. This interaction has been, and is, highly developed among human beings, and its consequences may be disastrous. Increased population density, now as in the past, leads to competition for food and eventually to famine; the need for living space causes increased aggressiveness and war. The increase in human numbers seems unstoppable, in that modern medicine has robbed of their effectiveness the diseases which for millenia kept the population within bounds. Scientific and technical advances have made possible sufficient increases in food production that for part of the world, at least, lack of food is no longer a controlling factor. We have yet to see how successfully man can adapt to high population density—perhaps with the aid of medicine and technology—and whether he can avoid the normal consequences of overcrowding. Social stress of course occurs among people as well as animals; its effects are quite similar to those seen in apes and mice.

In view of the accelerating growth of the human population, it becomes a critical question whether an eventual equilibrium—albeit at a very high level—will be reached, and what controlling factors can possibly bring about stability when the natural "emergency brakes" have lost their power. The production of food cannot be increased indefinitely, and space is limited. Moreover, man is poisoning his environment more and more; the phenomenon is similar to the regulating mechanism we have seen in insects living in food stores, but the consequences are much graver. It is up to the human race to find some intraspecific regulatory mechanism that will prevent overpopulation, and this must involve a voluntary slowing of the rate of reproduction. If this opportunity to establish "controlled competition" should be missed now—at the eleventh hour—a catastrophe that may extinguish our species is unavoidable.

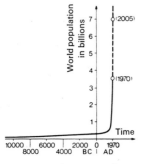

Fig. 10-7. The curve of world population *vs.* time shows a drastic rise in the rate of increase.

III. HABITATS AND THEIR FAUNA

Introduction
Habitats and Communities

By J. Illies

In the preceding chapters of this volume we have considered the paired concepts "environment" and "adaptation." We have learned to appreciate the different animal species as beings that have become adapted to the conditions characteristic of their particular habitat (their species-specific environment). The abiotic and biotic factors affecting them have been taken up one at a time, and it has been shown that body form, organ function, and behavior of the animals are molded by adaptation to these environmental conditions. But it was made clear at the outset, in the diagram of the structure of the science of ecology (Fig. 0-5), that the approach which concentrates upon the individual factors is, so to speak, only the ground floor of the ecological edifice.

In the chapters that follow we shall proceed to build upon this description of the single factors, so as to complete the construction. The constellation of different factors prevailing in each part of the world inhabited by organisms forms a biotope; of the totality of animal species, each adapted to its particular environment, the group occupying a certain area forms a community. This new pair of concepts enables us to express a new, fundamental ecological insight: particular environments (biotopes) are the frames, and in a sense the containers, for particular entities, the associated communities (biocenoses). The two together—the vessel and its living contents—in each case constitute an ecosystem. Whenever in the following chapters the word "community" is used, the reader should bear in mind that the community is inseparable from the ecosystem and can only be understood in that sense.

The community

The community *per se* is clearly defined in ecology. Not every possible grouping of animals is included; "artificial" associations brought about by man are not communities, nor are chance, transitory associations that may occur in nature. The community in the scientific sense was first recognized by the zoologist Karl Moebius in 1877, as he investigated the oyster beds in Kiel Bay. He suggested that the term be used only for *a group of living beings of which the number and types of species and individuals correspond to the average external conditions, which are subject to reciprocal influences, and which maintain themselves permanently in a specified area by reproduction.*

This definition is long and sounds rather cumbersome, but it contains not one superfluous word and it remains valid even today. When we consider its terms one by one, the several fundamental points reveal that communities are living entities with a high degree of intrinsic organization, which have a long history of evolution in close association with certain climatic conditions and which are just as susceptible to harm, and even destruction, as are individual organisms. It is not a matter of a chance gathering of animal species which have collected as a result of an arbitrary mixture of climatic factors at a certain spot but which could exist just as well in any other place in some other combination. A community, as seen by the ecologist, is an organic society the essence of which is its particular species composition. In saying, as Moebius expressed it, that the community *corresponds to average external conditions*, the definition summarizes the fact that a community is dependent upon quite specific ranges of temperature, light, humidity—all the climatic factors—in its biotope, and therefore cannot be found everywhere but, just like an individual species, has an ecological habitat, a certain biotope. The phrase *number and types of species and individuals* refers to the facts that the members of a community form a particular list of species of which certain ones are referred to as the "dominant species," and that the abundance of each of these species is regulated according to certain principles. The individuals composing the community are *subject to reciprocal influences*; the intimacy of the reciprocal relationships between the components of a community has already been indicated in the discussion of the circulation of matter at the beginning of the book (see Fig. 0-3) and will become apparent again and again in the following chapters. Our ecological "understanding" of a community primarily depends upon the degree to which we can obtain insight into the web of such interactions. Only a clarification of these relationships can put us in a position to explain how such communities, in the words of Moebius, *maintain themselves permanently in a specified area.*

In an undisturbed community, beneficial and detrimental effects are in balance; there is an equilibrium between the supply of food and the selection pressure exerted by enemies or other disadvantageous environmental influences. The resulting network of interrelationships fluctuates with the seasons and also over longer periods, but on the average all these fluctuations occur about a fixed norm. This is true for each single species in its ecological niche; if the equilibrium were to be permanently disturbed, the species would die out. The presence of a species in itself indicates that it is capable of adapting to its environment in the manner necessary for its existence. And the same can be said of the community as a whole. If it were not able to persist through centuries despite all the variations in favorable or harmful influences, it would not be in existence; the community, too, is adequately adapted to its environment.

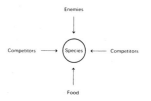

Fig. 00-1. Upon each species in a community various influences are exerted, both beneficial and harmful. As long as all these factors are in equilibrium, the species continues to maintain itself, but if the balance were permanently impaired, the species would gradually die out.

On the other hand, just as the individual species changes in the course of evolution, under the pressure of genetic and climatic modification, and eventually—though perhaps not until millennia have passed—is replaced by another, so the whole community can change and develop. This process, however, is much more difficult to comprehend than the evolution of single species, for it is not a matter of all the component species marching in step into the future. Some of the species fall by the wayside, new species may join in, and certain species may persist throughout but change their role in the community. Finally, the life of the community is itself a factor that can bring about long-term modifications of the biotope; it can happen that a community puts an end to its own further evolution and makes room for a successor. Such "succession," in fact, occurs quite commonly in nature and is the basis of the diversity we see in the landscape and its gradual, orderly alteration. For example, every pond in the course of decades or centuries turns into dry land, and even quite large lakes exist for only a few thousand years. The final stage in a succession is called the "climax" and represents the terminal, stabilized community toward which the developmental or "pioneer" stages have evolved. In a given climate, each shallow lake becomes bog and finally moorland, and every clearing grows back into forest in the course of time. Over longer periods there may be changes in the climate, and in this case the climax communities are modified correspondingly. If the water table falls, woodland is converted into steppe and steppe into desert; a rise in the temperature shifts the timberline upward so that alpine meadows are changed to alpine forests.

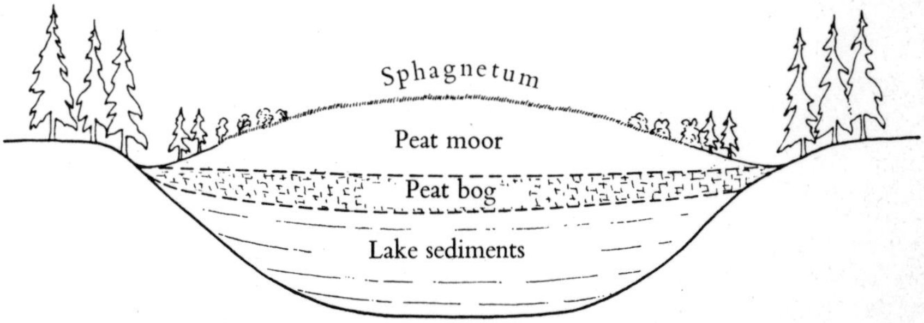

Fig. 00-2. Every community can change, as certain species die out and others become dominant. In so doing, communities modify the face of the earth. The drawing shows the progression from a lake to a flat marsh and eventually to a partially wooded hill with a plant community dominated by *Sphagnum* moss (Sphagnetum).

Scientists have established that there are certain general rules—fundamental ecological principles—governing the formation, subdivision and durability of communities. These hold for all the habitats on earth, and they show that the diverse species and environmental factors mesh to form a functional unit, following well-defined laws.

Four principles of ecology

The first fundamental principle was stated by August Thienemann in 1918—that is, *the greater the variety of the environmental conditions and resources for the organisms of a biotope, the greater the number of species in the associated community.* As an example, let us take a tropical jungle. Here we find an extraordinary number of different ecological niches in the various strata of the soil and the vegetation, there are a great number of different shrub and tree species forming each stand, and the special "microclimates" in separate small areas are quite variable. Accordingly, this habitat offers the greatest variety of animal species. Thousands of species of insect, and many dozen bird species, can exist side by side, each in its own specific environment. Because there are so many species, the number of individuals in each is usually small. Therefore, as all entomologists who have collected in such a tropical forest know, it is easier to find a hundred different butterfly species than to gather a hundred butterflies of any single species. Conversely, according to the first principle, in very uniform and constant habitats such as ground water, the bottoms of deep lakes, and deserts, one finds in the few niches only a small number of species; these, in most cases, have an abundance of individuals.

The second fundamental principle was also formulated by August Thienemann, in the same year: *The further the conditions for life in a biotope depart from the norm and from the optimum for the organisms, the fewer and more characteristic are the species in the community (and the more abundant is each species).* The "departure from normality" meant here occurs primarily in biotopes where certain climatic factors differ widely from the most favorable situation for animal life; this is the case, for example, in saline lakes, hot springs, the poorly oxygenated bottoms of lakes, the ice deserts near the poles, and in mountains at high altitudes. It is also the case in biotopes that have been damaged by man. Polluted waters and industrialized regions retain only a small remnant of the original list of species, while a few species specialized for survival under polluted conditions expand into the deserted niches and eventually can be found in great numbers.

The third fundamental principle was proposed by H. Franz in 1952: *The more continuous the evolution of the environmental conditions in a biotope and the longer it has remained the same, the more stable is the community and the larger is the number of species.* That is, old climax communities are characterized by high species diversity and great stability. Particularly good examples are coral reefs, tropical rainforests, caves, and the older lakes (Lake Baikal, for example). Such old habitats are the home of relicts of communities from earlier geological periods—especially the Tertiary— which have become extinct elsewhere. Thus the ecologist can infer the age of the communities in certain habitats or the length of time during which the climate has remained constant. For example, the presence of cold-adapted mountain-brook species on some Pacific islands like New Caledonia and New Guinea indicate that since these islands separated from the adjacent land masses a similar or colder, but never a warmer, climate has prevailed.

Finally, we shall state here for the first time a fourth basic principle: *Closely related species usually do not appear at the same place, at the same time, or in closely related niches; a community therefore, often includes only one of the many species in a genus or other related group.* This principle refers to the fact that any habitat may become "saturated" since the number of possible ecological niches is limited. Ordinarily only one of all the species potentially adapted to a type of niche can actually occupy it. Since similarly adapted species very often belong to the same genus, it follows (however odd this may at first appear) that one species of a genus will frequently exclude the others. This state of affairs has been expressed in various formulations such as Gause's Law and Jordan's Rule; behind all of these is the recognition that as species are the basic units of genetics, life-form types (and thus genera or higher-level taxa) are the faunal elements of communities—the basic units of ecology.

Though these four fundamental principles may not be mentioned explicitly in the following chapters, it will become clear that they have shaped each of the different communities discussed.

11 Cold Latitudes and the High Mountains

Arctic deserts, tundra, and the type of coniferous forest called taiga occupy large areas in the northern part of Eurasia and North America. It is characteristic of these polar cold zones that even in summer the temperature is low, there are seasonal changes of climate and biological processes, both genera and individual animals are few, and the ecosystems are unstable.

Cold zones, by A. A. Kistschinski

North of the tree line in Eurasia, North America and on the arctic islands there extend zones of tundra and ice desert; here the summers are short and the winters long. The period during which plants can grow and the total time when the temperature is above freezing are the shortest found anywhere in the northern hemisphere. The temperature in winter rarely falls below $-30°$ to $-40°C$, but as a result of the continual strong winds and snowstorms in this harsh season not many organisms can survive, at least in open country. An additional factor is the length of the polar nights. From September or October until May or June these arctic cold regions are covered by snow—not particularly deep, but extremely firm and distributed in a nonuniform way. In the spring certain spots thaw out while the air temperature is still below $0°C$, and these are a welcome stopping place for migratory birds. Insects and spiders awaken from their winter sleep and crawl out onto the still snow-covered surfaces, glistening in the sun, which from May to July sets only briefly or not at all. The summer is short, cold, and humid with a great deal of rain and fog. The temperature normally does not exceed $10°C$, or in the polar regions $2–4°C$; the northern boundary of the tundra in general coincides with the July isotherm (the line connecting places at the same temperature) for $10°C$.

Tundra and the arctic

The lack of heat is such that even the resistant boreal trees cannot grow here. The vegetation consists of mosses, lichens, small evergreen shrubs and long-lived grasses—it comprises sedges, cotton grass, saxifrage, milkvetch (*Oxytropis* and *Astragalus*), *Hedysarum*, *Dryas* and other plants. Shrubby willows, birches and alders are found only in the southern marginal regions; further north there are a few species of willow of more prostrate habit, the branches growing along the ground among the grass and moss. Large regions are occupied by lakes and swamps overgrown with bog moss (*Sphagnum*), green mosses, sedges and cotton grasses. For eight or nine months a year the lakes are covered with ice; during the spring thaw the water floods the low-lying areas, forming many temporary lakes and swamps which later dry up. On the shores of these there nest migratory birds such as gulls, ducks, phalaropes and sandpipers.

The soils are extraordinarily poor, and beneath them is permafrost. The root systems of the plants, together with the mosses, form a dense mat which conducts heat poorly; even toward the end of summer the soil under this layer has thawed to depths no greater than 30–50° cm. The ice deserts on most of the arctic islands offer almost the worst conceivable environment for terrestrial animals and plants. Here the summer lasts little more than a month, and even in July the thermometer almost never rises above 5°C. A large fraction of the continental land is covered by glaciers and fields of permanent snow; in other regions bare stone predominates, on which only lichens can thrive. Between these extremes are isolated spots where there grow mosses, lichens, a few flowering plants, and the prostrate, polar form of willow that spreads out through the moss. Since the sun never sets in summer, the soil and the plant-covered surfaces warm up; at this level the temperature can be 5–8°C higher than, for example, the air temperature at the height of a man's head. Thus soil-dwelling animals are at a greater advantage than one would ordinarily suppose, as far as climatic conditions are concerned.

For all these reasons, the fauna of the tundra is meager with respect both to the number of individuals and to the overall biomass (the weight of all organisms living in a given space); the average tundra biomass amounts to only 100 kg per hectare. The chief inhabitants of soil and the mat of moss are springtails (order Collembola), earthworms and ehcytraeids (family Enchytraeidae); in some places one also finds crane-fly larvae (genus *Tipula*). On the surface of the ground there are many ground beetles and spiders. In summer bumblebees and butterflies are conspicuous; though their numbers are not great, they are responsible for most of the work of pollinating plants. Mosses, swamps and lakes are the home not only of springtails and annelids, but also of numerous midge larvae of the genus *Prionocera*. One can see how characteristic of the tundra these animals are from the fact that their average density there is 10,000–20,000 springtails and 150–200 *Prionocera* larvae per square meter—considerably more than in the temperate zone. In the waters are small crustaceans, beetles, and the larvae of various insects, caddis flies and above all gnats and other Diptera. Diptera (midges, flies and their relatives) are altogether the most common insects in the tundra, and they have penetrated further northward than any of the other animals. At the end of June and into July, especially in the southern regions of tundra, the countless mosquitoes and black flies become a real plague.

Fig. 11-1. Some invertebrates characteristic of the tundra: a pierid butterfly (1), a mosquito (2), a springtail (3), and a chironomid larva (4).

Other groups of invertebrates are poorly represented in the tundra. There are hardly any herbivorous insects; the vegetation feeds primarily mammals—rodents and ungulates. Typical examples are the lemmings (*Lemmus* and *Dicrostonyx*). The size of the lemming population fluctuates with a three- to four-year cycle and when the mass migrations occur (see Chapter 10) it can increase almost a thousandfold. In the years when they are most abundant one encounters dozens or hundreds in a hectare; in other years even special search operations fail to discover a single animal. Lemmings are preyed upon by arctic foxes, owls and buzzards—the population density of which depends in turn upon that of this favorite food—as well as by ermines, gyrfalcons, skuas and gulls. Usually the fauna of the tundra also includes some species of field mouse and ground squirrel.

In the spring herds of caribou, with thousands of animals, migrate into the tundra. They have spent the winter in the taiga and forest-tundra and come to graze in the open country until autumn. They are followed by wolves. Certain populations of caribou live permanently on arctic islands such as Spitzbergen, New Siberia and the islands of the northern coast of Canada. In the parts of Eurasia where the reindeer has become domesticated, this wild form of the same genus is now almost completely absent. The musk ox, an inhabitant of the Canadian and Greenland tundra, does not make such long migrations.

The most conspicuous, to the human observer, are the many birds of passage which arrive in the cold zones in spring. During the winter one only occasionally sees a bird—a grouse, a ptarmigan, an arctic owl or a raven. But as soon as the sun's elevation rises, the newcomers appear, first snow buntings, other species of ptarmigan and geese, followed at the end of May and the beginning of June by sandpipers, plovers, various species of duck and goose, Lapland buntings and pipits. In June the tundra is filled with courtship song. Despite all this variety, there are fewer birds here than in the mixed forests of Europe—only a few hundred per square kilometer, on the average. Even the most common species (for example, the Lapland bunting) in the best habitats of the arctic are represented by at most two or three breeding pairs per hectare. In the ice deserts few bird species can be seen, apart from sea birds.

Most of the birds leave the tundra as soon as the young are able to fly. In many genera, the birds not engaged in caring for young depart even earlier. For example, at the end of the courting period male long-tailed and eider ducks and some of the sandpipers leave, as do many other birds that have not found mates. Among the phalaropes it is the females that leave early, since the males are responsible for raising the young. Only the ptarmigans and owls stay until late autumn.

The ocean plays an important role in the life of the tundra birds. Many birds that rely on the sea for food breed on rocky coasts—murres, auks, gulls and cormorants, to name only a few. Their breeding colonies, in Russian called "bird markets" (ptitshyi bazare) are to be found in specially

Fig. 11-2. The large white owl (1) lives in the open tundra and feeds primarily upon lemmings. The caribou (2) spend the winter in the taiga and the forest-tundra; in spring herds of them move into the tundra. The ground squirrel (3) often stores up food for the winter, to eat when it awakens from hibernation

great numbers on the coasts of the North Atlantic. Moreover, most of the ducks and swamp birds of the tundra spend the time when they are not breeding (i.e., nine to eleven months of the year) on the sea or the coasts; unpaired birds or birds not yet sexually mature are to be found there practically throughout the year. As far as the birds of the ice deserts are concerned, all their activities take place, at least part of the time, on the coasts. On the rocks of arctic islands single breeding colonies may include millions of gulls, murres, guillemots, little auks and fulmars. Where there are beaches, the fauna also includes certain mammals. In autumn, for example, walruses move onto the sandbanks. Polar bears migrate to the islands, where the females make caves in which they bear their young. All these animals find their food in the ocean and on ice floes; they play no special role in the communities of the ice desert, since their numbers are remarkably small.

The ecosystems of the tundra are still very young. They did not begin to form until the first part of the Pleistocene, the Ice Age that followed the Tertiary and froze large areas of the northern hemisphere. For invertebrates, the conditions here are less favorable than anywhere else on earth. Almost no forms are restricted to this region (i.e., endemic). Only the most resistant northern genera, which can develop from egg to adult at very low temperatures (and often require several years to do so), can withstand the harsh winters and the long periods during which soil and water are frozen. Even among the mammals only a few groups are endemic to the far north—these include, for example, lemmings, a few species of voles, the arctic fox and the musk ox; these play the leading roles in this ecosystem. Other mammals, such as the arctic hare, wolverine and caribou, live in the taiga as well as the tundra.

By contrast, the bird fauna in the far north is not only very abundant, but there are many species which breed there exclusively. The ability to make long-distance migrations enables the birds, more than other groups of animals, to invade the tundra at least during the time of courtship and brooding. As has already been mentioned, not only birds but also mammals like the caribou and arctic fox move south for the winter. It is not characteristic of these animals to store up food for the winter and to hibernate; where these behavioral traits do exist they are less well developed than in related species living further to the south.

From a zoogeographic viewpoint the tundra zone is rather uniform. Sometimes the communities on the different continents vary in that certain genera or species are replaced by other closely related forms, but many species are to be found all around the Pole. Some of the birds, such as the red-breasted goose and Ross' gull, are quite restricted in range. But there are in general no great impediments to prevent animals that can live in the ice desert at all from settling naturally in various places throughout the habitat.

Probably the most striking aspect of life in the tundra is the abruptness

Fig. 11-3. The most resistant typical animals of the far north: musk ox (1), arctic fox (2), lemming (3) and northern vole (4).

in the spring, before fresh supplies appear.

and magnitude of the seasonal changes. For eight or nine months in winter, life dies out almost completely, except for the rodents and the few ungulates. At the beginning of the summer, vast hordes of dipteran larvae, mainly midges and the like, appear in the waters and the matted vegetation. These are the food of the breeding ducks, phalaropes and sandpipers. Toward the middle of the summer most of the insect larvae metamorphose into adult insects; a large fraction of the birds that fed upon them—all that need not stay to care for their young—then leave the tundra. In the so-called "lemming years," when the population of these rodent swells enormously, the lemmings eat most of their food plants down to the ground; at the same time, the number of predatory mammals and birds that feed upon the lemmings increases. In subsequent years, when there are fewer lemmings, the vegetation is restored and the predators must turn to ducks, ptarmigans and other prey, the populations of which consequently decline. In especially cold years many species of birds—geese, for example—have no offspring at all.

Some animals are profoundly influenced by the fluctuations in climatic conditions, since when these are unfavorable the animals' reproduction cannot keep pace with the losses caused by predatory animals and human hunters. The musk ox is a good example; the populations in Greenland, especially, declined markedly when the humidity changed for a period of years, and the species could be saved only by resettling the animals in other areas. The caribou, too died out almost completely on various arctic islands and had to be replaced by domesticated reindeer in order to maintain the basic food source of the humans living there. There are many such examples, and these events can transform the entire exosystem. The impermanence of ecosystems as a result of seasonal and longer-term changes in climatic conditions and occasional drastic reductions in the rate of reproduction is perhaps the most distinctive characteristic of the tundra and ice desert.

▷
Above: Edge of the König glacier in Spitzbergen, from which pieces break off into the sea. Below: Musk oxen; their thick fur protects these characteristic mammals of the northern cold zones from the extremely low temperatures.

Fig. 11-4. The global extent of tundra (1) and taiga (2).

The coniferous forests south of the tundra, which comprise only a few species of trees, are called "taiga" (a Siberian word that has been taken into the Russian language and adopted by ecologists worldwide). Although its boundaries depend upon the local climate, in general one can say that the taiga extends south to between the 50th and 55th parallel (but in parts of

Taiga

Typical landscapes and distinctive animals of the tundra and taiga:
Upper left: Moorland with a pond and cushions of cotton-grass in the Alaskan interior.
Lower left: Lapland tundra in bloom (June).
Right, top to bottom: Caribou (*Rangifer arcticus*) in Alaska.—Lemming, one of the most common small mammals in the far north.—Taiga in Siberia.

northern Europe only to 60° north latitude). The greatest area is occupied by the taiga of Siberia and Canada.

Here the prevailing climate is sharply seasonal, with long cold winters and short summers, quite hot in places. The "cold pole" of the northern hemisphere is not in the real polar regions, but in the taiga zone, near Oimyakon in the Cherski Mountains of northeastern Siberia, where winter temperatures may be as low as −70°C. There are especially pronounced temperature contrasts in the eastern Siberian taiga and in the Canadian northwest; the climate in the European taiga and in areas near the coast is milder. Strong winds are rare in the taiga; this alleviates to some extent the harshness of the winter.

In general, taiga is restricted to those regions where the temperature is above freezing for only two to four months. For over half a year the in-fertile soil is covered by loose snow, more than a meter deep in places, and under the soil one finds permafrost almost everywhere. In contrast to the forests of the tropical and temperate zones, the taiga comprises few species of tree; in each area there may be up to three dominant species. In northern Europe and America spruce are dominant, while in western Siberia the dominant species are pine, cedar and Siberian larch, and in eastern Siberia another species of larch (*Larix dahurica*). In the mountains and in its southernmost parts the taiga is more varied. For example, in the forests of central Siberia there are many birches, and in Canada one can see the trembling aspen (*Populus tremuloides*). There, when the conifers have been logged off, deciduous trees often take their place.

Usually people imagine the taiga as dense forest with huge trees and an impenetrable undergrowth of shrubs. But this holds for only the southern parts, especially the mountain forests. There little light penetrates, the close-packed conifers; the floor of the forest is covered with green mosses and clumps of beard-moss (actually lichens, of the genus *Usnea* and others)

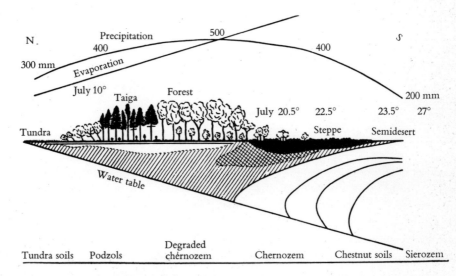

Fig. 11-5. Schematic classification of climate, vegetation and soil in a cross section through eastern Europe from the northwest toward the southeast, as far as the Caspian lowlands.

hang from the branches. In the undergrowth berry bushes of the family Ericaceae manage to survive, but there are few species of grass. In more open clearings and at the edges of the forest there are mountain ash, willow, honeysuckle and wild rose, as well as an abundance of different grasses In contrast. large areas of the northern taiga zone are covered by monotonous expanses of pine, spruce, and larch forest; these trees have an open habit of growth with thin trunks, and are sometimes quite deformed and stunted.

Although the number of animal species living in the taiga is small, it far exceeds that of the tundra. For many of these species the northern edge of their range coincides with the boundary of the forest. Among the ground animals earthworms, small mites, and insects predominate. Numerous insects live in the grass or upon the trees, eating leaves, needles and wood—for example, there are weevils, leaf beetles, and bark beetles. Characteristic of the taiga are the many insects that live only on certain species of tree or even parts of trees (cones, rotting tree stumps, or fallen trees); these include lepidopterans of the families Noctuidae, Geometridae and Bombycidae. The last of these sometimes reproduce at an extra-ordinary rate, so that their larvae consume all the needles of the trees in a wide area and leave only the bare, dead trunks. In summer the taiga is full of bloodsucking mosquitoes and black flies, gnats and horseflies; on hot days they torture the ungulates and render large parts of the forest uninhabitable by men.

Among the mammals, rodents, which feed on plants or their seeds, are represented in considerable numbers; to name but a few, there are redbacked voles and squirrels (of the genera *Sciurus* and *Eutamias*, and the flying squirrels *Pteromys* and *Glaucomys*). In the Canadian taiga lives the northernmost arboreal North American porcupine *Erethizon dorsatum*. The arctic hare (*Lepus timidus*) represents the order Leporidae. Invertebrates living in the soil or its plant cover are the food of the shrew and the mole. Artiodactyls of the taiga include elk and caribou, and in Siberia the musk ox. Characteristic carnivores are the lynx, wolverine, brown bear and—in North America—black bear. In addition to the Siberian sable, famous for its beautiful pelt, there are other marten species in the taiga of both the Old World and the New; in northern Asia, for example, lives the Siberian weasel (*Mustela sibirica*). In the southern taiga one can also encounter mammals more typical of deciduous forests, such as the red deer, the roe deer, and other cervid species. In the waters of the forest there live beaver, muskrat, otter, mink and water rats.

All the birds of the taiga are definite forest species, such as tits, woodpeckers, waxwings, the Siberian jay, the golden-crested wren, the pine grosbeak, crossbills, and hawk, Lapland, Ural, Tengmalm's and pigmy owls. In Eurasia one also finds birds typical of mixed forest: various songbirds, flycatchers, thrushes, nightingales, finches and buntings. Time and again the nutcrackers attract attention by their periodic mass migrations

Fig. 11-6. A large part of the bird population migrates south for the winter. But certain species can withstand the sharp frosts in the taiga, among them the crossbill (1) and the nutcracker (2).

from the taiga to western Europe. The North American taiga forests are the home of songbirds of the genera *Dendroica*, *Seiurus*, *Vermivora* and *Wilsonia*, buntings (*Junco*, *Spizella*, *Passerella*, *Zonotrichia* and *Melospiza*), the wood thrush (*Hylacichla*) and tyrant flycatcher. Grouse (family Tetraonidae) occupy a special place, with a biomass amounting to as much as 50% of the total for all birds; they are the main consumers of flowers, berries, needles and other parts of plant shoots. In the river valleys and by the lakes nest many species of duck, as well as gulls and swamp birds, though there are far fewer of these here than in the tundra.

The biomass of the animals is larger in the taiga than in the tundra, but it is still small—100 to 400 kg per hectare. Altogether, the taiga too can be described as sparsely populated by organisms, for it is rare to encounter an animal there. Even if one spends the whole day wandering through one of the northern woods, one often sees only a few squirrels. The silence of these monotonous woods is broken only now and then by the sounds of tits and songbirds. Even during the courting period in spring, few bird voices can be heard. The density of the bird population, as in the tundra, amounts to only some hundreds per square kilometer, and even in the years when it reproduces most abundantly that of the red-backed vole is measured in dozens per hectare. The open larch woods of northeastern Asia have even smaller animal populations.

The taiga, as a distinct feature of the landscape, has existed since the beginning of the Tertiary. Endemic plants and animals are particularly common in this habitat; groups restricted entirely to the taiga are most often found in eastern Siberia and in northwestern Canada, where one can justifiably refer to a "taiga fauna." Only a few species range all the way around the Pole, in both Old and New Worlds. But the trees of the Eurasian coniferous forests are frequently replaced in America by related forms of the same genus. Once humans invaded the taiga, a metamorphosis began; areas of deciduous woodland, modified forest fringes, and cultivated land came into being. This made it possible for animals typical of the forests of the temperate zone to move further north.

The seasonal change in environmental conditions is also very pronounced in the taiga. In winter, the snow cover plays an especially important role. Invertebrates then enter diapause and remain in this dormant state, with all vital processes more or less suspended, for as long as six to eight months. Many of the birds go south, but many others, in particular the true tree-dwellers, can stay for the winter, unmindful of the sharp frosts. The latter birds include seed-eaters like the pine grosbeak, crossbill and nutcracker, as well as grouse, which feed on buds and needles, and insectivorous birds, for which an adequate food supply is available under bark and in the leaf litter. Many of these birds, the grouse especially, spend the nights buried in the snow. Certain mammals, such as mice and shrews, can remain active under the snow cover during the cold season; others (for example, the bears and some squirrels) pass the winter in a

3

4

Fig. 11-7. Other species wintering in the taiga are the pine grosbeak (3) and grouse (4).

state of dormancy, though this is not a true hibernation. Finally, there are animals like the hares, deer and elk, which normally eat grass and leaves but in winter manage to live on tree bark and the twigs of the trees and shrubs. Musk oxen eat the lichens from trees, while reindeer dig away the snow to find dry grass and moss. Winter stores are laid up not only by mammals, but also by certain groups of birds—for example, the nutcracker, nuthatch, and arctic owl.

The populations of herbivorous animals undergo wide fluctuations. Mass outbreaks of waxwings (*Bombycilla*) have long been observed in certain years, and grouse populations display similar "cycles." Every three or four years red-backed voles appear in unusually large numbers, and arctic hares do so every seven to twelve years. Indirectly, in such times, the populations of predatory mammals and birds that feed on these species also increase, and so do those of the animals which in leaner years serve as a "substitute" food for these predators. The number of waxwings can increase a thousandfold and that of the hares, a hundredfold. At intervals of four to twelve years the trees give an especially good yield, and this is the reason for the fluctuations in numbers of squirrels, crossbills and nutcrackers; when the harvest is not so good, these animals migrate away. Population cycles, then, may be brought about by interactions between plants and animals. When one considers time spans not of years and decades but of centuries, one finds that the populations and ranges of larger, more conspicuous mammalian species like lynx, sable and elk are also subject to considerable fluctuation. Changes in the composition of the taiga forest must be responsible for this. In summary, the ecosystems of the taiga are by nature dynamic and impermanent.

The intervention of man has an ever greater effect upon the fauna of the taiga; these influences include not only hunting but cutting of the forest, exploitation of underground resources, and the construction of water-based power stations and transportation systems. An instructive example of the consequences of unrestricted hunting for fur is offered by the sable. In the 1930's it almost became extinct, and the species was saved only by the introduction of special protective measures. The number of water birds was also severely diminished by the activities of humans. In view of the low rates of reproduction and the instability of these northern ecosystems, such interference can be extremely dangerous. It is necessary to recognize now the environmental changes taking place in the taiga, so that countermeasures can be taken which will preserve these habitats for the future.

"Alpine" is generally used to refer to organisms living in mountains above the tree line (though the more precise word "alpestrine" is preferable in strict scientific usage). There are certain mountain ranges, in central Asia and certain parts of the Andes, where the alpine zone is not easily defined since the climate is so dry that there is no altitude-limited forest. Alpine regions are also characterized by certain geological formations,

Alpine habitats, by H. Janetschek

sharp ridges and peaks that have resulted from glaciation in the Ice Age and by contemporary glaciers, as well as by immature soils with large amounts of mineral debris which are subject to "solifluction" (soil flow, here largely as a result of the seasonal expansion and contraction of soil water). The alpine region begins at lower altitudes, the further away from the equator; the pattern differs in the northern and southern hemispheres (see Fig. 11-8). In the tropics the boundary lies at altitudes above 4000 meters, and in the cold-winter zones it is at the upper limit of the coniferous forests which are usually present. In tropical South America the timberline is much lower than in the subtropics, probably because the root systems of the trees growing in those mountains are too sensitive to low temperature.

The tree line

One may ask, why should there be an altitude limit upon forestation in the mountains, under natural circumstances? The reasons can be explained with reference to the Alps of Europe. Apart from possible limits set by rock walls, scree, stone falls and slopes swept by avalanches, a fundamental factor is the decrease in temperature at higher altitudes. As a consequence of lower temperature, photosynthesis begins later in the season and ceases earlier; at higher and higher altitudes, eventually a point is reached at which the growing season is too short to allow enough photosynthesis for the development of trees. In addition, the water balance of plants suffers especially in late winter, since the leaves are warmed by the sun and lose water which the roots, in still-frozen ground, cannot replace. Exposure to wind much affects water balance of plants, and thereby location of the timberline. The timberline, then, is in part a thermal boundary, but its location is much influenced by other environmental factors. Furthermore, at altitudes above the tree line the symbiosis between fungi and the roots of trees, upon which the trees depend to obtain trace elements and other nutrients essential for the complete maturation of new shoots, no longer operates adequately.

Vegetation levels

The tundra zone above the tree line can be subdivided into different levels. Just above the forest one finds isolated groups of short trees, separated by areas covered by dwarf shrubs (the "dwarf-shrub heath"); at still higher altitudes there are expanses of grasses and sedges of various hardy species, forming a steppelike "grass heath" which merges gradually with the dwarf-shrub level. Near the climatic snow line the plant cover, closed at lower altitudes, becomes more open; as a result of the lower temperature and the increased amount of solifluction, the alpine grasses here are found only in patches. Interspersed between them are cushion plants and areas of exposed rock and debris, sometimes with a loose covering of mosses and lichens. The grass patches are increasingly restricted to spots with a favorable microclimate, where they are protected by rock walls. The large snow-covered basins on these uppermost slopes are filled with rock debris, or at most have the characteristic plant cover of "snow soils," which can withstand being buried under snow for long periods. At the real snow level, which lies above the irregular course of the "orographic" snow line, the ground is covered by perpetual snow wherever the terrain permits. The tongues of the glaciers characteristic of this level can sometimes reach deep into the valleys—in New Zealand almost down to sea level, and near the South and North Poles actually into the sea. At alti-

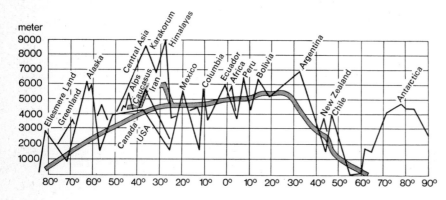

Fig. 11-8. Highly schematic diagram of the altitude limit (shaded band) of flowering plants in different mountain ranges of the earth.

tudes (or latitudes) approaching the orographic, visible snow line the "pioneer grasses" mentioned above are followed by a region in which flowering plants growing in the form of cushions are predominant; this is the "cushion-plant level." Still higher, the cushion plants are increasingly

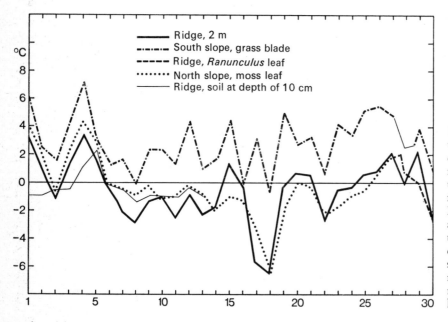

Fig. 11-9. Range of variation of mean temperatures during the daytime on a ridge at the snow level of the Ötztal Alps of Austria in August, 1968 (the Hoher Nebelkogel, altitude 3184 m), showing the differences in microclimate within a small space. The air temperature, measured at 2 m above the ridge, is represented by the heavy line.

replaced by mosses and lichens, and the zone in which these finally predominate is called the "cryptogam level." Even here many plants and animals can find places, especially well-protected spots, where life is possible, but few species of flowering plants are able to establish themselves at this altitude. In a broad sense, one can speak of an upper and a lower snow level; in the former, which includes the cryptogam level, the terrain does not become entirely free of snow every summer. The lower snow level can be considered to include the zone of cushion plants. In the antarctic—the only part of the earth which is still in the Ice Age—there are only cryptogams, except for the northernmost part of the Palmer Land peninsula, which projects well up toward South America and is the habitat of two species of flowering plants. Here, then, the "alpine zone" begins with a cryptogam level at zero altitude.

How can the few flowering plants native to the snow level survive, in the face of permafrost, low air temperatures, and restricted photosynthesis and growth? The highest-altitude flowering plant of the Alps, *Ranunculus glacialis*, in favorable spots has only 70 days per year (after subtraction of the days of snow and ice) in which to grow and lay up reserves, and in less advantageous places the growing period may be 20 days or less. Now, the alpine snow cover depends not only upon the direction and steepness of a slope but also upon the degree to which the snow is shifted by wind, so that in different years the conditions for plant and animal life may vary widely in a given place. It has been observed that *Ranunculus* plants at 3200 meters altitude survived after being covered by snow without interruption for almost three years (about thirty-three months); when the snow finally melted they resumed photosynthetic activity. A constant snow cover lasting forty-five months, however, was fatal.

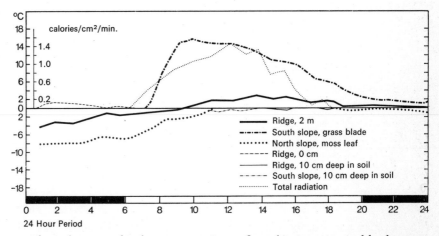

Fig. 11-10. Range of variation of temperature within a single August day at the same place as in Fig. 11-9 (the Hoher Nebelkogel, August 20, 1968). The air temperature at 2 m above the ridge is shown by the heavy line. The total radiation (sunlight plus skylight) measured 5 cm above the ground is also shown. The curve for light intensity would follow the same course as that for total radiation, with 1.2 calories per square centimeter per minute (on the scale insert at left) equivalent to about 100 kilolux.

Plants have evolved a great variety of mechanisms to enable them to live under extreme conditions. The cushion plants growing on south-facing slopes or on ridges swept free of snow by the wind, so that they stay green all winter, are insensitive to wide daily temperature fluctuations. Unlike *Ranunculus glacialis*, the "sun leaves" of which function best with high temperature and light intensity, these cushion plants (for example, the mosslike *Saxifraga bryoides*) carry on photosynthesis at the maximum rate even when the temperature is low and the light is dim. The achievements of lichens are even more remarkable; they are generally more common in cold regions than anywhere else, and represent the furthest out-posts of life on rocks and scree, both at high altitudes and near the poles.

Lichens have been found in the Himalayas at altitudes as high as 7000 meters, and it is certain that they must live even higher. They manage to exist on rocks (nutataks) projecting above the inland ice near the South Pole at latitudes of 86° or more (that is, 400 km from the Pole). They can withstand the most severe cold, wide fluctuations in temperature and long periods of dryness; they obtain the water they need from the vapor in the air. Alpine lichens can assimilate carbon dioxide at temperatures well be-low freezing, some species even at −24°C. Only ten minutes after a deep-frozen lichen has thawed out it can resume full activity. Mosses are also quite resistant; antarctic forms, at least, can stay frozen for three or four years and become fully active again once the temperature has risen. Many microscopic plants (microphytes) living in the soil are found beyond the limits of distribution of vegetation visible to the naked eye; among them are fungi, unicellular green and blue-green algae, actinomycetes and vari-ous groups of bacteria. In the inland mountains of Antarctica, the cryptogam zone is followed by a zone of microphytes, and it is only beyond the far boundary of the microphyte zone that terrestrial life is truly absent. The range of the microphytes depends upon whether occasional warming of the soil melts enough snow to provide them with water; extremely low temperatures in themselves are not necessarily a limiting factor. As another example of life under extreme conditions, it is known that in the eastern Alps blue-green algae form a fine film under the surface of the soil. So far they have been found at altitudes between 3100 and 3300 meters.

The high-altitudes zonation in humid regions often differs markedly from that in arid climates. If enough moisture is available there can be a closed grass cover extending as far as the snow level. In dry zones, on the other hand, the snow disappears almost entirely during the season of drought, even from the highest slopes; for this reason one finds here only open communities of xerophytes, in many cases with externally distin-guishable mechanisms for protection against drying out.

The alpine fauna, which we shall discuss later in more detail, is also greatly dependent upon the available water. In the Spanish Sierra Nevada darkling beetles (family Tenebrionidae) are common; in the lowlands, these beetles are ordinarily inhabitants of steppe and desert. In tropical mountains, where the climatic changes occurring within twenty-four hours are a more pronounced and characteristic feature than the annual climatic variation and the ground is not covered by snow at any season, certain large animals graze all year round on the meager pastures below the snow level. Examples of these in the alpine zones of the Andes are the llama and alpaca, Indian domestic animals descended from the guanaco, and the vicuna, a related species now faced with extinction which ranges up to the glaciers. Because of the "diurnal" rather than "seasonal" climate, there are no hibernating mammals in the Andes.

▷
Examples of the fauna of the arctic and antarctic zones:
Upper left: The goose *Anser brachyrhynchus* with young, Spitzbergen. Only during the short arctic summer can these geese, among the rare herbivores of the arctic, live in the far north. They begin breeding very early. When the long cold season begins again, they migrate to their winter quarters on the North Sea coast.
Below: Characteristic arthropods of the Antarctic continent. In the middle of the picture is the wingless midge *Belgica antarctica*.
Upper right: The "bird rocks" of the northern oceans offer a safe breeding ground to thousands of sea birds, since predators have great difficulty in reaching the helpless young. Under the breeding sites the accumulated excrement of the birds encourages a rich vegetation, which forms the food of herbivorous animals (most of them arthropods).
Bottom: Adelie penguins (Antarctica) migrating across the frozen sea from the breeding colony (the slope in the background) to open water, in search of food.

Colonization of the high mountains

The zonation of the alpine vegetation is also based upon geological factors. Where the rock walls rise too steeply or are too chalky, and where there is exposed igneous rock, which is very resistant to breakdown into soil, plant communities are very sparse even below the potential timberline. In places where such rock formations extend down into the valleys, one can find on low-lying expanses of stone and debris—just as in the avalanche areas—plants and animals ordinarily typical of the alpine zone. However, one cannot really speak of one typical alpine fauna; the differences between the various mountain ranges of the earth are so great that the local alpine flora and fauna can be properly understood only in comparison with those of the adjacent lowlands.

Alpine flora and fauna

As a consequence of their long and varied history of colonization by plants and animals, not only mountain ranges and individual mountains but even subdivisions of mountains display a number of endemic taxa—subspecies, species, genera, or families. It is thus justifiable to refer to a characteristic flora or fauna of the Alps, the Dolomites, the Andes, the Himalayas, or Kilimanjaro. Colonization of an alpine region is initiated by the organisms living at lower levels. Species may invade considerable altitudes while remaining unchanged or developing only nonhereditary modifications, but eventually the highland dwellers undergo genetic modifications which lead to the evolution of subspecies, species and higher taxa. These become established the more readily because of the many possible isolating mechanisms in the alpine habitat. For example, certain hummingbirds (*Oreotrochilus*) are found only at great altitudes in South America. In the New Zealand Alps lives the kea (a parrot, *Nestor notabilis*), which nests in crevices in the rock and ranges through the grass heath level almost up to the glaciers, and there is a monkey, the colobia *Presbytis entellus schistaceus*, that can stay all winter in the high, snow-covered forests of the Himalayas and is sometimes found there at altitudes above 4000 meters.

This basic "indigenous" fauna was joined by other animals, many of which immigrated from distant regions. Some of these retained their original form, while others evolved into new subspecies or species. During the Ice Age, the Alps and other southern European mountains recieved a flood of refugee plants and animals from the far north, some of which survive today as "arctic-alpine" flora and fauna. A number of animal and plant species endemic to certain mountains or groups of mountains evolved with relatively little disturbance during the glacial epochs, in areas they had colonized earlier above the Pleistocence ice and on the massifs at the edges of the Alps which remained free of ice, projecting above the large glaciers that flowed through neighboring valleys toward the foothills. To some extent, the Ice Age facilitated the process of evolution, since it increased the isolation of such populations. The valleys which had been filled with ice during the Pleistocene and the slopes just above them, previously covered by perpetual snow, were colonized by widely distributed forms

◁
Above: Ibex on the "ancient pastures" at the grass-heath level of the Swiss Alps.
Below: The Aletsch glacier (22 km long, 800 m depth perpendicular to the surface), the largest and longest glacier of the Alps; south of Bern, Switzerland.

after the Ice Age was past. But the alpine fauna also includes species of more or less worldwide distribution, most of them microscopic plants and animals with extremely resistant stages in their life cycles which make it easy for them to extend their ranges.

One of the most important cosmopolitan animals from an ecological point of view is man. Human influence reaches far up into the alpine zone; people are responsible for lowering the timberline to the point of total destruction of the forest, and for causing chemical imbalances along favorite climbing routes and near shelter huts. The lower parts, at least, of many alpine habitats have been exposed to the influence of man for millennia. For thousands of years the South American Andean highlands have fed large native populations. The people of the Andes have settlements at altitudes up to the snow line, higher than 5300 meters; it is likely that during the time of the Incas, a civilization which was centered in this area, their population amounted to about 40% of all the human beings inhabiting the southern hemisphere before the advent of the Europeans.

Now there live in the Andean highlands more than ten million people; taken together, all the regions of the earth at altitudes of 3000 meters or more have a population of over twenty-five million. Their numbers will probably increase as the world population grows. The International Biological Program of UNSECO did well to promote research into the ability of humans to adapt to great altitudes. Everyone accustomed to life in the lowlands suffers at high altitudes from a characteristic discomfort syndrome, associated particularly with the cold and the lack of oxygen, and physical symptoms such as a rise in hemoglobin concentration and arterial pressure in the lungs. Highland Indians and other groups that have lived at great heights for generations show evident physiological adaptations to altitude, but we do not yet know the extent to which heredity is involved. There are, of course, limits to such adaptation. For example, the Himalayan mountain people called Sherpas are among the most sought-after guides and bearers for climbing expeditions. But even a Sherpa in top condition has trouble with the low oxygen content and humidity in the air at the highest altitudes. To establish a permanent settlement, or even to stay for a long period, at over 6000 meters is impossible.

The composition and subdivision of animal communities in alpine habitats depends not only upon climatic factors, but even more upon the amount of harvestable vegetation available—that is, upon the "productivity" of the plants. For invertebrates, the low oxygen content mentioned above apparently plays no ecological role. The upper limits of the ranges of breeding birds and mammals depend primarily on the food supply, but certain species are known to be specially adapted to particularly high-altitude conditions. For example, the blood of the vicuna is capable of binding oxygen strongly even when its partial pressure is low. Some migratory birds (for example, the goose *Anser indicus*) fly on a route that passes over the main Himalayan chain.

Man and the alpine habitat

Table 11-1. Altitude distribution of the spiders in the northern Tyrol. The table shows that as altitude increases the diversity of species becomes less and the proportion of small spiders becomes greater. (From estimates by K. Thaler)

| Altitude level | North Tyrol, total | Web-trappers | | | | | Hunters | | | | | |
| | | Small spiders | | | | | | | | | | |
		Theridae	Erigonidae	Linyphiidae	Araneidae	Agelenidae (funnel-web spiders)	Lycosidae (wolf spiders)	Gnapho-sidae	Clubio-nidae	Thomi-sidae (crab spiders)	Salticidae	16 other families
	Number of species (percent)											
Cryptogams	14 (2.6)	—	6 (5)	6 (6)	—	—	2 (5)	—	—	—	—	—
Cushion plants	40 (7.4)	3 (7.5)	15 (13)	10 (10)	—	—	4 (10)	1 (3)	1 (3)	2 (5)	4 (11)	—
Grass heath	100 (19)	6 (15)	28 (24)	25 (25)	3 (8)	1 (5)	8 (20)	7 (23)	5 (14)	6 (15)	9 (26)	2 (4)
Timberline and dwarf-shrub heath	205 (38)	12 (30)	45 (39)	44 (44)	12 (34)	8 (40)	19 (47)	13 (43)	10 (28)	13 (32)	15 (43)	14 (28)
Total number of species	540 (100)	40 (100)	115 (100)	100 (100)	35 (100)	20 (100)	40 (100)	30 (100)	35 (100)	40 (100)	35 (100)	50 (100)

Disregarding the transitional stages, we can divide the alpine fauna into three altitude categories, based on the maximal size of the animals permitted by the productivity of the plants at each level.

1. The large-form level, characterized by expanses of pasture land inhabited by large grazing mammals. In addition to the predatory birds and mammals, some of which feed on these herbivores, the majority of birds breeding in the alpine zone are found at this level. Moreover, the vertebrates are most abundant and varied here, because of the relatively thick, humus-rich topsoil and the many herbaceous plants. "Large" forms, at least in relative terms, are typical for each animal group making up the community—annelids, myriapods, spiders, beetles, butterflies, flies, hymenopterans and grasshoppers. But the total biomass, as well as the number of different species, is much less than in the forested levels. There are no wood-eating insects at all, nor are there birds that breed in holes in trees; but tree-nesting birds can convert to nesting in rocks. Large burrowers like marmots may be present here in considerable numbers. In sum, this is basically a high-steppe, fauna with evident relationships to that found on sunny, open terrain at lower altitudes. Men use these natural meadows as grazing land for domestic animals such as llama, alpaca, yak and sheep; sometimes the system common in the Alps is adopted, whereby the animals are taken to pasture above the tree line and on cleared land during the summer, and kept in the lower-lying settlements for the rest of the year. South of Mount Everest land is cultivated up to 4350 meters, and settlements of shepherds are found in the puna of southern Peru at altitudes as high as 5200 meters.

2. The small-form level, the region of open cushion-plant and cryptogam vegetation below the orographic snow line. Here small mammals and small plant-eating birds, especially songbirds, can still exist. Vertebrates subsisting upon meat, refuse and carrion appear only as transients, passing through in search of food. Since ground-dwelling mammals cannot dig burrows in this region, they use crevices in the scree and rocks instead. The snow vole *Microtus nivalis* can be found in the Alps at heights above 4300 meters, and in the Andes and Himalaya chinchillas and hares, respectively, go as high as 6000 meters. The invertebrates are represented by many sorts of "small forms," living chiefly in the uppermost layer of the soil, the adjacent strata of the vegetation, and suitable cracks in rocks. The upper parts of the plants are used by flying insects as feeding stations and places for reproduction. The more demanding soil animals are absent from this level, for the soil lacks a humus horizon, is shallow and full of rock debris, and contains very little dead organic matter. Practically the only animals that can live under such conditions are mites, springtails, soil midges and small spiders.

Often this raw soil has a stony, pavementlike surface formed by wind erosion, under which many animals find dwelling and feeding places. Decomposition of the organic remains in the soil is slow, because of the low

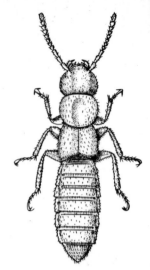

Fig. 11-11. Wingless soil beetle (*Chionostiba janetscheki*) of the snow level in the Dauphine region of the western Alps. Actual size 2.8 mm.

temperature. Occasionally large mammals enter this level, while changing territory or during their seasonal migrations. Many migratory insects can fly over mountain chains as high as the Alps, and there are a respectable number of birds which regularly migrate even over the high passes of the Himalayas. Some of these wanderers, of course, come to grief, and it is not at all uncommon to find their bodies on glaciers and fields of perpetual snow.

3. The microform level, the highest outpost of terrestrial life. At first sight the landscape here seems utterly lifeless, since the rare, and for the most part microscopically small, plants and animals live hidden under the surface of the soil. In the alpine regions of the antarctic interior, where as a result of low humidity or the action of the wind there is no snow, there are microphytes and a fauna consisting of only a few primitive animals, rotifers (Bdelloidea) and perhaps tardigrades and nematodes. All of these can hold out under the most arduous conditions by entering a state of anabiosis, in which all vital processes are almost completely suspended. Apart from the above animals there appear occasional springtails and a few species of mite, which can find sufficient food in the sparse microvegetation. It may well be that the situation is similar in other alpine cold deserts —for example, above the cryptogam level in the Himalayas, in parts of the Andes, and in the land being invaded by glaciers in the Alps. In mountains where the direction of air movement is not constantly downward the winds blowing uphill bring with them all sorts of organic substances such as the remains of plants, pollen and small arthropods, especially flying insects, and thus have a certain fertilizing effect. This becomes obvious when one looks at the surfaces of glaciers and fields of permanent snow, as any mountain climber knows; the many dead or dormant flying insects which accumulate there, preserved by the cold for long periods, constitute the chief element in the so-called "dead snow fauna." All life in this region is concentrated in those layers of the raw soil, under the hard, stony surface, where the temperature occasionally rises high enough to melt the ice in the soil and make water available. If there is no ice or influx of water from a neighboring snow field, or if the soil temperatures never rise above zero, there can be no life in the soil.

There is a fourth category, not based on size or altitude, which includes the interesting fauna of the glaciers and perpetual snow above the orographic snow line. Winds blowing up the mountain and, to an even greater extent, those blowing from the peaks deposit on these surfaces so-called "glacier dust," consisting of a mixture of inorganic and organic matter including the above-mentioned dead snow fauna. Here certain "snow algae" can live; the best-known of these is the chlorophyacean alga *Chlamydomonas nivalis*, which causes the phenomenon of "red snow," or "water melon snow." It occurs not only in the high mountains, but in polar regions as well. The temperature of these habitats is around zero in the summer months, so that the pools formed on the glaciers by local melting freeze over at night and in bad weather. The fauna here includes

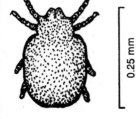

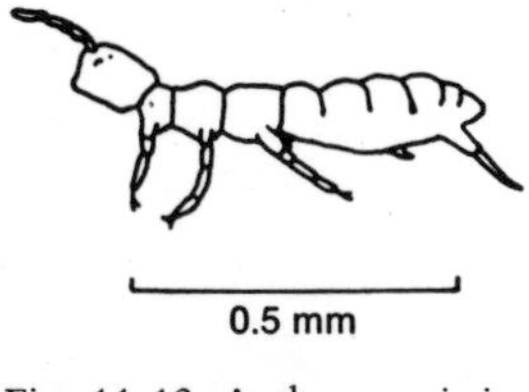

0.25 mm

Fig. 11-12. The arthropod best able to withstand the extreme alpine conditions of the interior of Antarctica is this minute orange-reddish mite (Prostigmata: *Nanorchestres antarcticus*).

0.5 mm

Fig. 11-13. A characteristic springtail of the microform level in alpine Antarctica, transparent as glass when alive: *Antarcticinella monoculata.*

an unknown number of protozoans, such as ciliates and heliozoans, as well as porcupinelike rotifers (Bdelloidea), tardigrades, springtails and in some alpine regions so-called "glacier worms." Springtails worthy of special mention are the famous *Isotoma saltans* of the Alps and the similar glacier springtail I discovered in the Himalayas, *Isotoma mazda*.

The "glacier worms" are either relatives of the earthworm belonging to the family Enchytraeidae, or midge larvae (family Chironomidae). The glaciers on the west coast of America are inhabited by the annelid *Mesenchytraeus solifugus*, which appears on the surface only in late afternoon and vanishes again by morning. Midge larvae have been found chiefly on the glaciers of New Zealand; they also occur in other alpine regions, but there—in contrast to the situation in New Zealand—they are usually in glacier pools.

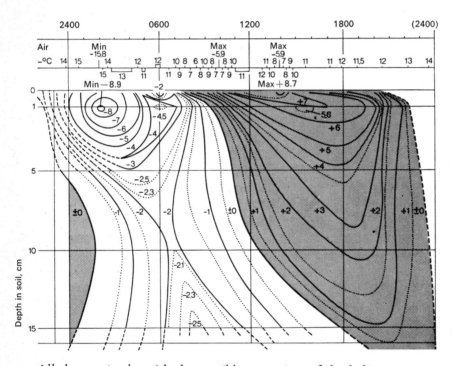

Fig. 11-14. Progression of soil and air temperature during a "midsummer" day, in a place without recognizable vegetation at the microform level of the antarctic mountains (altitude 1830 m), where a few species of springtail and mite still manage to live. While the air temperature oscillates between about −16° and −6°C, never going above zero, the soil temperature near the surface varies from about −9° to +9°C (January 12, 1962; 77° 10′ S, 160° 43′ 26″ E).

All these animals, with the possible exception of the heliozoans, are intensely colored: the rotifers are reddish-yellow, the ciliates and tardigrades dark brown to violet, one springtail of the Swiss Alps (*Onychiurus alborufescens*) yellow to rust-red, and the remaining species black. The "black snow" of the high Alps is produced by *Isotoma*, spread out like soot over wide expanses of perpetual snow. In general it is assumed that these intense colors serve to increase the absorption of sunlight, an important source of heat in view of the low air temperatures. Most likely, though, they act primarily to protect the animals against the intense short-wavelength radiation in the high mountains.

Fig. 11-15. A glacier tardigrade (*Hypsibius klebelsbergi*) found in "glacier dust" in the Ötztal Alps of Austria at 2450 m. Actual size about 380 μm, coloration black-brown.

Adaptations to high altitudes

Isotoma, as the predominant member of the glacial fauna, has been the subject of a series of investigations, and a good deal is known about it. It tends to keep to the "dry" system of pores in ice and perpetual snow, at depths as great as 30 cm and temperatures between 0° and −4°C. Higher temperatures are less well tolerated, and it actively avoids temperatures of 12°C or higher. But when it comes to the surface in summer, at midday when the sun is shining, to forage for food (chiefly the pollen of conifers) it temporarily enters environmental temperatures above 0°C. This springtail is also active in winter, when it lives in the layer between the surface of the glacier and the snow cover, at temperatures between −5° and −3°C. Probably it is the melted snow trickling down to this layer in spring that signals the time to leave winter quarters. In view of the low temperature, the embryological development of *Isotoma* is relatively short; when raised at temperatures between 4° and 8°C, it took 65 days to hatch from the egg. Young animals can survive the winter. In its metabolism, as judged by oxygen consumption, this springtail is also a prime example of adaptation to an extreme habitat.

Poikilothermic mountain animals display another striking adaptation, viviparity. Well-known examples of this are the viper *Vipera berus* and the lizard *Lacerta vivipara*, and the alpine salamander; the latter is limited to quite moist places. Finally, there are viviparous flies in the alpine habitat, probably a great number of them. The gestation period is often extended, because of the low temperature and the general slowing of vital processes. At the upper edge of its range, the alpine salamander sometimes has a gestation time of over three years, thus exceeding even the elephant.

Another mechanism enabling species to survive in the cold high-altitude climate is rapid growth. Small animals grow at a relatively greater rate, and thus reproduce sooner, than large ones; as a result, they are more certain of reaching in time a stage capable of surviving the winter. This is clearly demonstrated by the mites of the antarctic. The southern boun-

Table 11-2. Altitude distribution of lepidopterans in the northern Tyrol. The table shows that the diversity of species decreases with increased altitude, and the proportion of small forms increases. The altitude categories refer to the caterpillar stage.

Altitude level	Macrolepidoptera No. of species	%	Microlepidoptera* No. of species	%
Cryptogam level	10	0.9	30	2
Cushion-plant level	25	2.2	70	5
Grass-heath level	50	4.5	110	8
Dward-shrub level	90	8.0	200	14
Forest level	315*	28.0*	350	25
Valley	630*	56.4*	640	46
Total	1120 =	100	ca. 1400 =	100

* Estimates (from data of K. Burmann)

daries of the ranges of the species living there vary as a function of body size, the smallest species being found nearest the South Pole. Small-bodied animals can better endure the shortening of the "warm.' season ,in which they are capable of active life. The stage of development that must be reached before the onset of winter varies; in insects, for example, it may be the egg, a larval stage, the pupa, or the imago. Species that manage to live through several winters extend their period of feeding and growth, and these may be relatively large members of a community ordinarily composed mainly of small forms. For example, the jumping bristletails (order Thysanura, family Machilidae) continue to molt and thus to grow throughout their lives; the fact that alpine species like *Machilis fuscistylis*, of the eastern Alps, can be distinctly larger than their lowland relatives is probably associated with this ability. Numerous largish holometabolous insects living at high altitudes have been shown to pass several winters in the larval stage. Accordingly, it is only at intervals of a few years that one can find considerable numbers of the adult beetles or butterflies.

A typical characteristic of many alpine animals is the daily rhythm of their activity. When one turns over stones in the alpine meadows at midday one often finds hardly any insects at all, whereas the same places are swarming with life in the cooler mornings and evenings. Many flying insects withdraw to shelters during the warm hours of the day, swarming again briefly in the late afternoon before they settle down for the night. The number of night-active species is a good deal smaller, but even at altitudes of 3000 (in the Alps) or 4000 (Himalayas) meters it has been shown that quite a few insects come to lights at night, some of them even in snowstorms. In general, though, the "nocturnal" animals of the high mountains are probably active mainly at twilight and in the early hours of the night, while the heat stored in their surroundings is still adequate.

As altitude increases, flying animals make less and less use of this ability, and at great heights flight is used only to enable the two sexes to find one another quickly. Here spiders, primitive insects and other wingless groups predominate; in insect orders composed chiefly of normally winged animals, like the Coleoptera, Lepidoptera, Diptera and Orthoptera, the proportion of flightless species is greater in the mountains. Even within a single species the populations at high altitudes can have regressed wings. But this phenomenon is not so pronounced in alpine habitats as on islands exposed to strong, steady winds.

Moreover, as altitude increases the number of plant species and the supply of animal refuse declines; hence it is understandable that the variety of animals specializing in certain foods is less. This holds also for parasites, which find a much smaller selection of transmitters, hosts and intermediate hosts at higher altitudes. Nevertheless, even those lepidopteran caterpillars found at the greatest heights are infested by braconid and chalcidoid wasps, and the highest-altitude mammals are the hosts of parasitic protozoans, worms and mites. Of interest for zoogeography is the fact that par-

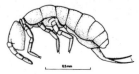

Fig. 11-16. The Himalaya glacier springtail *Isotoma mazda*, with deep black pigmentation.

Fig. 11-17. Jumping bristletail (*Machilis fuscistylis*) of the rock faces and ridges at the cryptogam level of the eastern Alps. Its coloration and patterning camouflage the animal superbly when it is on stone or lichens.

thenogenesis (reproduction by females alone) can appear in invertebrates at certain altitudes. Parthenogenesis facilitates an increase in the basic number of chromosomes (polyploidy). For example, the moth *Solenobia triquetrella* is found as a bisexual species in the region of peaks which towered above the ice during the Würm glaciation. A parthenogenetic form, equipped with two sets of chromosomes, inhabits the lower mountains and foothills, from which the ice first disappeared. The most recent form, with four sets of chromosomes, lives in the valleys, the last area to become free of ice.

Apart from the rain that falls during the season when no snow lies on the ground, it is the cover of snow which determines the local water supply and hence the nature of the community at any altitude. Animal species requiring particularly large quantities of moisture gather at the melting edges of the snow blanket; in dry-summer mountains like the Spanish Sierra Nevada, particularly, they are quite conspicuous both there and in moist depressions. Land isopods for which the "high steppes" are otherwise too dry can be found in European mountains at the upper boundary of the grass-heath level. In "wet" mountains above the high steppe in the snow level, where in general water is abundantly provided by the melting snow, the proportion of hygrophilous species is also large.

Are there truly alpine animals?

One often hears the opinion that there are characteristic alpine animals, specially adapted to the conditions at great altitudes by virtue of their morphology, physiology and behavior. Opposed to this view is the fact that severe cold and dryness, with all their effects upon thermal and water relations of organisms and upon the supply of food, are not limited to alpine habitats; for example, all the phenomena associated with the high mountains are also found in the polar lowlands. Fundamentally, then, one can consider as exclusive adaptations to high altitudes only those properties which enable animals to cope with low air pressure and oxygen content, and plants to survive despite low concentrations of carbon dioxide. All the other adaptations discussed—the increase in size of warm-blooded animals, the regression of appendages, the greater thickness of pelt or plumage—are appropriate to cold climates in general.

In some mountain ranges of the northern hemisphere, various species of mammal and bird change color in the winter. Some of them, such as the alpine hare, weasel and ptarmigan, become almost completely white. Strictly speaking, these are not mountain animals but species of the far north; there seasonal adoption of a white coat is more common, and some animals even stay white the year round. In the Ice Age such species were distributed widely in Europe. When the ice disappeared they withdrew, some to the north and some into the mountains. Many gallinaceous birds of the eastern European and Asian mountains never turn white, nor do the piping hares (or pikas, genus *Ochotona*), the many alpine rodents and most of the ruminants of mountain regions. The chamois, in fact, is considerably darker in winter than in summer. In general, the horned animals living at great heights—the ibex, wild sheep, tahr and others which nowadays are regarded as typical of the mountains—have close relatives in the nearby lowlands. One can even suppose that some of them have only gradually been crowded out into these mountain retreats. There is a high-altitude artiodactyl closely related to the ibex, the Rocky Mountain goat (*Oreamnos americanus*), which stays white all year, but in this case again the inference of polar origin seems justified.

Contrary to what is commonly supposed, there is no animal that can be unmistakeably described as an "alpine form" on the basis of external appearance. There is no alpine structural type; all the animals living at great heights can be assigned to the general morphological and "life-form-type" categories. From specially cold-adapted species like *Isotoma* to species that have withdrawn to the mountains only because they cannot survive under more intense competition, the alpine fauna comprises a wide range of life-forms. Many could also exist elsewhere, if they were not prevented from extending their range by various barriers or the pressure of competition. The diverse patterns of distribution of the alpine animals and plants are shaped not only by contemporary environmental conditions; rather, they reflect in a variety of ways the conditions of the past, the influence of the Pleistocene Ice Age being especially clearly evident. A large number of animal species live both on the flat land and on the lower mountain slopes, gradually disappearing at higher and higher altitudes.

This sort of distribution is particularly prevalent among birds and mammals, which because they are warm-blooded have a sort of "internal climate" of their own, maintained under a great variety of external conditions as long as the animal can obtain enough to eat. Birds are restricted to a certain extent by the requirements of breeding and raising the young. Moreover, flapping flight is more difficult at high altitudes because of the lower air pressure. All land vertebrates, and probably all the alpine invertebrates, compensate for the low oxygen concentration by making better use of the oxygen that is available. In higher vertebrates the respiratory surface of the lungs is increased, as is the number of red blood cells and their affinity for oxygen, the activity of the heart is intensified, and the vessels supplying the lungs expand. The best-known phenomenon is the enlargement of the right ventricle, which functions to force blood into the lungs. But even this is not exclusively characteristic of mountain animals; heart enlargement is also found in inhabitants of other cold regions, in this case for the sake of heat regulation.

Finally, a few remarks about the significance of the high mountains to the overall balance of nature and thus to humanity are in order. This can best be expressed in the words of the 1971 UNESCO report on the International Research Program "Man and Biosphere," which we give here in condensed form.

A considerable fraction of the water in rivers and reservoirs of ground water, the report says, comes from mountainous regions. Many substances are carried into the lowlands and eventually to the sea. Climate, sunlight, good air and the comparative lack of pollution in the mountains combine to enhance the health and well-being of the people there. In many respects the mountains can be thought of as "islands on land," which are extremely vulnerable to human interference. Mountain forests play a large role in maintaining the water supply and the climatic conditions in the plains below them.

Deforestation, poor forest management, unwise cultivation, over-grazing, and the construction of mines and transportation routes often result in soil erosion, the exposure of rock faces, and eventually the creation of stony deserts. Catastrophic flooding, landslides, the drying up of rivers and springs, the disappearance of fauna and flora—all these are typical signs of the improper use of meadow, forest, and water ecosystems in the mountains. The damage so caused is felt not only in the mountains themselves, but far away from them, in the valleys, the plains, and down to the mouths of the rivers.

12   The Temperate-Zone Forest

Between the tropical-subtropical forest region and the treeless northern tundra there is a broad zone of temperate climate. Here, wherever there is sufficient precipitation, grow forests with the species composition dependent upon the local climate and soil conditions. Since the land masses tend to lie mostly in the northern hemisphere, the forests here play a much greater role than in the southern temperate zones.

By G. Sperber

With increasing distance from the equator, and with increasing altitude in the mountains, the growing season becomes shorter. As a result, the natural forest communities in the temperate and northern zones, as in the mountains, have a simpler structure and comprise a smaller number of species than in the tropics. An additional factor is the temperature; the lower the temperatures, for a given availability of food and water, the smaller the total number of organisms.

The natural forest regions

The belt of temperate rainforest nearest the equator is distinguished by an almost tropical character. Adjacent to this in maritime climates is the sclerophyll region, where because of the prevailing lack of precipitation there are fewer plants and animals. In cooler and continental climates winter-deciduous forests occur instead of sclerophyll communities; these forests also are poorer in species than the warm-temperate forest and the tropical rainforest. The paucity of plants and animals in the taiga, the broad belt of forest circling the northern part of the hemisphere, has been described in Chapter 11. Woodland ends altogether wherever, in the far north or on the higher mountain slopes, the growing season amounts to fewer than sixty days per year.

The rainforests of the warm-temperate zone still show a strong similarity to tropical forests (see Chapter 16), insofar as man has not destroyed or altered the original vegetation. The combination of warm summers, mild winters with rare frost, and abundant rainfall throughout the year makes possible the development of luxuriant, multilayered forests. The dense undergrowth of tree ferns, low palms and species of bamboo, together with the woody lianas and the epithytic ferns on the trees, enhance

Temperate rainforest

the similarity to a tropical jungle. But in this zone we find among the evergreen trees deciduous species, which lose their leaves in winter.

That is the natural state; but these forests have been much affected by human activities, in clearing the trees excessively and converting woodland to crop and pasture land. Quite large remnants of the temperate rainforest are still to be found in southern Chile. There the dominant tree species are the southern beech genus *Nothofagus*, the equivalent of the *Fagus* species of the northern hemisphere. In addition there are certain remarkable coniferous species, such as the well-known *Fitzroya patagonica* and the gymnosperms of the family Araucariaceae. The temperate rainforests of New Zealand are also dominated by *Nothofagus*.

In eastern Asia, as a result of thousands of years of civilization, only small remnants of the original forest survive. The bamboo-covered areas in central China indicate the former presence of such forests. In southern Japan one can still find small stands of evergreen species of oak, the camphor tree (*Cinnamomum camphora*), magnolias, and various coniferous species such as *Pinus thunbergii* and *Crytomeria japonica*.

Among the warm-temperate forests in the southeastern part of North America are the oak (*Quercus* sp.) and magnolia (*Magnolia grandiflora*) woodlands. On poor soil the southern yellow pine (*Pinus palustris*), widely used for parquet floors, once formed vast forests. In the backwaters of the rivers there used to be thriving tree communities, typically dominated by the bald cypress (*Taxodium distichum*). Now most of the virgin forests of this region have been cleared, and in the woods that have grown up to replace them (the secondary forests) the southern pines have become the dominant species.

Sclerophyll forests

In the warm-temperate maritime climates, wherever dry hot summers alternate with mild wet winters, there have developed sclerophyll woodlands. The characteristic plants here are evergreen trees and shrubs with small, leathery leaves; beneath the short to moderately tall trees is a dense undergrowth and a ground flora including many herbs and plants growing from bulbs and corms. Such woodlnands are typical of the Mediterranean region, the southwestern corner of Cape Province, the coastal mountains of California, the mountains of central Chile between 1000 and 2000 m, and southwestern and southeastern Australia.

In the Mediterranean countries the sclerophyll zone is called "maquis." Here species of oak occupy a special place, particularly the evergreen hollyoak (*Quercus ilex*), the scarlet oak (*Quercus coccifera*), and the economically important cork-oak (*Quercus suber*). Of the many coniferous species we shall mention here only the Aleppo pine (*Pinus halepensis*), the stonepine (*Pinus pinea*), and the Italian cypress (*Cupressus sempervirens*). During the Greco-Roman civilization the forests of the Mediterranean region were already being destroyed by clearing for cultivation, overexploitation of the timber, and the grazing of goats; introduced (intentionally or not) plant species changed the face of the landscape. For example, men planted olive and fig trees far outside their natural range, started orchards of orange and lemon, and more recently introduced agaves and cactuses which then began to grow wild.

At altitudes above 400 m in some parts of the Metiderranean region, the maquis gives way to winter-deciduous forests. These differ from the more northern winter-deciduous forest (see below), in the prevalence of heat-loving species such as the turkey oak (*Quercus cerris*), *Quercus pubescens*, *Ostrya carpinifolia*, and the flowering ash (*Fraxinus ornus*)—trees which are found in the deciduous forests north of the Alps only in a few places where the local climate is especially favorable. Now, however, the edible chestnut *Castanea vesca*, encouraged by the people in the area, dominates the region, to the disadvantage of the other species.

The California chaparral is very like the maquis of the Mediterranean, and it too has been severely altered by man. Here, again, evergreen oaks are typical, as are deciduous oaks, other species of chestnut, cypresses and pines (for example, *Pinus radiata*). But the sclerophyll woodlands of Australia differ from these; they are characterized by species of eucalyptus, usually in stands of tall trees of a single species. In addition there are acacias and the largely endemic *Casuarina* (the only genus in the family Casuarinaceae).

Other parts of the temperate zone in the northern hemisphere have a climate such that the precipitation is relatively uniformly distributed over the year and is relatively abundant (700 to 1500 mm annually), with the growing season interrupted by a winter rest period lasting four to six months. The winters are not particularly cold; in the coldest month the average temperature falls no lower than $-5°C$. Nor is the summer heat very great; the average temperature barely exceeds $20°C$ in the hottest month. Originally the natural forest communities here were dominated by winter-deciduous trees and conifers were rare; the present wide distribution of evergreens is the result of human intervention.

Deciduous forests

The winter-deciduous forests comprise considerably fewer species than those of warmer climates, and the subdivision into strata is not so pronounced. Usually the tree stratum forms a single uniform canopy; two tree strata may occur however, and then they result from the mixture of light-requiring and smaller shade-tolerant trees. Because of the alternation between the dense foliage of summer and the bareness of winter, the ground flora blooms and bears fruit only at certain times of year; many herbaceous plants flower before the leaves of the trees expand. These ceciduous forests grow primarily on brownearth soils (see Chapter 14) which are poor in minerals if they are on a sandy substrate, through which water percolates rapidly, and can be of the pseudogley type (alternately wet and dry) if the subsoil is less permeable and occasionally allows stagnant water to accumulate. Ordinarily wet (gley) soils are to be found in the meadows along the valleys of rivers and brooks.

The litter of leaves, branches and other plant materials—about two to ten metric tons per hectare annually—is broken down more slowly than in the tropical and subtropical forests. In dense forests of beech and oak the dry weight of fresh and decomposing litter plus the superficial humus layer can amount to between ten and twenty tons per hectare. Earthworms play a decisive role in the decomposition of these substances.

The type and state of development of the ground flora, which differs from one wooded area to another, is of crucial importance to the large herbivores. In natural forest communities, however, there are relatively few higher animals. For example, in a 120-year-old stand of trees it was found that the biomass of vertebrates living above ground was only 8.5 kg per hectare, of which birds accounted for 1.3 kg, large mammals 2.2 kg, and small mammals 5 kg. The soil fauna, on the other hand, amounted to 1000 kg per hectare, the largest fraction being contributed by the different species of earthworm.

Three extensive regions of the northern hemisphere were orginally covered with winter-deciduous forest; eastern Asia, most of Europe, and eastern North America. By now the advanced civilizations of the world have brought about the destruction of more than two-thirds of this forest; only a few rapidly vanishing patches of real virgin forest remain.

Loss of species in the Ice Age

In the winter-deciduous forests of eastern Asia and North America there grow (or grew) the same genera of trees and shrubs as in Europe, but the European flora has notably fewer species. Geological history offers an explanation of the close relationship between the plants in the Old and New Worlds. In the Tertiary there was a broad land bridge between Eurasia and North America, which made it possible for a quite uniform flora to evolve. At that time almost all the plant genera now native to North America and eastern Asia also thrive in Europe, including the giant sequoia, bald cypress, magnolia and many others.

The subsequent Ice Age was a catastrophe for the European flora. Mountain chains extending between the eastern and western oceans prevented the plants from escaping the ice as it spread southward, and kept the various species from expanding their range again in the periods between the glacial epochs. As a result, most of the tree and shrub species were driven back to the foot of the mountain glaciers or to the seashore and there perished. Most of the "refugees" that were saved, apart from a few that were preserved on the Iberian Peninsula, found shelter in the Balkans; some of these, like the Serbian spruce (*Picea omorica*) and horse-chestnut (*Aesculus hippocastanum*), which has again become widespread through being planted as a tree in parks, survive there even today.

By contrast, the north-south orientation of the mountains in North America enabled the plants to withdraw from the encroaching mass of ice. The winter-deciduous forests of eastern Asia remained free of ice during the Pleistocene and for this reason are characterized by an abundance of species. The degree to which the Ice Age affected the flora of Europe can be seen from the fact that North America has over 800 species of trees and central Europe, only 51. In North America, for example, there are around 70 species of oak and 35 of pine, whereas in Europe north of the Alps there are only three native forms.

The deciduous forest regions in Europe can be considered as having three subdivisions. In the east the English or pedunculate oak predominates; it may be associated on poorer soils with pine, silver birch, aspen and alder and in more fertile places with ash, small-leaved linden, English elm, Norway maple, and hornbeam.

The nearness of the Atlantic affects the western part of the European deciduous forests, including Great Britain and western France. In the natural state—before human intervention began—the predominant plants were English and durmast oaks, mixed with hornbeam, birch and other deciduous trees.

Toward the north the proportion of conifers increases until finally, in the broad belt of taiga, they become the dominant trees. Further east and southeast these deciduous forests gradually give way to savanna and steppe.

Deciduous forests in Europe

Fig. 12-1. Beech forest: The greater part of the forests originally covering central Europe was occupied by communities of beeches. Shade tolerance and ecological adaptability made them extraordinarily good competitors against other species of tree, so that they formed pure stands over a broad area. The new growth filling openings in the stand was also mostly beeches.

The central subdivision, between these eastern and western parts, is by far the largest; it includes essentially all of central Europe. The climate here is temperate in every respect, providing the best possible conditions for growth of the copper beech. In comparison with other tree species, the copper beech is distinguished by high tolerance of shade, growth in height which is maintained for a long time, and little susceptibility to pests; because of this and its adaptability it managed to prevail against its competitors. The original forests of central Europe in many cases were pure beech forests. Not until the forests had been exploited by man for centuries were other tree species more dependent upon light, such as oak, linden and hornbeam, able to become widespread.

▷

Sub-alpine larch-spruce forest near the timberline in the Taurbachalm region of the Alps.

Forests in river valleys

◁

Some examples of the
European mixed-forest
fauna:
Upper left: Courting
wood grouse in its moun-
tain territory.
Upper right: Herd of red
deer on a mountain
meadow.
Lower left: Wild boar
standing in front of young
spruce trees.
Lower right: Badger in the
autumn woods.

Bog forests

Deciduous forests of eastern North America

Eastern Asian decid-uous forests

Montane forests of the cool-temperate zone

Montane mixed forest in Europe

In very damp habitats the copper beech is less prevalent; here the woodlands are characteristic of wet meadows. These woods near rivers are composed primarily of different species of willow, together with black and white poplars; all of these are adapted to such habitats in that they seed readily and are insensitive to flooding and mechanical injury. Further away from the river bed, where flooding is less common, the composition of the woods is different, with ash, elm, the common maple, hornbeam and English oak; beneath these grows a rich shrub layer comprising privet, cornelian cherry, dogwood, spindle-tree, and other species. A dense layer of herbs and grasses covers the ground. Twining plants such as travellers' joy and honeysuckle give these forests an appearance of tropical luxuriance. The upper reaches of the streams, finally, are bordered by narrow ashwoods in which alders are mingled.

In regions where the water table is high and fairly constant, the soil is fertile, and there is sufficient oxygen, one encounters bog forests, dominated by alder. On acid soils with water poor in oxygen it is joined by the downy birch, and in eastern central Europe by the pine as well. The soil flora of these forests begins to show characteristics of the bog; peat mosses, cotton-grasses and dwarf shrubs such as the crowberry. As dampness and oxygen content increase, the undecomposed organic mass accumulates, eventually forming true bogs.

The parts of Canada and the USA east of the prairie (see Chapter 14) were originally almost entirely covered by winter-deciduous forest. More than three-quarters of this woodland was destroyed by the clearing operations of white immigrants; only scattered remnants (0.1% of the former area) still display something of the glory of the virgin forest. The most extensive stand of virgin forest has been preserved in Great Smoky Mountain National Park.

In eastern Asia, too—in northeastern China, Manchuria, the Amur region, Korea and parts of central and northern Japan—broad areas were originally covered by deciduous forest. In China almost all of this forest has been cleared for cultivation. The bits that remain, particularly in mountains difficult of access, bear witness to the former multitude of tree species. The tree specialist Ernest Henry Wilson in 1899-1911 discovered no less than 400 new species of woody plants in the mountains between the Yangtze Kiang and the Hwang Ho.

As temperature decreases and the growing season becomes shorter in the temperate zones, the conifers become ever more prevalent. At the northern limit of the deciduous forests, espeially at fairly high altitudes, there appears a mixed forest of deciduous and evergreen trees which eventually gives way to pure coniferous forest. Here we shall describe in detail only the mixed-forest region of the European mountains and the splendid coniferous-forest region of western North America.

The European beechwoods become mixed with silver fir at altitudes of about 600 meters and more (in cool regions the change becomes ap-

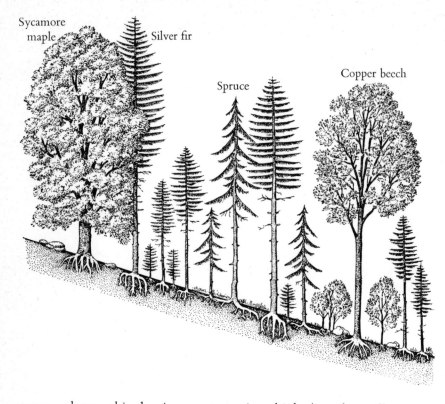

Sycamore maple · Silver fir · Spruce · Copper beech

Fig. 12-2. Montane mixed forest: At altitudes above 600 m in the central European sub-alpine mountains and on the fringes of the Alps, the beechwoods include silver fir, and at higher altitudes they are mingled with spruce. Montane mixed forests with trees of different ages in a small area are among the most durable and highest-yield types in our latitudes. But in most such forests the original combination of species and the admixture of younger trees are lost because of mistaken forestry practices and excessive grazing by deer.

parent at lower altitudes, in warmer regions higher), and at still greater heights the spruce also grows. This montane mixed forest is economically the most productive in Europe. At altitudes above 1100 meters beech and fir disappear; here are pure stands of spruce, most of them extending to the natural timberline. In the interior of the Alps where there is little precipitation, both beech and fir are absent; the predominant species here are pine, larch and stone-pine.

Even today, the forests of giant redwoods in the coastal regions of southwestern Oregon and in northwestern California are the most impressive of all woodlands. *Sequoia sempervirens* can grow over 100 m tall. To the north of the sequoia forests lie large forests of western hemlock (*Tsuga heterophylla*) and *Thuja plicata*, associated with Douglas fir (*Pseudotsuga menziesii*). The cooler slopes of the southern and central Rocky Mountains are occupied by dry coniferous forests comprising species of *Pinus* and *Pseudotsuga*. At altitudes between 1400 and 2500 meters in the southwestern Sierra Nevada one again encounters forests of giant trees; here they belong to the species *Sequoiadendron giganteum*.

In the temperate zones of Eurasia and North America, the faunas show numerous points of correspondence, which can be ascribed to their common origin in geological time. These common features are especially pronounced in the very similar habitats of the northern temperate coniferous forests. As described above, the Tertiary land bridge between Eurasia and North America permitted the development of a relatively uniform

Montane coniferous forest in western North America

Animals of the temperate forest

flora. Toward the end of the Tertiary this bridge sank into the sea; but in the subsequent Pleistocene the ice tied up huge amounts of water, lowering the sea level enough to reconnect Alaska with Siberia. It was over this new bridge that most of the species passed which are now found in both Eurasia and North America. Among them are the ancestral forms of the large herbivores such as red deer, elk, bison and wild sheep, as well as predatory mammals like the brown bear, wolf, lynx, wolverine and red fox, and finally an enormous number of bird species.

The cool climate prevailing during the Pleistocene excluded a number of bird and animal species from immigration. Other species found their environmental niche in the New World already occupied by forms that had evolved in America, so that they could not become established. Even man, starting from Asia, colonized the American continent during the last glacial epoch, before the land bridge was finally submerged by the melting of the Pleistocene glaciers. In the 12,000 years or so that the two continents have been separated many species and subspecies of animals evolved in North America as a consequence of isolation and natural selection; gradually they have become less and less like their Eurasian relatives.

Whereas the communities of the northern coniferous forests still, to a considerable extent, retain their original appearance, in the rest of the temperate zone man has cleared large sections and caused profound changes in the composition of both flora and fauna. The zones of sclerophyll and winter-deciduous forests are especially favorable for the establishment of human settlements. As the forests were driven back, higher civilizations developed—first in the Near East, eastern Asia, and Europe, and after the discovery of the New World, in North America. Three-quarters of the forests in central Europe and eastern North America were cleared to make way for agriculture, and in China only insignificant remnants were left. The forest became restricted to those places little suited to cultivation or use as pasture.

Such clearing necessarily restricted the habitat of the forest-dwelling animals. During the last two centuries eastern North America has lost more bird species than any other continent, as a result of the destruction of the woods. For example, as the large forests in the southeastern USA vanished, so did the ivory-billed woodpecker (*Campephilus principalis*). Of the many millions of passenger pigeons (*Ectopistes migratorius*) that once lived in the extensive forest regions of eastern North America, not one is left; the last died in 1914 in the Cincinnati Zoo. The wild turkey (*Meleagris gallopavo*), which formerly ranged as far as Canada, still exists but has disappeared from the regions where the wood has been cleared. Moreover, the reduction of the forests made it easier to hunt the large animals, and thus paved the way for their eventual eradication in wide areas.

On the other hand, new habitats were created, and these became occupied by a quite different fauna. Forest fringes and the hedges between fields were good places for species of shrub and tree with higher light requirements to grow; the cultivation of grain offered an opportunity for immigration to animals originally inhabitants of the steppes. In Europe the hare, hamster, field mouse, partridge, quail, bunting and meadowlark invaded the land cleared for crops. Men were followed even into their villages by adaptable small mammals like the house mouse and brown rat, and by the animals that prey upon them—the polecat and beech marten. Since domestic fowl is easy prey for animals so inclined, man was also soon followed by foxes, other martens, weasels and predatory birds.

The very first islands of cleared land in the forests were surrounded by belts of relatively sparse woodland, where cattle grazed. Later, cattle were driven into nearly all the forests during the summer. Since the new growth was bitten off by these animals, regeneration of the forests was impossible. Shrubs protected by spines and thorns began to take over. In this way, juniper (*Juniperus communis*) became the characteristic plant of the pasture land. Excessive grazing caused the tree line in the Alps to recede. Acorns and beechnuts—which contained the seeds of oak and beech trees—were eaten by swine. Even in classical antiquity, the sclerophyll woodlands of the Mediterranean were ravaged by excessive grazing by goats, which prevented any new growth of trees. Clear-cutting followed by goat pasturing destroyed these forests, once so extensive, and on slopes created conditions for erosion and left the soil dry, stony and infertile. More recently, a similar destruction of forests has occurred in southern Chile. There clear-cutting was followed by years of primitive agriculture, after which the former enormous wooded areas were grazed, turning progressively into an infertile region where nothing could live without difficulty. The man-made steppes and deserts of the world have been estimated to cover a total of 450 million hectares.

Hand in hand with the conversion of forest to pastureland went a merciless persecution of the large predatory animals, which naturally began to hunt the cattle wandering freely in the woods. The transition to keeping cattle in barns, in the second half of the 18th Century, was associated in Europe with a particularly harmful form of forest exploitation; to save straw, which was then in short supply, the litter on the forest floor—leaves, needles, and ground plants, along with the humus layer—was used as bedding for the animals in their stalls. Unimaginable quantities of organic matter were thus taken from the forest and eventually, mixed with manure, put on the fields. This robbery, carried on through almost 200 years, of course depleted the soil of nutrients; the sandy soils, naturally infertile in any case, suffered the most and finally could support only stunted, deformed growth.

On top of all these unwise activities, people used far too much of the wood itself. Until the 19th Century was well underway wood was almost the only fuel, the most common material for buildings, furniture, and other man-made objects, and the most important source of energy for craftsmen and early industries. The more the taller timber of the central

Forest grazing and removal of ground litter

Excessive use of timber

Fig. 12-3. The present composition of the oak-beech forests of Europe is associated with the economy of the region from the middle ages through the beginning of the 19th Century. The upper stratum, consisting mainly of oaks, provided timber for building. A lower tree stratum, with hornbeam, linden and smaller oaks, which grew back especially well from the cut stumps, was chopped down every 20-30 years to serve as fuel. Alongside these could grow trees that seeded themselves readily, like birches, trembling aspen and willow, and species with seeds distributed by birds, such as sweet cherry and mountain ash. These forests, shaped by man, contained more species of plants and animals than the natural oak-beech communities.

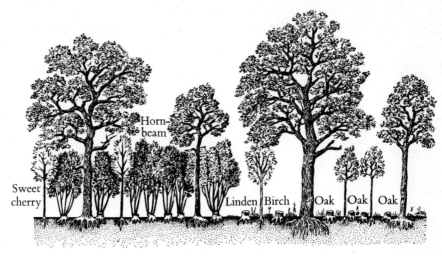

European forests was cut, and the more often the undergrowth was cleared away, the more room was made for light-requiring plants such as birches, willows, aspens, mountain ash, and all sorts of shrubs. Where conditions were suitable, there resulted mixed forests comprising a large number of species (see Fig. 12-3).

The fauna in these forests was correspondingly diverse. The hill forests of Europe had, next to the riverside forests, the greatest variety and population density of birds. Species like the hawfinch *Coccothraustes coccothraustes*, which lives on the hard-shelled fruits of trees, and the middle spotted woodpecker *Dendrocopos medius* are especially characteristic of these mixed forests created by man.

The large, closed forests of the sub-alpine mountains of Europe were once used primarily for hunting by the local rulers. In still earlier times, people had used the streams of the Alps and higher sub-alpine mountains to float the highly-prized softwoods from the mountain forests down to the harbor cities. Enormous consumption of wood for fuel, as charcoal, and as ash for the manufacture of glass and in iron foundries contributed a great deal to exhausting the supplies of wood. When these factories were finally given up as no longer economical at the beginning of the 19th Century, the sub-alpine mountains, with their rigorous climate, were full of populous settlements which could barely manage to feed themselves. It became necessary to assist these people by giving them extensive rights over the surrounding woodland. As a result, especially because of the depletion of ground litter, the fertility of the soil in most of these mountain forests was destroyed.

The end of the 18th Century marked the end of the "Age of Wood." The central European forests were in a desperate state hardly imaginable today; the supply of wood was exhausted, and the soil was pitifully depleted. Natural regeneration was prevented by excessive grazing by both cattle and the greatly increased population of red deer. Much of the former woodland had long since been changed into waste ground, heath or meager pastures. The beneficiaries of this change were the moorhen, woodlark, and plover-like thick-knee; the wood grouse, too, found a home in the open stands of trees with an abundance of dwarf shrubs growing among them on the acid topsoil. The roe and red deer—both of which, as the preferred game animals, had been carefully preserved by the hunters—found more food and thus better conditions in this new woodland than in the original forests.

In North America similar events occurred; the forests were destroyed by clearing for agricultural purposes and by rash exploitation of the timber. But the strength of the soil was not sapped, as it had been in Europe, by grazing and the removal of litter, so that gradually a natural secondary forest came into being; this consisted of rapidly-growing pioneer tree species, which provided an ideal habitat for a few adaptable herbivores such as the white-tailed deer.

The 19th Century brought a turning point in the attitude of men to the forest in central Europe. Professionally trained foresters and forestry scientists directed their efforts toward a reforestation of the waste land, primarily with commercially valuable species like pine and spruce. Huge areas of bog were drained and planted with conifers. The large rivers were dammed up and the fringe forests that still remained were cleared, except for a few patches. All this brought about a further change in the forest communities.

The century of forestry

Moreover, considerable effort was made simultaneously to raise closed stands of beech and oak. These endeavours were aided by the marked decline in the numbers of deer that occurred about the middle of the 19th Century, as well as by improved agricultural methods, the introduction of artificial fertilizers, and the use of coal once a network of railways had been constructed. The old stands of beech and oak now found in the central European forests date from that time.

But the deciduous forests originally covering central Europe were displaced only temporaily by the plantations of pine and spruce. A search was begun for other suitable tree species, and there was large-scale planting of the European larch as well as imports from North America—Douglas fir and white pine, red oak, Canadian poplar, Sitka spruce, and coastal fir species. The black locust has now become an inseparable element of the landscape in all central, eastern and southern Europe. Of the introduced eastern Asian species, only the Japanese larch has really become established as a forest tree over considerable areas. On the other hand, countless North American and eastern Asian trees and shrubs are cultivated in parks and gardens, along avenues, and as isolated specimens in woods. Ginkgo, magnolia, *Ailanthus, Thuja,* bald cypress and many other trees have been returned by man to the land where their ancestors, in the Ice Age, became extinct.

The transformations of large parts of the central European beech and oak forests into softwood plantations had a profound effect upon the entire forest community. The ground flora now comprised elements from the original deciduous forests as well as undemanding plants from neighboring communities and typical plants of the natural coniferous forests, which were often several hundred kilometers away. The fungi which were symbionts of certain conifers followed them into the plantations. As in the raw humus of the northern coniferous forests, fungi and springtails took over the job of gradually decomposing the organic debris.

Bird species typical of the northern and alpine coniferous forest invaded the softwood plantations; among them were Tengmalm's owl, nutcrackers, crossbills, the siskin *Carduelis spinus*, the crested tit, and the coal tit. On the whole, the communities of the planted coniferous woodland comprise far fewer species of both plants and animals than do the natural forest communities, and they are correspondingly more vulnerable to pests of all kinds.

This was demonstrated toward the end of the 19th Century to an extent never before experienced. Certain moths, among them pine beauties (*Panolis flammea*), black arches (*Lymantria monacha*), and the geometrid *Bupalus piniarius*, defoliated tens of thousands of hectares of pine and spruce plantations in central Europe. After periods of drought or storms the numbers of bark beetles increased. At first there was no defense against these pests; in the 20th Century highly effective insecticides came into use, but these brought with them quite different dangers, which will be described later.

Fire which has a decisive effect upon life in natural coniferous forests, can be very effectively contained by men in the deciduous forest region—despite the considerable increase in the likelihood of its occurrence as a result of flying sparks from locomotives, neglected campfires and the like. Set against this are the detrimental activities of the new pests introduced accidentally in greater numbers as traffic between the different parts of the

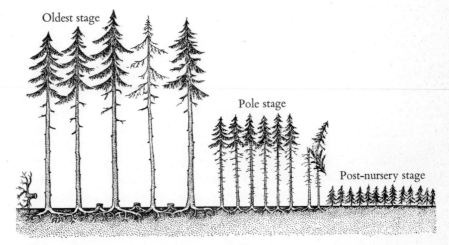

Oldest stage

Pole stage

Post-nursery stage

Fig. 12-4. Stands of spruce planted by foresters are composed of trees of the same age, each age-group with a special descriptive name (three of the five categories used in Germany are shown). Such uniform plantations give a high yield per acre, but are very vulnerable to damage by storms, snow, fungus disease of roots and trunks, and infestation by insects.

earth increased. A fungus disease that originated in Asia destroyed large numbers of chestnut trees, in both eastern North America and the Mediterranean region. Cultivation of white pine (*Pinus strobus*) in Europe was set back severely by another fungus (*Peridermium strobi*). From Europe this fungus was carried to the North American home of the white pine, where it caused immeasurable damage. Both in North America and in central Europe the fungus *Graphium ulmi*, which is spread by the bark beetles *Scolytus scolytus* and *Scolytus multistriatus*, threatens the various species of elm.

By the end of the 19th Century the reasons for the discouraging state of the large softwood plantations had become clear. In southern Germany and Switzerland, particularly, a determined attempt was made to encourage their conversion to mixed forest. The idea was that there should be a basic framework of native deciduous trees to which the more commercially valuable conifers should be added, but only to such an extent as would not disturb appreciably the balance of the community.

The crucial obstacle to such an undertaking was the excessive population of deer in central Europe. Ordinarily the planned vigorous mixed forest could actually be brought into being only behind kilometer-long fences to keep the deer out. At present 80% of the funds allocated to forest conservation in Germany is spent in prevention of damage by red and roe deer. The conversion of stands of conifers to mixed forests was most successful in central Europe after the Second World War. Mechanical cultivation, liming and mineral fertilization improved the soil, counteracting the long depletion by the removal of litter. The impoverished communities were strengthened by the addition of accessory plants with a beneficial effect on the soil, such as alder, broom and blue lupine. Artificial breeding holes for bats and insectivorous wood birds such as tits, nuthatches, and pied flycatchers served as a substitute for the hollow trees now no longer tolerated. The tits, estimated to be the most helpful in pest control, were further encouraged by providing them with food in the winter, and protection and artificially extended distribution of the red ant (*Formica rufa*) increased the usefulness of this extremely active destroyer of insect pests.

The changes in their environment, and even more the various forms of direct human intervention such as hunting, pest control, protective measures and the purposeful establishment of new species have brought about fundamental alterations in the animal populations of the temperate-zone forests. At first men tried to eradicate the large predators, regarding them as competitors for food. In eastern North America the puma, grizzly bear and wolf were destroyed; the same thing happened in central Europe during the first half of the last century to the wolf, lynx and brown bear, a few of which saved themselves by withdrawing to mountain forests that were hard for men to reach. From there, with luck, they could extend their ranges again, as the lynx has begun to do in recent years by making forays toward the west from the Carpathian mountains. In the northern part of

The mixed-forest concept

Man's effect on the fauna

eastern Asia the Amur leopard and Siberian tiger, despite all attempts to hunt them down, have remained the northernmost representatives of their species; but the few remnants of the population that are left are now threatened with extinction.

Among the ungulates considered by hunters as valuable game the largest species, such as the aurochs, had already been eradicated by unrestrained hunting in the late Middle Ages, or like the bison, reduced to a few protected herds. By contrast, the red deer was and is still the most important game animal of the ruling classes in the European forests; as a result, its numbers grew over the centuries until it became an unbearable burden to agriculture. Not until the beginning of the last century, when the rulers could no longer shut their ears to the complaints of the peasants, was the free-ranging red deer largely exterminated. The bottled-up passion of the people for hunting broke loose in the 1848 revolution in a terrible "free-for-all" that soon killed nearly all the roe deer, chamois and wild boar in central, western and southern Europe. During these years the idea of game conservation was developed in Germany and Austria; the concept of animal husbandry was applied to the wild fauna, and populations of selected game species began to build up again under the care of the gamekeepers.

The "enemies" of game animals, the wild carnivores, were attacked even more vigorously. After the large predators had been exterminated, all but a small fraction of the wildcats and otters were destroyed. When fur prices reached record heights in the 1930's, the beech marten and the European pine marten were hunted so intensively that they became quite rare in certain places. Even the extremely adaptable red fox, with its high reproductive capacity, suffered a temporary decline at that time. And birds met with the same fate—the golden eagle, which was driven into the Alps, the eagle-owl, of which there are only scattered remnants in the varied habitats of the Jura and on the fringes of the Alps; and the "common" raven, now found only in the Alps and in Schleswig-Holstein.

Birds of prey, in particular, were destroyed indiscriminately and in the most brutal way, with shotguns and nets; in their ignorance, the hunters did not care which species were their victims. The effectiveness of this hunting became apparent in Germany in the first years following the end of the Second World War; there the temporary disarming of the hunters produced an astonishing—but unfortunately only short-lived—recovery of the populations of predatory birds.

Hand in hand with the extermination of "destructive" species went the conservation of the wild animals declared to be "desirable." Closed seasons, and above all the practice of winter feeding, caused a rapid increase in their numbers. In earlier times the populations were limited not only by the (now eliminated) predators but by the shortage of food in the winter. Aged, sick or juvenile animals were the first to succumb to starvation in winters of heavy snow. When food was provided, even the weak could survive. The populations of red and roe deer rose to many times their original density.

Since 1850, the concern of the huntsmen has been directed especially toward the adaptable roe deer. Now there are more of these deer in central eastern, and northern Europe than ever before. This excessive increase has had a marked effect upon the food situation. Over large areas of Europe the ground flora, including the tree seedlings, has suffered more and more. In the montane mixed forests the grazing of deer in our century has annihilated the new growth of silver fir, the most ecologically important tree, almost everywhere. The red deer also does considerable damage, with direct economical consequences, by rubbing off the bark of trees.

Overpopulation in a given species affects not only the plants that serve it as food, but the animals themselves. Lack of food and the absence of natural selection result in lowered body weight, inadequate development of antlers, and a greater susceptibility to disease and parasites. The chamois of the Alps suffer from epidemic illness, and roe deer are infested to an alarming extent by gastrointenstinal parasites; an attempt is being made to control the latter with medication. In eastern North America the white-tailed deer, like the roe deer in Europe, have adapted to their agricultural environment and have multiplied so that they are now the most important game animal. In western North America their place is taken by the mule deer. Both species have now grown excessively numerous and do considerable damage to the forests.

Like the practice of winter feeding, the idea of "new blood" has been taken over from animal husbandry. Toward the end of the last century a large-scale effort was made to introduce specimens of stronger subspecies in order that they might cross-breed with the native game. The best-known of these experiments were those intended to "improve" the native red deer by interbreeding with strong Carpathian deer. The enormous antlers of the Siberian roe deer (*Capreolus capreolus pygargus*) repeatedly tempted gamekeepers to try to cross it with the smaller European subspecies; such attempts failed, because of the lower resistance of the Siberian deer and the hybrids to disease in the lower latitudes.

More momentous results were achieved in the introduction of exotic species, which became fashionable around the middle of the last century. The impetus was given by the hunters, who were always on the lookout for new, exciting objects for their passion. The pheasant, originally distributed in central Asia from the Caucasus to Japan, is now found throughout Europe as far north as Scandinavia. Each new attempt to establish it was preceded by campaigns to eradicate possible enemies, especially birds of prey; even small predators like the ermine and the mouse weasel were not spared. The progeny of a few North American muskrats that were set free in 1905 in Bohemia have today dispersed over almost all of central and western Europe. Since the damage they did to dams far outweighed their value as game, control measures soon became necessary.

▷

From left to right and top to bottom:
Deciduous-forest soil over basalt.—Wheat-field soil over sand.—Growth of lichen on a stone (island in the Gulf of Bothnia). A biotope in eastern Fjeld-lappland (September): the birches are beginning to turn yellow, and crow-berry (*Empetrum hermaph-roditum*) carpets the ground in red.—A growth of lichen (*Cladonia cariosa*) with red fruiting bodies, on a stone in eastern Fjeldlappland.—The stump of a larch cut three weeks previously (April); it has not yet been infested by wood insects.

A stump that was inhabited by ants, which have now left it (May).—The small red ant *Formica polyctena* is beginning to build a nest over the stump of a spruce (September).—A stump almost completely over-grown by fungi, the discharged spores of which cover the top surface (October).

Fruiting body of a fungus on a beech stump, characteristically hung with the excrement sacks of various caterpillars (October).—Decomposition of a stump: nine- to ten-year-old oak stump, collapsed in the middle and over-grown with moss (April).—Under the bark of a stump: a millipede (*Polydesmus* sp.) guards its egg chamber (June).

Introduction of new species

◁

From left to right and top to bottom:
Decomposition of a stump: oak stump, about ten years old, in the last stage of humification (June).— Differently colored layers in beach sand on Amrum (one of the North Frisian Islands): white- or gray-yellow layer (3–5 mm) sometimes containing diatoms; green layer (as much as 5 mm) with blue-green algae and diatoms; red layer (2–5 mm) with red bacteria; black layer with hydrogen-sulfide-forming bacteria.—Slice of of the trunk of a central European birch (large piece; 35 years old, diameter 27.4 cm) and a birch from northern Lappland (small piece; 150 years old, diameter 4.6 cm); growth of the latter is slow because of the short growing season.
Leaf litter in a stand of beech (June) with a tile-red snail (*Arion rufus*) crawling over it.—The dark-colored duff under the litter proper, near a beech stump.—Soil fungi growing in leaf mold layer (September); at the right a beech leaf that has been mined by a moth living in the crown of the tree. Soil profile under a stand of deciduous oak and beech: a dense root zone extends down into the fine sand.—Soil profile of an evergreen stand (spruce): the roots form a shallow plate, and the trees are more easily blown down.

Forests in danger

In the forests remaining in eastern North America, the European wild boar was introduced, and pheasants and partridges were also brought to North America to serve as gamebirds. The sparrow and starling were brought because of their usefulness in destroying insects, and the goldfinch because of nostalgia for the familiar birds of the old country. But it proved impossible to establish the red cardinal, probably the most striking songbird of eastern North America, in Europe. Red deer set free in New Zealand and Argentina multiplied to such an extent that they began to crowd out the native fauna of the Argentinian mountain forests; today they are treated as pests in New Zealand. In Europe attempts have been made to introduce a total of forty-seven species of mammal and at least eighty-five species of bird.

Other efforts to transplant animal species to different parts of the world have been made with the intention of preserving them, when they are threatened by extinction in their homeland. For example, the sika deer, endangered in eastern Asia, found a new home in Europe, New Zealand and Australia. When the wild rabbit and the wild sheep, the mouflon, were introduced to central Europe it was simply a matter of reestablishing the original distribution of species that had been driven south during the Ice Age. The mouflon, continually on the point of becoming extinct in its native Corsica and Sardinia, is now widespread in the deciduous forests of central Europe, with the greatest concentration in Czechoslovakia, and its preservation is assured.

The most prized game animals have been reintroduced to areas from which they had been exterminated by unrestrained hunting in the previous century. Examples are the red deer in the Böhmer Wald and Bayerischer Wald, in the Pfälzer Wald and at various places in France, and the wild boar in the Netherlands, Denmark and England. But even today the efforts of conservationists to renew the native populations of predatory birds and mammals encounter resistance, particularly in hunting circles. Nevertheless, in Switzerland a number of lynxes have been set free, and in Germany similar experiments are planned in the Harz, in the vicinity of the Alps, and in the Bavarian National Forest. It also proved possible to increase the numbers of the eagle-owl, which had become rare in West Germany, though a considerable effort had to be made and the losses were high.

Today overpopulation, industry, transportation technology and the methods of mechanized agriculture are placing more and more stress upon the former forest regions of the temperate zone. The residues of poisons used to protect plants are a threat, for example, to a number of species of predatory birds—and this just at a time when even among hunters it is becoming accepted that birds of prey and carnivorous mammals are of great significance to the maintenance of the balance of nature and ought to be protected.

In North America, the National Park movement has been able to preserve for the future the remnants of temperate-zone virgin forest. In central Europe an effort is being made to set aside relatively slightly altered regions of forest and mountains as national parks, and to repair, as far as possible, the ravages caused by earlier human interference. But even now such obviously vital measures encounter opposition and are fraught with difficulty.

The shrinking of the natural forests in the temperate zone was accompanied by the development of advanced human civilization. Whereas only vestiges of the forests remain today, and these have been profoundly altered with respect to both flora and fauna, the human population has continued to grow until it has reached, and in many cases already exceeded, its limits. And it is precisely under these conditions, when the capacity of the environment to support all these people is being strained so severely, that forests are most important—less for their value as timber than for their role in maintaining a favorable environmental water balance, cleaning the air, offering a place for animals and plants to live, and providing a refuge for city dwellers in need of rest and recreation. In the struggle of humanity for a better future—indeed, for survival—the preservation, in an optimal functional state, of the forests we have left cannot be urged too strongly.

13   Life in the Soil

By A. Brauns

Soil organisms and soil fertility—these are inseparably related, and the combination, a subsection of the total complex "biotope and community," is emphasized more and more of late by zoologists concerned with the soil. We have already seen the extent to which all life in the litter and soil strata of a diciduous forest floor affects the overall environment and the situation is the same in the great variety of other soils. In agriculture, all the measures taken to preserve and encourage biological activity in the soil protect and increase the vigor of the plants growing on it; they are thus the focal point of applied soil biology. There can be no doubt that this field is just on the threshold of a highly promising stage of development. It is difficult to draw a dividing line between the biology of the soil animals and that of the growing plants, which provide food for many soil-dwelling animals. Moreover, research into soil organisms must extend to the problem of increasing production in two of the most important areas of the economy, agriculture and forestry. For these reasons, soil biology has a vital contribution to make to applied research on productivity.

By "soil" we mean the loose part of the earth's crust, which has been formed by weathering, humus formation, and mixing of the products of these processes. This loose covering over stone or sand (see Color plate, p. 221) may be ralatively thin and yet support various types of vegetation. "Weathering" in the broad sense is brought about not only by climatic factors but—and these are of the most interest here—by biological processes, associated with the activity of animals and plants. Algae, lichens (see Color plate, p. 221), fungi and mosses colonize the surfaces of rock, penetrate the cracks caused by freezing, and thus contribute to the factors hastening the weathering of the stone. Lichens actually secrete acids that attack the stone surface. In the eastern part of Fjeldlappland (northern Finland) there are many springtails under the lichen encrustations on rocks dating from the Ice Age (see Color plate, p. 221); these primitive insects ordinarily inhabit ground litter, which is very sparse in this region.

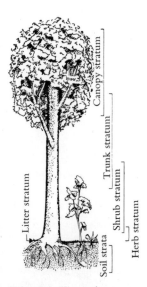

Fig. 13-1. Vegetation strata in deciduous woodland.

The processes of "humification," which in times past converted weathered rock into the soil we have today, are of course still going on. Humification is the breaking down of organic matter to form humus; it requires adequate (though not necessarily very much) oxygen, sufficient moisture, and moderate temperatures. Mineral nutrients needed by plants are freed, and more or less dark colored "humic substances" are formed, sometimes in many separate steps. Humification thus requires different conditions than do the processes of decay or peat formation, though all these forms of decomposition depend upon the microclimate and upon the participation of soil organisms.

An impressive display of ongoing humification is offered by the decomposition of tree stumps in a forest. As a tree stump is converted to humus, a specific succession of organisms appears upon it, several of which are shown in the Color plate, p. 221. Soon after the tree has been cut, soil animals move into the foot of the former tree. In the first three years after a tree is felled in the autumn the stump is usually inhabited by the larvae of specialized wood insects, such as buprestid and cerambycid beetles or the beetle *Hylecoetus*, which feed on fungi in tunnels in the wood. But they share their home with the larvae of another beetle (in the family Pyrochroidae), a carnivorous species which hunts the other beetle larvae and limits their numbers.

As soon as ants infiltrate the stump with their passages and chambers, they have such a great requirement for food that the larvae of the wood insects usually disappear from the scene. Only in the nests of the small red ant *Formica polyctena*, which are built over a stump, are certain species allowed to share the dwelling. In the three years that follow, blue-green algae colonize the cut surface of a stump not occupied by ants, and these are eaten by snails; often various fungi grow there at the same time. Where the excrement of the snails is deposited, moss begins to grow over the stump. Under the moss there lives a diverse fauna ordinarily found only under the surface of the soil. When the stump is nine or ten years old the cut surface is entirely covered by moss; now, or sometimes even earlier, the top of the stump collapses and fallen leaves or needles drift into the depression. There are many insect larvae living under the mossy covering at this stage, including forms not present before; these are the prey of larvae of snipe flies (family Rhagionidae), long-legged flies (family Dolichopodidae), and flies of the family Xylophagidae, as well as "wireworms" (larvae of beetles of the family Elateridae). Even in stumps that have been standing for eleven or twelve years remnants of the sides are still discernible, but the central part is continuous with the general ground litter (see Color plate, p. 222).

Once decomposition of the stumps is approaching completion, numerous insect larvae from other strata of the vegetation move into it toward the end of autumn. Evidently the temperature and humidity in the stump or its vicinity at this point in the process is especially favorable, for with

▷
From left to right and top to bottom:
Burning straw and stubble on the fields after harvest (September).—Very large molehills are characteristic of the coastal pastures with their high water table. Pasture in the black forest with typical ridges made by the walking cattle (September).—Meadow near Garmisch-Partenkirchen with mounds where trees once stood (June); the mountain in the background is the Wank. Intentional flooding of a meadow by the Hunte river near its junction with the Weser (January)—Fields near Turku, Finland (September).
Plant cover is being established on the bare earth of this Braunschweig coalmine (July), but soil erosion hampers the process.—Gradual forestation of a pile of rubble near the Röchling iron and steel works (Völkingen, Saar).

the onset of winter the density of the populations of true soil animals and overwintering insects from the trunk and crown strata increases. In the following spring the small animals move out in all directions into the soil and litter.

Humification is the normal and desirable process by which stumps are broken down, even in a forest under professional management. But decomposition by this means does not proceed according to a definite pattern, nor is it always completed within a certain time. The felling of trees in the autumn, as is customary, delays by some months the real beginning of the process. But if the timber were taken in the spring, the sap exuded from the stump would attract quite different animal species, less important in humification; stumps left from an autumn felling are ready in the following spring for colonization by wood-decomposing animals.

The processes by which soil is developed produce a layered structure comparable to the horizontal strips of color caused by microorganisms in the sand on the seacoast (see Color plate, p. 222). The different soil layers are called "horizons," and their nature and relative depth determine the "soil profile." This, too, is well demonstrated by the forest floor (see Color plate, p. 222). The stratum of ground litter is a much more crucial concern to the forester than the stage of decomposition of the stumps. The amount of litter produced per year varies with the type of forest; stands of spruce lead the list with six metric tons per hectare, and they are followed by pines (4.1 tons), oaks (3.9 tons), and larches (2.7 tons). The amount also depends upon the age and species composition of the stand. The fact that an old forest soil differs considerably from that of agricultural land, in profile, microclimate and fauna, is due chiefly to the prolonged influence of the trees and the litter they produce.

Intensive investigations of the mineral and nitrogen balance in the forest floor have shown that over two-thirds of the nutrients withdrawn annually from the soil by the plants is returned to the soil in the litter and thus reenters the local circulation of these substances—as long as the litter does not simply lie on the surface, but is decomposed as rapidly as possible (see Fig. 13-4).

There can be no doubt that the microorganisms found in the ground litter play a significant role in its humification, but the organic detritus accumulated on the ground is also processed by other animals, many of which leave characteristic traces of their activity. For example, it is common for inhabitants of the litter layers to construct cases of various sorts (Fig. 13-3). Any observer can easily distinguish the topmost layer of detritus (the "litter proper"; for example, the most recently fallen needles or leaves), which has hardly been touched by the soil organisms, from the lower levels of detritus, the "duff" and "leaf mold" layers (see Color plate, p. 222). Duff has undergone sufficient decomposition that its origin is no longer recognizable, and it serves as the food of many small

◁
From left to right and top to bottom:
Research methods in soil biology:
Core sampler containing a core of soil.—Taking a sample in the hard soil of a beet field.
After taking a sample from an irrigated wheat field, where only the upper layers are to be studied.—Berlese funnel for quantitative separation of the organisms. The sieve of a Berlese funnel with a soil sample.—Storage of the samples: after systematic sorting of the material the small animals are kept in alcohol-filled tubes, each of which is labelled with the exact place and time the sample was taken.

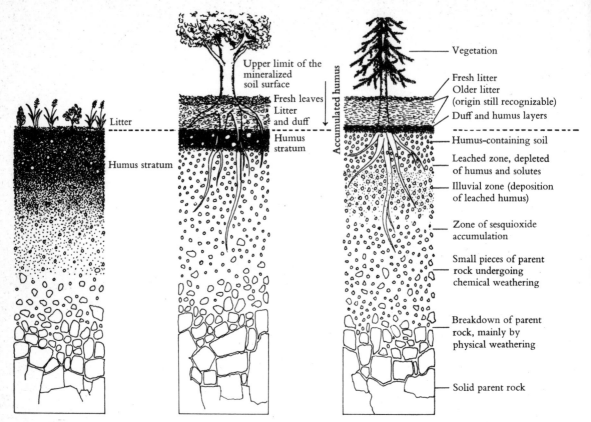

Vegetation

Fresh litter
Older litter
(origin still recognizable)
Duff and humus layers

Humus-containing soil

Leached zone, depleted
of humus and solutes

Illuvial zone (deposition
of leached humus)

Zone of sesquioxide
accumulation

Small pieces of parent
rock undergoing
chemical weathering

Breakdown of parent
rock, mainly by
physical weathering

Solid parent rock

Accumulated humus

Upper limit of the
mineralized
soil surface

Fresh leaves
Litter
and duff

Humus
stratum

Litter

Humus stratum

Fig. 13-2. Soil profiles showing the different types of humus (left to right): raw humus (mor), brown earth with leaf mold; brown earth with mild humus (mull).

soil animals. This layer also contains a great variety of fungi, often conspicuously colored, with branched mycelia. Below this comes the humus layer, in which decomposition is complete and mixing with the mineral components of the soil begins.

Just as each person's handwriting is distinctive and tells something about that person, so we can learn by the study of soil samples what is the nature of the soil where the sample was taken. Moreover, by studying the soil profile exposed in a bank or the side of a trench, we can find out a good deal from the state of the various horizons. The litter profile tells us what the soil organisms have to work with, and the lower horizons show how the biological activity is progressing (see Fig. 13-2).

The activity of animals in the detritus layer consists in preparing the way for the actual humus formation. The passage of the cast-off parts of plants through the digestive system is crucial because it is thus that they are reduced to smaller pieces; the surface of needles, for example, must be broken by animals before bacteria can enter them. In addition, the breakdown of cellulose is facilitated when lignins, which are very resistant to bacterial attack, are separated from it in the digestive tract; the excrement becomes filled with bacteria. Many soil animals, including isopods, earth-

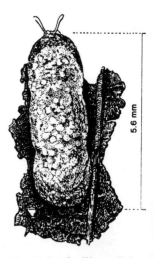

5.6 mm

Fig. 13-3. The "house" built by a litter animal: the pupal case of a crane fly.

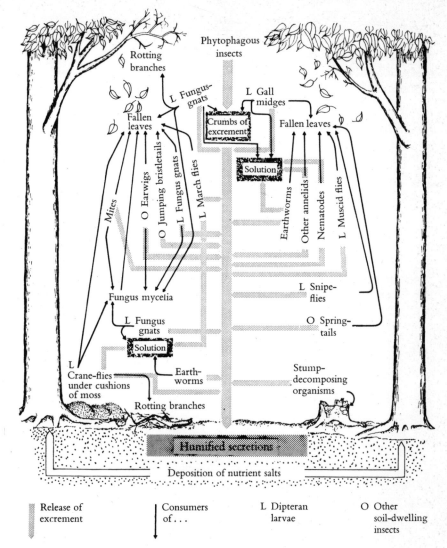

Fig. 13-4. Part of the cycle of matter in a stand of deciduous trees, indicating the different primary decomposers. The relationships of the predators to these are not shown.

Release of excrement	Consumers of . . .	L Dipteran larvae	O Other soil-dwelling insects

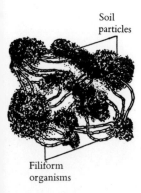

Fig. 13-5. Crumbs of soil joined by living, threadlike organisms.

worms and enchytraeids, send mineral material through the gut along with the organic substances; the humic acids formed in their excrement are bound into "clay-humus complexes" and thus retained in the soil. The casts of earthworms are firmer than other crumbs of soil, because they are glued together by the mucus of small organisms, and they can take up much more water than other soil particles. Threadlike organisms, notably the filaments of fungi, join the crumbs of soil in a living assemblage that can better withstand the destructive effects (microerosion) of water in the soil (Fig. 13-5).

From the viewpoint of soil biology the primary decomposers are the most significant of the litter organisms, because their excretions contain humus. Some of the animals that actually eat the detritus also harbor intestinal symbionts (microorganisms living in the gut, which are beneficial to their hosts and profit from the association themselves) which evidently can bind nitrogen in some form. The significance of those humic substances which cannot be regarded as direct plant nutrients cannot be easily explained, for there are many opinions as to what is meant by "humus." To the soil biologist humus is important chiefly because it keeps the soil in a porous, "spongy" state and affects the availability of water and nutrients (see Fig. 13-8).

A healthy soil fauna produces a desirable humus content of the soil, and the two are in a state of dynamic equilibrium. If any of the conditions that ordinarily bring about a high density of soil organisms should be lacking, the animals cannot process the organic material rapidly enough. The activity of the primary decomposers is very severely hampered, and in autumn of the following years a new layer of detritus is piled on the not yet decomposed remains. There is an excessive growth of fungi, the threads of which mat the litter to form a covering of raw humus not easily penetrated by water when it is dry, so that most of the precipitation runs off the surface. For the soil to recover from the lack of humus, the proper sequence of primary, secondary and subsequent decomposers must be reestablished—a succession that occurs automatically in stands where humification of the litter is proceeding well.

Forestry is often regarded as only a subdivision of agriculture. The two fields are without doubt related; both are concerned with making the best use of the soil, and there are overlap areas—for example, when animals are sent into the woods to graze and leaf litter is taken to the farms, neither of which practices are now as common as they were, or when forestation and cultivation are carried on together for the sake of soil improvement. But despite these similarities, one can find fundamental differences between the two applied sciences. Forestry deals with large areas, and is therefore in some respects not applicable to agricultural questions. The possibilities for mechanization are limited in forest management, whereas technological improvements play a great role in agriculture. Moreover, tilling and fertilization of the soil can be used only to a restricted extent in woodland; because of the length of time between seed and harvest this is not such a decisive factor in forestry as in fields and meadows. The production cycle in forestry is a matter of decades or perhaps a hundred years, whereas that of agriculture is completed within a single year.

As far as cultivated fields are concerned, modern farming techniques have already affected the organisms in the soil (Figs. 13-7 and 13-8). It is easy to see that the root systems of the crops are very important to the animals in the soil. They contribute to their vertical distribution and are a source of food for many animals. Each year's harvest leaves a considerable quantity of dead roots behind. There have been various recent developments in agricultural practice that have a crucial effect upon soil biology. Because the shortage of agricultural laborers is becoming increasingly severe, many farmers keep few or no cattle. Such cattle as there are remain

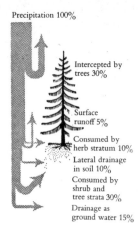

Precipitation 100%

Intercepted by trees 30%

Surface runoff 5%

Consumed by herb stratum 10%

Lateral drainage in soil 10%

Consumed by shrub and tree strata 30%

Drainage as ground water 15%

Fig. 13-6. Water balance in a "podzolized" forest soil.

in the pasture for months or stay in barns so constructed that practically no straw is needed. To dispose of the excess straw, fields are commonly burnt over after the grain is harvested (see Color plate, p. 227). Use of a mowing and threshing combine tends to encourage the growth of weeds; if herbicides are not to be used against the weeds, the burning of stubble in the fall is of value in that it destroys weed seeds and kills many pests.

Nevertheless, many soil biologists advise against burning off these raw materials for humus, particularly since the straw, if chopped and plowed under, could serve as food for microorganisms and small animals. Even well humified bits of straw can still be eaten by springtails and by the larvae of dark-winged fungus-gnats (family Sciaridae). Many years of research will be required to solve the question of the best method of dealing with the straw left on the fields after the harvest.

Almost 40% of the agricultural land in Eurasia is meadow and pasture land. In coastal regions where land is being reclaimed from the ocean, maturation of the soil is an important element in the process. When grassland is used as pasture, the activities of animals above the ground are closely related to the conditions in the soil strata. For example, a cowpat contains a remarkable community of animals. One ox deposits in a year nineteen times its weight of dung; in this mass of dung lives an insect population, consisting mostly of dipteran larvae, which amounts to about one-fifth the weight of the ox. These contribute to the breakdown of the dung and its eventual incorporation in the soil. On the other hand, trampling by the cattle compresses the pores in the soil, and this probably diminishes the number of small arthropods; at least, it must be disadvantageous to the soil insects. Mountain slopes are shaped in characteristic ways by grazing cattle (see Color plate, p. 227). On meadows in the sub-alpine mountains the wandering animals form the surface into ripples that are visible from some distance, and in the higher mountains clear-cut areas used as pasture land develop humps, since the cattle graze around the stumps of the trees.

Another factor potentially detrimental to soil fauna is flooding. In some coastal regions fields are intentionally flooded (see Color plate, p. 227), a practice intended to protect regions further inland from inundation when the rivers are dangerously high with melted snow. Sometimes earthworms, enchytraeids and other soil-dwellers can survive underwater for unlimited periods. Insect larvae which live in relatively dry habitats also are generally unhurt by flooding in autumn, winter or spring, but flooding during the hot summer months always presents a danger. When insect larvae from distinctly moist habitats are submerged, they usually retain their normal motility in the upper soil layers and do not swell up; in the deeper layers they often enter a sort of dormant state from which they can emerge as soon as conditions are more favorable.

Currently, as industrialization continues to expand, ecology and soil

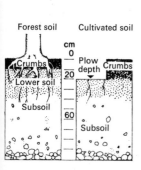

Fig. 13-7. Profile of an undisturbed (left) and a cultivated (right) soil; turning the soil by machine destroys the natural profile.

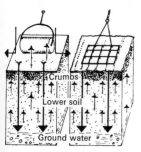

Fig. 13-8. The effects of different soil treatments: Rolling increases the upward movement of capillary water (upward-pointing arrows); harrowing prevents excessive evaporation by breaking the capillaries in the upper crumbly soil layer. Arrows pointing down represent percolating "gravitational" water.

biology are crucial areas of environmental research. Soil biology has developed a technological side with applications which are worth a brief discussion here. The cultivation of crops as it is widely practiced produces a great variety of deficiencies in the soil, and the techniques of soil biology can be used in general to relieve them. The emerging countries offer special challenge to the soil biologist, particularly in those regions where the population pressure is greatest.

Nothing is known as yet about the possible effects on life in the soil of a type of land "use" that is becoming more common every year; we refer to former agricultural land which is now allowed to lie fallow as a result of high wages and general prosperity. On the fringes of concentrations of population and industry such land is particularly evident. Another phenomenon that has not yet been clarified by large-scale, long-term investigations is the replenishment of the soil fauna from the boundaries of the fields, a characteristic aspect of the Finnish fields, which still show the effects of the Ice Age (see Color plate, p. 227). Farmers and agricultural scientists concerned with protection of the crops and disposal of refuse have realized, in recent decades, that they must understand and be guided by the effects of their operations on the environment; this is a particularly sensitive area, in which unwise practices could upset the system "soil organisms and soil fertility," with far-reaching consequences. Small animals are important indicators of the chemical processes occurring in the soil, and can be used to decide the category to which a particular soil belongs. It is evident from all this that the representatives of a variety of professions—agricultural entomology and microbiology, soil biology and chemistry, plant pathology and forestry—must work together to construct a scientifically based classification of soils which can serve as a basis for a program of soil improvement.

Man's manipulation of his surroundings has caused a progressive loss of natural countryside and has placed a heavy burden upon the biological scientists (soil biologists, of course, among them) whose job it is to save the situation—by conservation of what remains, repair of the damage already done, and planning for optimal land use in the future. One task, for example, is the stabilization of loose hills and mounds of rubble in industrial centers, by selective forestation. The point of this is less to obtain a crop of timber than to avoid the dangers associated with the dust from the loose materials (see Color plate, p. 227). In such a project, research by soil biologists is important and may be crucial, since before planting a number of measures may be necessary to condition the soil. Covering such heaps of waste soil with vegetation not only restores the harmony of the lanescape, but in many cases allows them to be used eventually in agriculture.

Most of the projects described above have been in the area of applied ecology, the goal of which is to find ways of improving conditions in the soil layers and making a wise use of the plant and animal communities.

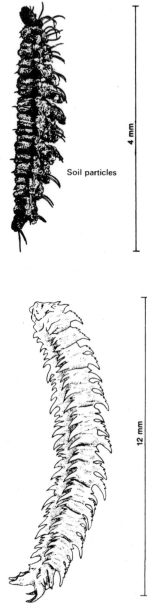

Soil particles

Fig. 13-9. Two soil-dwelling dipteran larvae: moth-fly of the genus *Pericoma* (above); midge of the *Triogma* (below).

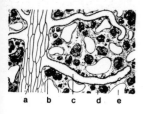

a Roots
b Grain of soil
c Root hair
d Water
e Air pore

Fig. 13-10. Structural components of the soil.

Careful experimentation can answer a number of questions. For example what are the practical effects of the relationships between different soil organisms or entire plant and animal communities? How does life in the soil as a whole affect the plants growing on it? In addition, the influences of the abiotic environment must be considered—the dependence of organisms upon the water and oxygen content of the soil, the soil texture and density, the temperature, and other conditions. Soil biology, the science of the animal and plant communities in the soil layers, is intimately interwoven with the study of the communities occupying the environment.

Conditions for life in the soil are of a very special sort. In the different horizons, water, air and the components of the soil vary in nature and are mingled in different proportions. The horizons in which organisms live are not dense and firm, but display a crumbly structure with many cavities or pores. These pores are filled with air or water, and are occupied by subterranean organisms. Large pores serve, so to speak, for soil respiration, intermediate pores of capillary size for the conduction of water, and the finest pores for the storage of water reserves that can be drawn upon in dry seasons (though water is also bound to humus and soil minerals). Depending on its location and structure, a soil has a particular micro-climate, so that one can speak of "warm" or "cold" soils. A very crumb-like structure, with many airfilled pores, is associated with a dense population of soil-dwelling organisms and encourages the formation of warm soils, whereas very moist soils can hold less heat and are therefore "cold." In the lowest strata inhabited by animals, darkness is a special factor; it is associated with regression of light-sensing organs in many of the small animals and, in the deepest layers, with an absence of green plants, so that the animals there must find alternative food.

The special conditions in the soil determine not only characteristic morphotypes but also characteristic behavioral traits (see Fig. 13-12) of the soil animals. Dipteran larvae, two of which are shown in Fig. 13-9, are good examples, for their biology has many interesting aspects and yet is very little known. Some are spindle-shaped or wormlike, but others are flattened and appear well adapted for locomotion through the litter layer. Moreover, many soil animals have been shown to be able to round up into a ball. Among these are bettle-mites, isopods and glomerid millipedes such rolling up has been interpreted as a means of defense against predators.

The "edaphon" (soil flora and fauna, from the Greek for "soil"), can be classified on the basis of general behavior as follows: 1. Organisms which attach to the soil; bacteria and fungi. 2. Organisms which swim through the soil water, among them flagellates, ciliates, and small nematodes. 3. Organisms which creep through the soil; these include rhizopods, rotifers, enchytraeids, certain earthworms, millipedes, isopods, mites, springtails and some insect larvae. 4. Organisms which burrow

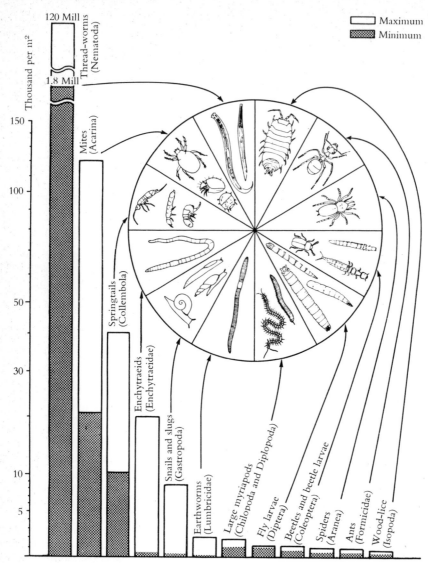

Thousand per m²

120 Mill   Thread-worms (Nematoda)

1.8 Mill

Maximum
Minimum

150

100

50

30

10

5

Mites (Acarina)

Springtails (Collembola)

Enchytraeids (Enchytraeidae)

Snails and slugs (Gastropoda)

Earthworms (Lumbricidae)

Large myriapods (Chilopoda and Diplopoda)

Fly larvae (Diptera)

Beetles and beetle larvae (Coleoptera)

Spiders (Aranea)

Ants (Formicidae)

Wood-lice (Isopoda)

Fig. 13-11. Density of the animal populations in a European meadow soil (one square meter) to a depth of about 30 cm.

through the soil; most of the soil annelids, many insects and insect larvae and other permanent soil dwellers as well as part-time soil animals like the mole and a number of mouse species.

Terrestrial communities must often manage with a minimal supply of water. To protect themselves during the occasional drying out of the soil some of its inhabitants, such as the amoebas, flagellates, ciliates, rotifers and tardigrades, form cysts; others—for example, certain nematodes— enter a state of anabiosis in which the water in the body is reduced to a minimum and vital processes are temporarily suspended. The environmental conditions prevailing in the soil make it necessary for the organisms to alter their vertical distribution from time to time and to make seasonal migrations to different levels; the migrations of earthworms can take them to depths as great as three meters.

Table 13–1. Approximate numbers and weights of the most important groups of plants and animals in European soils, calculated for a block of soil 1 m square on the surface and 30 cm deep (from Dunger, 1970).

Group	Average number of individuals	Optimum	Weight in grams (average)	Maximum weight in grams
Microflora				
Bacteria	1,000 billion	1 million billion	50	500
Actinomycetes	10 billion	10,000 billion	50	500
Fungi	1 billion	1,000 billion	100	1,000
Algae	1 million	10 billion	1	15
Microfauna (0.002–0.2 mm)				
Flagellata	500 billion	1,000 billion		
Rhizopoda	100 billion	500 billion	10	100
Ciliata	1 million	100 million		
Mesofauna (0.2–2 mm)				
Rotifers (Rotatoria)	25,000	600,000	0.01	0.3
Thread-worms (Nematoda)	1 million	20 million	1	20
Mites (Acarina)	100,000	400,000	1	10
Springtails (Collembola)	50,000	400,000	0.6	10
Macrofauna (2–20 mm)				
Enchytraeidae	10,000	200,000	2	26
Snails and slugs (Gastropoda)	50	1,000	1	30
Spiders (Araneae)	50	200	0.2	1
Wood-lice (Isopoda)	50	200	0.5	1.5
Millipedes (Diplopoda)	150	500	4	8
Centipedes (Chilopoda)	50	300	0.4	2
Other Myriapoda	100	2,000	0.05	1
Beetles and larvae (Coleoptera)	100	600	1.5	20
Fly larvae (Diptera)	100	1,000	1	10
Other insects	150	15,000	1	15
Megafauna (20–200 mm)				
Earthworms (Lumbricidae)	80	800	40	400
Vertebrates	0.001	0.1	0.1	10

How dense, then, are the populations of soil organisms? The litter and soil horizons house far greater numbers of plants and animals than is generally supposed, though the various estimates available are often not comparable (Fig. 13-11 and Table 13-1). Systematic statistical determinations of the organisms to be found in the various soil strata show that there are quantitative differences between soils and provide a measure of soil fertility, but lengthy sifting and selection procedures (see Color plate, p. 228) are necessary to achieve these. Extensive measurement and classification programs are involved as well, but with the current ominous lack of specialists in all branches of ecological research, such programs encounter difficulties which may soon become insuperable.

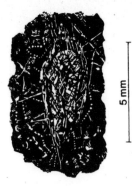

Fig. 13-12. A net to catch prey, spun by a sciophilid larva (Diptera) on the leaf of a copper beech. Springtails are paralysed by droplets of saliva and their body contents are sucked out by the larva.

▷
Above: Among the characteristic inhabitants of the African, South American and Australian grass plains are large ground birds. The picture shows a grassland savanna in northwestern Australia with two emus.
Lower left: Once the characteristic animal of the North American prairies, the bison now survives only in preserves; this herd is in Roosevelt Park, North Dakota.
Lower right: An Australian steppe scene with termite hills.

14   Steppes and Savannas

By T. Haltenorth

◁
Upper left: Zebras in the
African bush steppe at the
foot of Mt. Kilimanjaro.
Upper right: Thomson's
gazelles at the edge of a
dry lake-bed (Lake Lagaya,
Serengeti).
Lower left: Elephants in
Manyara National Park
(Tanzania).
Lower right: Typical arid
savanna in eastern Africa
(Kenya) with scattered
trees; antelopes at a water
hole.

The steppes

The extensive, more or less treeless plains of grass in the interior of the continents, under which the water table is low, are called steppes and savannas. The distinctive characteristic of both habitats is the abundance of monocotyledons, especially grasses (family Gramineae). Because of the special soil, vegetation and climate here, the number of species of both plants and animals may be smaller than in forest habitats, but each species is relatively abundant. This is most impressively evident in the herds of medium-sized to large mammals roaming the steppe; but these have been a favorite prey of humans since the ages when man subsisted by hunting, and with the passage of time many of them have been exterminated.

In some regions precipitation is so scarce that the steppe or savanna grades into semi-desert (or desert-steppe) and eventually into real desert, with no distinct boundaries. Such desert-steppes look like deserts during the dry season, but after it has rained a carpet of plants appears that can feed a quite varied fauna. There may also be a transitional zone between steppe and forest, in regions where the water table is higher; islands of shrubs and trees appear, and along the damp floors of valleys cut out by watercourses (which, in most cases, are still present) the forests extend far into the steppe. In such regions there is a belt of forest-steppe or of woodlands bordering the forest proper. In tropical grasslands there may be scattered single trees, acacias and other species, which can even survive the frequent fires that sweep through the grass. This is the savanna, a broad range of communities that in some tropical areas occur between closed forests and semidesert or thorn scrub.

Steppe, then, is the general term for grass-covered plains in the temperate zone, where plant growth is hampered by heat and dryness in summer and by cold in winter. Because of the low water table, no stands of even moderately large trees can develop. The prairies of North America may be classified as steppes, though they differ in some respects from the Eurasian grasslands, as we shall see below.

On black earth rich in humus (chernozem, from the Russian for black earth) grow the tall-grass steppes of taller mixed with shorter grasses; many of these are characterized by feather grass (*Stipa*) in Eurasia or bluestem (*Andropogon*) in North America, with an average annual precipitation of 300–450 mm, falling mainly in spring and early summer. The life span of grasses and herbs is short, as compared with that of trees. The generations fade and die in rapid succession, providing the soil with humus at a high rate; in fact, grassland soils contain five to ten times as much humus as do forest soils. They have a permanent crumbly structure, and they are well aerated. All these factors permit the development of a great variety of microorganisms and small animals, from protozoans to earthworms. As a consequence, steppe soils are very fertile, and can provide food for many animals, particularly rodents and ungulates. Because of their fertility, the tall-grass steppes give the highest yields when they are put under cultivation; wheat grows there especially well. Today almost all of them are planted with grain—that is, grasses especially selected for their value as crops. In the long run, this specialization is harmful, since a natural community of humus-producing plants, developed slowly over millennia, is thereby destroyed.

Tall-grass steppes on chernozem

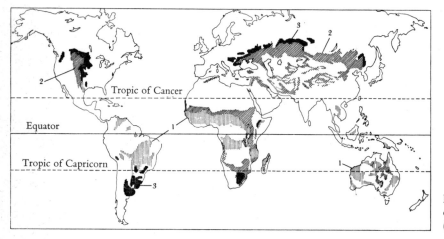

Fig. 14-1. The distribution of the savannas (1), steppes (2) and prairies (3).

As land plants gradually evolved, through algae, lichens, mosses, ferns, cycads, ginkgos and conifers to angiosperms, the quality of the soil steadily improved; at the same time, the number of species of small animal living in the soil increased. With the addition and evolution of flowering plants to the grasslands, soil quality reached a high point in the chernozem of the steppes. An important factor in the development of this high-quality soil was the pollinating activity of certain insects, in particular bees and butterflies. The best soil is produced when the grasses are mingled with insect-pollinated herbs, especially composites and legumes, in the right proportions. Of the grassland plants in the chernozem regions 20% of

Evolution of the steppe

the species are pollinated by wind, and 80% by insects. This 80%, about a third of which are Compositae and another sizable fraction legumes, significantly affect the quality of the soil. This is because grass, composite and papilionaceous species, which together comprise two thirds of all grassland species, produce about 97% of the humus. When men plow up the chernozem steppe and turn it into grain fields, they eliminate both natural grasses and forbs (grassland plants other than grasses); and man's crop plants are much less effective humus-producers.

Chernozems are widespread in northern China, the Ukraine, Rumania, Hungary, the vicinities of Vienna, Magdeburg, and the upper Rhein, midwestern USA, and southern Canada; a similar form is also found in the South American pampas.

Short-grass steppes on chestnut soil

If the humus content of the steppe soil is only 2–3% its color lightens to a chestnut brown; accordingly, it is called brown or chestnut soil (castanozem). The crumb structure is less pronounced and hence the soil is less well aerated; as a result the microfauna is not so diverse, nor the

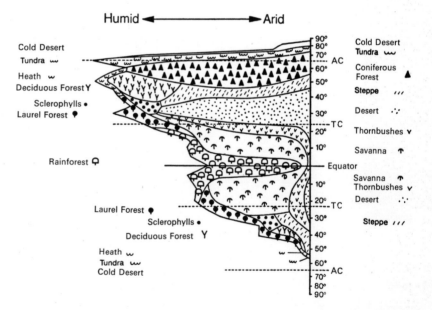

Fig. 14-2. Ecological diagram showing the distribution of vegetation at different latitudes as a function of humidity.

fertility as great, as in the chernozem steppe. But chestnut soil supports short grasses useful to man as pasture for his domestic animals, and it can be used for large-scale cultivation of grain. Chestnut soil adjoins chernozem on the relatively arid side—in the southern part of the Soviet Union north of the Caspian and Aral Seas and from there eastward along the northern edge of the central Asian mountains, and in North America west of the chernozem region.

In the spring, bulbs and perennial herbs put forth new growth between the bunch grasses and others characteristic of these steppes. Often dwarf shrubs, thorn bushes, semishrubs and succulents are also scattered among the grasses, and these may be used to designate particular regions—for example, in the terms wormwood-steppe, tragacanth-steppe, and so on. In the tropics, there are steppe grasslands on the cool upper slopes of the mountains and the plateaus; among these are the high plains of South Africa known as "veldt." *Savannas*

The tropical and subtropical grasslands, with either sparsely scattered trees and bushes or none at all, are called savannas. Here the average annual precipitation, concentrated in one or two rainy seasons, is 900–1500 mm. The scattered trees are mostly flat-topped acacias (Fig. 14-3), spurges, baobabs (Fig. 14-5), wax palms, and eucalyptus. The boundary between savanna and forest, which may be either sharp or indistinct, is usually determined by the nature of the soil, though fire or clearing by man can also be involved.

The savannas

Savannas with thorn trees or bushes are characteristic of Africa. Most of the thorny bushes and shrubs are acacias (Fig. 14-4) and other mimosoids, but some belong to other plant families. The climatic conditions are similar in the Australian savannas, but there the shrubs and low trees bear hardly any thorns, even though very many of them are acacias. In South America the place of thorny shrubs and trees is taken by the spiny cactuses. The prevalence of thorns in the African savanna plants is no doubt due to the great numbers of leaf- and twig-eating ungulates which, over millions of years of evolution, exerted strong selective pressure on the plants to develop defense mechanisms. In Australia such protective measures were not necessary, since before the continent was colonized by the white man there were no leaf- or twig-eating animals to speak of, apart from a few species of kangaroo.

Fig. 14-3. An acacia with the nests of weaver-birds hanging from it.

Regularly recurring fires not only keep the woods from invading the savanna, but also eliminate fire-sensitive plants and leave only those resistant to burning. When dry grass burns, minerals are freed to serve as fertilizer for the new growth; young grasses and herbs thus follow one another in more rapid succession and considerably increase the food available to the herbivores (Figs. 14-6 and 14-7). As the fire sweeps past it kills a number of small animals unable to flee in time, but since the heat barely penetrates the soil many escape by hiding in holes and burrows, under stones or in thick clumps of grass. When the fire has passed they emerge again, and those that have fled return to the new growth.

The large herbivores also help keep the forest at bay, by grazing the plains and biting off the tree seedlings with the grass. There is a state of equilibrium among natural animal communities such that they do not compete with one another directly for the individual plant species. Each animal species prefers certain plants, certain parts of the plants, or certain times of the year; some species range widely and others stay in one place. As long as this balance is maintained—and the predatory carnivores contribute to its maintenance—the vegetation suffers no damage. The African steppes and savannas show particularly clearly the consequences

Fig. 14-4. This acacia shelters an ant colony, living in the round galls on the branches. The ants in turn protect the tree from grazing animals (see Chapter 8).

Fig. 14-5. In its thick, shapeless trunk the baobab can store large quantities of water for use later, in time of drought.

of replacing the wild herbivores by domestic grazers; the grasslands can feed up to ten times as many wild as domestic animals. Cattle and the other domestic species do not browse indiscriminately in one spot at a time, but wander over considerable areas eating chiefly the grass; as a result, the proportions of the different plant species gradually change, and if grazing is excessive even the dense layer of grass just above the ground may be destroyed. While grasslands can produce about 12,000–25,000 kg of wild-animal biomass per hectare, the same area produces only 5000–7500 kg of highly domesticated animals and 2500–3500 kg of native cattle. Unfortunately, overgrazing has already transformed large areas of grassland into desert in all the warm countries.

Savanna is found in Africa between 15° north and 25° south latitude, but it is not limited to Africa; in South America it is known as chaco, campos and llanos, and in Australia as scrub. The South American llanos were originally called "savanna" by the Spaniards, and the name was later adopted for all grasslands of the same type.

Toward the end of the lower Cretaceous (about 70 million years ago), the angiosperms began a spurt of evolution that made them the largest of all plant groups, with about 250,000 species at present. Within the class Monocotyledonae evolved the grasses, the family Gramineae. This family soon dispersed throughout the world, and in many places became the dominant plant group; at present it comprises about 4500 species. Large grassy plains came into being, like those now found in the steppes and savannas. These represented a new, easily exploited source of food for the herbivorous mammals.

With the extinction of the dinosaurs and increasing abundance of angiosperms the mammals, which were already evolving rapidly toward the end of the Mesozoic, were given a powerful impetus to further development. The superabundance of vegetation served as the basic food for members of widely different orders—the rodents, ungulates, lagomorphs, a majority of the primates, and a number of marsupials (the phalangerids, wombats, and macropodids). They were joined by a vast army of plant-eating birds and invertebrates, chiefly mollusks and insects.

In contrast to animal prey, high in nutritional value but hard to catch, plant food is readily available but less nutritious, and must be eaten in larger amounts. Herbivores therefore had to evolve a number of morphological and behavioral modifications. For example, kangaroos, hyraxes, the ancient camels, and ruminants (i.e., chevrotains, deer, giraffes and bovids) each evolved independently the habit of cud-chewing, by which cellulose is made digestible with the help of symbiotic bacteria and protozoans. Another advantage of cud-chewing is that less time is required for the actual intake of food than if it were chewed immediately; the danger of attack by predators, greatest when an animal is grazing in the open, is thus reduced. Separation of the processes of intake and mastication allows each to be done at the most suitable time.

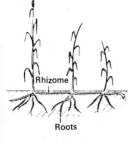

Fig. 14-6. Many grasses have highly branched root systems, with only the upper part approaching the surface. Thus they can grow back immediately after the shoots have been destroyed by fire or grazing.

Among these herbivores, between the late Oligocene and the early Miocene, there evolved groups specialized for eating the grasses, grass seeds, and forbs of the plains. Small and medium-sized mammals adapted themselves to the grassland environment in various ways; some came to live in underground burrows, others moved about through tunnels in the grass or became extremely rapid runners or jumpers. Large mammals like cattle and rhinoceros were protected by their size alone or—in the case of the antelopes and gazelles, for example—were so light and swift that they could outdistance their predators on the open plains. Some birds, too, can run very fast; among them are the ostriches, rheas, emus and bustards. Other members of the grassland fauna are the vulture, which finds a steady supply of carrion to eat, and grasshoppers and termites, billions of which feed on the various herbs; the total biomass of these insects can be enormous. In building their nests, a characteristic feature of the landscape, the termites move large quantities of earth. In all grasslands there come to be typical species, the general morphology and behavior of which bear the stamp of the grazing habit or of life in open country. As herbivores or carnivores, they exploit what the habitat offers in a variety of ways.

High-speed runners

Grasslands, then, are unmistakably an ecosystem in themselves. All their plants and animals, together with the conditions in their environment—the soil, the water, the air and the temperature—constitute a quite specific network of interactions which, despite local modifications, is fundamentally consistent throughout the world. In every grassland community on earth there are animals in the categories walker, runner, jumper, burrower, plains carnivore or bird of prey; the position of each in the ecosystem is equivalent everywhere.

In Eurasia many herbivorous species, such as the wild horse, camel, yak and *Equus hemionus*, have been almost or entirely exterminated— as have some of their predators, the leopard and cheetah. These steppes are still inhabited by the saiga antelope and other species of antelope and gazelle, and by such carnivores as the wolf, red dog and eagle. The corresponding herbivores in Africa are the wart-hog, wild ass, steppe zebra steppe elephant, wide-mouthed rhinoceros, many antelopes and gazelles, and the ostrich and bustard. These are hunted by lions, leopards, cheetahs, servals, caracal lynxes, hyenas, wild dogs and eagles. The North American prairies were once grazed by bison and the pronghorn antelope, which now are restricted to the national parks and other preserves, and by ancient perissodactyls and camels which became extinct toward the end of the Ice Age; the large carnivores here are the wolf, coyote and puma. In the South American pampas there still live small camels, though their numbers are steadily declining; the perissodactyls and ground sloths did not survive the end of the Ice Age. South American ground birds include two species of rhea. There are few large carnivores—the puma and the jaguar. The situation is similar in Australia, where the large kangaroos

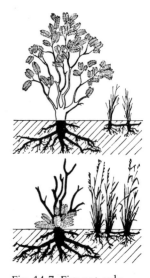

Fig. 14-7. Fire not only destroys, but can also encourage growth. The upper picture shows a mesquite bush, a North American leguminous tree, which suppresses the grass in the vicinity. After a fire the grass recovers faster than the bush and grows more vigorously now that there is less competition (lower picture).

and the emu play the role of herbivores, and the carnivores are represented by the marsupial wolf (probably exinct today) and sometimes the Tasmanian devil. The moas of New Zealand and the giant ostriches and prosimians of Madagascar had no natural enemies; they have all been killed off by man.

These, then, are the most important herbivores and carnivores of the grassy plains, but there are many less conspicuous animals as well. To name some of the medium-sized herbivores; in the different areas these include rabbits, marmots, ground squirrels, prairies dogs, pampas hares, viscachas, guinea pigs, wombats, rat-, hare-, and other kangaroos, prairie chickens, partridges, tinamous, francolins, bustards, lapwings and other birds. These are the prey of jackals, various foxes, maned wolves, martens, tayras, polecats, skunks, wild cats (*Felis sylvestris*), eagles, falcons and other birds of prey. The hordes of small grass-eaters include rodents like the hamster, vole, jerboa, jumping mouse, tuco-tuco, karroo rat, pocket gopher and many bird species; their predators are small mammals such as the weasel, grison, dwarf mongoose and small cats, and birds such as the buzzard, falcon and kite. Finally, there is a vast army of plant- and seed-eating insects and other invertebrates.

Many small animals of the open plains protect themselves from storms and predators by hiding in the ground; tunnels and underground chambers are dug by certain rabbits, most of the rodents, armadillos, aardvarks, and foxes. These structures are sometimes used by prairie owls, certain nuthatches, finches, snakes, lizards and tortoises, but there are also lizards, tortoises and frogs that can dig or burrow into the ground themselves. Burrows, especially those of ground squirrels and other small mammals, are the favorite shelters and breeding grounds of fleas, lice, and similar parasites. Since large numbers of these digging animals make their way through the soil, they increase its fertility considerably by aerating, loosening and redistributing it and by breaking up the large lumps. In so doing, they play an important role in the grassland community.

The herbivores that do not hide underground in the steppes and savannas depend upon speed for their safety. The grasslands are thus the home of many of the runners, hoppers, jumpers, as well as animals that slip through tunnels in the grass. These range from perissodactyls, antelopes, gazelles, wild dogs and some of the cats to the ostriches, bustards and gallinaceous birds, kangaroos of all sizes, marsupial jerboas, jumping and running mice, jumping hare, frilled lizards, grasshoppers and cicadas. The terrain is so flat and open that predators can be spotted at a great distance. The large mammals and birds, on their long legs, are easily able to keep watch, and their vision is often very acute. The smaller mammals have more trouble seeing over the grass, but many of them—various rabbits, rodents, and small carnivores—are adept at sitting up on their hind legs to scan their surroundings.

When animals of the same species gather in groups, they are more likely to detect their enemies in time, and in some cases are able to fight them off. For this reason, the grassland fauna contains a greater number of social species than that of woodlands. Grassland animals often form flocks or herds, some of them consisting of several species of ungulate, or a mixture of ungulate and bird species (for example, the zebra-gnu-ostrich societies). Predators like the wolf, the African wild dog, and the red dog hunt in packs; others, like the lion, operate as family groups. Ground-dwelling birds, such as the prairie chicken, partridge and guinea fowl, gather in "coveys," and rabbits and rodents form "colonies." These colonies may be very densely populated, as in the case of ground squirrels, or may extend over some square kilometers, like the "towns" of the prairie dogs, which before man invaded the prairies often comprised millions of inhabitants.

Of all the continental habitats, the grasslands produced the greatest animal biomass per unit area. As a result, they were from the very beginning the most attractive to man, the hunter. As a steppe-dwelling primate with upright posture, man was intrinsically well adapted to this habitat, and his mental powers developed as he struggled there for food, shelter and means of defense. He used his increasing intelligence to invent weapons and improve his methods of hunting and trapping, and this was the undoing of the large herbivores and the carnivores that depended upon them for food.

The role of man

There are still differences of opinion as to whether the primitive humans contributed appreciably to the extermination of any animal species, and the various views are often in direct contradiction to one another. Some maintain that as early as the Acheulian—the subdivision of the early Stone Age associated with hand-stone culture—man destroyed many animal inhabitants of the African steppes and savannas. The same thing is said to have happened in North America when man first immigrated over the Bering Strait, 40,000 years ago. It is a fact that in the late Ice Age about twenty-six African and thirty-five North American genera of large mammals disappeared. But those representing the opposed view argue that the weapons in use at that time were so inadequate that they could not possibly have caused such widespread destruction, and that the large mammals which became extinct toward the end of the Ice Age were the victims of large-scale climatic changes that affected the vegetation.

In any case it is certain that the islands Madagascar and New Zealand, reached much later by well-armed men and with faunas essentially free of any natural enemies, were disastrously affected by the continual hunting activities of these immigrants. In Madagascar no less than fourteen species of large prosimian, four species of giant bird, and presumably the aardvark and small hippopotamus became extinct in a relatively short time; in New Zealand, about nineteen species of moa and a considerable number of other bird species met the same fate.

But the most severe disturbance of the equilibrium between human and animal populations by the White Man has occurred since firearms came into use. Today the large animals of the steppes and savannas in all parts of the world have been to a great extent destroyed; the former grassy plains have been transformed into fields and pastures. As the original flora vanished, so did the small and medium-sized animals. Only in national parks and other nature preserves can one still see remnants of this unique community, evolved over millions of years. The human hunters of the savannas, who owed their development to this open environment, destroyed their homeland and the inconceivable numbers of animals which, as partners in the community, had brought the ecosystem "steppe and savanna" into being.

The holarctic steppe

The Eurasian steppe is a belt extending for about 7000 kilometers, from Hungary into Manchuria. The western outpost is the "Puszta" of Hungary, with a projection swinging north from the lowlands around the Neusiedler See and into Austria. Here the so-called Pannonian basin was filled in by alluvium from the Danube and Theiss rivers; before man had brought these rivers under control they often changed their courses, creating lakes and swampy regions so that the plains were enlivened by the presence of water birds. Sand dunes formed, interspersed with saline swamps and alkali steppes, and these too enriched the flora and fauna. Today the Puszta is almost all under cultivation; hardly anything remains of its former magnificence. Among the typical animals were the imperial, booted, and lesser spotted eagle, red-footed and saker falcon, great and pigmy bustard, pratincole, thick-knee and other species of bird; on damper ground there occasionally stopped enormous numbers of white-fronted geese, as well as large flocks of greylag and bean geese. In the swamps bred spoonbills, great white egrets, glossy ibis, terns and other swamp and water birds. The steppe itself was inhabited by small mammals like the hamster, the ground-squirrel, the palearctic mole rat and the Turkestan polecat.

Toward the east, the most prominent continuation of the Puszta is the southern Russian steppe. This extends from the eastern banks of the lower Danube in Bessarabia to the Ural River, and south to the mountains of the Crimean peninsula and to the Caucasus range. There are three bands of vegetation in this area, from north-northwest to south-southeast: forest-steppe, grass steppe, and arid steppe.

Forest-steppe belt

The forest-steppe marks the transition from woodland to grassland; it is a mosaic of strips of deciduous forest interspersed with grass steppe. The forest grows where the soil is light and coarse, and where the water table is high enough for the roots of the trees to reach; a hectare of forest consumes much more water than a hectare of steppe. The plants of the grass steppe, on the other hand, grow on fine-grain chernozem. In the north the forest predominates, and in the south the steppe. The forest-steppe is inhabited by both forest and steppe animals, since each of these groups can find a suitable environment there. The open areas are the home of the spotted souslik, Turkestan polecat, meadowlark, calandra lark, yellowhammer, whinchat, Montagu's and pallid harriers, great bustard and other plains birds; in the shrubbery and forest there are beavers and other rodents, various species of marten, and fox, roe deer, and elk. Among the many characteristic bird species are a great number of songbirds, wild pigeons, ravens, and birds of prey like hawks, sparrow-hawks, common and honey buzzards, kites and the golden eagle. The habitat is shared by certain reptiles (for example, sand lizards, slow-worms and Orsini's viper) as well as a number of frogs and toads.

The grass steppe adjoins the forest-steppe on the south, and its southern edge runs approximately from Kishniev in the west to Ufa in the east. The soil beneath it is deep chernozem, in which the black humus horizon extends as far down as 170 cm, growing lighter in color toward the bottom. In the upper layers the many dense roots provide an abundance of humus. Countless earthworms, insect larvae, rodents and other small animals provide a good mixing of minerals through the soil. This region of steppe is therefore characterized by an abundance of plant species; one can distinguish about twenty grasses, mostly medium to short species, and about 180 different forbs, of which peonies, dwarf irises, anemones, sage, the ranunculaceous *Adonis* and many other flowering plants brighten the green background with spots of color.

Toward the south, feather grasses predominate; in the flowering season, June and July, their long light awns make a waving sheet of silver. The northern belt of feather-grass steppe, with a plentiful admixture of forbs, grows on chernozem of intermediate depth, with a humus horizon as deep as 75 cm, whereas the southern belt contains fewer forbs and the humus horizon of the chrenozem extends only to 50 cm. Because the forbs of the feather-grass steppe are not as drought-resistant as the grasses, they not only grow fewer in number toward the south but also have shorter seasons for growth, flowering and ripening of fruit—all of which must be completed before the onset of summer drought. A few plants manage to flower later by virtue of very deep roots or roots that can store water (Fig. 14-15). The characteristic plant cover becomes lower toward the south and also more open, so that spaces are left for small annual herbs and bulb plants such as crocuses, tulips, and star-of-Bethlehem.

At one time wild horses, bison, aurochs, red deer and saiga antelope ranged the grass steppes. The horses, deer, aurochs and bison had their summer pastures there and in the fall migrated back to the forests along the river valleys or into the forest-steppe; the saigas were able to remain in the steppe all winter. If these animals had not been exterminated, and had the grass steppes not been plowed under except for small preserves, it would not now be necessary to worry about feeding people by agriculture; the wild game, if used carefully on a long-term basis would have

Grass steppe

Fig. 14-8. Characteristic grasses of the central Asian steppes: feather grass (1), sedge (2), and fescue (3).

Large herbivores

provided more protein than all the crops put together. Moreover, as in the African savannas, the wild herbivores keep the plant community well balanced; they graze off the superfluous leaves, so that they do not form a matted layer on the ground, help seeds to germinate by driving them into the ground as they walk, and provide large quantities of good fertilizer.

Other animals that contribute a great deal to the vigor of the grass steppe are the many small and medium-sized rodents. Steppe marmots dig their burrows so deep that they bring humus-free calcareous soil to the surface and distribute it around the entrances; ground squirrels pile the earth they excavate into small hills. On these there arises a different plant community, which gives way only gradually to the original plants. Where there are many rodent burrows together the whole aspect of the landscape is changed, with countless little hills and a bright mosaic of vegetation.

The density of rodent populations, particularly steppe marmots and ground squirrels, is often very high. Up to 35,000 animals have been counted in one square kilometer; in a day they can consume about two metric tons of green food. The exrement and urine they produce return as fertilizer to the soil. The amount of earth moved by such large rodents is also considerable. Each steppe marmot brings to the surface about 1000 to 2000 cubic centimeters of soil per year. With 35,000 marmots in a square kilometer, that amounts to between 35,000 and 70,000 cubic meters annually. The ground squirrels are smaller, but they live even closer together and thus altogether achieve just about as much in a given area. If one pictures thousands of square kilometers populated by such rodents, as was the case and still is in some parts of the Asian steppes, one can appreciate that these animals moved, aerated and fertilized millions of square meters of soil and were therefore important elements in the formation of the chernozem.

Small rodents like the vole, lemming, and various species of hamster make shallow burrows in the upper humus layer, which thus receives an extra amount of turning, aeration and fertilization. These animals gradually eat all the plants around the entrances to their burrows, some of them down to the roots; then they move out and build new burrows where the grass is thick. On the bare earth they have left behind, fertilized with dung and urine, a new plant community appears—first annuals, then biennials, and finally perennials, until eventually the old community is reestablished. Every four or five years the small rodents multiply enormously and lay bare large areas of soil. Then lack of food, bodily weakness and nervous strain resulting from the continual hostile confrontations between the animals bring about high mortality, and this is further increased by the predations of numerous carnivores. The sudden disappearance of the little rodents gives the plants time to grow over the bare spots and, in the sequence given above, reestablish the original type of community. Then the ungulates return to the area to graze.

Rodents

Fig. 14-9. When the steppe summer approaches its end, the ground squirrel family begins to build its underground burrow. The picture shows, from top to bottom, burrows one year, two years, and eight years old. Many other rodents dig through the steppe in a similar way, contributing to the maintenance of chemical equilibrium in the soil and thus to a greater diversity of plant and animal life.

Fig. 14-10. The European souslik (*Citellus citellus*) is the only species of ground squirrel also found in central Europe.

The populations of large herbivores were once kept in balance primarily by wolves; today the red fox and corsac fox, badger and a few species of marten hunt the smaller herbivores. A new predator has been introduced, the eastern Asian raccoon-dog. Otters and mink hunt along the rivers. Among birds the most conspicuous are the bustard, demoiselle crane, roller, bee-eater and a number of birds of prey; these live alongside larks, pipits and the rose-colored starling. Typical reptiles are Orsini's viper, the European whip snake, and the four-lined rat snake. When migratory locusts appear in great swarms, they present many birds, as well as small predatory mammals and a few rodents, with a high-protein supplement to their diets.

In the south and southeast the feather-grass steppe gives way to arid steppe. This is found mainly between the Volga and Ural Rivers, on what was once the bottom of the Caspian Sea; it has been exposed since the last Ice Age, when the water level was about two dozen meters higher. The chestnut soil here has only a thin layer of humus, and in places is so sandy that the arid steppe is replaced by semidesert. The dominant plants here are wormwood and other *Artemisia* species adapted to saline soils. The soils may have more or less high concentrations of salts derived from the former sea floor. Some of the many scattered brine pools and shallow lakes are so salty that no plants can grow in them and only a few highly adapted herbs grow even on the banks.

Characteristic mammals of the wormwood-steppe are the saiga antelope and ground squirrels—the little souslik and Aral yellow souslik. In April the sousliks wake up from their winter sleep; by the end of June they must have finished rearing their young, for soon the great heat and drought begin. To escape these harsh conditions, they withdraw into their burrows and again enter a state of anabiosis, with their metabolism turned down to the most economical rate. Thus they spend almost three-quarters of the year in a resting state, living on the fat stored in their bodies; when they appear again in the spring their water content is minimal and they have lost four-fifths of their original weight. When digging their burrows, the ground squirrels in certain regions bring saline soil to the surface, which attracts halophytes. But they can also do the reverse, bringing up soil which is not saline and thus decreasing the salinity of the surface soil, so that non-halophytic plants invade the area. Altogether, they have a large influence upon the vegetation (Fig. 14-9).

The saiga is also very well adapted to the extreme conditions in the arid steppe, with its dust storms in summer and snow storms in winter. By the early 1920's it had almost been exterminated by excessive hunting, but thanks to strict conservation measures in the 1930's, and to its high fecundity, it recovered sufficiently that there are now almost three million of these animals in the steppe of the Volga and Kaspi regions. By controlled shooting of 300,000 saigas per year for food, the people there obtain far more nutritional value than they could from domestic cattle, which

Arid steppe

Fig. 14-11. The saiga has little protection against predators in the dry, barren wormwood steppe. But the newborn antelopes can crouch down to resemble the hills of earth thrown up by ground squirrels and marmots, so closely that they can hardly be distinguished from a distance.

Fig. 14-12. When it walks the saiga stretches its neck far out in front.

Fig. 14-13. The miniature proboscis at the end of the saiga's snout is an adaptation to the dust storms in its habitat: the large spaces in the nose filter the inhaled air and keep back the dust.

would barely sustain themselves and destroy the vegetation in the process. Apart from saigas and sousliks, inhabitants of the arid steppe are small hamsters, running and jumping mice, the eared hedgehog, Turkestan and marbled polecats, corsac fox, and wolf. The birds are especially characteristic—the many species of lark; the sand grouse, which makes mass invasions of central and western Europe every few decades; and the houbara bustard and tawny eagle. The most notable reptiles are the sand boa, Haly's viper, the alligator lizard, and several species of agama.

On the other side of the Ural River the steppe continues eastward through Asia south of the taiga into Mongolia and Manchuria. Here, too, there is a broad belt of forest-steppe between taiga and steppe; toward the south the grass steppe gives way to arid or wormwood steppe, semidesert and in places eventually to true desert (for example, the Gobi and Kara Kum). In June, when most of the year's precipitation falls, the grass steppe becomes resplendent with flowers of all colors. In the arid steppe the carpet of flowers appears earlier, together with the spring rains in February and March. The crocuses and meadow saffron are followed by tulips, buttercups, and other plants, all of which must complete their growth, flowering and fruiting by the summer solstice, when the heat begins.

Sometimes little bushes, such as the papilionaceous *Caragana*, meadowsweet, broom and dwarf almond are scattered through the steppe, particularly where the land spreads out in shallow undulations as far as one can see. In the arid steppe, too, there is a semishrublike orache species growing between the wormwood, fescue, hair grass, and feather grass. The spring rains leave many pools behind in the grass steppe (particularly the wormwood steppe), since in some places there are soil strata impermeable to water at depths of about twenty centimeters; but by the end of spring they have dried up again. In summer, when the temperature rises as high as 38°C in the shade, the wind breaks the stalks of the dried grass, leaving a surface of straw above which one sees only the steppe thistle, with its red flowers. The winter brings icy winds and snow storms, with temperatures occasionally falling to −50°C.

At one time wild horses, camels and *Equus hemionus* wandered through the Asian steppes—large mammals which today are rare or nearly extinct. They were accompanied by saigas and various species of gazelle. In the wooded river valleys there were aurochs, bison and wild boar. Kiangs, wild yaks, chirus and wild sheep grazed on the high steppes. Of these, only the saigas and gazelles have remained in considerable numbers. Their predators too, the wolves, red dogs and inner-Asian subspecies of tiger, leopard and cheetah, have been almost or entirely eradicated here by the senseless behavior of humans. Eared hedgehogs, rabbits and a number of rodents (five-toed jerboas, mole-rats, and molelemmings, to mention a few) still live there, and there are large colonies of pikas, marmots and ground squirrels. All of these except the hares build burrows. Some, like the mole-lemming and mole-rat, live underground permanently or nearly so, digging tunnels down for as much as five meters and eating the roots, bulbs, and tubers of the steppe plants. They are hunted by red and steppe foxes, steppe cats, manuls, Turkestan and marbled polecats, as well as by the pallid harrier, snake eagle, common buzzard, kestrel, lesser kestrel, hobby, saker falcon and, if the forest-steppe margin is included, by the eagle owl. The imperial eagle and steppe eagle sweep in wide circles over the plains. Some corvid birds also feed on small mammals. The steppe birds mentioned above —the great and pigmy bustards, cranes, the partridges *Perdrix perdrix* and *P. dauuricae*, and many others—are also found here, as are Orsini's viper and the steppe agama (Fig. 14-14).

Fig. 14-14. In the food chain of the steppe-dwellers (Africa is used here as an example) the rabbits and rodents (3. Jumping hare; 8. Crested hamster; 9. Mole-rat *Heterocephalus*; 10. Northern ground squirrel; 11. Mole-rat *Heliophobus*) are the food of an army of predators. At night owls like the milky eagle-owl (1) hunt them by ear. During the day they are threatened by birds of prey like the Old World kestrel (2) when they are aboveground, and by snakes (4. Cobra) and the striped weasel (5) which can crawl into their burrows. The black-backed jackal (6) detects them by smell, and the big-eared fox (7) is guided by its sense of hearing. Both canids can dig the rodents out of their burrows. The rabbits and rodents protect themselves from all these enemies by great fecundity and effective defense mechanisms.

When winter comes, many of the birds move further south or migrate to distant winter quarters. Crows tend to remain in the steppes; they feed on carrion, which is more plentiful in winter. The smaller carnivores have a difficult time; they have no winter dormant period as do many rodents, and must depend for food upon other animals that are active during the winter—hares, pikas, mice, voles, lemmings and shrews; but all of these, except for the hares, live under the snow. When wolves and tigers were still living in the Eurasian steppes, the wolves found sufficient prey among the ungulates; the tiger, an inhabitant of the

The steppe in winter

reedy woodland in the swamps and fringing bodies of water, fed on the wild boar there. Large ungulates can range widely, and they will travel hundreds of kilometers to escape high snow and intense cold. If necessary, these steppe-dwellers will enter the forest-steppe, where the trees break the icy wind. The critical factor in these migrations, though, is the snow cover. If the snow lies too deep, the animals cannot push or dig it away to get at the plants below. Furthermore, it then becomes very difficult for them to move about, since their hooves are small compared to the weight they have to bear, and they sink deep into the snow. Only elk and reindeer find walking somewhat easier, since their hooves are very large and can spread wide apart; the gazelles are relatively well off because they are so light, and the wild boar because the regressed toe is long and can be spread away from the hoof.

Thanks to its broad paws, the wolf has little trouble in catching the ungulates it chases in deep snow. Packs of wolves used to decimate the ungulate populations in the winter. Now, since the saiga antelope is being established as the most valuable human food animal, hundreds of thousands of wolves are being shot, sometimes even from helicopters; as a result, they have practically become extinct in most places. In a single winter a wolf can kill around seventy saigas; most of these are bucks, which were severely weakened during the mating season in November and December and in the winter have no chance to regain their strength. Since the harshness of the winter itself often reduces the numbers of bucks to two or three percent of the population, it is questionable whether this mass slaughter of the wolves really makes sense.

A particular danger in winter is the hoarfrost that surrounds every stalk and twig with a coat of ice, making it so difficult for the ungulates to graze that they cannot obtain the necessary daily ration and lose strength. Ordinarily such conditions last for only a day or two, but every ten to twenty-five years they persist longer, up to one or two months. Then whole herds of ungulates succumb and vanish entirely from certain regions. The interval between two long periods of frost is usually enough to allow the populations to build up again. But if prolonged hoarfrost occurs in two successive winters it kills millions of ungulates; the Mongols have a word for it, *jood*, which means "mass death of hoofed animals." In fairly recent times persistent hoarfrost has completely eradicated the wild sheep in the Transcaspian and Transbaykal regions, the goitered gazelle in the upper Yenisey steppes, and the kulan in Kazakhstan. The elk has the best prospects of survival, since it shelters among the forest-steppe trees in winter; and those of the saiga are almost as good, for it travels rapidly in large herds and can quickly make good its losses.

The New-World counterpart of the Eurasian steppes is the North American prairie. Conditions are somewhat different here, since the amount of precipitation decreases not from north to south, but from

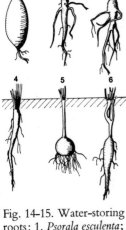

Fig. 14-15. Water-storing roots: 1. *Psorala esculenta*; 2. *Petalostemum candidum*; 3. *P. purpureum*; 4. *Oxytropis lamberti*; 5. *Liatris scariosa*; 6. *L. punctata*.

The North American prairies

east to west, and the different soil types form north-south belts. Before the prairie was plowed for agriculture it extended from northern Alberta and central Saskatchewan south to the Gulf of Mexico, and from the inland slopes of the Rocky Mountains to the belt of parkland and forest in the east. It covered an expanse about 3700 km long and 700–800 km wide. In the north it was bounded by the northern coniferous forest belt, in the east and southeast by the parkland and deciduous forest belt, and in the west by the montane coniferous forest; in the south the boundary was not distinct, for the prairie gave way gradually to sub-tropical savanna.

The prairie region as a whole is a plateau, descending gently toward the north from an altitude of about 900 m in the south. In the southwest there is a stepwise descent into the coastal plain of eastern Texas. It is drained primarily by the Missouri and the lower Mississippi, together with its western tributaries. As in the Russian steppe, most of the rain falls in early summer. At the eastern forest boundary of the prairie the precipitation amounts to an average of 500 to 1000 mm per year, increasing from north to south. In the tall-grass prairie just to the west of this the corresponding value is about 700 mm, in the central mixed-grass prairie about 500 mm, and in the western short-grass prairie about 420 mm. In dry years the rainfall may be diminished by 25% or more. The long periods of drought which occasionally occur dry up the vegetation, except for a few especially drought-resistant plants, so that a number of normal years in succession are required to restore the old composition of the plant communities. In the northern part of the prairie the mean temperature in January is $-20°C$ (and the temperature may fall to $-50°C$ in the course of the winter), whereas in the south the weather is so warm that the monthly average is above 0°C all year.

The length of the dominant prairie grasses decreases from east to west, in correspondence with the decrease in precipitation, so that in moving from east to west one crosses three belts of prairie with a north-south orientation: the tall-grass, mixed-grass, and short-grass prairie. Since the temperature rises toward the south, there is also change in the plant communities of each belt from north to south. In the south late-flowering tropical grasses, primarily species of millet, become dominant. The eastern part, especially the tall-grass belt, once had extremely good soil, but today hardly any sign of it remains; the region has been plowed and planted and now consists of giant fields of grain. The rest of the prairie serves mainly as rangeland for cattle.

The grasses of the gently rolling tall-grass prairie can raise their flowering heads as much as three meters above ground, where they grow in wet depressions; a man riding on a horse cannot be seen among them. Even in the dry, shallow valleys (the so-called lowland prairie) the grass grows one or two meters high, but on the plateau prairie it reaches no more than 50–100 cm. Among the different grass species

▷ Above: in the South American pampas herds of millions of sheep have crowded out most of the guanacos and pampas deer. Below: Llamas in the Bolivian puna, the high steppe region of the central Andes.

Tall-grass prairie

The geomorphological differences between deserts: Above: The Kara Kum in Turkmenia (USSR). Lower left: Typical shapes resulting from weathering in the Hoggar Mountains (Sahara). Lower middle: The Atacama Desert near La Serena (Chile). The cloud masses coming from the sea break up over the interior of the desert. Lower right: Scene in central Australia (northern Culgera).

there grow more than 180 species of forbs, including many composites and legumes, which flower from March to September. Almost half of all the species, however, flower most abundantly in late spring and at the beginning of summer, before the onset of summer drought.

The mixed-grass prairie is a transition zone between the tall-grass prairie and the western short-grass plains, with tall and short grasses growing side by side. As the climate becomes dryer, toward the west, the tall grasses gradually disappear. The westernmost belt of prairie, with the least rain and the least diverse vegetation, includes the Great Plains. Within this short-grass prairie lies the Missouri plateau, with the Black Hills and the Badlands, where brooks and rivers have eaten away the soil to form a desertlike landscape of cliffs and gullies. The high plains and the Staked Plain, through which runs the state line between Texas and New Mexico, are also part of the short-grass prairie.

During the previous century the White Man destroyed the last herds of bison in the Great Plains, which once numbered sixty million animals ranging through the prairie. Bison and pronghorn antelope, together with mustangs (originally domesticated horses that reverted to the wild state), grazed the prairie; their activities, and those of the numerous rodents and rabbits, maintained the prairie as a stable habitat and prevented the encroachment of the forest, particularly toward the east. Other factors acting against the spread of the forest were lightning, fires started by the Indians, and the occasional years of drought, with lowered water table and an insufficiency of surface moisture.

Toward the end of the Ice Age the prairie was inhabited not only by bison and pronghorns, but by ancient camels, perissodactyls, mammoths and mastodons as well. Almost all of these, together with the saber-toothed tiger and other cats as big as lions, disappeared immediately after the Ice Age, as a consequence of both the changed climate and hunting by men. The Indians were familiar with some of these now-extinct mammals. Only the bison and pronghorn survived and multiplied into the millions, until finally the "conquering of the Wild West" brought white immigrants and massive slaughter of these last representatives of a unique steppe fauna; now only a few remnants are left.

Before the land was taken over by the whites, the Indians had carried on agriculture in the river valleys and lived as hunting nomads on the open prairie. There they relied almost completely upon the bison for food and other necessities of life, but there were too few of them and their weapons were not sufficiently developed for them to do any permanent damage to the huge herds. From 1541 on, horses that had been introduced by the Europeans began to run wild; these mustangs also formed enormous herds ·on the prairies. The Indians took advantage of this, and on their mounts they could hunt the bison more efficiently, but still they caused hardly any reduction in the total population of these wild cattle. Not until the white settlers and conquerors slowly invaded the prairie did the ecological

Fig. 14-16. Range of the American bison, formerly (1) and at present (2).

equilibrium begin to change. The large-scale extermination that followed involved not only the bison and pronghorns, but other animals such as the prairie dog (*Cynomys*), a marmot genus that has been destroyed except for a few small, scattered populations and some large colonies in wildlife preserves. The stocks of bison and pronghonrs have now been built up so that there are over 30,000 of them in national parks and other preserves, but like the prairie dog they have no longer any role to play as true shapers and maintainers of the prairie.

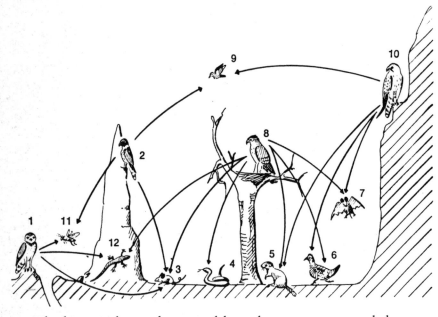

Fig. 14-17. The American prairie is the home of certain species of owl and other birds of prey, which nest and hunt here and hardly ever leave the habitat. The ecological diagram shows four of them, and their prey: 1. Burrowing owl; 2. American kestrel or sparrow-hawk; 8. Red-tailed hawk; 10. Prairie falcon.
Prey animals: 3. Small rodents; 4. Snakes; 5. Large rodents; 6. Prairie chickens; 7. Bats; 9. Small birds; 11. Insects; 12. Small reptiles.

The bison and pronghorns, and later the mustangs, grazed the grass and forbs down to such an extent that they could not build up a mat of dead and rotting vegetation over the soil. Moving about over the sod, they made it firmer, and they trod the seeds into the soil so that they germinated more readily; in addition they provided large quantities of dung. The prairie dogs helped by churning up the soil so thoroughly that there was essentially no large area not turned over, aerated and thoroughly dampened. They lived in enormous colonies, sometimes covering as much as 10,000 square kilometers and comprising several hundred million members. Apart from the prairie dogs, other animals made burrows in the prairie: voles, deer mice, white-footed mice, harvest mice, northern ground squirrels and other plant-eating rodents. There were also pocket gophers, which lived permanently underground, eating roots and tubers, as well as jack rabbits, cottontail rabbits, and the prairie chicken, with its unusual courtship ritual.

The larger herbivores were hunted by the wolf, black bear and puma; those of medium and small size were the prey of many carnivores, including the coyote, American badger, spotted skunk, black-footed ferret, long-tailed weasel, eagle, prairie falcon and rattlesnake. The grasshopper mice, which are entirely carnivorous, decimated the insect populations. Prairie dogs were the special food of the black-footed ferret, burrowing owl and rattlesnakes, which lived in the prairie dog burrows and thus had ready access to their prey. The White Man destroyed this intrinsically well-balanced community not only by exterminating the large animals but by driving out the prairie dogs, since they competed with the cattle for food and the horses broke their legs by stepping into the burrows. As a result, not only the prairie dogs, prairie chickens and burrowing owl have vanished, but the small carnivores as well. The black-footed ferret has become the rarest mammal of North America, and is about to become extinct.

The African savanna belt

The savanna is the most extensive and characteristic habitat of Africa. It forms a huge belt surrounding the central African rainforest on three sides. In the north the rainforest is bounded by the Guinea-Sudan savanna, 400–550 km wide and about 5000 km long, stretching from the Atlantic coast into the western part of the Bahr el-Ghazal. The basin of the White Nile interrupts the belt, and it begins again in the east at the Tana River in Kenya. From there it runs south as a 200-km-wide band for more than 2000 km, as far as the Zambesi valley and a little further on the other side. In the south the belt turns west again and, varying in width, extends for about 2500 km from the Pacific to the Atlantic coast. This southeastern curve of the savanna belt, reaching from northern Kenya to the coast of Angola, is the largest area in the world occupied by a uniform (and thus monotonous) plant community. Altogether, it covers no less than 800,000 square kilometers. If the *ca.* 250,000 square kilometers of the Guinea-Sudan belt are included, the savannas of Africa constitute a gigantic, distinctive habitat of more than a million square kilometers.

The Guinea-Sudan savanna

The Guinea-Sudan savanna is grassland in which grow only a few species of trees. In the northern part the trees are small, with little undergrowth, and they are spaced further apart than in the south; the trees in the south grow taller, and more species are represented there. The rainy season, from April to October, brings about 1000 mm of precipitation in the north and as much as 1500 mm in the south. The hot winds from the Sahara herald the season of drought, and cause the leaves to fade rapidly and fall. The desolate appearance of the savanna then is enhanced by the frequent fires that sweep through the grass. At some places, treeless swampy depressions or fringe woods along rivers break the monotony. The large rivers—the Senegal, Niger, Benue, Volta, Yadseram and Chari have formed wide flood plains, which by nature have a much more diverse fauna than does the true savanna.

The eastern African savanna

In eastern Africa the savanna is more arid, since the two short rainy seasons (in April and May, and in November and December) together bring only about 600 mm of precipitation. Bushes are just as abundant as low trees, and are equally thorny. Between the clumps of bushes grows grass; scattered rocks, mounds and chains of hills make the terrain more varied, and there are occasional isolated mountains, which attract enough moisture that forests can grow in the clouds shrouding the upper slopes and around the springs that emerge at lower altitudes. This type of savanna is called "nyika." The landscape is dotted by gigantic baobab trees, or by springs surrounded by greenery. A famous example of the latter is the Mzima spring in Tsavo Park, where the clear waters of the pond provide an excellent opportunity for observing hippopotamus and crocodiles. But on the whole, water is a rarity in this arid region.

Fig. 14-18. A colony of prairie dogs, showing the structure of their burrows.

From southern Tanzania toward the south and west, the trees become rather taller and stand closer together to form a woodland, and this community is called "miombo." The rainy and dry seasons each last half the year, as in the Guinea-Sudan savanna, and the total precipitation is about the same, but since this region is in the southern hemisphere the months are reversed—the rain falls from October to May, and the dry season lasts from June to October.

As the savanna belt surrounds the rainforest, so the grassland belt delimits the savanna. In the north is the Sudan grassland ("Sudan" is used here in the geographical sense), and in the south the bush veldt. In the east the orientation of grassland to savanna is reversed; the nyika is east of the grassland, which merges with the Nile basin in the west. Whereas there is usually a sharp boundary between savanna and rainforest, the transition from savanna to grassland is just as indistinct as that from grassland to semidesert. As a result, some savanna animals can also be found in the grassland, and grassland animals in the savanna or semidesert.

The grassland belt

In southern Africa, a western and an eastern bush veldt can be dis-

The veldt

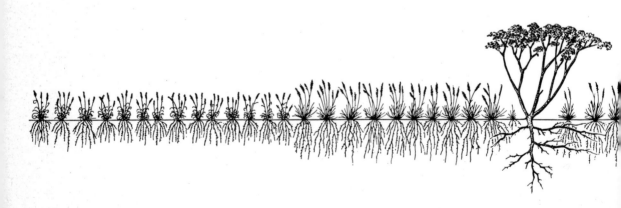

Fig. 14-19. The transition from grassland (left) to savanna (middle) and arid woodland (right).

tinguished, but the two are connected by the valleys of the Limpopo and other rivers. The hotter, bushier eastern veldt (laeveld) is at present largely within the bounds of the Kruger National Park, which covers 20,480 square kilometers. The western veldt (lowveld), an open acacia grassland, resembles that of the Sudan. Here, too, there is only one rainy season, from November to April. In the winter it is rather cool. There is also a feature resembling the isolated mountains of the eastern and southern savanna; the monotony of the grassland is interrupted here by the so-called "castle-kopjes," large blocks of plutonic rock weathered into strange shapes. Usually these rocky outcrops are overgrown with dense savanna forest, which makes them conspicuous from a great distance.

The fauna of the savanna-grassland belt

The savanna-grassland belt thus has a number of distinct subdivisions, which extend to its plant and animal communities as well. It is famous throughout the world for its abundance of large animals. As an old continent, Africa has been one of the main regions in which the major ancestral lines of animals have evolved. For a long time it was connected to Asia along a broad front, so that many immigrants joined the native fauna. In consequence, the variety of animal species became greater than in any other savanna habitat on earth. The number of mammals alone is so great that we can mention only a few of the most characteristic species, without going into a discussion of their habits.

Since there are no sharp boundaries between savanna and grassland, some species occupy both habitats, throughout the whole region. We find them in the northern part as well as in the east and south, although they may be represented by several subspecies in each section. Among these widely distributed mammals are the African elephant, wart hog, hippopotamus, giraffe, cape buffalo, antelopes such as the grey duiker, oribi,

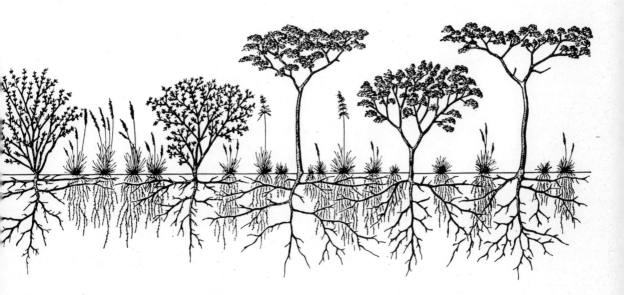

hartebeest, sassaby, eland, Buffon's kob, waterbuck, and reedbuck, the steppe baboon, and carnivores like the lion, leopard, cheetah, serval, spotted hyena, side-striped jackal, African wild dog, honey badger, the spotted-necked otter and otters of the genera *Aonyx* and *Paraonyx*, the zebra mongoose and the white-tailed mongoose. Hyraxes (or "dassies") are also found wherever clumps of trees or rocks interrupt the grassland.

Apart from these widely distributed animals, there are a number of species with a more restricted range, either being limited to one part of the savanna-grassland belt or inhabiting grassland or savanna exclusively. These include the bush pig, bushbuck, impala, gnu, various species of gazelle, springbuck, roan and sable antelopes, steppe zebra, red guenon, aard-wolf, black-backed and common jackals. In the flood plains of the large rivers and lakes there is a distinct, rich fauna consisting of species adapted to life in water and swamp; among them are antelopes (*Tragelaphus spekei*, *Adenota kob*, *Hydrotragus leche*, *Onototragus megaceros*) which sometimes appear in great numbers.

The fauna of the savanna-grassland belt also includes numerous smaller mammals and an enormous variety of birds, from the large bustard to small finches, as well as some reptiles (for example, snakes, tortoises, agamas and varanid lizards) and an army of insects and other invertebrates, of which the most conspicuous are the termites, of which the most conspicuous are the termites, with their huge nests. All these animals have adapted to the conditions in their particular habitat so well that they can make use of the varied food supply in the best possible way.

The number of different approaches there are to the herbivorous habit can be well illustrated by reference to just one group, the mammals. Burrowing rodents eat the subterranean roots and tubers of the grasses, forbs, bushes and trees; mice find their food close to the ground. The higher parts of the plants are eaten by gazelles, antelopes and zebras (Fig. 14-20). Leaf- and twig-eaters keep the bushes and trees at all levels compact in form; they range in size from the dikdiks and other dwarf antelopes through bushbucks, kudus and black rhinoceros to the gerenuk and giraffe. And these animals differ not only in terms of the height at which they graze, but also in their choice of plants, the way they eat, the "schedule" they follow and the particular locale they choose; in this way their requirements mesh with one another so that competition between the species is minimized. Some prefer soft grass and foliage while others choose the tougher food; some take only the tips of the shoots, others the upper parts of the plants, and still others the stalks and stems close to the ground. Certain species nibble here and there, others drift slowly, grazing as they go, and some animals tend to remain in one spot. In some cases food is sought exclusively in the savanna or in the grassland, depending upon whether it is the rainy season or the period of drought. For example, "harnessed" antelopes (*Tragelaphus*) are found in the bush, Thompson's gazelles in short, dry grassland, reedbucks in somewhat damper places

The food chain in the savanna-grassland belt

with taller grass, waterbucks in reeds at the edge of water, sitatungas in reeds and swamps, and Buffon's kob on flooded marshy meadows.

Since the large and small carnivores keep the herbivore populations in bounds, the African savanna-grassland belt has maintained an equilibrium that was not disturbed even by the natives, in their former sparse settlements. The fires they set at regular intervals in fact contributed to the maintenance of the habitat. All these factors account for the fact that the animals living here presented the greatest number of species, the greatest density of individuals, and thus the greatest biomass per unit area on earth. At certain seasons, for example, there were up to a million large ungulates in the *ca.* 13,000 square kilometers of the Serengeti. An eastern African region of thornbush-savanna covering about 15,000 square kilometers was recently estimated to contain an ungulate biomass of approximately 5000 kg per square kilometer, while that of small mammals was 400–500 kg and that of carnivores was about 850 kg. The vast hordes of small to very small herbivores in the grassland of eastern Africa have been found to amount to more than 25,000 kg biomass per square kilometer. A conservative estimate of the invertebrates in the thornbush-savanna sets their total biomass at about 10,000 kg per square kilometer.

If this production of animal biomass by the African savanna-grassland belt is extrapolated to its entire area, which amounts to an estimated two million square kilometers, the final figure is about twenty billion tons of animals. This animal mass feeds upon a much larger plant mass; the herbivorous mammals in the thornbush-savanna account for only around 20% of the vegetation consumed, the rest being eaten by invertebrates or destroyed by fire. This superabundance of life is the result of millions of years of precisely balanced interactions between plants, microorganisms and animals of all sizes, which have evolved to suit the local geological, edaphic, and climatic conditions. Here, too, it was with the advent of the White Man that large parts of the community were disturbed or destroyed. Even though the numerous national parks and wildlife preserves that have since been set aside are often of impressive size, these previously untouched areas cannot escape change; they are only islands in a vast expanse, and all the modifications of their surroundings must be reflected in them as well.

A good example of this process is given by the African elephant. The savanna and grassland elephants in particular are by nature wide-ranging animals that feed mainly on leaves and branches; when one of their herds passes through a stand of bush trees, considerable damage is done. An elephant is quite able to trample down any tree that offers tempting foliage in its crown. As long as the herds of elephants returned to a region only at intervals of a few years, the woods had enough time to recover. But now the wilderness is only a small part of the country, and humans have taken over the rest; the elephants can no longer move about as they once did. Should they enter the cultivated fields and woods, they are driven

Fig. 14-20. The mammals of the savanna-grassland together make use of the vegetation at all levels, so that each species can feed without excessive competition. From left to right: a dikdik, a gerenuk and a giraffe.

away or shot. The only undisturbed areas left to them are the national parks and preserves, and these are too small; the overcrowded elephants become instruments of destruction. In Murchison Falls Park they have already annihilated the trees, and they are about to do the same thing in Tsavo and Kruger Parks. This is why thousands of elephants have had to be shot there, as the only way to preserve the ecological balance. Wherever the law prescribes that nature must take its course without human intervention in the national parks, the "elephant question" raises a dilemma for the park administration.

It was not by accident that the former abundance of animal species in the open habitats of Africa provided primitive man with fundamental assistance in his struggle for survival. Ramapithecines and australopithecines, which are currently thought to be the ancestral human forms, probably lived in troops as hunters in the savannas, using the bushes, trees and gullies in the varied terrain for cover, to approach or escape undetected. Thus they first tested their skill on small and medium-sized animals, and were able to improve their abilities before risking a big-game hunt. This hunting and hiding behavior, evolved as a critical element of survival in the ecosystem of the African savanna-grassland belt, has remained as an inheritance of present-day humans. It is evident in many activities—for example, when one car chases another through streets full of traffic, in sports with a ball to serve as a "substitute game animal," and even in the tendency of people to choose a protected restaurant table in a corner or next to a wall, from which they can safely and calmly watch the "lions at their kill"—the other humans eating in the room.

▷
Upper left: A cactus desert in Arizona.
Upper middle: A cactus wren (*Campylorhynchus brunneicapillus*) leaving its nest, in which its offspring are protected by the spines of the cactus.
Upper right: The melon-like fruits of *Acanthosicyos horrida* store water that can be drunk by man and animals (near Gobabis in South West Africa).
Center: Sand dunes in Death Valley, California. The desert is not devoid of plants even here; there are isolated clumps of shrubbery.
Lower left: A river at the southern edge of the Luth desert in Iran, after a rain. In a few days the riverbed will be dry again.
Lower middle: A desert in bloom (the plant is *Genothera deltoides*); rain brought forth this brief display as if by magic.
Lower right: A flowering prickly pear (*Opuntia basilaris*) in the Colorado Desert.

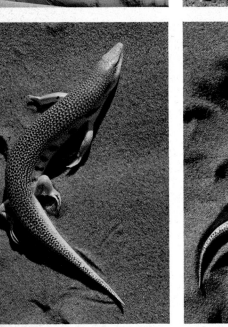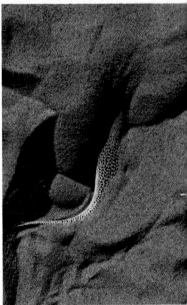

By U. F. Gruber

15 Plants and Animals of the Deserts

Upper row: Three forms
of the African Sahara:
Left: Sand desert with
grasses and tamarisks (the
erg).
Middle: Flat gravelly
ground (the reg).
Right: The hamada in
southern Morocco, covered
with large blocks of stone.

Types of desert and
their climate

Center: A common skink
(*Scincus scincus*) digs itself
into the desert sand with
a few quick movements.
Lower left: A Senegal
stand grouse lets its young
(which look like rough
stones) drink the water it
has brought in its breast
feathers.
Lower middle: A tene-
brionid beetle on a dune
near Beni Ounif in the
Western Erg of the Sahara.
The fans of hair on its feet
support it securely as it
marches over the loose
sand.
Lower right: A yellow
variant of the desert-dwelling spiny-tailed lizard
(*Uromastix acanthinurus*) in
the Algerian Sahara. This
reptile is one of the few
lizards that feed chiefly on
plants.

All around the earth, between the temperate zones and the tropical savannas and forests, the continents are spanned by a belt of aridity. In this dry region lie the great deserts: the Sahara in northern Africa, the Takla Makan and the Gobi in central Asia, the Namib and the Kalahari in southern Africa, the various deserts of Australia and North America, the Atacama in western South America, and the desertlike parts of Patagonia. One cannot draw a sharp boundary between the semideserts and arid steppes on the one hand and the deserts on the other. The transitions are so gradual that in the boundary regions it is impossible to decide whether one is still in the steppe or has entered the desert.

Many people picture the desert as a barren, hot place full of sand and stones, where it never rains, nothing grows, and no animal lives. In fact, though, it does sometimes rain in the desert, and this makes possible a sparse, characteristic vegetation and a special highly adapted fauna. It is generally agreed that the term desert should be applied to those regions with average annual precipitation less than 25 cm and with very high summer temperatures, so that as a result of lack of rain and great heat conditions of extreme drought arise. It is true that in parts of the deserts or on the coasts of America and Africa—for example, the Atacama or the Namib—the humidity is high because of clouds, fog and so on, but even here there is essentially no rain, so that hardly any moisture enters the soil. The clouds of water vapor are caused by cold ocean currents flowing along the coasts; in the ocean off the Atacama, for example, is the Peruvian Current, off the Californian coast is the Californian Current, and off the coast of southwestern Africa is the Benguela Current.

Though all deserts share a lack of moisture, they are not all permanently hot; there are large differences in temperature. The arid parts of the Australian interior are definitely hot, but in the Gobi and the Takla Makan it can be uncomfortably cold. In winter these central Asian deserts are frozen and swept by snow storms, while in summer they swelter in the sun. But the hottest place on earth is in the Sahara, near El Asisia, where an air temperature of 58°C in the shade has been measured; the 56.5°C measured in Death Valley, California runs a close second. The daytime and nighttime temperatures can also contrast sharply. Daily temperature oscillations over 35°C are no rarity. Even in the interior of the Sahara, where the merciless sun burns all day long, the nights are so cold that the desert-dwellers must wrap themselves in warm clothes and blankets.

Aridity is a common feature, but it differs in degree. There are places —for example, in the Namib or the Australian interior—where rain falls only once in a decade. When one of these rare desert rains does occur, it usually pours over the bone-dry land as a great flood. In the desert of Western Australia there once fell no less than 288 mm of rain on a single day. Often the entire rainfall for the year comes all at once; it can even happen that the raindrops evaporate while still falling, before they have reached the hot ground. Desert rains are always limited to a relatively small area, but the erosion caused by the force of the massive downpours can be extreme. In a matter of minutes a dry, dusty river bed can be filled with a thundering torrent of clay-yellow water, from a rainstorm kilometers away. A short while later, it is almost as though nothing had happened; only the steam rising from the floor of the valley bears witness to nature's recent display of power.

The rivers of the deserts almost never reach the sea. The gullies through which the water runs—the wadis of the Sahara, the sais of the Gobi, the laagtes of the Kalahari and the canyons of North America—dry up a short distance from the source of the stream. It might be thought that the Nile is an exception, but though this river flows through desert areas its water comes from tributaries originating in springs, in quite rainy regions.

The notion that deserts are nothing but an infinite sea of sand dunes is contradicted even by the desert that is perhaps most associated with such a landscape—the Sahara, the largest desert on earth. Measuring nine million square kilometers, this huge arid region extends for 7000 km from east to west and 2000 km from north to south. Less than half of it is covered with sand dunes, and it is still one of the sandiest deserts in the world. The Namib, too, consists in large part of sand dunes, some of which are as high as 150 or even 300 meters. In the deserts of North America, however, the sandy areas amount to only about 2% of the total. The other parts of the deserts are regions of stone and rock, plateaus, and mountains.

Three chief formations have been named in the Sahara, on the basis of the nature of the surface. First there is the erg, huge areas covered with sand dunes, among which are the Erg Idehan in Libya and the Erg Chech in Algeria. Second is the reg or serir, vast flat expanses of coarse sand, gravel or small stones ground down by the wind. Finally, there is the hamada, higher altitude rocky desert formed by large blocks of stone, shale, or plates of stratified rock. Each of these is characterized by extensive uniform terrain, in some places flat and in others hilly; from them there

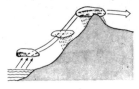

Fig. 15-1. Deserts can come into being in different ways, but in each case clouds are prevented from passing over them. The picture explains why deserts are often in the lee of mountains. The humid air coming from the sea rises over a mountain range and as it cools its moisture is precipitated—it rains. By the time the air has crossed the mountains it is quite dry, so that there is a "rain shadow," an arid zone, on the other side of the range.

Fig. 15-2. The most famous plant in the Namib is *Welwitschia mirabilis*; this specimen is still young, and its leaves have not yet been shredded by the wind. *Welwitschia* plants can live for more than 100 years.

arise the mountains of the Sahara (for example, the Hoggar Mountains, which reach altitudes of 3000 meters, and the Tibesti Mountains, with peaks towering above 3000 meters). But in the heart of the Sahara, in southwestern Algeria, lies one of the most desolate desert regions and the most dreaded by caravans—the Tanezrouft, the "land of drought and thirst."

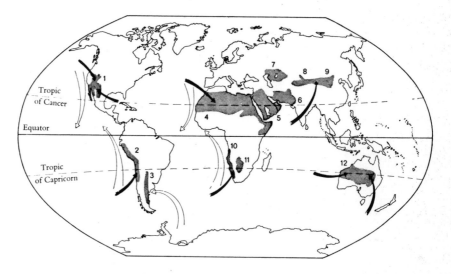

Fig. 15-3. Distribution of deserts on the earth:
1. North American deserts; 2. Atacama; 3. Patagonian arid regions; 4. Sahara; 5. Arabian desert; 6. Indo-Iranian deserts; 7. Turkestan desert; 8. Takla Makan; 9. Gobi; 10. Namib; 11. Kalahari; 12. Australian desert.
White arrows; cold ocean currents. Black arrows: main directions in which the great storms move.

The Sahara was not always so inimical to life. During the relatively wet rainy periods in the Quaternary, the flora and fauna of the Mediterranean moved south and those of the Sudan, northward. As evidence of this less arid past, Nile crocodiles survive as relicts in the oasis lakes at the foot of the Hoggar and Tibetsi Mountains. This instance of the presence of crocodiles is of extreme interest; the well-known ornithologist Günther Niethammer observed considerable numbers of these animals as recently as 1954 at the Gelta Archei. Cave drawings represent a large number of steppe animals, adding to the evidence that the Sahara had much more water in prehistoric times than it does today, and that at least parts of the present desert region were then a steppe full of game. Relicts of that time of Mediterranean, humid climate are the Barbary sheep (*Ammotragus lervia*) and the Nubian ibex (*Capra ibex nubiana*). Today the Barbary sheep has withdrawn into the massifs of the Hoggar, Tibesti and Air Mountains, and the Nubian ibex is found only in the Karakora Mountains in the Sudan, on a few mountain chains in Egypt, and in particular on the Sinai peninsula and in the Negev Desert of Israel. There these horned animals find conditions somewhat more favorable than in the deserts at lower altitudes. But their environment is still so severe that both species have had to evolve considerable adaptations to the desert climate.

To the biologist, deserts are testing grounds for studies of the modifiability and adaptability of plants and animals. Here he can investigate a great variety of physiological and morphological adaptations used by organisms to ensure the proper functioning of their metabolism despite extraordinary heat, dryness and scarcity of food. Many forms resemble one another in appearance and behavior, even though they belong to different genera and families. All the groups of rodents called "jumping mice," which are by no means closely related, look almost the same everywhere and behave in much the same way. The desert jerboa *Jaculus jaculus*, of the family Dipodidae, lives in the Sahara; the jumping hare (*Pedetes cafer*), which belongs to a different family (Pedetidae) more closely related to the squirrels, lives in the South African deserts; the many kangaroo-rats of the genus *Dipodomys* (family Heteromyidae) lives in the deserts of western North America; and there is a marsupial jumping mouse, *Antechinomys*, in the deserts of western and central Australia. All these animals have hind legs longer than the front legs, so that they can make powerful jumps; other common characteristics are large ears and eyes, and a long tail ending in a bushy tuft, which helps in steering the jump. Such correspondence in form of unrelated animals is called convergence. Other examples of convergence are found in the Saharan gazelle species, the mule deer of the North American deserts, and the desert kangaroos, all of which graze in arid country and have become modified accordingly. Certain animals protected by bad-smelling secretions, such as the New World skunks and the zorillas of Africa and the Near East, also represent cases of convergence.

All life in the desert depends upon the ability to take up and retain water. Moreover, every organism, whether animal or plant, provides the necessities of existence for another. A chain of organisms is formed, each of which both makes life possible for and depends upon the others. We have encountered the "food chain" before in this volume, but nowhere is it so obvious as in the desert. At the beginning come the plants; they capture the precious moisture brought by the rare desert rains and use the energy of the sun and the carbon dioxide of the air to turn it into organic matter. The desert, of course, is not devoid of plants, though the vegetation is scant. The key to existence for desert plants is to make the best use of the rain in the shortest possible time, and then to survive the period of drought until the next rain falls. They have used a variety of methods to accomplish this. After a violent downpour the desert is soon covered by a green carpet, with magnificent splashes of color, of forbs and grasses. With their bright flowers, sweet scent and nectar, the different plants attract their insects; verbenas, fumitories and legumes are pollinated by bees, columbine and phlox by moths, and *Castillea* and lilies by butterflies. In an unbelievably short time these plants flower and seed themselves. Then they wither and vanish; only the seeds remain, but these can withstand years of drought if need be, until a rainfall brings forth new flowers and fruits. Other species endure the periods of drought as bulbs, tubers or thickened roots—the bushmen of the Kalahari use some plants of this sort.

Fig. 15-4. The desert plants have adapted to the scarcity of water in different ways:

The giant cactus sucks up water with a root system that fans out near the surface of the ground, and stores it in its tissues.

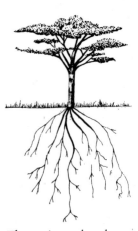

The acacia, on the other hand, sends its roots far down into the soil so as to take up every drop that may percolate through in a rainstorm.

Fig. 15-5. Four examples of convergence:

The jerboa *Jaculus jaculus* (family Dipodidae).

The kangaroo rat *Dipodomys ingens* (family Heteromyidae).

The marsupial jerboa (*Antechinomys spenceri*; family Dasyuridae).

The jumping hare (*Pedetes capensis*; family Pedetidae).

There are also plants that do not live as seeds or underground regenerative organs from one rain to the next, but have adapted to the dry desert climate by succulence. That is, they are able to store water in their leaves, branches or stems. Among them are the cactuses, agaves and euphorbias. Often their leaves and branches are protected against evaporation by a coating of wax or a covering of matted hairs. Some of the perennial plants, especially trees and bushes, can reach the ground water at certain spots with their deeply penetrating roots. Acacias have been found to have roots that can draw water up from a depth of eight meters, and the mesquite bush in North America sends roots down as far as thirty meters. The trees in the Sahara, tamarisks and acacias, tend to stand along the dry wadis, where the water table is higher than elsewhere; there they sometimes form an open fringe forest along the (usually absent) river. A striking aspect of many desert plants is their armament of thorns; in the Sahara, especially, there are great numbers of thorny shrubs. Probably the thorns protect the plants from grazing ungulates. The root and branch systems of the thornbushes are refuges and homes for many animals— ground squirrels, kangaroo rats, and certain lizards, snakes, and birds.

Most of the perennial plants grow in a very open distribution on the desert soil. They need a great deal of room for their extensive root systems, which must capture every last drop of moisture whenever it rains. Because of the pressure of competition, each plant stands alone. Only in the dry river valleys and oases can more closed plant communities develop, and this permits the development of a more diverse and abundant fauna. One plant deserves special mention; this is *Welwitschia mirabilis*, discovered by the Austrian physician and botanist Friedrich Welwitsch. It grows in the Namib, and is restricted to sandy ground in a strip of stony desert located 50 km away from the coast. A gymnosperm, it has a short stem shaped like a beet and as thick as a man, and two large leaves which split into ribbons. With its long taproot it can draw up water from deep in the ground. It can live for well over 100 years; individual *Welwitschia* have been said to be as much as 500–600 years old (Fig. 15-2).

The desert flora, sparse as it is, is the basis for the existence of the desert animals. These include vertebrates (in particular reptiles, birds and mammals), insects (locusts, beetles and ants), and spiders (scorpions, sun-spiders, and wolf spiders). The number of species is remarkably small, and the populations are spread out so that the density is also low. This of course corresponds to the openness of the plant cover. In summary, then, the factors determining the low density of the animal populations are lack of water, heat, temperature fluctuations, scarcity of food, and finally the open terrain itself.

Water is the biggest problem for all desert organisms. All animals must obtain water from time to time and must protect themselves from excessive water loss. In the oases, water is relatively easy to find, and even amphibians manage to live there; in the Sahara there are green toads

(*Bufo viridis*), leopard toads (*Bufo regularis*), pantherine toads (*Bufo mauretanica*), and frogs (*Rana ridibunda* and *Rana mascariensis*). The toads are so well adapted to dryness that they can bury themselves in times of drought and enter a state of anabiosis.

Even in the open desert there are many animals that must drink water from time to time. One of the people most familiar with the fauna of the South West African Namib, E.G.F. Sauer, has made detailed observations of the habits of the Namib ostriches. He saw these large birds going to drink at the rare water holes together with oryx, springbucks and mountain zebras. In such company, the ostriches are very low-ranking and often must stand about waiting for a long time before it is their turn to drink. The very last in line are the young ostriches, usually shepherded by a few "aunts" and "uncles." Not until all the other animals have finished and left do the young birds stride into the turbid water on their long legs and take deep gulps—always prepared to flee at the slightest disturbance.

Other desert birds, too, must drink water at more or less regular intervals. It is not so hard for them, since they can fly for long distances. But the desert larks in the Sahara are quite irregular in their drinking habits, and can on occasion go for weeks without a drink. Another group of true desert dwellers is related to the pigeons—the sand grouse (family Pteroclididae). They build their nests deep in the desert, far away from any source of water. To provide their young with the moisture they need, they take up water with the breast feathers when they drink, and carry it all the way home to the nest. When the soaked feathers are offered to the nestlings, they suck the water out (see Color plate, p. 268).

There are also mammals that can manage with only occasional drinks of water. Dassies of the genus *Provacia* can go without water for several months, but eventually even they must find a source of moisture. The classical example of a desert animal that seems impervious to thirst is the dromedary. It draws upon the water stored in the tissues of its body; these can lose as much as 40% of the water they contain without damage, though of course the camel's weight falls drastically in the process. When the animal does have a chance to drink, it can make up the entire loss all at once. Certain other ungulates can do this as well; among them are the addax antelope *Adax nasomaculatus* and the wild ass *Equus asinus*. And finally, many arthropods also fall into this category. It must be assumed that spiders, mites, myriapods and beetles at least lick up dew when they have the opportunity.

In addition to the groups of animals that take in water by drinking, there are others even more radically adapted to the dryness of the desert. These can do without any intake of water as such, and obtain what they need from their food. The chief representatives of this category are vegetarians such as rodents and many insects, but it also includes a reptile, the African spiny-tailed lizard (*Uromastyx acanthinurus*; see Color plate, p. 268). The gerbil *Psammomys obesus* feeds on fleshy plants and can even make use of the water in the halophytic Chenopodiaceae. The urine it excretes is four times as concentrated as sea water. The kangaroo rats (genus *Dipodomys*) of the Californian deserts also meet their water requirements exclusively by consuming plant juices. And even the animals that depend upon seeds for food can get all the water they need from that source; it is freed by chemical processes during digestion.

Nor need the carnivores drink water. Owls (for example, *Bubo ascalaphus*) and other predatory birds, as well as mammals like the fox, fennec and jackal obtain enough fluid from their prey. Camels are similar in a sense, but it is their own bodies from which their water is derived; when the stored fat (or the vegetable food they eat) is broken down by metabolism, the hydrogen set free can combine with respired oxygen to form water. The camels can endure a loss of 25% of their total body weight; but of course, as mentioned above, they must eventually replace it by drinking water.

Fig. 15-6. The giant cactus plays an important role in the ecology of the desert. The Gila woodpecker (1) chops out a nest hole in the stem, and the elf owl moves into this shelter as soon as the woodpecker has abandoned it. Elf owl and red-tailed buzzard (3), both of which nest in the arms of the cactus, protect it from rodents that eat young plants and seeds. In spring bats (5) come out at night to feed on the pollen of the large cactus flowers; in so doing they help pollinate the flowers. Finally, the fruits of the cactus are eaten by the white-winged dove (4), which also has assisted in pollination.

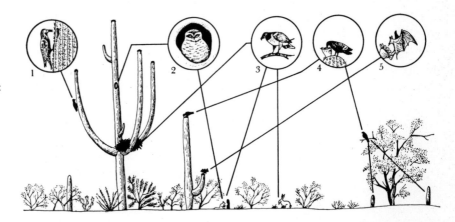

All these animals must conserve the water they obtain, from whatever source, as carefully as possible. Only a very little can be excreted. Reptiles and birds remove the nitrogen-containing metabolic wastes from their blood in the form of uric acid, which easily compacts to a firm mass containing essentially no water. The poikilothermic reptiles are especially well adapted to living under arid conditions. Their scaly epidermis is impermeable to water and their excrement is almost powder-dry; the water supplied by the insects, birds and small mammals they eat is enough for their needs. The difficulty of eliminating wastes in a dry form has been met by the spiny-tailed lizards in a special way; they can excrete excess salts by way of glands in the nasal passages. Many desert mammals, especially rodents, must excrete urine, but it is so highly concentrated that the water loss is minimized. Whereas human urine, for example, is as much as 92% water, that of kangaroo rats is only 70% water. This ability to reduce the amount of water in the urine, to some extent at least, is a fundamental characteristic of all desert mammals. The arthropods, too—the insects, spiders, scorpions and nyriapods—are protected from evaporation by a chitinous exoskeleton and lose very little water in any other way.

Perhaps the second greatest problem for desert animals is the heat. They must all find some means of keeping their body temperature from rising to a lethal point. Large mammals like antelopes and gazelles achieve this by sweating and panting; the evaporation of water from their bodies cools them. Birds and many reptiles, such as the spiny-tailed lizard and desert monitor, can increase the rate of evaporation by panting and more rapid breathing, and are thus protected from overheating. Some Australian desert-dwelling kangaroos of the genus *Wallabia* have an unusual behavior; they not only pant, but they lick their whole bodies so as to be cooled by the evaporating saliva.

Many desert mammals have particularly large ears and long limbs. This tendency is expressed by Allen's Rule: in homiothermic animals, the relative size of ears, tail and limbs is larger in warmer than in cooler regions. This seems particularly applicable to the Cape hare (*Lepus capensis*) and the fennec (*Fennecus zerda*) in the Sahara, and for the kit fox (*Vulpes macrotis*) of the western North American deserts. The oversized ears of these animals are certainly "cooling organs"; the larger the relative body surface, the more heat is lost by evaporation (Fig. 15-10).

A number of vertebrates living in the desert can even raise the temperature of their bodies slightly. The critical temperature limits for lizards are between 40° and 46°C; the corresponding values for snakes are 38–42°C, for birds 43–46°C, and for mammals 39–44°C. But the heat in the open desert is often so great that the animals must hide in cooler shelters. Insects, reptiles and small mammals escape into the soil; rodents, agamas and iguanas look for shady subterranean crevices. If the heat is prolonged, these animals can stay there in a sort of anabiosis or dormacy for days or even weeks, with respiration, metabolism and body temperature much reduced. Anabiosis is probably induced by lack of food. It is known to occur, for example, in the fat-tailed mouse (*Pachyuromys prasi*) of the Sahara, the jerboa *Jaculus jaculus*, which ranges from the Sahara to the Near East, and the Australian kangaroo mouse (*Notomys cervinus*); it also happens in reptiles and gastropods and in insects which spend the period of greatest heat in the egg or pupa stage. The snail *Helix desertorum*, under certain circumstances, can awaken to active life after five uninterrupted years of anabiosis.

Amphibians can survive the hottest times only if they are in moist places. The pelobatid spadefoot toad *Scaphiopus* burrows backwards into the soil of the North American deserts, using horny, wartlike processes on the hind feet. It makes an underground chamber, lines it with mucus, and there enters anabiosis for the summer. This can last as long as eight or nine months; but with the first rains they emerge and make their way to the nearest water-hole. The males call females to join them, and the eggs are laid and fertilized immediately, before the water can evaporate. After one

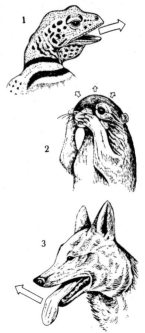

Fig. 15-7. In the heat of the desert animals must protect themselves from overheating, which could be fatal. Reptiles (1) and birds give off heat through their skins and by evaporation of water from the oral mucosa. Mammals have various methods; here a ground squirrel (2) is rubbing itself with saliva, while the coyote (3) cools itself by panting.

or two days the tadpoles hatch. In a week they are almost full-grown, and before a month has passed they have metamorphosed into small frogs, able to make burrows for themselves when necessary.

Many reptiles escape the heat by digging into the sand. Among them are the cylindrical skink *Chalcides ocellatus*, the sand boa (*Eryx jaculus*), and the common skink (*Scincus scincus*; see Color plate, p. 268), which paddles through the sand with its short legs in a way that has given it the local name "sandfish." The horned viper (*Cerastes cerastes*) of the Sahara burrows into the sand with a most unusual series of movements; it moves the ribs at the sides of the body back and forth, so that its sides cut into the sand like the edges of shovels. The movement begins at the tail and proceeds up to the head, and in the process the animal sinks into the sand until only the horns and eyes reveal its presence. But most reptiles protect themselves from overheating by shifting their position repeatedly between sunny and shady sites or going underground; thus they keep their body temperature approximately constant. This is why there is continual movement among populations of iguanas and agamas. Suddenly an animal will vanish into a hole or crevice in the rock; then its head emerges just as quickly and with rapid movements it slips into the sun, only to disappear again soon after. It is probably the parietal eye that controls temperature regulation. When the parietal eye was removed from spiny lizards, or was covered so that no light reached it, they were indifferent to the glaring sun and stayed out long enough to suffer severe injury.

Birds, like many large mammals, can quickly move to shady places when necessary; but to raise their young they must find a nest site where the temperature is always moderate. For this reason species like the wheatear *Oenanthe moesta* and the Saharan subspecies of the little owl breed in holes underground and in the burrows of rodents. The snow finches of the central deserts of Asia prefer the burrows made by pikas as their nesting places. In the Ennedi Mountains at the southern edge of the Sahara the ground temperatures have been measured; at a depth of 10 cm the average temperature was 26°C in the morning, 32°C at noon, and 30.5°C in the evening. The amplitude of the daily fluctuation decreases with depth; 20 cm under the surface the sequence was morning 27°C, noon 29°C, and evening 29°C, and the soil at 30 cm stayed a constant 28°C. Thirty centimeters underground is thus the best place for the birds to nest, as far as temperature is concerned, and also offers the best conditions to other animals seeking shelter from the heat.

In the desert, as in every other habitat, the plants begin the food chain; they are the only organisms capable of producing organic matter from inorganic raw materials. The next link, the herbivore or primary consumer level, has representatives in all animal groups but is concentrated here in the insects and rodents. Shortly after a rain these animals find a feast set out for them, but in times of drought they must make do with hard stems, and roots or even with seeds alone. Seeds, however, are always

Fig. 15-8. A pelobatid spadefoot toad digs itself into the ground backwards, to sleep through the summer in a subterranean chamber. Horny projections on the hind feet make them more effective shovels.

in adequate supply, though it may not appear so when one looks at the drought-ridden desert landscape.

The harvester ants (genus *Pogonomyrmex*) of North America spend the brief morning and evening hours of each day carrying seeds into their nest, built four or five meters underground. Two particular species of plant are clearly preferred; in the rainy periods they will take other seeds as well, but during drought they return to these two species. In view of the fact that these ant colonies are extremely populous and carry in new supplies every day, there must be enormous numbers of seeds on the desert floor. Quantitative estimates suggest that there are about 1.45 billion seeds in an area of 4000 square meters—far more than the animals living in this region could ever eat.

Whereas the rodents feed chiefly on seeds or on the leaves and stems of water-containing plants, only a few species of bird are plant-eaters; examples of these are the sand grouse and pigeons. It is even less common to find herbivorous reptiles. In the Sahara the abovementioned spiny-tailed lizards depend almost exclusively upon plants for food; their counterpart in the deserts of North America is the chuckwalla (*Sauromalus ater*). A special situation prevails in the Namib and the Atacama, where the wind blows in bits of plants and dead animals which serve as food for certain insects.

The final link in the food chain is represented by the carnivores. It is actually divided into "sub-links," for many a carnivore eventually be-

Fig. 15-9. The significance of water to life in the desert: At the beginning of the food chain are the plants, which capture the rain water and turn it into organic matter. After a downpour the barren landscape is covered with a flowering carpet; this attracts pollinating insects and rodents, which are the main vegetarian animals. The last and largest link in

comes the food of another. At this level, then, it would be better to speak of a "food web." At one end of the web are insects, spiders, mites and rodents. Upon these feed, for example, lizards and snakes; these in turn are the prey of foxes, lynxes, owls and other birds of prey. For example, the lanner falcon (*Falco biarmicus*) and the desert golden eagle catch primarily lizards and snakes. But all the carnivores are fundamentally dependent upon the number of herbivores available; they ultimately limit the food supply of the hunters. Relatively more young animals tend to be eaten. Herbivore communities are dynamic, in a constant state of flux due to high rates of reproduction combined with rapid changes in the age composition of the population.

Some birds have found an unusual way to adjust to the fluctuating availability or their animal food sources in the desert. They breed after a rainfall or at a time of year ordinarily associated with an abundant food supply. When one of the rare rainstorms has occurred, many insects emerge from their pupal cases, cocoons or other anabiotic states and resume active life. At this time insectivorous birds are assured of sufficient food, and they are able to synchronize their breeding and raising their young accordingly. Seed-eating birds also find the best food supply shortly after rain has fallen. Some Australian estrildine finches, such as the zebra finch (*Taeniopygia guttata*), live permanently in pairs, so that they are always ready to begin breeding, whenever one of the unpredictable downpours occurs. As the first drops fall they begin to build their nests and

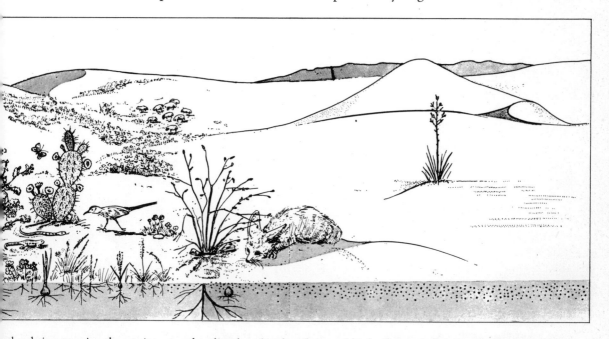

the chain comprises the carnivores, such as lizards and snakes, foxes and birds of prey. Each animal makes the best use it can of the temporary abundance of food. When the moisture has drained away, the desert appears barren again; only the seeds of the plants and their bulbs, tubers and roots survive, until another rain brings the desert to life again.

proceed to lay eggs; the young hatch just when the vegetation that has sprung up is producing vast quantities of seed for them to eat. The whole process is completed in an unbelievably short time, for the season of abundance is very brief. In the Sahara there are two species of falcon which time their breeding season to coincide with the migration of songbirds, great flocks of which stream over the desert once a year. The lanner falcon breeds in the spring and feeds its young with the birds returning to their northern homes. The sooty falcon (*Falco concolor*), on the other hand, lays its eggs in late summer or early autumn and feeds its young with the birds migrating to their winter quarters.

The extreme climatic conditions in the desert have imposed a pronounced behavioral rhythmicity upon the animals living there. We have already mentioned the almost explosive onset of animal activity after a rainstorm. In addition to this seasonal and often very irregular rhythm there is a strict periodicity associated with the day/night cycle. In the glowing heat of noon nothing stirs throughout the desert. Not until evening approaches do insects, reptiles, birds and mammals appear on the scene to feed or mate. A midday break in activity, even among animals normally active by day, is also found in the Mediterranean fauna—for example, in lizards on the Aegean islands. No one seeing the barren, motionless midday desert would imagine the lively and varied activity that prevails in twilight and darkness. Jumping mice, kangaroo rats and pocket gophers then scurry over the stones; iguanas, agamas, skinks and geckos intently hunt their prey insect, while fennecs, kit foxes and desert lynxes lie in wait for mice, lizards and snakes; owls and bats glide soundlessly through the air. In this all-embracing search for food, the smaller and weaker animal always becomes the victim and the meal of the larger and stronger.

The migratory locusts occupy a special place in the desert fauna. They are found in many arid and desert areas, with the exception of western South America; there are a total of nine species, belonging to three different families. Mass outbreaks of locusts occur in the semideserts which border the true desert areas. There are two phases of development; in one phase, the animals migrate in great swarms, and in the other they stay in one place and are not so gregarious. In external appearance the two phases are quite different, but genetically they are identical. When the supply of food is especially good, many more eggs than usual are laid, and it is then that the gregarious phase appears. The insects eat up all the plants they can find in the place where they were born, and grow very fat. For the final great flight preceding mating, vast swarms of locusts rise into the air and fly until they have used up their stores of fat. Then they descend to earth again, consume everything edible in the area, mate, lay their eggs in the ground, and die. If the food situation is worse in the following year, only a few locusts develop, of the non-migratory phase; these are enough to assure the survival of the species. But if conditions are again favorable, there is another gregarious phase which repeats the migration.

Fig. 15-10. According to Allen's Rule, the homoiotherms in warmer regions have larger ears, tails and limbs than those in cold regions. From top to bottom: arctic fox (*Alopex lagopus*), the European red fox (*Vulpes vulpes*) and a desert fox (*Fennecus zerda*).

Fig. 15-11. Range of distribution of locust swarms.

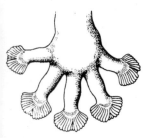

Fig. 15-12. The fanlike expansions of the toes of the gecko *Ptyodactylus hasselquistii* act as "sandshoes" to facilitate walking on the sand dunes.

Locomotion by "sidewinding"

Jumping animals

In adapting to desert life, a number of desert animals have evolved characteristic forms of locomotion. Sandy soils present a special problem, and walking on them can be exhausting. Many insects, such as the tenebrionid beetle *Pimelia angulata* (see Color plate, p. 269) of the Sahara and the locust *Comicus arenarius* of the Namib, have fans of fine chitinous bristles on their legs, which help them to run through the dunes. Reptiles and mammals also have broadened feet that act as "sandshoes." The addax and slender-horned gazelle in the Sahara walk on very broad hooves. The paws of the fennec, the sand cat and the jerboa are covered with thick hair and spread out like snowshoes. The tracks of the sand cat differ from those of other cats in that the balls of the feet make no impression. Geckos living on the ground in the desert also frequently have toes spread into fans at the tips, so that the contact surface is much enlarged. Such toes are found in the geckos *Ptyodactylus hasselquistii* of the Sahara and *Ptenopus garrulus* of the Namib and the Kalahari.

Foot expansion is taken to an extreme by the Namib gecko *Palmatogecko rangei*. Its feet are reminiscent of the webbed feet of water birds, but they are of less use in locomotion than in digging; the gecko uses its feet as shovels to excavate a burrow in the sand. Other lizards—for example, the common skink in the Sahara and the fringe-toed lizard (*Uma notata*) of the Californian deserts—"swim" through the sand, paddling vigorously in order to bury themselves.

Certain species of snake that live in different deserts and even belong to different genera have evolved the same unusual manner of locomotion —"sidewinding." Such a snake moves with part of the body pushed forward in an arc, past the head. Not all parts of the snake touch the ground at once, but rather only two short sections, progressing from the front to the hind end. This allows the animal's weight to be better distributed over the yielding sand and to work against greater resistance. Furthermore, the snake can move faster in this way, since both head and body are shooting forward simultaneously. A Saharan horned viper (*Cerastes cerastes*) moving by sidewinding appears to be flying over the surface of the sand. Other sidewinders are the extremely poisonous saw–scale viper (*Echis carinatus*) in desert regions from North Africa to western central Asia, the dwarf puff adder (*Bitis peringueyi*) in the Namib and Kalahari, and the sidewinder rattlesnake (*Crotalus cerastes*) in the deserts of North America.

But it is not only to moving over sand that desert animals have become adapted; rocky surfaces also demand a special sort of locomotor behavior. The jumping animals have evolved a particularly useful technique for dealing with such a habitat. Among the animals with greatly elongated hindlegs are the kangaroo rats of America, many jerboas of Africa and Asia, and the rat kangaroos of the arid parts of Australia. Other rock dwellers are extremely agile and quick, disappearing into their holes in the blink of an eye when danger threatens; examples of such animals are the chuckwalla in North America and the spiny-tailed lizard in the Sahara. Moreover lizards of these two species can puff up their bodies, once they are safely in a crevice in the rock, to such an extent that it is impossible to pull them out again.

Deserts affected by cold ocean currents have a character of their own. The Namib of South West Africa and the South American Atacama are deserts of this sort. Winds blow landward over the cold ocean water, releasing precipitation there and warming up again once they are over land. Hence both of these coastal deserts are characterized by cloud formations which provide essentially no rain. Nowhere is there a continuous belt of vegetation, and in some places there are no plants at all. Here and there grow isolated tillandsias and various species of cactus.

The coasts of the Atacama, because of the cold Peruvian Current, are enormously fertile. The massive growth of algae here provides a base for a varied fauna. The gigantic schools of anchovies in the Pacific Ocean, off the South American coast, feed many sea birds which leave deposits of excrement, or "guano," on certain desert islands—among them the Chincha Islands of Peru—that can be as much as 60 meters thick. The annual production of guano, used as a fertilizer because of its high phosphate content, has been estimated at 200,000 metric tons. Some of the most important guano birds of South America are the guanay cormorant (*Phalacrocorax bougainvillei*), the brown pelican (*Pelicanus occidentalis*), and various species of booby such as the masked booby (*Sula dactylatra*), *Sula nebouxii*, and *Sula variegata*. On the southern island of the Chincha group alone there is a colony of about 360,000 guanay cormorants in an area of 60,000 square meters. The Humboldt penguin (*Spheniscus humboldti*) makes its nest holes in the guano. The overfishing of the Peruvian Current and the processing of the anchovies to make fish flour presents a danger to the millions of guano birds on the coast of the Atacama; in recent years many of the populations, once so imposing, have already declined considerably.

Man's attempts to change the conditions of life in the deserts can be beneficial, when it is a matter of oases that can exist only under human care. In such places it becomes possible for many plants and animals to live which could not exist permanently outside the oases. But often human intervention has destructive consequences. Near the beginning of recorded history deserts were already beginning to expand as a result of overgrazing and of agriculture without fertilization in dry fringe areas. Even true desert regions suffer severely from overgrazing, and become wasteland in the course of time. Another kind of detrimental interference is hunting; man's tendency to satisfy his passion for the chase regardless of the consequences has caused a particularly large number of animals to become extinct in desert regions. And the situation is not improving—hunters have recently begun to use motorized vehicles, often with motives of simple greed for trophies or commercially valuable skins. The introduction of exotic species also often has undesirable results and has completely altered

The guano birds

Man's influence on the desert

the ecology in some regions. A prime example of this is the introduction of the wild rabbit in Australia. The boundless multiplication of the rabbits was finally controlled there by use of the myxomatosis virus, but it is still not clear what consequences the spread of this disease will have for other organisms.

European red foxes were also set free in Australia, in order that the people might have fox hunts. But the fox soon became a major hunter itself, killing so many small native marsupials that some species were almost exterminated in certain areas. The desert is especially vulnerable to human interference, for its ecological relationships are complex and delicately balanced. One can only hope, now that man is becoming conscious of the need for environmental protection, that he will soon realize the full extent of his responsibility for the desert regions.

16 Tropical Rainforest

Wherever the climate is warm and humid all the year round, one finds tropical evergreen rainforest—the kind of forest that is commonly called simply "jungle." It is an ancient habitat, and probably the most important in the evolution of terrestrial organisms. Of course, it has not always been exactly the same; in the course of the earth's history, as the face of the planet was transformed and the climate fluctuated on a worldwide scale, the boundaries of the rainforest have changed and its subdivisions have shifted, become larger or smaller, or been broken up and separated. But it seems that in all parts of the world there have been extensive, permanently humid warm forests without interruption for almost a hundred million years; here the superabundance of plants and animals we now find had time to evolve.

By E. J. Fittkau

Many plant and animal groups of the temperate zone are thought to have evolved in warm rainforests. There is no other continental habitat in which so many phylogenetically ancient forms have survived. Even today, for example, the tropical rainforests house many species of Onychophora, a group that stands between the annelids and arthropods and contains some of the oldest land animals still in existence. Whip scorpions (suborder Uropygi), and spiders of the suborder Amblypygi and the order Ricinulei, ancient forms of arthropods, are found here and almost nowhere else. There are also ancient representatives of other arthropod orders in the rainforest—daddy-long-legs, spiders, centipedes, millipedes and many groups of insects.

The home of ancient animals

And the same is true of vertebrates. The amphibians evolved in the rainforest region, and the number of amphibian species here is still greater than in other habitats. In the jungle soil live the wormlike amphibians called caecilians (order Gymnophiona), which despite their specialization still display many primitive characteristics. Reptiles and birds, too, have attained their greatest diversity in the equatorial forests, and some representatives of ancient groups still survive. And the earliest marsupials—the agile, arboreal opossums (family Didelphidae) and the ratlike members of

▷
Tropical montane rainforest on Mount Bosavi in New Guinea (altitude about 1800 m).

the family Caenolestidae—have survived in the American jungles, the equally primitive flying lemurs (order Dermoptera) and tree shrews (family Tupaiidae) in the tropics of Asia, and some specially old groups of insectivores, such as the tenrecs (Tenrecidae) and golden moles (Chryso-chloridae) in Africa and Madagascar. The Lemuroids (lemurs and their allies) inhabit Madagascar, the Lorisoids (lorises, pottos, etc.) live in the tropical forests of southern Asia and Africa, and the Tarsiidae (tarsiers) are native to the Sunda and Philippine Islands. Other representatives of very old mammal groups that are found in rainforests and in some cases are extremely well adapted to this habitat are pangolins and scaly anteaters (order Pholidota) in the Old World and armadillos, anteaters and sloths (order Edentata) in the New.

Before the Ice Age, the rainforest extended as far north as Europe, but today it is essentially limited to the tropics. By this we mean the band around the equator, from the Tropic of Cancer in the north to the Tropic of Capricorn in the south, which until very recently was the most densely wooded region on earth; 40% of the area was forested. About two thirds of this—approximately ten million square kilometers—was evergreen rainforest. In the less humid marginal areas there was a transition to semideciduous or entirely deciduous monsoon forests, savannas and steppes, and in the humid tropical mountains at altitudes above 500–1000 meters its place was taken by montane rainforests.

But in most tropical regions clearing by fire and the establishment of large plantations have brought about catastrophic losses of forest; and recently there has been additional widespread destruction resulting from the use of chemicals—defoliants and preparations of arsenic, diesel oil and other substances. The severity of the resulting damage to the environment has already become apparent. To mention only a few of these consequences, there has been soil erosion, loss of soil fertility, filling of the rivers with sand and mud, disturbance of large-scale water relations (for example, wide fluctuations between high and low water), an increasing incidence of floods and serious climatic changes. The rainforests contribute to the balance of nature in many different ways. Not only do they protect the quality of the soil, but they store enormous quantities of water; as they disappear even the amount of reradiation from the earth's surface can change, which cannot fail to affect the atmosphere and thus the plant, animal and human life on our planet.

In the constantly humid tropics the mean monthly temperatures lie between about 24° and 26°C, with maxima of 33–36°C and minima of 18–20°C. The average variation in temperature in the course of a day, then, in these forests is only about five to eight degrees; and even this is several times greater than the fluctuation over a year, which often averages only one to two degrees centigrade. The humidity, averaged over a month, is never less than 75% and usually it is considerably higher. To maintain such a high average value, the forests require at least 1800

Extent of the rainforests

◁

Samples of the tropical rainforest fauna:
Above: the three-fingered sloth, a mammal fully adapted to arboreal life which feeds on leaves and buds exclusively (Amazonia).
Middle left: The hoatzin (*Opisthocomus hoazin*), a leaf-eater which lives only in trees and is found only in the regularly flooded forests of northern South America. The young birds have retained two fingers on each wing, which they use to hold on to the branches.
Middle right: The blue crowned pigeon, the world's largest pigeon species; it occupies an ecological niche in the New Guinea forests which in the forests of South America is taken over by other birds, among them the curassows.
Below: Butterflies perched on a decaying fish (upper reaches of the Xingu, southern Amazonia); in the carrion they find nutrient salts not adequately supplied by their usual food.

mm precipitation per year, and it must be distributed more or less uniformly throughout the year. The optimal rainfall is 2000 mm or more. During the so-called tropical summer there must be no more than two or three months in succession with less than 50–100 mm of rain. Where there is a longer period of diminished rainfall, or where there are one or two months with no rain at all, evergreen rainforests cannot survive despite a high average annual precipitation; there it is replaced by a semideciduous forest, in which some of the trees lose their leaves during the dry months.

The largest uninterrupted area of tropical rainforest covers—or covered—the Amazon Basin and three countries on the northeastern coast of South America, Cayenne, Surinam and Guayana. On the eastern slopes of the Andes, in the coastal regions of eastern Brazil, and in Central America grow montane rainforests, though these too have suffered greatly in some places from human activities. In Africa there is a relatively small equatorial nucleus of evergreen forest, in Cameroon, Gabon, the Congo countries and the coast of the Gulf of Guinea; in places this gives way to isolated montane rainforests, and it is enclosed by a wide belt of semi-dediduous forests, steppes and savannas. This African rainforest region once spread over about 218 million hectares, but it has now shrunk to around 60% of its original area. Before the recent clearing operations, the eastern part of Madagascar was also covered by rainforest. The rainforest regions of southern and southeastern Asia include the islands of Indonesia, the coastal regions of Indochina and Malaysia; there are also rainforests in New Guinea and to a lesser extent in northeastern Australia. The proportion of montane rainforests is higher in Asia than in Africa and America. But even here, in southern and southeastern Asia, more than 15 million hectares of forest are lost by clearing every year.

Fig. 16-1. Distribution of rainforest over the earth.

☰ Evergreen tropical rainforest

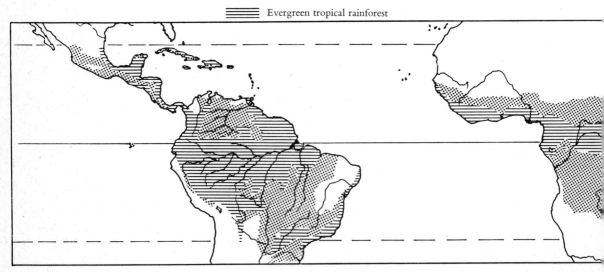

All three great tropical forest regions of the world—insofar as they remain in their original condition—are similar in the structure of their ecosystems. It is evident that in each case organisms similar in appearance, habits and role in the community evolved independently; the exchange of flora and fauna was sometimes interrupted for long periods.

There is an enormous variety of plant species in the different forest regions. On the island of Borneo alone there are about ten thousand species, rather more than on the Malaysian Peninsula; in the Amazon the number of species is considerably greater. About 3000 species of tree grow in the South American "hylaea" (as Alexander von Humboldt, one of its early explorers, called the Amazon rainforest), not even including the many lianas and palms. Herbaceous plants play a very subordinate role on the floor of the forest, but they are found as epiphytes (plants that grow on other plants but are not parasitic since they feed independently) on the trunks and in the crowns of the trees. Although some trees and shrubs are in bloom or bearing fruit at all times of the year, the flowers are not conspicuously colorful against the varied green hues of the foliage.

Ordinarily the rainforest trees are thirty to forty-five meters high. Taller species, up to sixty or in rare cases even seventy meters, are found in appreciable numbers only in the Asian rainforests, especially the montane forests, and not in those of Africa and America. The intermingling of many different trees, palms and lianas is fundamental to the composition of the forest. Because of the different heights of the various species, a deep, open canopy is formed; in a forest thirty to forty-five meters high, for example, the canopy is most dense between about twenty and thirty meters, and nearer the ground there are often several distinct strata. Taller trees are scattered more or less uniformly through the forest, projecting here and there above the canopy of leaves. About

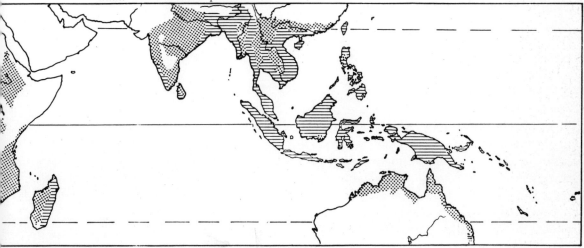

Semideciduous tropical rainforest

99% of the total radiation incident upon the forest is intercepted by the leaves of the plants. As a result, the interior of the forest has a climate of its own; from the uppermost crowns of the trees to the ground the light becomes progressively dimmer and the temperature and humidity become more and more constant. In the central Amazon rainforest the temperature at about 15 cm underground is 24–25°C, varying by little more than one or two degrees in the course of a day or year. The soil never really dries out, even on the surface. Despite the abundance of vegetation the plants on the forest floor are almost always so widely spaced that a man has little difficulty moving among the trees.

All the tropical rainforests appear little populated by animals, even though the fauna comprises so many species. One reason for this is that it is hard to see very far in the dim, overgrown jungle, and another is the nocturnal habit of many of the inhabitants. But it is true that the tropical rainforests house relatively few large, conspicuous animals. And in most regions the number of individuals in each species is small, so that despite the many species the overall density of animals remains low. Apart from the social insects, the termites, ants, wasps and bees, it is rare to encounter even moderately large groups of animals of the same species, regardless of body size. Usually it is easier to collect thirty different species of beetle or butterfly in a day than to find thirty individuals of one species. The larger gregarious animals—for example, parrots, pigs and certain primate species which often live in fairly large troops—wander like nomads through extensive territories, but these represent only a small fraction of the forest fauna.

The fauna of the tropical forests has never been adequately studied. The vertebrates, conspicuously large beetles and beautiful butterflies have almost all been given scientific names, but often little is known about their behavior or ways of life. And the same is true of the huge army of smaller insects and invertebrates, most of which have not even been named and classified. The total number of animal species in the forest regions is probably many times that of the plants. Within the animal groups that have been thoroughly studied by systematists, the greatest number of species is in the South American rainforests, and the smallest in those of Africa.

The vertical layering of the forest vegetation is usually so pronounced that it is useful to think of the habitat as divided into strata, each with its own animal community. The strata are characterized by particular food chains and climatic conditions, which change more or less gradually from the ground to the treetops. Animals not so strictly limited to a particular substrate, humidity or light intensity make the boundaries more indistinct, and dividing lines are of course harder to draw where the substrate itself is not clearly layered. For example, even the soil is not limited to ground level, for it accumulates between epiphytes, on branches and on old tree stumps; it can form an adequate habitat for a

Fig. 16-2. Characteristic roots of tropical trees:

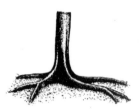

Superficial roots (*Entandrophragma angolense*, Nigeria).

Boardlike roots (*Mora excelsa*, Amazon region).

Prop roots (*Uapaca staudtii*, western Africa)

Fig. 16-3. Section of a central Amazonian rainforest, showing the division of the habitat into strata: forest floor, tree canopy, and the intermediate trunk region. Number and height of the trees are shown in the proportions determined for an actual area of forest. The forest shown covers an area 20 m long and 5 m wide. The trees and palms growing on this 100 square meters weigh a total of 10 metric tons, and there is an additional *ca.* 1 ton of dead wood and leaf litter. The animals in such a section of forest weigh an estimated total of only 2–3 kg.

true soil fauna even in the crowns of the trees. Moreover, attempts to delimit strata fail when one of the giant trees has fallen and enough light can penetrate for a canopy of leaves to form near the ground; then a temporary habitat is created which corresponds more' or less closely to that of the fringe forests along rivers and around clearings.

In the soil and the layer of litter covering it is hidden the most diverse fauna of the forest, and one particularly important in the cycling of nutrients. It is directly or indirectly responsible for the rapid decomposition of the dead leaves, woody fragments and other detritus from the plants. The soil fauna constitutes by far the largest fraction of the animal biomass in the rainforest ecosystem, even though it consists chiefly of small organisms such as mites, springtails, cockroaches, beetles and their larvae, dipteran larvae, ants, termites and other insects. Other soil-dwellers are land planarians, leeches, earthworms, gastropods and onychophorans, as well as centipedes, millipedes, many scorpions, spiders and related groups. Certain vertebrates like the caecilians and ringed lizards play a role in conditioning the soil that must not be overlooked, and there are armadillos, pangolins, scaly anteaters and aardvarks that live on the floor of the forest.

Certain groups which constitute a large fraction of the soil fauna in temperate latitudes (ground beetles, for example) are much less well represented in the tropics. In many cases the omnipresent ants take their place; in Amazonia alone there are about 400 species of ant, many of them armed with stings. And earthworms of the family Lumbricidae, so common in the temperate zones, are rare here. Instead one finds in South America related worms of the family Glossoscolecidae, some of which are of impressive size. They do not eat old leaf litter, but rather lick up microscopic animals and plants from the litter and the surface of the soil, using their eversible proboscises. There is one exception to this general rule; in the rainforests of Asia live numerous species of the lumbricid genus *Pheretima*—brightly colored, flattened worms which, because of the high humidity and the abundance of food, can live on the bark of trees.

The constantly humid jungle climate has also made it possible for another group of annelids (the leeches, order Hirudinea) and for planarians (class Turbellaria) to evolve large terrestrial species. The New World leech *Liostomus* lives in and on the forest soil and litter, preying upon insects and earthworms. In contrast, terrestrial leeches of the Old World tropics, especially in Asia, suck the blood of vertebrates. In expanses of rainforest with very acid soils low in calcium carbonate, like those of central Amazonia, there are no gastropods with shells.

The feeding habits of the small soil animals, and perhaps the absence (with the abovementioned exception) of lumbricid worms, suggest that the litter on the rainforest floor is usually lacking in nutrients, so that it cannot be used directly as food but is recycled by way of bacteria, fungi and protozoans. In any case, those members of the soil fauna in the forests of the central Amazon region which are not carnivorous feed primarily upon fungi; among them are species belonging to groups which outside the tropics ordinarily eat decaying vegetable matter.

Next to the ants, most of which are predatory carnivores, the termites are probably the most successful animals of the rainforest. They digest their food with the help of intestinal protozoans, so that they are able to subsist in large part upon wood. But there are many "food specialists" among the termites. Phylogenetically younger species seem to prefer rotting wood or litter infested with fungi, and some even cultivate fungi in the well-controlled climate of their nests. By building tunnels in which to travel, these soft-skinned animals, sensitive to light and dryness, protect themselves from predators and are able to leave the forest floor. In this way they can not only move into the higher strata of the forest, where climatic conditions are much less stable, but they can even colonize the occasionally drought-ridden steppes and savannas, where their large nests are a conspicuous feature.

The New World leaf-cutting ants (genus *Atta* and others) are also very well able to cope with the difficulties of finding food in the rainforest. They carry fresh leaves, which are still relatively nutritious, into their subterranean nests, and on the chewed mass of leaves they cultivate a fungus which is their only food. In building their nests, ants and termites can make a considerable contribution to turning over the upper layers of the soil.

Aside from the invertebrates, all of which live more or less in the litter or soil except for a few spiders, grasshoppers and flying insects, the fauna of the forest floor and shrub strata is sparse, in terms of both species and individuals. Only relatively few vertebrates have been able to become completely adapted to life on the ground in the jungle. In the New World, these include certain frogs and toads, two species of tortoise (*Chelonoidis carbonaria* and *Chelonoidis denticulata*), and a few lizards, snakes, birds and mammals. Some of the amphibians and reptiles, though, are quite large—the giant toad (*Bufo marinus*), the Columbian toad *Bufo blombergi*, the huge snakes (*Boa* and others) and the bushmaster (genus *Lachesis*).

Mammals of the forest floor

The mammals restricted to the forest floor are, in general, small. Striking exceptions in Africa are the rare okapi, the bongo, the giant forest pig and the gorilla, and in Asia the orangutan and Malayan tapir —all species found only in very limited areas. In South and Central America the lowland tapir and Central American tapir are the largest animals of the forest, whereas the fourth species of tapir, the mountain tapir, lives only at higher altitudes. Many of the medium-sized and large inhabitants of the jungle stay near bodies of water full of plants; among these are the tapirs, the New World brockets (deer of the genus *Mazama*), the capybara (a rodent), the western African pigmy hippopotamus, the bush pigs of Africa, and finally the Asian two-horned rhinoceros and the great Indian rhinoceros—though the latter are not pure forest animals. Mammal groups distributed chiefly in open terrain are represented in the forests by especially small species; for example, in the forests of western Africa lives the royal antelope, the smallest of all antelopes, standing 25–30 cm tall from hoof to shoulder. The smallest ungulate is a chevrotain (family Tragulidae); this is the lesser Malay mouse deer (*Tragulus javanicus*) of Indochina, only 20 cm high. Even the cattle, usually rather ponderous, have produced a small forest form, 60–100 cm tall—the anoa, the dwarf buffalo of the Celebes.

Apart from the relatively uncommon chevrotains and the brockets of the New World, the herbivorous mammal fauna of the rainforest floor in South America consists predominantly of rodents like the agoutis and pacas. In Africa there are the antelopes called duikers (subfamily Cephalophinae) and in Asia, the muntjacs (the deer subfamily Muntiacinae); there are wild boars (family Suidae) in the Old World and peccaries (family Tayassuidae) in the New, though neither of these feed exclusively upon plants. Almost all these mammals—except for the boars and peccaries, which usually stay in fairly large troops—are active mainly at night. They orient primarily by hearing. Their bodies are adapted to life on the forest floor, being low-slung, with wedge-shaped head and shoulders carried close to the ground. The deer and bovids have regressed antlers or horns and enlarged eyes and ears.

Some species of mammal which feed on insects and small animals are remarkably large. But these are not restricted to the rainforests; rather, various species or subspecies also occur in the savannas and steppes. In this category are the two larger species of anteater and the giant armadillo of the New World; their biological counterparts in the Old World are the aardvark and the scaly anteaters. Nor do large carnivores like the jaguar, leopard, tiger and puma stay entirely within the rainforests, although they are good climbers; they also spend time in open country. True rainforest carnivores include the South American bush dog, the ocelot and its relatives, and a number of Old World viverrid cat species.

In the tree trunk stratum and the lower regions of the crowns there are relatively few animals; most of them are small and live as climbers or even flyers. Through the motionless, humid air in Amazonia glide the world's largest butterflies (*Caligo*) and the morphos (family Morphidae), the blue wings of which light up when a sunbeam falls on them through the jungle twilight. Here, too, there flutter numerous butterflies of the families Heliconiidae and Ithoniidae and the species that resemble them so deceptively, discussed in the chapter on mimicry (see Chapter 9). Outsize dragonflies, which hatch out in the water collected in the bromeliads, dart through the air. Hummingbirds flit up to the hidden flowers. The nests of termites, ants, wasps and bees are attached to tree trunks and branches. Cicadas, camouflaged by magnificent colors and

▷
Upper left: flooded forest (igapó) on the banks of the Rio Negro at low water. Below: Epiphytes (Araceae) in central Amazonia.
Upper right: Settlement at the edge of the untouched tropical jungle in Amazonia.
Below, from left to right: Tree ferns in the tropical cloud forest of the Sierra de Santa Marta (Columbia) at an altitude of 2000 m.— Tree ferns in the foothills of the Serra da Neblina (near the border between Brazil and Venezuela).— Epiphytic fig in the flood region of the Amazon.

strange shapes, suck on the rather thin bark of the trees and at certain times of day, together with frogs and toads, produce the sounds that characterize the jungle. Many insect-eating species of bird, most of them inconspicuous in color, shelter in this stratum. Some find favorably situated places where they lie in wait for passing prey, while others, like the antbirds (family Formicariidae) follow the columns of driver and army ants and eat the animals they flush out of hiding. Still others, like the woodpeckers so common in the rainforest, seek their food on tree trunks and on the ground.

There are a large number of rainforest trees with flowers located directly on the trunk or on branches below the crown. This is assumed to be an adaptation to pollination by animals; in the tropical rainforest not only insects serve as pollinators, but bats and birds as well—for example, hummingbirds in America and sunbirds in Africa.

In general, the tree canopy is the rainforest stratum with the most abundant animal life. The vegetation, too, is best developed here; most of the trees, lianas and epiphytes flower and bear their fruits in this stratum. There are a great number of different niches available to the various organisms. Plants and animals requiring shade and much moisture must keep to the lower regions, more protected from the sun, for in and on the canopy stratum temperature, humidity and air motion change considerably during the day as a function of the position of the sun. In order to survive here, many epiphytes in sunny locations store water —the orchids in the outer tissues of their aerial roots and the New World bromeliads in the axils of the leaves; thus they create for themselves almost aquatic habitats in the crowns of trees. The same thing is achieved by the Asian pitcher-plants (genus *Nepenthes*). Other epiphytes attach in the light, near the treetops, and let their roots hang down to the ground to obtain water; among them are arums and others of the family Araceae, which is widespread in the tropics. The many lianas have solved the problem similarly, rooting in the ground, sending up long thin stems, and often spreading out their branches on top of the canopy formed by the trees supporting them. Almost all epiphytes collect humus and soil between their leaves, shoots and roots, and often suitably adapted ants also gather there. In fact, such accumulations of soil provide the crowns of the trees with a variety of habitats for a true soil fauna, some of which can shelter and feed even large species.

The fauna adapted to life in the tree canopy is extremely varied. The individual crowns overlap so extensively that amphibians, reptiles and mammals can move from tree to tree without difficulty, never needing to descend to earth. But the food supply of the leaf- and fruit-eaters is more or less limited. Fruit-bearing trees of the same species are usually widely separated and can be visited in succession only by highly motile animals—birds, bats and apes. Often the fruits are hidden within a thick woody case which can be broken only by large rodents on the ground.

◁
Above: View of the montane forest on the southern Brazilian coast (Serra do Mar). The purple flowering trees are *Tibuchina mutabilis* (Melastomaceae).
Lower left: An Amazon parrot, a characteristic inhabitant of the South American rainforest.
Lower right: Mountain gorillas in the eastern Congo forest.

The irregular timing of leaf abscission and new growth may well make it more difficult for the plant-eating insects to find young leaves. Older leaves quickly grow tough or become unpalatable because of poisons deposited in them. Certain trees (acacias and other ant trees) are guarded by stinging ants, to which they provide cavities for shelter and food from specialized organs (see Chapter 8).

The many forms of mimicry (see Chapter 9), often achieving a high degree of perfection, among cicadas, bugs, grasshoppers, stick insects and caterpillars is evidence of the ubiquity of insectivorous animals, which ensure that there are no mass outbreaks of individual insect species. Nevertheless, it sometimes happens that certain species of caterpillar or spider appear in great numbers, and then they behave like social insects; the caterpillars rest close together during the day, and the spiders build huge communal nests.

Often frogs, lizards, geckos, snakes and birds are cleverly matched to their surroundings, both in color and in shape. A large flock of green Amazon parrots is most difficult to detect in the canopy of a tree. On the other hand, many species display colors of unexcelled brilliance and striking shapes—for example, the brightly colored, extremely poisonous tree-climbing frogs of the genus *Dendrobates*, the coral snakes and their mimics, and the macaws and birds of paradise.

One of the most remarkable adaptations to life in the treetops is the ability to hover or glide, evolved by certain amphibians, reptiles and mammals of the Old World tropics (Fig. 16-5). The frog *Rhacophorus nigropalmatus* of Borneo has enormous membranes between its toes, which act as a parachute when it jumps from a tree. Similarly, a Malaysian gecko spreads folds of skin out from the body during a jump, which expand its body surface enough to permit it to glide at an angle of about forty-five degrees. The highest development of gliding flight is found in the flying dragons (the agamid genus *Draco*) of southern Asia and the Indonesian islands. In this case the expandable folds at the sides of the body are supported by several ribs, so that they form fanlike "wings." Even the flying snakes (genus *Chrysopelea*) can broaden and flatten their bodies to such an extent that they fall through the air more slowly and can steer themselves in a certain direction. A very flat, long-distance glide is achieved by the flying squirrels (subfamily Pteromyinae), the African scaly-tailed squirrels (family Anomaluridae), and the south-eastern Asian flying lemurs (order Dermoptera). When Amazonian primates, parrots and toucans are in danger—perhaps having been surprised by a cat or bird of prey—they simply drop from the branch on which they are sitting. But in all the tropics of the New World, with their great variety of animal species, there are no animals specialized for gliding. Perhaps the tall forests of the mountainous regions of Asia, with clear vertical "steps" on the slopes, were better suited for the evolution of gliding animals than the forests of the Amazon lowlands.

COMMENTARY ON THE FOLLOWING ILLUSTRATION ▷ ▷ SCHEMATIC REPRE-SENTATION OF THE FOOD CHAIN IN THE TROPICAL LOWLAND RAINFOREST OF SOUTH AMERICA. The shaded sectors correspond to the estimated percent of the total animal biomass represented by the different trophic types. The inner ring includes the pure herbivores, the PRIMARY CONSUM-ERS, by far the greater fraction of which feed on dead plant matter. The most important members of this group are the termites and beetles. The middle ring comprises omnivores, PRIMARY AND HIGHER-LEVEL CONSUMERS. The most significant groups here are the ants and wasps. In the outer ring are the carnivores, the SECOND-ARY AND HIGHER-LEVEL CONSUMERS, some of which also live underground. The largest percentage, by weight, of the rainforest fauna is represented by the soil fauna, small animals and microorganisms in the litter layer and the upper layers of the soil. Most of these are insects, which do not feed on the litter directly but rather on fungi and bacteria which break down the plant detritus.

PRIMARY CONSUMERS feeding only on dead vegetable matter:
1. Termite (*Nasutitermes*); 1a. Termite nest; 2. Longhorn beetle (*Acrocinus longimanus*); 2a. Larva of a longhorn beetle; 3. Bess beetle (*Passalus*); 4. Bark beetle of the family Scolytidae.

PRIMARY CONSUMERS feeding only on living plants:
5. Two-toed sloth (*Choleopus didactylus*); 6. Parrot (*Amazona* sp.); 7. Howler monkey (*Alouatta*); 8. Curassow (*Crax*); 9. Red fruit bat (*Vampyrum*); 10. Butterfly (*Heliconius* sp.); 11. Hawkmoth (family Sphingidae); 12. Leaf-cutter ant (*Atta* sp.); 13. Tree-hopper (family Membranacidae); 14. Stick insect (family Bacteriidae); 15. Paca (*Cuniculus paca*); 16. Lowland tapir (*Tapirus terrestris*).

PRIMARY AND SECONDARY CONSUMERS (omnivores):
17. Capuchin monkey (*Cebus*); 18. Toucan (*Ramphastos*); 19. Coati (*Nasua*); 20. Hummingbird (*Urochroa*); 21. Wasp (*Polybia*); 21a. Wasp nest; 22. Army ant (*Eciton*); 23. Peccary (*Pecari tajacu*); 24. South American mouse opossum (*Marmosa*).

SECONDARY AND HIGHER-ORDER CONSUMERS (carnivores, carrion-eaters, parasites):
5. Praying mantis (family Mantidae); 26. Parasitic wasp (family Ichneumonidae); 27. Frog (*Phyllomedusa*); 28. Anole (*Anolis*); 29. Anteater (*Tamandua tetradactyla*); 30. Leaf-nosed bat (*Phyllostomus*); 31. Woodpecker (*Scapaneus*); 32. Harpy (*Harpia harpyja*); 33. *Boa constrictor*; 34. Bird spider (*Lasidora*); 35. Scorpion (*Tityus*); 36. Jaguar (*Panthera onca*); 36a. Armadillo (*Dasypus*); 37. Leech (*Liostomus*); 38. Centipede (*Scolopendra*); 39. Caecilian (order Apoda); 40. Mite (order Acarina); 41. Springtail (order Collembola); 42. Cockroach (family Blattidae); 43. Earthworm (family Glossoscolecidae); 44. King vulture (*Sarcoramphus papa*); 45. Dung beetle (family Scarabaeidae); 46. Mosquito (*Sabethes*). The king vulture (44), a carrion-eater, and the blood-sucking mosquito (46), a parasite, are higher-level consumers.

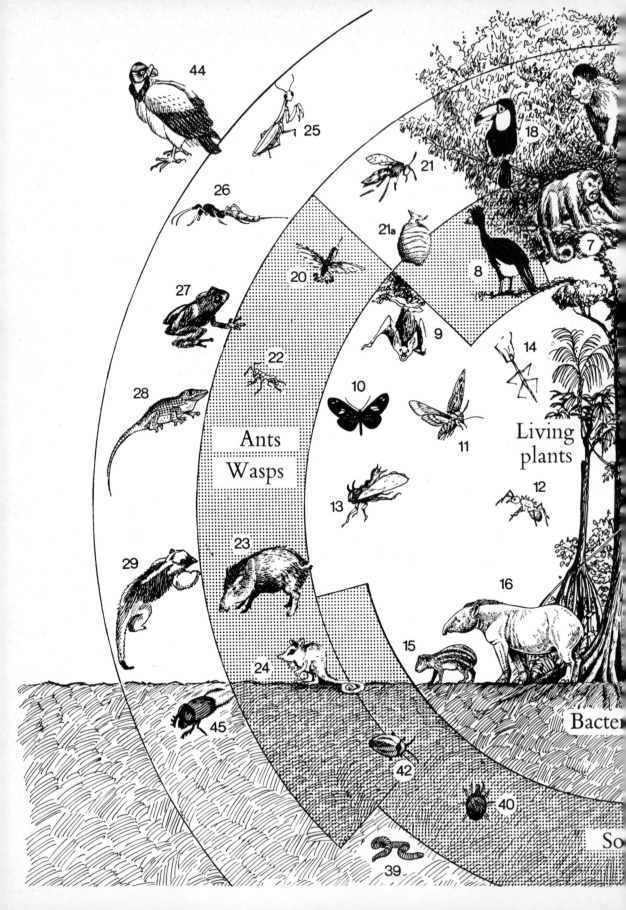

44

25

26

21

21a

20

8

9

14

27

22

10

Living
plants

11

28

Ants

Wasps

13

12

29

23

16

24

15

45

42

40

Bacter

39

So

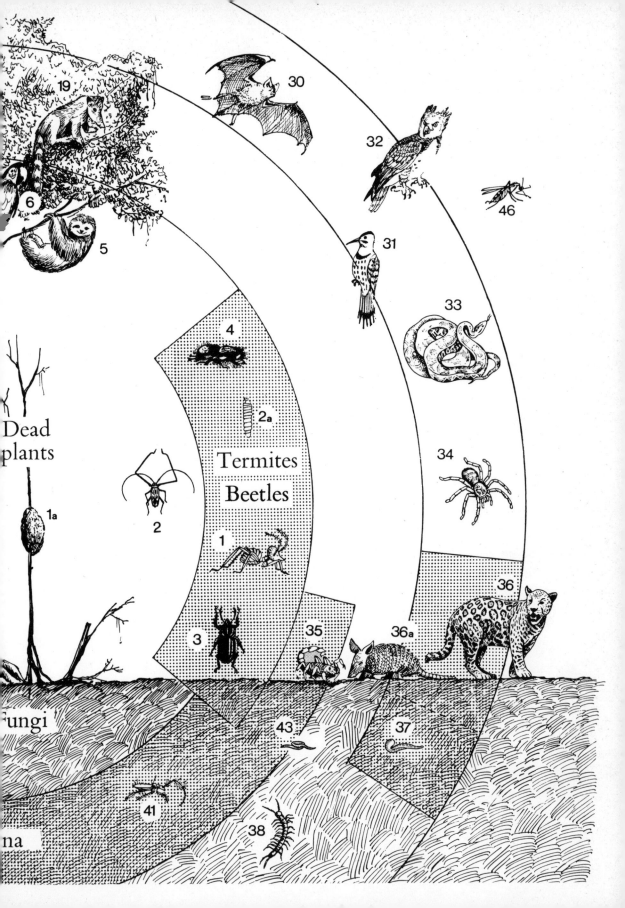

19

30

32

6

5

31

46

4

33

2a

Dead
plants

Termites

Beetles

34

1a

2

1

35

36

3

36a

Fungi

43

37

na

41

38

Many animals of the canopy stratum are well adapted in other respects to life high above the forest floor. For example, some amphibians have evolved various ways to reproduce independently of water on the ground. Numerous birds that stay in the crowns of the trees cannot fly particularly well. This is especially striking in the case of the large gallinaceous birds, which feed on leaves and move relatively slowly; there are also fruit- and flesh-eaters which walk and hop through the trees—the toucans of South America, the externally similar but unrelated hornbills of the Old World tropics, and the touracos of Africa. Parrots, on the other hand, are excellent flyers and climbers; living gregariously, as most of them do, they must be highly motile in order to obtain enough food. The pure leaf-eaters among the tree-dwelling mammals, the sloths and porcupines, climb cautiously; so do the prosimians, the anteaters *Cyclopes* and *Tamandua*, and the scaly anteaters (which eat not only ants but also termites), assisted by their prehensile tails. The simians, too, are mostly arboreal. Many of the New World monkeys use their tails in climbing, while those Old World species with tails use them to control direction and balance. A few carnivorous mammals of the tropical rainforest also have prehensile tails; among them are the kinkajou and the binturong. Many smaller cat species—including the Margay cat (*Leopardus wiedi*), which has achieved near perfection in climbing and swinging from branches—hunt a great variety of prey in the crowns of the trees.

The bats, the group of mammals having the greatest number of genera and lower taxa in the tropics—hundreds of species—are also well represented in the rainforest. Only some of them catch insects; most species feed upon fruits and flowers or suck nectar. There are also bats, like the "false vampires," which supplement their diet of fruit and insects with small vertebrates. The true vampire bats (family Desmodontidae), on the other hand, feed exclusively by sucking vertebrate blood. Fruit-eating bats tend to sleep in the treetops, sometimes in large groups in the open and sometimes in smaller groups hidden among the leaves; other species, however, withdraw to holes in trees or rocks during the day.

The open air above the canopy of the forest seems sparsely populated by insects. Only a few birds spend most of their time there—swifts, New World vultures and other birds of prey. The most conspicuous accipitrid birds flying over the treetops are the African crowned eagle (*Stephanoaëtus coronatus*), the monkey-eating eagle (*Pithecophaga jefferyi*), which is almost extinct in its Philippine homeland, and the South American harpy (*Harpia harpyja*); all of these (Fig. 16-8) eat monkeys, and *Pithecophaga* eats practically nothing else.

There are many sorts of reciprocal relationship between the forests and the lakes and streams, together with their fauna, that arise in the forests or flow through them. In the shady jungle brooks, over which the tree canopy closes, there is hardly any plant life. Here the food chain

Fig. 16-5. Some gliding animals of the Old World tropics:

The frog *Rhacophorus nigropalmatus*.

Kuhl's gecko (*Ptychozoon kuhli*).

Flying dragon (*Draco volans*).

Flying lemur (*Cynocephalus volans*).

Fig. 16-6. Some epiphytes of the tropical rainforest. Epiphytes are plants that grow on other plants, particularly trees, without taking nutrients from them.

Orchid (*Cattleya* sp., Amazon region).

Bromeliad (*Guzmania* sp., Amazon region)

Fern (*Asplenium africanum*, western Africa).

begins with the flowers, fruit, leaves, insects and other organic matter that fall into the water or are washed in by rain. Nevertheless, there is an extremely rich fauna in the waters of the rainforest, consisting primarily of insects and their larvae but also including fish, crustaceans, amphibians and mammals. Where the brook expands into a river, many animals take advantage of the gap in the forest as a place to fly, especially since along the shores the tree canopy reaches down to the water.

Probably all the vertebrates of the tropical rainforest—except for a few New World primates, the gibbons, and the lemurs—are good swimmers; even the sloths, which hardly ever descend to the ground, can swim across large bodies of water without difficulty. It has already been mentioned that the larger forest vertebrates, in particular, live in swampy regions near the water; this is because the food preferred by herbivores is usually more abundant here than in the part of the forest not submerged even when the water level is highest. The seasonal flooding of the river valleys, which in some regions lasts for a long time, is associated with a specially adapted type of forest—rather low, open trees between which it is often possible for grasses and herbs to grow on the forest floor and along the river banks. But the only parts of the forest subject to flooding which are really rich in animals and plants are those that the river fertilizes by bringing new soil, newly weathered stone, and deposits from its upper reaches. Brooks and rivers arising in forest lowlands themselves very infertile cannot, of course, increase the fertility of the flooded soil with their sediments.

In central Amazonia the waters generally are colored a more or less deep brown, because of the humic acids dissolved in them. The forests growing along their banks—low, open stands with few species—are submerged under as much as ten (or even more) meters of water for half the year. The local name for these forests is igapó. Even when the water drains away hardly any herbs will grow on the ground, although the light is quite strong in places. The igapó is the habitat with the fewest animals in the New World tropical rainforest. Termites, ants and other invertebrates which live here permanently escape the high water by moving up into the crowns of the trees. During the flooded season fish swim into the forest; they evidently find a better food supply there than in the river itself. Among the few animals adapted to this habitat are the siliceous sponges. Their rounded or flattened colonies, often quite large, are conspicuous sights on the branches and trunks of the trees or shrubs during low water.

Where the rainforest extends from lowlands into mountains, its composition changes fundamentally with increasing altitude. As low as 300–500 meters the species characteristic of the flatland begin to disappear. Among the new plants are tree ferns, which take the place of the lowland palms and even resemble them in form. At altitudes between 1000 and 2000 meters, the epiphytes are most abundant. Above 2000 meters the leafy trees gradually give way to conifers, shrubbery and areas of grass. On steep slopes the tree canopy becomes more open, so that more light reaches the forest floor. Rocky outcrops and weathered stone provide enough mineral nutrients for a luxuriant undergrowth of herbs. Thus the varying slopes and the associated differences in microclimate, together with the change in the vegetation, provide a great number of new niches, often within a very small space; as a result, there is a rich fauna that is largely unknown in the lowlands.

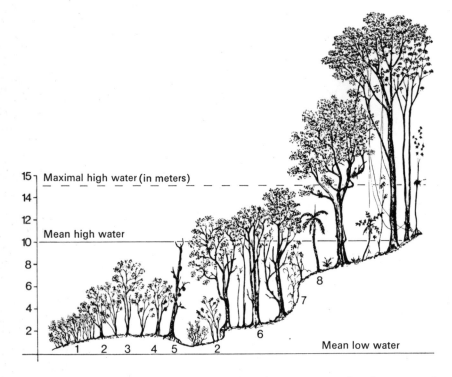

Fig. 16-7. Igapó (periodically flooded forest in the Amazon basin) near Manaus on the lower Rio Negro. During the annual flood season, which lasts for several months, the level of "blackwater" in the forest is high; often the forest floor is not dry even when the water is lowest. Most species of tree keep their leaves while they are submerged. Some of the common species: 1. Pixuna (*Coccoloba* sp.); 2. Araça (*Eugenia inundata*); 3. Acapurana (*Campsiandra laurifolia*); 5. Dead tree to which are attached sponges of the genera *Metanea* and *Drulia*; 6. Tree species of different families, forming a stand 13–15 m tall; 7. The grass *Scleria tenacissima*; 8. Iara palms (*Leopoldina pulchra*).

Again and again one hears it said that the enormous development of the flora and fauna in the tropical rainforest is the consequence of great fertility in those regions. But the soils of large parts of the rainforest are extraordinarily low in nutrients, which is understandable in view of the prevailing climate. High temperatures and heavy precipitation do accelerate the weathering of stone, the liberation of nutrients and the formation of soil; but at the same time they favor the rapid removal of weathered substances, especially from hilly terrain. In areas where the ground is being levelled and sediments deposited, the upper layers of the soil continue to be rapidly leached. But it is just on such level, alluvial ground, usually formed quite a long time ago, that the large, dense forests stand; and this is where the greatest diversity of plant and animal life is found.

The factors responsible for this abundance of species are probably the great age of humid tropical forests, their large spatial extent, and the fact that during their varied history they were occasionally split up into isolated areas. But it is still puzzling that so very many plants and animals can exist in an orderly manner in such close proximity, without one species spreading to crowd out others. Evidently this is an exceedingly complex ecosystem, evolved through geological epochs, which still continues—as long as man does not interfere—to regulate and control itself in many ways by mechanisms of which we have only a vague notion.

For millions of years the plants and animals of the tropical forests have had more or less uniform environmental conditions in which to maintain themselves and evolve further. But in order for the situation to remain stable in the extensive lowlands, with their very limited or even exhausted reserves of nutrients (for example, in Amazonia), the nutrients that are available—those bound in the living and dead organic matter of the forest—must all be recycled without loss. The humid tropical climate accelerates the synthesis of organic matter as well as its decomposition. Unavoidable losses of nutrients—for example, through leaching by ground and surface water—cannot in the long run be made good by the soil. Evidently the ecosystem is capable of keeping these losses so small that they can be compensated by the nutrient materials the rain brings down from the atmosphere. The equilibrium between losses by leaching and the slight gain of nutrients from the soil and the air must be the more stable, the shorter the period of nutrient cycling; that is, stability is increased the greater the certainty that all nutrients, whether provided by rain or by remineralization, can immediately be returned to the ecosystem. The recycling of nutrients in the rainforest must, accordingly, be more complete the more diverse the stand of plants in a given area. Each plant takes up through its leaves and roots different amounts of nutrients, depending upon the season, its age, and its species. The more different species there are, the more completely and efficiently one can expect the released or introduced nutrients to be used. Therefore it seems reasonable to regard the great diversity of the vegetation as a successful adaptation to the infertility of the tropical habitat, where apart from the paucity of the nutrient reserves the environmental conditions are extremely favorable to plant life.

In this connection, it is interesting to consider a detailed analysis that has been made of a stand on extraordinarily nutrient-poor soil in a central Amazonian rainforest; this example also illuminates the role of the animals in the nutrient cycles of the community. Geologically, the area consists of continental, sandy-clayey Tertiary sediments, weathered to a considerable depth and with a superficial layer of the characteristic acid tropical red-clay soils (latosols). In one hectare more than 90,000 plants were counted, of which about 10,000 were taller than 1.5 m and belonged to more than 500 different species of trees, shrubs and palms. The number

The circulation of matter

of species of plants less than 1.5 m tall, mostly seedlings and young plants, was not determined. The living plant biomass in the hectare investigated amounted to about 1000 metric tons, of which around 250 tons comprised the total root mass and twenty tons, the leaves. In addition, there were on the same area about 100 tons of dead plant matter, such as leaves and wood. The animal biomass was determined by sampling and estimates; in this region there was only about 0.2–0.3 tons biomass per hectare. Of this amount, vertebrates contributed 13–20 kg and invertebrates made up the rest; most of the latter were arthropods of the soil fauna.

The share of the animals, especially the vertebrates, in the total biomass of the rainforest is thus very small, and in central Amazonia it is particularly low. Although it might be several times greater in other rainforest regions, the same explanation for the small animal biomass as compared with other habitats holds for all—the limitation on the food supply discussed above. As we have already mentioned, the plant-eating soil animals feed chiefly upon fungus mycelia; presumably the leaf litter is not sufficiently nutritious, since the trees draw a great deal of the nutrient substances back out of the leaves before they fall. Fungi that decompose the litter are in symbiosis with higher plants (such associations of fungi with roots are called mycorrhizae); as a result, nutrients can be recycled to the plants by a short pathway or even directly. A dense network of fine roots ensures that all the nutrients released on the soil surface are taken up. In the central Amazonian forest investigated the dried fine roots in the upper meter of the soil of a hectare weighed about forty tons, and of this about seventeen tons were in the upper fifteen centimeters. At depths greater than one meter hardly any fine roots could be detected.

In addition to the variety of means by which rainforest plants protect themselves from damage by animals, they have developed many ways of using nutrients economically and they are frequently quite thrifty in their production of seeds and fruits. For example, the Lecythidaceae (a family including the well-known Brazil nut tree) in infertile Tertiary sedimentation regions of Amazonia produce thickly encapsulated seeds that are small and few in number. But on more fertile soils, formed on weathered crystalline or plutonic rock or consisting of recent alluvia, there grow species with large fruits and many seeds. In this case, then, the supply of animal food improves as the fertility of the soil increases, although the climatic conditions are the same. There are many similar examples, all of which go to show that a forest well supplied with nutrients by the soil, other things being equal, offers a more generous supply of food to the animals; in such cases the proportion of species with leaves, seeds and fruits that can be eaten by animals is greater. But with the increased fertility of the soil and the clearly associated increase in plant biomass the total number of different species—at least among the plants

Fig. 16-8. Characteristic accipitrid birds of the tropical rainforest:

Crowned eagle (*Stephano-aëtus coronatus*, Africa).

Monkey-eating eagle (*Pithecophaga jefferyi*, Philippines).

Harpy (*Harpia harpyja*, South America).

—actually seems to decrease; that is, in a comparable area there are more large trees of the same species, while the population density of the animals increases accordingly. Even under these conditions, though, the tropical rainforest is the domain of the plants; animals have invaded their domain, but remain entirely subordinate to the flora.

Animals as elements of the ecosystem

Simplifying the situation greatly, one can divide the rainforest animals into three groups of different ecological significance. All the species directly necessary for the maintenance of the plant cover belong to the first group. Among them are those insects and vertebrates active in pollination and seed dispersal, as well as the numerous invertebrates which bring about the rapid decomposition of the plant detritus and thus speed up the recycling of nutrients. The latter—particularly the wood-eating termites, beetles and beetle larvae, but also the small organisms in the soil which decompose litter and fungi—represent the largest fraction of the animal biomass.

The biomass of the second group is not so large, but it is composed of a much greater variety of species and forms. These are the carnivores, which keep the entire fauna, including the members of the first group, within the necessary limits and in so doing ensure that the surplus animal biomass is returned to circulation in an appropriate way.

The third and smallest group comprises the true herbivores. Their numbers are notably few in the nutrient-poor regions of the forest. In addition to insects, the group includes some vertebrates; to the extent that they live on the ground, like the many miniature forms of ungulates, they are essentially of no significance in the ecology of the rainforest. The herbivorous mammals in particular, which reach a peak of development in open terrain and are major contributors to the ecosystems of steppe and savanna, in the rainforest are represented by hardly any large animals; this fact betrays the degree of their subordination in this habitat.

Man and the rainforest

What is true of the animals holds for humans as well. It is not without reason that the Amazon region has been called a "green hell"; until recent times it has repelled men looking for new lands to conquer, except for a few tribes that live by hunting and gathering (see Chapter 20). It was neither disease nor dangerous animals that limited the exploitation of Amazonia, but rather the difficulty of obtaining food. Large parts of former Asian and Central American rainforest regions, where there is fertile, volcanic soil, became densely populated only after the forest had been destroyed. The remaining forests are still the least populated major regions of the world, even though the climate is by no means unfavorable to human life. Nowhere have the few groups of men that have been living in the forests for millennia managed to achieve a real, full development of culture and society. Indeed, there are many signs that repeatedly, in the course of human history, tribes that were subordinate to other human communities were driven into the jungle and there experienced a cultural decline—if they could survive in these retreats at all. The only

IDENTIFICATION OF ELEMENTS IN THE COLOR PLATE ON THE FOL-
LOWING PAGES ▷▷ THE MAIN GROUPS OF ORGANISMS PARTICIPATING
IN THE FOOD CHAIN OF THE OCEAN:
1. Diatoms (Bacillariophyceae); 2. Flagellate algae (Flagellata); 3. Copepoda; 4. Sea
butterflies (Pteropoda); 5. Medusae; 6. Krill (Euphausiacea); 7. Crustacean larvae; 8.
Heteropoda; 9. Ctenophora; 10. Arrowworms (Chaetognatha); 11. Polychaeta; 12. Clupeoid fish; 13. Giant sharks; 14. Flying fish; 15. Coryphaenid fish; 16. Blue whales,
17. Bottle-nosed dolphins; 18. Seals; 19. Tuna; 20. Bonitos; 21. Mackerel; 22. Clupeoid
fish; 23. Squid (Cephalopoda); 24. *Maurolicus*; 25. Sharks; 26. Swordfish; 27. Sperm
whales; 28. Large squid; 29. Gasteropelecid *Argyropelecus*; 30. Red deep-sea shrimp;
31. *Anoplopoma*; 32. Greenland shark; 33. Gonostomatid *Cyclothone*; 34, 35. Chaulio-
dontid fish; 36. Angler fish; 37. Octopus (Cephalopoda); 38, 39. Black swallowers
(*Chiasmodon*); 40. Saccopharyngid fish; 41. Lantern fish (Linophryne); 42. Grenadiers
(Macrouroidei); 43. *Bathypterois*; 44. Squid; 45. Sea stars; 46. Brachiopods; 47. Sea lilies;
48. Hexactinellid sponges.

▷
Some of the shells washed
up to the high-tide line on
the North Sea coast
(*Cardium*, *Mytilus*, tellinid
and mactrid clams, etc.).

The food chain in the ocean: a simplified diagram. Organic substances are synthesized in the euphotic zone, using energy from the sun, by a variety of planktonic plant species. This microscopic phytoplankton serves as food for the small animal plankton (zooplankton) and certain small fish. These in turn are the basic food of many larger carnivorous fish and mammals (nekton). The organic matter moves to the deepest parts of the ocean as a result of active daily vertical migrations, especially at depths down to 600 m, and by the sinking of dead organisms.

In the shallow neritic waters additional vegetable food is provided by seaweed; moreover, nutrients are washed into the neritic zone by the rivers.

The bacterial decomposition of animal bodies sets free nutrient salts. In some coastal regions these are more rapidly brought to the euphotic zone by upwellings, and there they enhance the growth of the phytoplankton.

tribes which could survive were those that adapted themselves completely
to the forest. They were forced to adopt a nomadic way of life, travelling
in small groups, and their struggle for existence left little opportunity
for the development of a material and intellectual culture.

That is why we can still find humans in the jungle—that is, in extraordinary social and geographical isolation—who appear to belong to the
stone age. Wherever men were able to develop beyond the stone age,
they destroyed the rainforest community. The rainforest does not give
a high enough yield to suit modern man; he would prefer to convert it
as quickly as possible to pastureland and cultivated fields. Where the
soils are fertile it may be justified to destroy part of an ecosystem that
has taken countless millions of years to develop. But where there are
large areas of forest on extremely infertile soil as, for example, in central
Amazonia, where experience shows that even after clearing by fire one
or two harvests completely exhaust the soil—in such places, the destruction of the forest is senseless. For centuries, but to a much greater degree
in the last few decades, man has caused the worst possible damage to the
rainforest environment. If he continues to destroy the jungles at the same
rate as before, he will soon have transformed large regions with the most
elaborately developed organisms and communities on earth into barely
inhabited eroded areas and finally into leached-out deserts.

◁
Above: Mangrove forest
(Red Sea). The much-
branched root systems of
the *Avicennia* trees send up
aerial roots, so that oxygen
can enter the system and
the fine root hairs can keep
within the upper layers of
the soil
Lower left: The mudskip-
per *Periophthalmus koelreu-
teri* lives in mangrove
swamps. In the breeding
season these amphibious
fish build funnel-shaped
nests in the mud, which
reach down into the
ground water. There the
young grow, until they
too have adapted to life on
land.
Lower right: At ebb tide
the mud is alive with
fiddler crabs searching for
food. When the tide turns,
they hide in their tunnels
again, covering the opening
with a lump of mud.

314

17   The Ocean

The marine habitat is the largest on earth. The oceans and smaller seas together cover 71% of the earth's surface, 61% in the northern hemisphere and 81% in the southern. This in itself indicates their importance in our overall environment, and further quantitative comparisons emphasize it. For example, the oceans contain 98.5%, and the inland waters only 1.5%, of the earth's water and ice. Whereas the average altitude of the continents is only 840 meters, the oceans have an average depth of 3800 meters.

With respect to the effects of external influences and to its biology, the marine habitat can be subdivided into geographical regions and depth zones. As on the continents, the climate determines the geographical divisions; that is, one can distinguish polar, temperate, subtropical and tropical regions. In all parts of the oceans there is a comparable zonation in terms of structure of the ocean floor and depth in the open water. But these zones are modified by the local conditions, and change in character according to the prevailing climate.

Subdivisions of the ocean, by H. Thiel

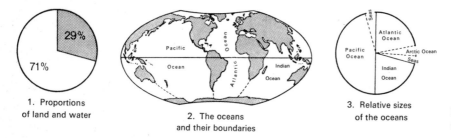

1. Proportions of land and water

2. The oceans and their boundaries

3. Relative sizes of the oceans

Fig. 17-1. The oceans of the earth.

The boundary between land and sea, with which humans most often come into contact, is characterized by the ebb and flow of the water, the tides. Under the influence of sun and moon, with a period of about twelve and a half hours, the water recedes and leaves the shore more or less exposed; then it returns and the beach is submerged again. In the intertidal

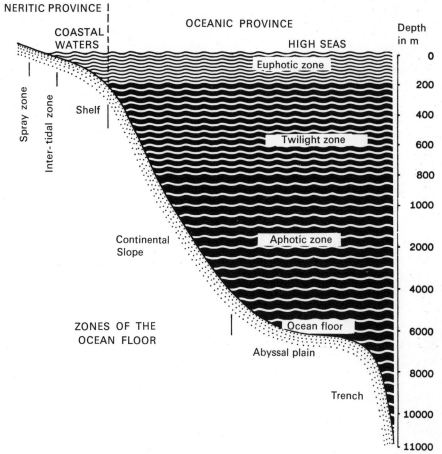

Fig. 17-2. The horizontal and the vertical (scale greatly expanded) subdivisions of the ocean.

(or "eulittoral") zone, then, the environmental conditions change drastically in a fairly rapid rhythm. The tidal zone varies in size on the different coasts of the world. In the smaller seas—for example, the Baltic and the European part of the Mediterranean—the water level varies only a few centimeters between high and low tides, whereas on the coasts of the open oceans the difference in water level may be eight meters and on the French coast of the English Channel, as much as thirteen meters. Above the intertidal zone there is a strip that lies beyond the average high-water mark and thus actually counts as land, but is still influenced by the ocean— the supralittoral or spray zone. This zone is especially evident on rocky coasts where the surf is heavy.

On the seaward side of the intertidal zone is a constantly submerged region with special characteristics. This shelf or "sublittoral" zone extends from the low-tide line down to an average depth underwater of 200 meters; since the slope of the ocean floor here is less than 1%, the horizontal extent of the shelf zone is considerable. Above it is the "neritic" region of the ocean. A characteristic aspect of the shelf and neritic habitats is the exchange of organisms, food and dissolved nutrients between the two. Many animals that live on or in the ocean floor here have a free-swimming larval stage; later, when the larva has drifted through the water to another place and metamorphosed into the adult animal, it returns to life on the bottom. Organic particles sink from the upper layers of water and serve as food for the bottom-dwelling animals. Such substances—dead animals, algae, and clumps of excrement—would accumulate in the mud there if the bacteria did not decompose them and release the smaller molecules and elements of which they are made. These then become dissolved in the water and serve as nutrients for the sessile and free-swimming algae, and these in turn feed the animals.

The zone in which plants grow extends from the lower spray zone through the intertidal and into the shelf zone as far as adequate light can penetrate the water. On the underwater slopes of oceanic islands algae can grow at depths as great as 100 m, but in the less clear coastal water the limit is 30–40 m.

Exchange processes like those described for the shelf and the neritic province also occur in the other parts of the ocean, but as the distance from the coast and the depth of the water increase, such processes become less important. The oceanic province (the open water beyond the continental shelf) differs from the neritic in its smaller content of plant nutrients; in consequence, the number of microscopic algae, and hence that of the animals, is less. When travelling across the ocean one can detect this difference in the blue color of the clear oceanic water; the higher concentration of nutrients and organisms makes the neritic water more turbid and green.

The depth zonation of the oceanic water is also based upon a biological process, the photosynthesis of living matter from dissolved nutrients by algae. This process can continue only as long as sufficient sunlight is available. Since the light is absorbed by the water, the depth to which it can penetrate is limited. In the open ocean, therefore, there is a lighted region (the euphotic zone) in which the algae synthesize more organic matter in the course of twenty-four hours than they require for themselves in the same time. That is to say, algal productivity shows a positive balance in this zone. The euphotic zone extends to a depth of at most 200 meters. It is followed by a twilight zone, where there is still some light but only enough to permit a negative balance in productivity; the algae cannot synthesize at a sufficient rate to meet their own needs. Finally, below 800–1000 meters, there is an aphotic zone in which the only light ever seen is the occasional flash of an animal's luminescent organ.

Beyond the shelf, the floor of the ocean is divided into three zones, distinguished by depth and angle of inclination. From the shelf zone down to about 3000 meters is the continental slope. Here the inclination amounts to 3–6% in the upper part, and 0.1–1% in the lower part. This lower part, called the continental rise, marks a transition to the abyssal plain, which lies between 3000 and 6000 meters deep and has an inclination of less than 0.1%. Both the slope and the plain are interrupted in places by undersea ridges and isolated mountains, some of them so high that they rise as islands above the water surface. Depths of more than 11,000 meters have been measured, but only in the third zone, the narrow deep-sea trenches, where the inclination of the sides is as much as 10%.

This system of ocean-bottom and open-water zonation is the result of more than a hundred years of oceanographic research. The different zones arise in a comparable way in all parts of the ocean, by virtue of characteristic properties of the chemical and physical factors in the environment and by reciprocal relationships of the organisms. Between the different zones and provinces, however, there are no sharp boundaries; the transitions are always gradual. This is also true of the many types of communities that inhabit these regions. The biology and interactions of marine organisms and their relationships to their particular environments will be described in the following sections, on the basis of the different individual habitats and their communities.

The neritic and shelf zones, by H. -P. Bulnheim

The neritic province includes those parts of the ocean immediately off the coasts and above the continental shelves. A shelf is the submerged base of a continental land mass; the shelves surround continents and the larger islands like flat undersea terraces. The width of the neritic province varies from place to place; it extends from the coastline to a depth of about 200 meters. The volume of the neritic water is only 0.2% of that of the whole ocean, but its surface area amounts to 7.8%; this surface area is equivalent to almost one-fifth of the total land area of the world. Most of the shelf is covered by sediments, three to six kilometers deep, washed out to sea from the land and deposited there. In the temperate latitudes it is rather uniform in contour, but further from the equator there are often quite pronounced patterns in relief. Even at lower latitudes, however, the activity of reef-building corals can give the bottom underlying the coastal waters a considerably varied form.

In some places the neritic zone occupies large discrete bodies of water; among these are the North Sea, Baltic Sea, English Channel, Hudson Bay, and Barents Sea. About two-thirds of the total neritic area is in the northern hemisphere; part of this, including the shelf regions off Siberia, Alaska and northern Canada, is covered by ice almost all year. Because of its closeness to land, relative shallowness and great economic significance, the neritic province is one of the most thoroughly studied regions of the ocean.

Littoral habitats are distinguished by a great diversity, and this is reflected in an extraordinary variety and abundance of animal and plant communities. The outposts of this concentration of marine life, the communities nearest the dry land, inhabit the spray zone, the transition region between land and sea. Only when the tide is extremely high or during a storm does the surf wash over them. The organisms living in this zone are exposed to drastic fluctuations in environmental conditions.

Fig. 17-3. The distribution of the shelf regions (black) around Europe.

They are endangered by rain, which dilutes the salt water on and around them, as well as by the sun and wind which threaten to dry them out, and they are subjected to large and rapid changes in temperature. Accordingly, they have evolved protective mechanisms and structural modifications that enable them to survive in the face of these abrupt swings from one extreme to another.

In the intertidal zone, which is dry at ebb tide and submerged at high tide, conditions are somewhat more favorable. The imposed fluctuations of environmental factors are similar, but on the whole less pronounced. Therefore the flora and fauna here display a greater variety of species than those in the spray zone.

The shelf zone is always submerged; it is larger in area than the other zones and is inhabited by the most species. The atmosphere and the dry land affect this realm only indirectly. Environmental factors fluctuate considerably less widely than in the higher zones, and the fluctuations decrease progressively with increasing depth of the water.

In each of these zones live certain animal and plant communities, specially adapted to the local conditions and food supply. One of the most decisive environmental factors is light, the primary source of energy for the assimilation of carbon dioxide by plants, in which carbohydrates are formed and oxygen released. This is the fundamental process in the synthesis of the organic compounds by which all animals, directly or indirectly, are fed. Only in the illuminated upper waters of the neritic and oceanic provinces can unicellular and multicellular marine plants live and directly support animal life. Light can also affect animals in other ways—for example, by controlling certain rhythms and as a reference for visual orientation.

Another critical factor in the shelf region is temperature. Its chief effect is upon the distribution and activity of the marine organisms. Depending upon latitude and depth, there may be wide temperature fluctuations in the course of a day or a year; these are especially pronounced in the spray and intertidal zones. Intertidal organisms are exposed to a rapid warming by the sun when the tide ebbs and a sudden cooling when the water rises again. In neritic zones at temperate latitudes the average temperature of the surface water varies by 10° or at the most 20°C in the course of a year, whereas at higher and lower latitudes the variation is considerably less. Near the equator the temperature of the surface water can rise to 30°C, and it can be as much as 50°C for brief periods in shallow pools on tropical coasts. By contrast, the upper temperature limit of the coastal waters in the arctic and antarctic is about 5°C.

Salinity, relatively constant in the oceanic province, plays an important role in the waters over the continental shelf. Sea water contains an average of 35 grams of various salts per liter; that is, the salt concentration by weight is about 3.5%. Even though the proportions of the different components are to a great extent constant, the total salt concentration may vary. Departures from the average oceanic salinity are brought about chiefly by variations in the amount of precipitation and by different rates of influx of fresh water and evaporation. In the Red Sea the salt concentration is over 4%, and in certain isolated marine regions in the tropics it can be considerably more. Wide fluctuations in salinity occur in the intertidal zone, especially in the pools that collect in the rocks of the spray zone and near the mouths of rivers. Sea water of less than average salinity is called brackish water. In many lagoons and nearly isolated seas such as the Baltic, the sea water has been more or less diluted with fresh water. For certain physiological reasons, only a few marine organisms are capable of invading brackish water or surviving in places where the salinity fluctuates widely (see Chapter 5).

There are numerous other environmental factors that may affect the

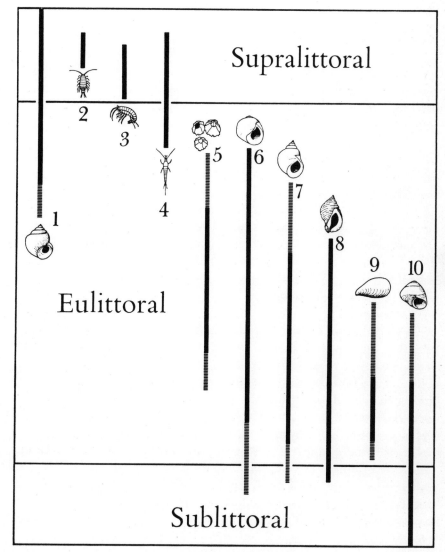

Fig. 17-4. An example of vertical zonation of the rocky-coast fauna in the spray zone (supralittoral), intertidal zone (eulittoral) and shelf zone (sublittoral) on the southwest coast of England. The species indicated, or their close relatives are also found in Helgoland 1. Small periwinkle (*Littorina saxatilis*); 2. Isopod *Ligia oceanica*; 3. Beach flea (*Orchestia gammarella*); 4. Jumping bristletail (*Petrobius maritima*); 5. Barnacle (*Balanus balanoides*); 6. Smooth periwinkle (*Littorina obtusata*); 7. Common periwinkle (*Littorina littorea*); 8. Snail *Nucella lapillus*; 9. Edible mussel (*Mytilus edulis*); 10. Snail *Gibbula cineraria*.

composition of neritic communities; chief among them are the motion of the water and the nature of the bottom. Water movement is a very complex phenomenon; it takes the form not only of ocean currents and the ebb and flow of the tides, but also of waves and surf. Continual water movement facilitates the distribution of food particles and dissolved nutrients and gases, and assists in dispersing the marine fauna. But the force of the surf represents a constant danger to the shore animals, for it can crush them, tear them from their moorings, or bury them under sand. And the constant alternation between wet and dry, as we have already mentioned, brings a special set of problems which the intertidal animals have met in different ways.

The nature of the ocean floor—whether it is rock, sand, or mud—is a critical determinant in its colonization by plants and animals. The "benthos" (a collective term for bottom-dwelling organisms) forms typical communities, characterized by different dominant species, in each of these habitats.

Rocky bottoms are common on the Mediterranean coast and can also be found in the North Sea near Helgoland. This kind of substrate presents many different "microhabitats" in the form of smooth surfaces, cracks, caves, overhangs and loose stones. Sea-walls built of stone, cement or iron can offer corresponding habitats. An important factor in the composition of the fauna on such hard substrates is the type of vegetation there. On rocky coasts with heavy surf usually only small algae can grow, but where the surf is moderate large algae can also attach, and these provide shelter and food for many marine animals.

Sessile forms predominate on solid substrates. A colorful underwater "garden" develops here, with many different sponges, hydroid polyps, sea anemones, tubicolous polychaetes, bryozoans and tunicates. Quite a few of them live as colonies. But the communities also include more or less actively moving animals—for example, various gastropods, echinoderms, crustaceans and benthic fish.

The spray and tidal zones on rocky coasts are usually readily accessible to an observer and offer instructive examples of the way position with respect to the water level limits the distribution of numerous organisms. Many species are very narrowly restricted to particular subzones, although the upper and lower boundaries of their ranges depend on local conditions. Such limitations are associated with the degree of resistance of the animals to environmental factors, with the amount and type of food available, and with competition by other species. Proceeding up from the low-water line one encounters a sequence of species: barnacles (*Balanus, Chthamalus*), limpets (*Patella*), periwinkles (*Littorina*) and other animals. These fringe members of the marine fauna counter the dangers of the transition zone between water and land by having thick armor or conical shells that can be tightly closed, or by moving about to suit the circumstances.

Communities in the benthos

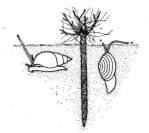

Fig. 17-5. Animals living in the ocean bottom: Left: a buried snail (*Nassa reticulata*) with the siphon, a tubelike extension of the mantle, extended. The snail tests the respiratory water sucked in through the siphon for the scent of prey.
In the middle: the polychaete *Lanice conchilega* in its tube, built of small stones and other particles. Above the sand the tube forms a "crown," to which food suspended in the water sticks so that it can be collected by the many thin tentacles.
Right: a tellinid clam (*Angulus tenuis*) with outstretched foot and siphons; water is swept in and out through the latter. The incurrent stream carries microorganisms, etc., that serve as food.

Fig. 17-6. A community of various sessile animals on a piece of seaweed (*Fucus vesiculosus*):
Hydroid polyps (*Dynamena pumila*), skeleton crabs (*Caprella*), barnacles (*Balanus*), bryozoan colonies (*Membranipora*), and serpulid worms (*Spirorbis*).

The communities on rocky beaches also include a number of highly specialized animals capable of boring into rock (especially limestone) or wood to find shelter. Various sponges, polychaetes, bivalves and crustaceans are equipped with boring mechanisms.

At lower levels, near or under the water, rocky coasts usually become more stony and eventually sandy. Sandy beaches and bottoms are formed by deposits of granular material of varying diameter. Coarse grains tend to be deposited where there is considerable water motion, and finer grains accumulate where the currents are less strong. Usually fine-grained bottoms are richer in nutrients, since more organic matter settles out and is retained in the sand. The availability of nutrients and the degree of mixing of the water near and in the bottom play a large role in determining the composition of the fauna here.

Sandy bottoms and broad sand beaches are found in large parts of the North and Baltic Seas. In the spray zone of such beaches there is a very transitory and changeable habitat: the debris left by the high tide. This consists of dead algae, seaweed and driftwood together with other objects such as the shells of clams and snails; its fauna is composed both of immigrants from the sea and of land animals. Typical animals here are various species of small crustaceans called "beach fleas," springtails and flies. The tidal zone and the sand bottom which is always underwater are the home of relatively few species. Among the free-moving animals are a variety of crustacean and gastropod species. Sessile forms are not at all obvious, for they are buried in the sand all or part of the time; there are a number of these, including bivalves, polychaetes, amphipods, shrimps, echinoderms and lancelets. Many of the animals that move about actively are superbly camouflaged by their shape or coloration and—as in the case of flatfish or cephalopods—are well hidden even when on the open sand. In the system of interstices between the sand grains there live a large number of small organisms of various animal groups, all remarkably well adapted to their surroundings in structure and habits.

There is often no clear dividing line between sand and mud bottoms, and mixtures of the two in all proportions can occur. The relative amounts of sand and mud affect the type and density of the animal populations. Mud bottoms are formed by the sedimentation of fine clay particles and organic substances, and tend to be situated in protected parts of the coast and near the mouths of rivers. The intertidal zone is usually flat, with channels through which the water moves during the ebb and flow of the tide. Because of the high organic content of these substrates, their fauna is more diverse than that on and in sand. Most of the animals living here are free-moving; this "epifauna" includes turbellarians, polychaetes, isopods and ostracods. But there is also a typical "infauna" living in tunnels or tubes in the mud. These are polychaetes, bivalves, gastropods and echinoderms, most of which feed on the organic contents of the mud or by filtering the sea water. At low tide one can see parts of their burrows;

those of the lugworm (the polychaete *Arenicola marina*) are an especially characteristic sight on the sandy mudflats of the intertidal zone along the coasts of Germany. The large size of the animal populations place the mudflats among the most fertile marine habitats. Because of the abundance of food in and on the mud, the coastal waters over muddy bottoms are a sort of nursery for young of many economically important fishes.

Other quite distinctive shallow-water communities, the mangroves and coral reefs of the tropics, will be discussed in subsequent sections of this chapter.

Dense stands of marine plants form a bottom habitat quite different from those mentioned thus far. The plant communities may be "lawns" of small threadlike algae, forests of tall brown algae, or expansive meadows of *Zostera*; they offer homes, refuges and breeding and feeding grounds to a number of animals which, as on the rocky substrates, are sessile or reluctant to move far. In general these animals are rather small, and often they are well camouflaged. Among them are sponges, hydroid polyps, bryozoans, various of the Aschelminthes, polychaetes, amphipods and isopods. Colonial species can attach to the plants to form clumps covering large areas of the plant surfaces.

The animals and plants of the open water (the pelagium) fall into two groups: the plankton, with little or no locomotor ability, which drifts with the water, and the nekton, actively swimming organisms which can move about independently of the ocean currents. The marine plankton consists of an enormous army of species of microscopic and larger animals (the zooplankton), some of them so transparent as to be nearly invisible, and a no less diverse world of unicellular algae (the phytoplankton) restricted to the euphotic zone. Altogether, the plankton is the most important part of the marine fauna.

The communities of the neritic pelagium are distinguished from those of the oceanic pelagium, though numerous organisms can be found regularly or occasionally in both regions. For example, plankton may be carried from one province to the other by currents of water or wind. The neritic zooplankton primarily consists of animals that live in open water only during certain stages of development, such as the pelagic larvae of benthic animals. Floating in the water, they are carried away from the place occupied by the previous generation; in this way even sessile or slow-moving animals—coelenterates, polychaetes, gastropods, bivalves and echinoderms—can become widely dispersed. In almost every phylum of the animal kingdom there are at least a few species in this category; only the sponges, aschelminths, and ascidians have no free-swimming stage. On the other hand, there are purely pelagic animals—radiolarians, siphonophores, ctenophores, arrow-worms, the gastropods called "sea butterflies" (Pteropoda), and salps. The eggs and larvae of many fish also form part of the drifting world of plankton.

Among the organisms that propel themselves through the water, the

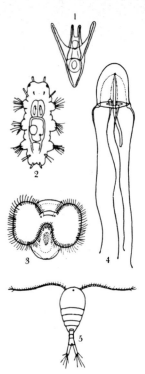

Fig. 17-7. Planktonic animals of the neritic province (North and Baltic Seas): 1. Larva of the sea urchin *Psammechinus miliaris*; 2. Larva of the polychaete *Nereis pelagica*; 3. Larva of the periwinkle *Littorina littorea*; 4. Medusa (*Sarsia tubulosa*); 5. Copepod (*Temora longicornis*), which in contrast to the other species is entirely plank-tonic.

Communities in the pelagium

Fig. 17-8. Characteristic root systems of some mangroves:

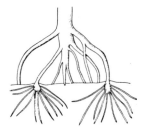

Prop roots of the red mangrove (*Rhizophora*).

Aerial roots of *Sonneratia*.

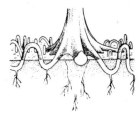

Bruguiera obtains oxygen through the "knees" formed by the roots.

The pelagic food chain

Mangrove swamps, by S. A. Gerlach

nekton, are the most highly evolved marine animals: cephalopods, fish, dolphins, whales and other vertebrates. Moreover, there are sea snakes, marine turtles and lizards, and certain crocodiles which have made the tropical and subtropical neritic—and in some cases even oceanic—waters their home. Seals and sea cows are also considered to belong to the nekton.

The neritic phytoplankton is considerably more diverse than that of the oceanic province. Since these drifting plants are the basis of the marine food chain, their abundance and variety in the shelf regions permits the development of an abundant and varied fauna. Fish find conditions here particularly good for feeding and spawning; though the number of fish species is relatively small, the number of individuals is great. For this reason the neritic province is of the most importance to fishery; the yield from neritic waters is about 90% of the world total. Some of the large catches—chiefly of cod, herring, flatfish and mackerel—come from the North Sea, the Baltic Sea, and other regions over the European shelf. Other sea animals useful to man, such as the crustaceans and bivalves, find an optical environment in the neritic zone, and in suitable places men have established "farms" for oysters and mussels, the production of which is considerable.

Why is the neritic province so extremely fertile? The continual mixing of the water from top to bottom, which occurs in shallow and in cold regions of the ocean, provides for a maintained circulation of dissolved and suspended substances. Wind and tidal currents ordinarily bring about a mixing of the whole mass of water and a uniform distribution of phosphates, nitrates and other nutrient salts which, along with adequate light, are crucial requirements for a vigorous growth of planktonic algae. The nutrient salts are released from the sinking, dead plants and animals by bacteria, and they also dissolve slowly from the bottom and enter the sea in the water of rivers.

The first link in the food chain of the ocean is the unicellular algae of the phytoplankton. The amount and quality of these determines that of all organisms further along in the chain. Planktonic animals, among which small crustaceans predominate, as well as bivalves and other filter-feeders and even some fish (for example, sardines) feed upon these microscopic algae. The secondary consumers, which eat these animals, include a number of fish important in the human economy. And these in turn are eaten by larger fish, cephalopods, odontocete whales, and sea birds—the natural terminal links in the marine food chain. Finally, man too uses the products of the sea, from several levels in the chain, as feed and as raw materials for manufacture.

Mangroves are trees of various species of several families which grow only where they can contact sea water or brackish water. Mangrove swamps are found at the edges of tropical seas, in bays, lagoons and estuarine regions. Among the most important mangrove trees are the red mangrove (*Rhizophora mangle*), the black mangrove (*Avicennia nitida*) and other species of those two genera as well as *Sonneratia*, *Laguncularia*, *Bruguiera*, *Aegiceras* and *Lumnitzera*. All these trees, except for *Laguncularia*, are found in the Indo-Pacific mangrove forests. *Laguncularia* grows only in the "western" mangrove forests, together with the red and black mangroves. In the transition zone between swamp and dry land the mangroves are joined by other plants—in South America by *Hibiscus*, on the Indo-Pacific coasts by the palm *Nipa*, and everywhere by the fern *Acrostichum*.

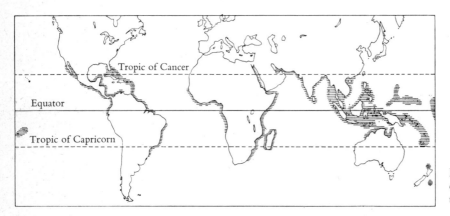
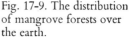

Fig. 17-9. The distribution of mangrove forests over the earth.

The mangroves share with shore and salt-marsh plants the ability to maintain a suitable water balance in spite of the salinity of the sea water; some of them excrete salts from their leaves. Special adaptations have also been necessary to anchor the trees firmly in the mud. Tap roots would be of little use here, since the mud is poorly aerated and only a little way under the surface contains no oxygen, but only poisonous hydrogen sulfide. Instead, the trees are supported by prop roots or by flat root systems that spread out just under the surface of the mud. *Avicennia* and *Sonneratia* have evolved special aerial roots to ensure that the deeper roots are supplied with oxygen, and the roots of *Bruguiera* arch above the surface here and there as "knees" with a similar function. The fine

Fig. 17-10. Mangrove swamps may be of the coastal, coral-reef, or estuarine type. The double-page illustration below shows the sequence of plant zones in the coastal mangrove forest of eastern Africa.

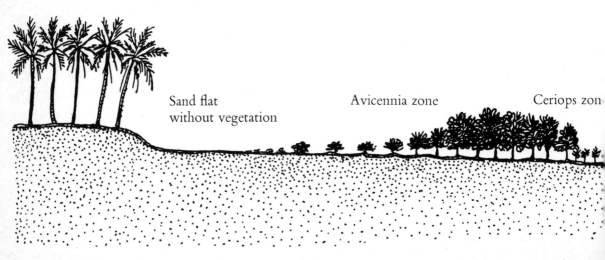

Sand flat
without vegetation

Avicennia zone

Ceriops zon

root hairs of the mangroves can take up nutrients only in the uppermost, oxygenated layer of the mud. But since mangrove forests tend to grow just where sediments continually accumulate and the anaerobic zone steadily rises, the upward growth of the roots must keep pace with the progressive sedimentation. Aerial roots (see Color plate, p. 312) and "knees" are adaptations to these conditions.

Finally, mangrove plants must have special means of colonizing newly created mudbanks. In the red mangrove and other species the seedling grows directly from the flower; when it eventually falls, it is either driven like a stake into the mud below the parent tree or it is carried away by the water and strikes roots somewhere else (Fig. 17-14). Without adaptations like those described, no tree could exist in a mangrove swamp; it is remarkable that trees of different families have independently acquired the necessary modifications.

Luxuriant mangrove forests grow on coasts bordered inland by tropical rainforest; the rainforest merges directly with the mangroves. A uniformly high temperature and precipitation amounting to more than 200 cm per year favor the growth of mangroves, so that they can become as tall as 25 meters. In tropical regions of dryer climate and in subtropical regions, where the winters are cold, the mangroves grow to a less impressive size, and at the extremes of their range they appear only as scattered bushes; the northern limit in western Africa lies at about twenty degrees north latitude, and there are mangrove swamps on the shores of the Ryukyu Islands south of Japan and on the southern coast of Florida, just north of the Tropic of Cancer.

Mangrove forests require still water; they cannot grow on unprotected coasts beaten by surf, but thrive where an offshore coral reef breaks the waves, behind promontories and near the mouths of rivers. At the outer margins of the swamp the mud is very soft, and a man walking on it sinks in deeply. But in the interior of a mangrove forest real soil can form. The mud becomes mixed with the detritus from the trees, bits of leaves,

Fig. 17-11. Mangrove forests do not grow on open coasts with strong surf. Along the coast of eastern Africa near Tanga, for example, they are found in places protected by the offshore coral islands and reefs.

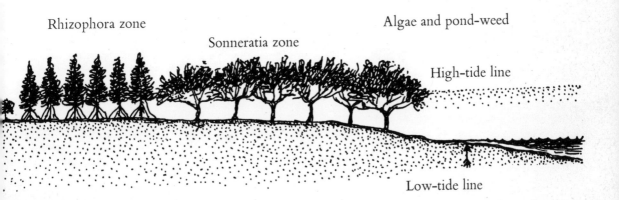

Rhizophora zone

Sonneratia zone

Algae and pond-weed

High-tide line

Low-tide line

trunks and branches, so that humus accumulates and sometimes actual peat-bogs develop.

The position of mangrove forests with respect to sea level is strictly fixed. They extend from the lowest to the highest high-tide mark—a zone which is flooded ten or fifteen times in a month, but not at every high tide; the parts of the trees above the mud are in the water at most 40% of the time. The mangrove forests are thus in the upper part of the intertidal zone, the region occupied by the succulent glassworts (*Salicornia*) and salt marshes on the coast of the North Sea.

Often there is a discernible zonation of the different species in a mangrove forest (Fig. 17-10), but the local differences are too great to allow a generally valid classification. Probably, one determining factor is which species of seedling happens to alight first on freshly deposited mud. Moreover, man has altered the mangrove habitat on many tropical coasts. The straight stems of the red mangrove and of *Bruguiera* are prized as structural material in Arabian countries and are imported from Africa. To a certain extent, mangroves also serve as the raw material for tannin and paper factories, and they are widely used as firewood. In some regions mangrove forests have been under professional management since as early as 1900, so as to achieve the highest possible long-term yield of wood. But in other places the mangroves have been irresponsibly exploited, and have vanished or been reduced to pitiful remnants.

For the mangrove-swamp fauna, the habitats of land and sea overlap. In the crowns of the trees forest-dwellers can move seaward; on the surface of the mud marine animals can migrate inland, as far as the salinity permits. And on the trunks and roots of the mangroves live marine animals, attached in the same way as they are on rocks elsewhere. Many of these animals are also found in habitats other than the mangrove forest; the distinguishing characteristic of the mangrove community is the great variety of land and water organisms that live together there.

In the crowns of South American mangroves there are iguanas. In Borneo the treetops are occupied by proboscis monkeys, which eat the leaves. The flowers of the red mangrove are pollinated by bees, and in Australia the mangrove *Aegiceras* is actually of economic importance to apiarists. Bats are thought to pollinate the *Sonneratia* flowers, which have no scent and do not open until evening. Ants put together nests of mangrove leaves and feed on scale insects that suck the mangrove juices. These animals represent a continuation of the tropical rainforest community in the mangrove forest. Some pigeons and parrots use the mangrove regions as a protected place to sleep. Migratory birds have their winter quarters here; cormorants, herons, ospreys and kingfishers nest in the mangroves. With few exceptions, these are the same species otherwise encountered on the riverbanks in their respective regions.

Terrestrial and marine animals meet in the trunks of the mangroves and under their bark. Beetles and crickets, caterpillars and ants shelter in

▷
Protozoans, coelenterates and worms of the interstitial fauna:
Top, left to right: Two ciliates (genus *Condylostoma*) of the family Trachelocercidae.—The dwarf medusa *Halammohydra*.—*Turbanella*, a gastrotrich of the order Macrodasyoidea.
Middle, left to right: A gastrotrich (*Macrodasys*).—A widespread morphological type of sand-dwelling nematode.—An unusual nematode, of the family Epsilonematidae, with locomotor bristles on the ventral surface.—The turbellarian *Coelogynopora*, as an example of threadlike elongation of the body (1 cm).
Bottom, left to right: Hind end of the turbellarian *Bothriomolus balticus*, with adhesive papillae.—*Postbursoplana fibulata*, of the turbellarian family Otoplanidae, a characteristic species of the surf zone.—The flatworm *Gnathostomula paradoxa*, full view (showing the anchoring organ at the hind end) and anterior end.

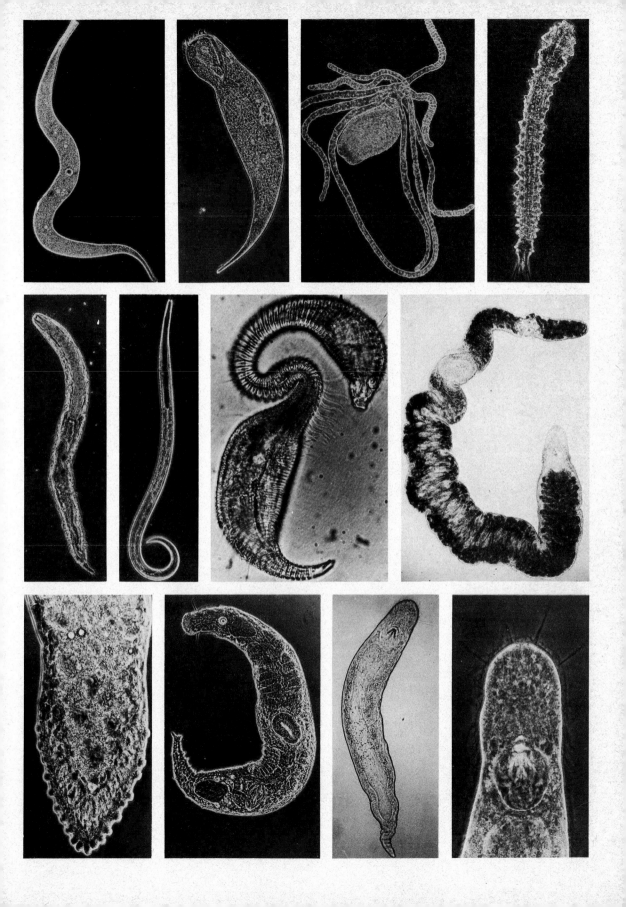

the soft wood; where the wood is soaked with sea water, the ship worm (the molluscan genus *Teredo*) bores in. On the trunks live beach snails (*Littorina* and *Melampus*), which always stay above the water, wandering up and down with the tides and grazing on the coating of microscopic algae that covers the trunks. Crabs of the family Grapsidae, the relatives of which live in rocky habitats on the seacoasts, climb about on the prop roots of the mangrove trees and as a rule never descend, either into the water or onto the mud; the genus *Metapograpsus* is common in the Indo-Pacific mangrove swamps and *Goniopsis* in those of South America. The mangrove crab *Aratus pisoni*, of the Caribbean and Brazilian swamps, also prefers not to flee into the water when pursued, but rather climbs up into the finest branches of the trees; it feeds in part upon the mangrove leaves.

Just above the mud, where they are more regularly submerged in the sea water, all sorts of marine animals attach to the trunks, prop roots and aerial roots of the trees: barnacles, oysters and sometimes tunicates. They feed only on plankton, so that they can obtain food only when covered by the high tide. Here one also finds an association of characteristic red algae (*Bostrychia*, *Catenella*) found elsewhere only in the shady crevices in coastal rocks. Small animals like nematodes, copepods and midge larvae live among the threads of algae, where they are protected from desiccation.

The association of animals on the mangrove trunks is thus a typical marine solid-substrate community, reminiscent of communities on rocky coasts and man-made structures in harbors. Where the soil under the mangroves is sandy, all sorts of sand-dwellers can be found, but the typical mangrove-swamp soils are muddy sediments and support about the same type of animal life as is found on other muddy bottoms along tropical coasts.

In contrast to other mud-bottom habitats, however, the mangrove swamps support large stands of trees, and this effects even the bottom-dwellers in a number of ways. The animals living here must be able to cope with the unusual admixture of organic matter in the mud. Usually there is no free oxygen at all only a few millimeters under the surface. Where the material under the mud is not calcareous sediment but rather products of the weathering of igneous rock, the large quantities of woody fibers, which are slow to decompose, cause the formation of humus, humic acids and to some extent peat in the mud. As a result, the soil water is quite acid, and the acidity extends to some of the water in the channels running through the swamp. Sea water in general is well buffered and alkaline; but the mangrove waters can have a pH between 6 and 7, an unusual situation for the marine animals. For example, mussels and clams may well encounter difficulty in building up their calcareous shells here.

On the other hand, life in the mangrove swamp can have advantages

◁

Polychaetes, mollusks, crustaceans and tardigrades of the interstitial fauna: Top, left to right: The polychaete *Petitia amphophthalma*, from the sand in the surf zone of the Mediterranean coast.—*Microphthalmus sczelkowii*, a hermaphrodite with male anterior and female posterior end (large egg cells).—The archiannelids *Protodrilus* (with two large palps on the head) and *Diurodrilus*. Middle, left to right: Minute sand-dwelling gastropod of the genus *Unela*.—The archiannelid *Trilobodrilus axi*, from a North Sea beach. Bottom, left to right: The mystacocarid crustacean *Derocheilocaris remanei*, Mediterranean coast.—Two typical tardigrades of the suborder Arthrotardigrada, *Stygarctus bradypus* and *Batillipes mirus*.—The sand copepod *Paraleptastacus spinicauda*.

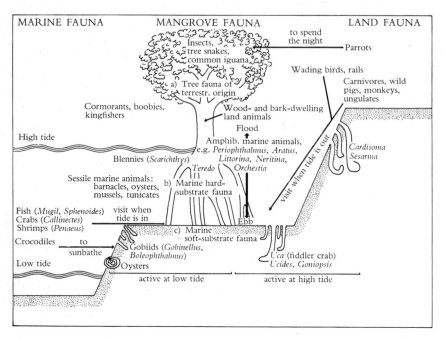

MARINE FAUNA   MANGROVE FAUNA   LAND FAUNA

Insects,
tree snakes,
common iguana

to spend
the night

Parrots

Wading birds, rails

Carnivores, wild
pigs, monkeys,
ungulates

a) Tree fauna of
terrestr. origin

Cormorants, boobies,
kingfishers

Wood- and bark-dwelling
land animals

High tide

Flood

Amphib. marine animals,
e.g. *Periophthalmus, Aratus,
Littorina, Neritina,
Orchestia*

*Cardisoma
Sesarma*

Blennies (*Scarichthys*)

Teredo

Sessile marine animals:
barnacles, oysters,
mussels, tunicates

b) Marine hard-
substrate fauna

visit when tide is out

Fish (*Mugil, Sphenoides*)
Crabs (*Callinectes*)
Shrimps (*Penaeus*)

visit when
tide is in

Crocodiles

to
sunbathe

c) Marine
soft-substrate fauna

Ebb

Gobiids (*Gobinellus,
Boleophthalmus*)

Uca (fiddler crab)
Ucides, Goniopsis

Low tide

Oysters

active at low tide   active at high tide

Fig. 17-12. A schematic
diagram of the mangrove
habitat.
In the mangrove forest
marine and land animals
meet. Many animals are
active only during one
phase of the tides, either at
high tide or when the mud
is exposed.

as compared with that on open mudflats. The canopy of the mangroves gives protection from the burning rays of the tropical sun; it is not quite as hot in the mangrove forest as it would be at the same time of day on a mudbank without vegetation. It is, of course, rather muggy among the trees, since no wind clears the air, but for marine animals taking their first step toward life on land the high humidity is an advantage, protecting their bodies from drying out. Finally, there is an abundant food supply here, not only for the abovementioned mangrove crabs but for other genera as well—the crab *Sesarma*, which eats fallen mangrove leaves, and other animals which graze the surface of the mud. They find a dense growth of siliceous algae there, and after every high tide the sea leaves behind a film of dead planktonic organisms.

Whereas a mud flat exposed by low tide on the German coast seems practically uninhabited, with only tracks and holes in the mud to bear witness to the hidden animals, the surface of the mud in the mangrove swamp is populated by a lively crowd of crabs and fishes when the tide is out. In the Indo-Pacific mangrove swamp gobies of the genus *Boleophthalmus* and ocypodid crabs eat the feast spread out on the mud, and the highly noticeable fiddler crabs (genus *Uca*) find conditions even more favorable here (see Color plate, p. 312, and Fig. 17-15).

The gobies take up particles from the surface of the mud and then, by some mechanism still unknown separate the nutritious components from the inedible mud in their mouths. The fiddler crabs accomplish this separation with specially developed mouthparts, the first and second maxillipeds. These have hairs with spoon-shaped ends which hold on to

Crabs of the mangrove
swamps

the sediment granules while other hairs brush them off, and the bits of food so obtained are washed into the mouth with water. When everything edible has been removed from the sample of mud, the crab shapes it into a neat pill and sets it down on the surface. By the time the tide rises again, the mud is covered with these pills in many places—a good indication of the extent to which fiddler crabs and related forms turn over the surface mud. In the Malaysian mangrove swamps one commonly sees conspicuous mounds, made by the axiid crab *Thalassina anomala*; this crab, like its distant relative, the hermit crab, has no hard shell of its own. It shelters in a tunnel it has built under the mounds of earth and apparently feeds on unsorted swamp mud, as other tunnel-building crustaceans perhaps also do. Finally, as already mentioned, there are land and rock crabs of the families Gecarcinidae and Grapsidae, the most common of which is *Sesarma*, which are omnivorous but concentrate on the leaves and young shoots of the mangroves.

All these crustaceans, even those living on the trunks of the mangroves, have one thing in common: they have become more or less independent of sea water. Crustaceans of course, being fundamentally aquatic animals, are gill breathers; many mangrove crabs breathe with gills even in air, by making sure that the body cavities in which the gills are enclosed are always filled with water, though the crab may be running about on dry land. It is as though the gills were kept in little aquariums that the crabs carry around with them; and like aquariums, they need to be aerated in order to replace the oxygen consumed. The fiddler crabs actually pump bubbles of air through the water around the gills, whereas *Sesarma* pumps the water out of the gill cavities, lets it run over special paths of hairs on the body surface where it becomes saturated with oxygen from the air, and sucks it back into the gill chambers. Naturally, these crabs must replenish the water in the gill chambers now and then; to do this, they dive into their burrows, which extend down past the water table. But other crabs, such as the white crab (*Cardisoma guanhumi*), have regressed gills; to take their place, the wall of the gill chamber has been modified into a sort of lung. Both *Cardisoma* and another inhabitant of the Caribbean the red land crab *Gigantinus lateralis*, can withdraw such water as they need from the moist substrate. In this case the name "land crab" is really appropriate, for these animals can live indefinitely with only slight amounts of water. On the other hand, the larvae of all mangrove crabs develop primarily in the open water of the ocean.

Among the mangrove-swamp fishes there are also some, like the gobies *Boleophthalmus* and *Scartelaos*, which have become partially independent of water. They jump about on the damp mud, and when danger threatens or when the tide begins to turn they burrow into the ground. In these fish respiration is taken over by the skin; well-vascularized papillae on the back and the sides of the body allow an exchange of gases between the humid air and the blood. Another fish has gone a step further; this is

Fig. 17-13. A grapsid crab among the roots of the red mangrove (*Rhizophora*).

the mudskipper (genus *Periophthalmus*; see Color plate, p. 312), which belongs to the same family and is represented by large numbers of species on all tropical seacoasts of the Old World and particularly in the mangrove swamps. They live almost entirely out of water. As the tide comes in, some species of mudskipper actually flee from the water, clinging to the trunks or prop roots of the mangroves some centimeters above the water surface. When the water recedes, they descend and hunt for midges and crabs on the mud. In the breeding season these fish build funnel-shaped nests in the mud; they lead down to the ground water, where the young grow until they have become adapted to life on land.

At low tide the mudflats under the mangrove forests are attractive feeding grounds for herons and shore birds, and even wild boar and monkeys come here to hunt crabs. At high tide, on the other hand, fish and shrimps come from the channels or from the sea itself, and they too hunt the crabs that have not returned to their holes in time or have not hidden themselves deep enough under the mud. Water snakes even pursue the crabs into their holes. In the Indo-Pacific swamps there is a frog that is very resistant to high salinity, the crab-eating *Rana cancrivora*; its tadpoles can withstand sea water with a salt concentration of 2.6%, which is extremely rare among amphibians. Crocodiles feed on all these animals. And man, finally, takes his toll as well, by setting nets to catch fish and shrimps on their way to the feeding grounds. It is not yet possible to make a good estimate of the role the mangrove swamps play as nurseries for those fish and shrimps which, as adults, have great importance to fishery in the offshore waters.

The mangrove forests excite the interest of ecologists because of the dovetailing of communities which in themselves are quite different. The habitat unites hard and soft seacoast substrates with the tree trunks and leafy canopy of the rainforest. Moreover, mangrove swamps are a habitat in which an unusual number of adaptations to temporary or permanent life on land have been evolved by animals with very different ancestry. Mangrove-swamp animals can in a sense be considered as models which answer a question of burning interest to man as a land animal—how was it possible for aquatic animals to conquer the land?

Sandy ocean beaches—nowadays one of the most attractive types of vacation spot—are the habitat of a great community of microscopic animals. In just a handful of beach sand we can easily find several thousand animals adapted to life between the sand grains, the so-called interstitial fauna or "psammon." They are found in the damp subsurface sand as well as in the surf zone, where it is hard to imagine anything surviving the churning movement of sand and gravel under the force of the waves.

Let us take as an example the eastern shore of the island of Sylt, in the North Sea off the coast of Germany. Here, when one walks from the dry foot of the dunes toward the ocean for forty or fifty meters, into the flat, sandy intertidal zone, he has crossed a strip of land in which over 500

▷
Top, left to right: Hind end of the gastrotrich *Turbanella* with two groups of adhesive papillae, and those of the polychaetes *Hesionides* and *Saccocirrus*, with two adhesive lobes.— Jaws in the proboscis of the turbellarian *Diascorhynchus* (suborder Kalyptorhyncha); a highly differentiated organ for catching prey in the interstitial system.

Feeding grounds in the swamp

▷
Middle, left to right: Specialized part of gut reinforcing the head of the turbellarian *Nematoplana nigrocapitula*: the dark-appearing structure in front of the brain (with two eyes).—Highly vacuolated epidermis of the turbellarian *Cystiplex* (view from above) and the gastrotrich *Macrodasys* (in the middle of the intestinal tract).
Bottom, left to right: The polychaete *Microphthalmus aberrans*, showing an everted copulatory organ on the right.—The polychaete *Pisione remota*; copulatory organs on the parapodia of the middle body segments.—The polychaete *Hesionides arenaria*; female with sperm packets on the right at the level of the pharynx.
Eggs and egg-masses of interstitial animals.

The interstitial system by P. Ax

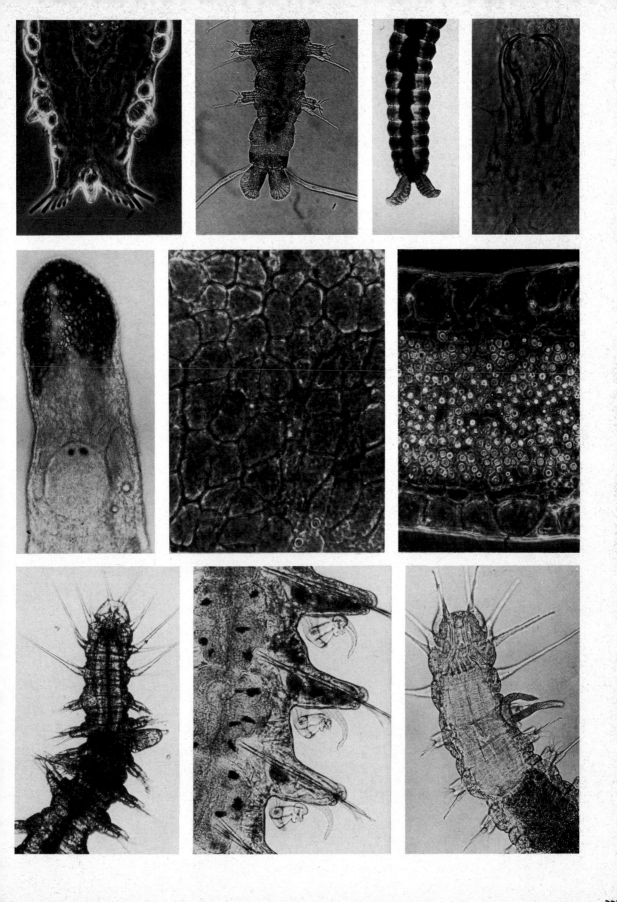

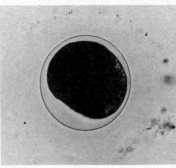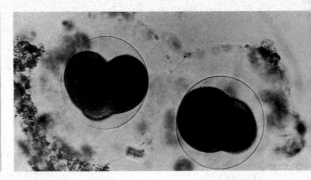
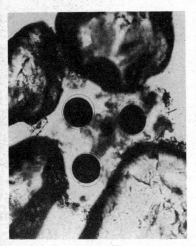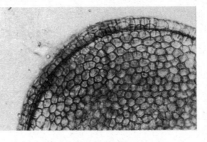
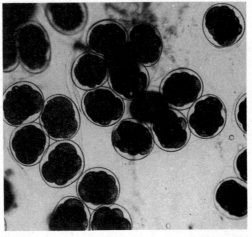
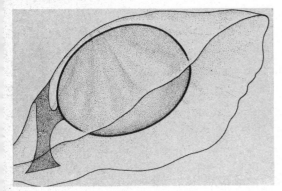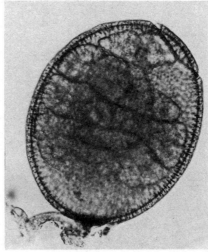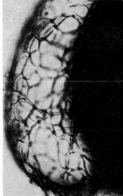
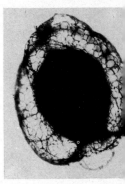

different animal species live. In the top ten centimeters of the sand there are forty to fifty million individuals per cubic meter. But this microfauna of the sand is by no means limited to the beach. It inhabits the coastal sands far out to sea, to depths of fifty meters underwater or more; recently a deep-sea expedition of the research ship *Meteor* brought up living animals typical of the interstitial fauna from a depth of 2000 meters. In the shores of fresh-water lakes and in sandy river beds there is a comparable interstitial fauna, though the number of species is considerably less.

What we know about the interstitial animals we have learned relatively recently. The plankton, for example—the microfauna of the open water—was being studied intensively before the turn of the century, but it was not until about 1930, when Adolf Remane began to publish his work on the subject, that people became aware of the teeming world in the sand of the Kieler Bucht. Historically, then, the study of the psammon is the last stage in biological research on the large marine habitats. Even today we face many unsolved problems in this area, and current research is steadily producing new fundamental information.

The two factors most critical in determining what animals can live in this habitat are the small size of the interstitial spaces and the looseness of the sandy substrate. The dimensions of the pores between the sand grains set a clear limit to the size of the animals that live in them. They must be minute, and in fact the smallest members of many classes in the animal kingdom are to be found here. Examples are the nematocyst-bearing coelenterates (subphylum Cnidaria) with the 0.3 to 0.4-mm-long genus *Psammohydra*, the free-living flatworms (class Turbellaria), of which the smallest members are about 0.3 mm long, the polychaete annelids (class Polychaeta) with the genus *Diurodrilus* (also 0.3 mm), and the tardigrades (phylum Tardigrada), which are often only 0.1 mm long. Strictly speaking, the pore system limits only the diameter of its inhabitants and many ciliates, worms and small crustaceans have adopted an obvious way of escaping the restriction by evolving long, threadlike bodies. Particularly impressive examples of this are the turbellarians *Coelogynopora* and *Nematoplana* and the archiannelid *Protodrilus*, all of which twist and twine through the sand as extremely fine threads one to one and a half centimeters long.

The motion of water in the coastal region disturbs the upper layers of sand. The amount of displacement ranges from the relatively stable, permanently wet sand well below the surface to the pronounced churning and shifting experienced by the superficial sand in the surf zone. The interstitial fauna is subjected to three crucial effects of this instability: an animal may be buried, it may be washed out of the sand and swept away, and it may be pounded and squeezed by the whirling grains of sand and gravel. In the course of time, the interstitial animals have evolved a great number of different adaptations to these conditions.

To begin with, nearly all of them are motile organisms and many are capable of great expansion and contraction. Particularly quickly moving

◁
Top, left to right: eggs of the archiannelid *Trilobodrilus axi*; unprotected egg immediately after laying.—Separation of egg membrane.—Formation of a thick, protective gelatinous envelope.
Middle, left to right: *Trilobodrilus axi*. A batch of three eggs attached among the sand grains.—Egg mass of the turbellarian *Archaphanostoma agile*; numerous eggs embedded in the muscus from the body of the mother.—Egg-capsule of the otoplanid turbellarian *Itaspiella helgolandica*, with a firm capsule wall and an elastic stalk of cement-gland secretion.
Bottom: Further devices to protect the egg-capsules of turbellarians: Left: *Bothriomolus balticus*, with a cap of cement-gland secretion.—Middle: Protective cushion with a regular honeycomb pattern on the egg of *Diascorhynchus rubrus* (whole capsule, with section at higher magnification above it).—Right: Thick protective cushion of shell-gland secretion on the egg of *Diascorhynchides arenaria* (whole capsule and enlarged section).

animals are typical of the surf zone. Among these, turbellarians of the family Otoplanidae are especially noticeable, and in fact shores with strong surf have been termed the "otoplanid zone." Giant swarms of otoplanids shoot through the sand grains, suddenly becoming motionless for a fraction of a second and in the next instant darting off in another direction. The organs of this remarkable locomotion are an extremely well-developed ciliation of the ventral surface and a powerful musculature under the skin.

But rapid movement alone is not an adequate protection against being washed away by the water. Interstitial animals must be able to anchor themselves in the substrate, and to the annoyance of zoologists they manage this very well. Many wormlike species hold themselves in the sand so firmly, at the slightest disturbance, that it is almost impossible to get them out. If one does eventually outwit them and suck them up in a fine pipette, they stick—sometimes permanently—to the walls of the pipette. This ability to adhere to objects involves a number of different mechanisms. In the simplest case there are adhesive glands scattered in the skin of the body. These may be connected to long papillae, and these in turn may be arranged in fields or in rings around the body, all of which increase the effectiveness of the sticky secretion. Sometimes the rear end is so shaped as to provide mechanical attachment, either having platelike expansions or being drawn out into a long appendage that reaches down into the substrate and on which the animals—unicellular or multicellular—can ride at anchor in the shifting sand.

Protection from pressure and impact can be provided by the fine structure of the body tissues and cells. There are two contrasting possibilities, both of which are characteristic adaptations to this habitat. In turbellarians of the genus *Acanthomacrostomum* and some small sand gastropods there are tiny calcareous needles under the skin; sometimes they are arranged in regular layers so that they obviously form a reliable armor. Other turbellarians, as well as polychaetes and gastrotrichs, take the opposite approach by developing an elastic pillow to cushion the blows; the skin is modified to form a layer of bubblelike cells with large vesicles containing fluid, which makes the tissues turgescent.

A comparable vesicular tissue is found in the threadlike turbellarians *Coelogynopora* and *Nematoplana*; oddly enough, it is in the gut. A large branch of the gut reaching forward over the brain has been modified so as to consist entirely of vesicular cells; it forms an elastic supporting rod in the middle of the body which assists the animal in burrowing through the sand. And evolution has gone a considerable step further. In the North American turbellarian *Nematoplana nigrocapitula* there is not only a turgid projection of the gut over the head, but the entire dorsal surface of the gut has become a strand of vesicular cells. This organ is called the chorda intestinalis; its discovery has led to the suggestion that the notochord of cephalochordates and embryonic vertebrates may have arisen directly from vesicular cells on the roof of the gut.

Fig. 17-14. The mangroves have evolved a special adaptation to permit the colonization of new mud banks:

A seedling grows directly from the flower on the mangrove tree.

This seedling drops off and either sticks upright in the mud or is washed away by the water, to strike roots elsewhere.

Soon a highly branched root system had developed.

We have now described a number of adaptations of the interstitial animals to the unstable system of microscopic pores in which they live, and we have mentioned quite a number of specific animals. The question now arises: Which groups of the animal kingdom have been able to invade the spaces between the sand grains in the face of the unusually severe conditions there? The answer is astonishing: Almost all animal phyla are represented there, though some are much more common than others. One can group the interstitial fauna on the basis of ecological and phylogenetic considerations as follows:

1. There are at least three different pathways by which large classes in other habitats have sent a few specialized representatives to join the psammon. For example, gastropods and sea cucumbers are present in great variety on the floor of the ocean. In the interstitial system there live several minute shell-less gastropods (*Pseudovermis*, *Microhedyle*), as well as sea cucumbers of the order of a millimeter long (*Rhabdomolgus*, *Leptosynapta*). Certain dwarf medusae (*Halammohydra*) moved from the open water into the sand, the bell becoming regressed in the process. Even classes with ordinarily sessile members have produced some interstitial animals, which of course had to acquire motility. Among the 3500 species of colonial bryozoans there is a single genus, *Monobryozoon*, which crawls about slowly in the sand. In appearance it is very like a number of minute ascidians, which belong to the Chordata; even this phylum, then, which includes the vertebrates and thus the human race, is represented in the interstitial fauna. There are some solitary forms (*Psammostyela*, *Heterostigma*) and even small colonies of four to six animals (*Arenadiplosoma migrans*), equipped with sticky processes to hold themselves to the sand.

2. The majority of the animals living among the sand grains belong to a few classes almost entirely composed of small forms. In many coastal sands the thread-worms (class Nematoda) make up 50%, copepods of the suborder Harpacticoidea 20–30%, and turbellarians 10-15% of the metazoan population. Protozoans, of course, are also in this category and are represented in the sand by the class Ciliata. In all these classes there are whole families, with many species, that have evolved entirely in the interstitial habitat. Among the turbellarians these are the Otoplanidae, already mentioned as typical of the surf zone, and the Karkinorhynchidae and Diascorhynchidae. The last two families have complicated hooks on the proboscis, with which they are very adept at seizing their prey. The polychaetes do not really belong to this category since there are many large forms living on the ocean floor but there are also a great number of characteristic interstitial forms in the class. For example, *Hesionides arenaria* runs about like a centipede in the sand of the surf zone. Small worms in which many polychaete attributes have regressed (members of the order Archiannelida)—for example, *Polygordius*, *Protodrilus*, *Trilobodrilus* and *Nerilla*—live in the beach sand.

Fig. 17-15. One of the lively inhabitants of the mud banks is the fiddler crab (*Uca*). Its name comes from the waving motions of the large claw, which are especially important in courtship.

Fig. 17-16. When the tide is out mudskippers (*Periophthalmus*) move nimbly over the mud surface, hunting midges and crabs.

3. Finally, there exist orders and even whole classes of animals that are altogether restricted to the interstitial system. To this category belong the orders Macrodasyoidea (of the class Gastrotricha) and Arthrotardigrada. Not until 1943 was the crustacean subclass Mystacocarida discovered in the subsurface coastal sands. In 1956 I described the most recently established class of the animal kingdom, the Gnathostomulida; it has now been shown to be represented by countless species in sandy beaches throughout the world.

It is evident, then, that the interstitial habitat has not just taken up the "overflow" from other habitats in the course of phylogeny. Rather, it is a distinct and certainly ancient center of evolution for large sections of the animal kingdom.

If anything is to be discovered about the dynamic processes that take place in the interstitial zone, it is necessary to make regular monthly surveys of the number and distribution of its fauna. In the climate of the North Sea coasts the population density of interstitial animals changes predictably with temperature. On the sandy beach of the eastern shore of Sylt, near List, in late summer there are an average of 750 metazoan animals in 100 cc of sand, while in March and April there are only 250. Several hundred different species are involved, which differ from one another in their behavior. By studying the life cycle of a given species during a year one can make surprising discoveries. Zoologists in general used to think that the minute interstitial animals could live for only a few weeks and therefore must reproduce at short intervals. Now we know that many turbellarians and polychaetes live in the beach sand for at least a year; they reproduce only once a year, and their reproductive season is sometimes limited to a few weeks in the summer.

A notable example is given by the polychaete *Hesionides areharia*; its one-year life cycle involves characteristic migrations up and down in the sand. It reproduces in June and July in the superficial layers of the sand. As the weather deteriorates in the fall, the new generation migrates into the depths, withdrawing far into the ground-water region. From January to March not a single specimen is to be found in the sand of the beach; not until spring, when the temperature rises, does *Hesionides* emerge from the ground water.

There is another important question concerning the reproductive behavior of the interstitial animals. Are the transmission of sperm, the laying of eggs, or the development of the young also specially adapted to this unique habitat? In view of their small size, it is understandable that the animals produce only a small number of gametes. Therefore the sperm must be transmitted in the most "economical" way. Again, the polychaetes offer a good example. The large polychaete species in other habitats all simply release their eggs and sperm directly into the water and fertilization occurs there, outside the parents' bodies. In contrast, small interstitial polychaetes have evolved complicated copulatory organs

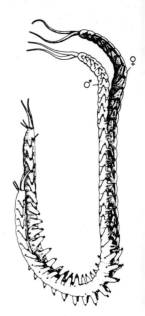

Fig. 17-17. The polychaete *Pisione remota* during sperm transfer.

and a variety of behavioral mechanisms to ensure successful mating. In the genus *Microphthalmus* there are one or two muscular copulatory organs in the anterior part of the body. *Pisione remota*, remarkably, has up to twenty pairs of copulatory organs, formed in the reproductive season from parts of the parapods of the middle segments. The male creeps onto the back of the female and pushes his copulatory organs down into the female genital apertures, equal in number, on either side of her body (Fig. 17-17 and 17-18).

The behavior of *Hesionides arenaria* is quite different. In this case the sperm is accumulated in little packets (spermatophores). Two of these tubular packets emerge from each of two pores on the head of the male, and the packets are attached to the skin of the female anywhere on her body (Figs. 17-19 and 17-20). The sperm must bore through the skin and migrate through the body cavity to the ovaries. And there are still other methods, too many to mention, of direct transfer of sperm.

When only a few eggs are produced, it is helpful if they are somehow anchored and specially protected from mechanical injury. Here, too, there is an array of appropriate mechanisms among the interstitial animals. The egg membrane itself can swell up into a gelatinous mass, as in the eggs of the archiannelid *Trilobodrilus*. Moreover, skin glands can secrete a gelatinous mucus, a soft mass in which the eggs are embedded between the sand grains; this is done by turbellarians of the order Acoela and by polychaetes. One species of the polychaete genus *Microphthalmus* even uses a method very like that of the terrestrial earthworms—it makes a firm, spindle-shaped cocoon for its eggs.

Finally, the egg capsules of some higher turbellarians (superorder Neoophora) are quite specialized. Glands in the reproductive system which participate in forming the capsule wall and a stalk for the egg capsule, in these animals produce additional protective envelopes. In the otoplanid genus *Bothriomolus* cement glands make a protective cap which is drawn like a floppy hat over the egg capsule and the edge of which is glued to sand grains. On the other hand, there are shell-forming glands which can make an elastic cushion to cover the eggs—in the form of a honeycomb, as in *Diascorhynchus*, or a thick envelope with irregular braces and a viscous fluid inside it, as in *Diascorhynchides*. This is an interesting parallel to the vesicular tissues, described above, in the skin of some interstitial animals.

Embryological development also displays adaptation to the interstitial habitat. A free-swimming larval stage, which might be carried away by the water, is no longer part of most life cycles; development takes place in the sand. This is true even of gastropods and polychaetes, which in other habitats are known for their motile larvae—the veliger of the gastropods and the trochophore of the annelids; the interstitial members of these classes suppress such stages.

Altogether, then, the complexities of the interstitial habitat and the

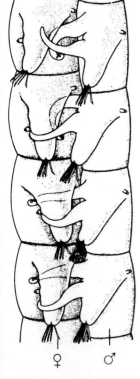

Fig. 17-18. *Pisione remota*. The copulatory organs being introduced into the female genital apertures.

♀   ♂

structure and habits of its fauna are intimately related. From the size and shape of the body to the fine structure of tissues and cells, from the seasonal migrations of whole populations to the smallest details of reproductive behavior, the sand fauna is stamped by adaptations acquired during its evolution under the unusual conditions of its environment. However insignificant the animal life between the sand grains may at first appear to the casual observer, this "world in miniature" is extremely interesting in the comparative study of life forms. The examples described here must be counted among the most informative discoveries yet made in this field of ecological research.

The term "coral reef" refers to wall-like formations in the coastal regions of tropical oceans, which lie just under the surface of the water but can extend to considerable depths. These reefs are occupied by numerous organisms—not only the various types of coral, but sponges, many other animals, and large numbers of small and large algae.

Each coral reef is a biological and ecological unit, found only in tropical seas, and formed of the calcareous supporting structures produced by living animals. Whereas present-day coral reefs are limited to the warm waters of the Atlantic, the Pacific, and the Indian Ocean, none being further north or south than twenty-two degrees latitude, at earlier times in the earth's history they could also be found in other parts of the world. From the Triassic period of the early Mesozoic until the Tertiary of the Cenozoic mighty reefs were growing, for example, where the Alps stand today. The climate of southern and central Europe was tropical then; the area now occupied by the Mediterranean and the Alps was all submerged under part of the Tethys Sea, which was connected to the Indian Ocean and inhabited by the same tropical marine fauna. The calcareous strata widespread in the Alps are to a considerable extent derived from one-time coral reefs; the Dolomites of the southern Tyrol also came from coral reefs. On Monte Bolca near Lugano one can find fossil remains of fish of the same genera that now swim in the Red Sea and the Indian Ocean.

As early as the oldest geological era, during the Devonian, long coral reefs ran through a shallow tropical sea over large parts of what is now West Germany. The Eifel Mountains were largely built up by reef organisms, and even today, more than 350 million years after they were formed, one can still find distinct pieces of coral to remind him of the original builders. From the composition and shape of the corals and the other reef inhabitants, which are readily discernible in the fossilized remains, it is often possible to infer the structure and position of a former reef, as well as its relationship to the water currents prevailing then; as is the case today, the earlier reefs were not all the same, but differed considerably in form and organization.

There are three types of present-day reefs:

1. Fringing reefs, which parallel the shore and are separated from it

▷
Top: Gardner Atoll in the Pacific Ocean (aerial photo.)
Lower left: The upper surface of a reef, with a forest of antlerlike corals (*Acropora* species). Great Barrier Reef, Australia.
Lower middle: Upper part of the slope of an outer reef, with a profusion of different coral and fish species. Red Sea.
Lower right: Deeper part of the slope of an outer reef, with a sandy terrace below. Red Sea.

Coral-reef communities, by W. Klausewitz

▷▷
Above: A dead table-shaped head of coral, overgrown with other corals and sponges. The photographer's flash reveals especially well the magnificent colors of the coral and its inhabitants, which find shelter and food there. Left in the background is the typical blue of the underwater landscape. Great Barrier Reef, Australia.
Lower left: Corals and fish at the edge of a reef in the Red Sea.
Lower middle: Part of a coral reef in the Caribbean Sea, showing the diveristy in form and color.
Lower right: A dead head of coral serving as the habitat of calcareous algae, sponges, alcyonarian and madreporarian corals, crinoids, and fish.

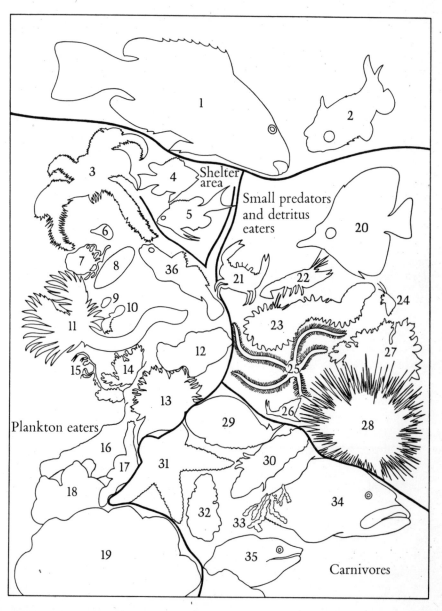

Left, top to bottom:
Tube worms on a head of coral.—Crinoids on gorgonarian corals and encrusting anemones (right).—*Abudefduf* near the slope of a reef.—Extended and retracted polyps in a coral (*Goniopora*). These corals are not always attached; they can also lie loose on the bottom. The *Goniopora* species stretch out their long polyps even by day.—All pictures from the Red Sea.

Right, top to bottom:
A giant clam (*Tridacna*) with mantle margin outspread between *Goniastrea* corals. The outer margin of the mantle bears a row of dark dots, the light-sensing organs. Red Sea.—Blue sea stars (*Linckia laevigata*) on the sand of the upper reef surface, between corals. Great Barrier Reef, Australia.—*Anthias squamipinnis* over an antler-shaped coral (*Anthias hemprichi*). Red Sea.—A many-armed sea star, the "crown-of-thorns" (*Acanthaster planci*) with everted stomach digests the polyps of a coral (*Acropora*) and thus destroys the coral reef. New Hebrides.

IDENTIFICATION OF THE ELEMENTS OF THE PLATE OPPOSITE:
FAUNA ON A TROPICAL CORAL REEF IN THE MALDIVES.

1. Parrot fish (*Callyodon*); 2. Porcupine fish (family Diodontidae).—In the shelter area: 4. *Dascyllus aruanus*; 5. Demoiselle (*Cromis coeruleus*).

Plankton eaters: 3. Crinoid (order Comatulida); 6. Boring gastropod (*Leptoconcha*); 7. Boring sponges (*Cliona*); 8. Boring clam (*Lithodomus*); 9. Boring crustacean (*Cryptochirus*); 10. Cirripede (*Pyrgoma*); 11. Tube worm (family Serpulidae); 12. Tunicates (*Ascidia*); 13. Sea anemone (Actinia); 14. Bryozoan; 15. Skeleton shrimp (*Caprella*); 16. Alcyonarian coral (*Lobophytum*); 17. Vermetid gastropod; 18. Sponges; 19. Giant clam (*Tridacna*); 36. Gobies (family Gobiidae).

Small predators and detritus-eaters: 20. Butterfly fishes (*Chaetodon*); 21. Crab (*Trapezia*); 22. Snapping shrimp (*Alpheus*); 23. Polychaete worm; 24. Amphipod; 25. Brittle star; 26. Gastropod; 27. Sea cucumber; 28. Sea urchin.

Predators: 29. Snail *Cypraecea*; 30. Opisthobranch gastropod; 31. Sea star; 32. Flatworm; 33. Red algae; 34. Grouper; 35. Moray eel.

by a lagoon—shallow water over a sandy bottom. The lagoon can be several hundred meters wide but is often much narrower; it is rarely deeper than thirty meters. The reef itself usually is no more than fifty meters wide. Fringing reefs are found, for example, along the eastern African coast and off the islands of the Indo-Australian archipelago.

2. Barrier reefs are modified fringing reefs. They are several kilometers away from the coast; the lagoon between coast and reef is significantly deeper and the reef itself is much bigger, often several kilometers wide and many kilometers long. A prime example is the Great Barrier Reef off the northern coast of Australia, a formation 1200 kilometers long and 30–150 kilometers wide.

3. Atolls, or circular reefs, have grown up to the surface from deep in the ocean. An atoll always surrounds a lagoon thirty to sixty meters deep, forming a sort of water-filled bowl. Most of them are found in the central part of the Indian Ocean, near the Laccadive and Maladive Islands, and in the western and central part of the Pacific. There are some smaller atolls in the Red Sea.

The formation of a fringing reef along a coast can be explained relatively simply. Reef building organisms settle on the rocky substrate under shallow water off the coast and gradually, as they grow, a living wall develops. In contrast, it is considerably more difficult to explain the way in which a barrier reef or an atoll is formed.

The classical theory of the origin of both types of reef was formulated by Charles Darwin, who found time during his five-year voyage in the Beagle to study a number of coral reefs. He proposed that as an island gradually sank, the fringing reef which had already formed around it continued to grow, rising upward and spreading over the underwater parts of the island. As a result, the lagoon between island and reef gradually became wider, as did the reef itself, until the dimensions were those of a barrier reef. If the island became entirely submerged, only the ring-shaped reef remained, and an atoll was born.

Some opponents of this "sinking" theory proposed as an alternative the theory that parts of the ocean floor—undersea mounds, ridges, or even volcanoes—were lifted up; the surfaces were stabilized by sediments (the skeletons of sponges, clamshells, deep-sea corals, etc.) and continued to rise, so that they provided the substrate for a growing reef.

According to a third opinion, the atolls were formed not by rising of the sea floor nor by sinking of islands, but as a result of wide fluctuations in water level. Lowering of the water level would expose large areas of reef and create conditions suitable for the formation of new reefs, whereas a higher water level would stimulate the old or new reefs to more rapid growth; in this way fringing reefs could eventually give rise to barrier reefs or atolls. In fact, such eustatic (prolonged and widespread) fluctuations in sea level have occurred repeatedly in very recent geological times; during the glacial epochs of the Pleistocene so much sea water was tied

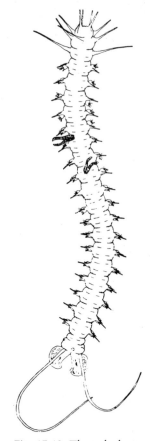

Fig. 17-19. The polychaete *Hesionides arenaria*. Female with two double spermatophores attached to the middle of her body.

Fig. 17-20. *Hesionides arenaria*. Transfer of the spermatophores to the body wall of the female. Adhesive apparatus, prey-grasping organs, vesicular tissue and sperm transfer in interstitial animals.

Fig. 17-21. General plan of the earth's coral-reef belt, with arrows showing cold ocean currents.

Subdivisions of the reef

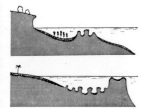

Fig. 17-22. Cross section through a fringing reef near the coast (above) and a barrier reef (below) farther out, with individual reefs forming in the lagoon between the main reef and the coast.

up in the giant ice caps that the sea level was as much as 200 meters lower than it is today. Conversely, during the warm periods between the glacial epochs the level was as much as fifty meters higher than at present.

Many scientists concerned with coral reefs combine these theories. In their view, there was sinking and reef formation in Darwin's sense at some places, and in others lifting of the ocean floor occurred; the fluctuations in sea level contributed to the pattern of reef formation as well. One may infer from the deep-sea cores drilled by American scientists at various locations in the Pacific that all three processes have played a role; some of the atolls are supported by stabilized sediments or volcanic rock, and others have been formed on plutonic rock like that of the continents.

Often one finds "miniature atolls" within ordinary atolls, and sometimes they occur in other places, such as in the Red Sea off the coast of Saudi Arabia. In this case there is no doubt that they arose from small rounded pillars of reef which grew up from the floor of the lagoon; when such a reef block reached the surface it died out in the middle but proceeded to grow vigorously around the edges. Thus an originally uniform mass of coral gradually transforms itself into a ring-shaped reef. The exposed calcareous material left in the middle of the upper surface is brittle and wears away, forming a shallow depression at first and eventually deepening, over quite a long time, to become a lagoon. The well-known underwater researcher Hans Hass was the first to point out this manner of atoll formation.

A coral reef is by no means a uniform structure. Flying over such a reef, one can see that it is pierced at many points by small channels or wide passages. The outer side of the reef, exposed to the waves, looks quite different from the side toward the quiet water of the lagoon. In the lagoon isolated "miniature reefs" have often formed.

Charles Darwin himself had perceived the basic elements of which a reef is composed. Most recently, certain American scientists and the German coral specialist Georg Scheer have investigated the reef zones and their characteristic corals in great detail. The various subdivisions can best be seen in an atoll reef.

The upper surface, or reef flat, is usually only a few meters wide in the case of a fringing reef, but in an atoll it can be as wide as several hundred meters. On the seaward side, where the waves beat against the reef, there is an elevated rampart. The individual corals—if there are any there at all—are small and compact, so as to offer little resistance to the surf. The firm edge of the reef consists mainly of flat calcareous algae, lying side by side almost like slabs of cement and producing a protective crust over the coral. This algal ridge prevents the wall from being pounded to bits and eaten away by the waves, which if permitted would gradually destroy the whole reef.

On the reef flat the corals grow close together. The further they are from the edge, and thus from the destructive effect of the waves, the more widespread and bushy they grow.

Where the reef flat is especially wide, as on a barrier reef and even more so on an atoll, the corals often die out in the middle of the area. The dead corals break up, so that there is first an accumulation of rough debris and later a layer of white calcareous gravel and sand. In this way, the middle of the reef can become an island, which can develop into a piece of land several hundred meters wide and some kilometers long. In the tropical oceans the creation of such "corallogenic" islands is no rarity. For example, the approximately 20,000 islands of the Maldive archipelago, in the middle of the Indian Ocean, came into being by this process alone. Moreover, the countless South Sea islands of the Pacific to a great extent grew up from the sea as deposits of debris and sand on reefs far from land. Where the surface of a reef is interrupted by an island, the two sides are called the outer (seaward) and inner reefs.

On the outer side of a coral reef, where a high surf constantly breaks, the upper part of the slope is flatter and there are channels cut out along it, within which some of the water flows back to the sea. The few corals growing here are short and little branched. In the case of an atoll, this description fits only the windward side of the outer reef, where the surf is strongest. The lee side of the outer reef, the side away from the wind and the main force of the waves, looks quite different. There the surf does not eat away the reef, and the waves and currents are not strong enough to make grooves in it. The slope is significantly steeper; just below the edge, corals begin to grow, and at relatively shallow depths there are large, spreading tablelike corals—an indication that in these places the effects of the waves are ordinarily not felt very far below the surface.

The coral heads on the slope of the lagoon-side reef spread just as broadly, and in many cases are delicately formed and fragile. There are tidal currents here, but no surf, so that the algal ridge is absent. The growth of coral on the inner-reef flat is continuous with that on the slope. The miniature reefs growing in the lagoon of an atoll or a fringing reef are similar in structure, for they, too, are ordinarily sheltered from the surf.

Both animals and plants contribute to the building of a coral reef. Most of the animal builders are stone corals (order Madreporaria). Each species grows into a head of characteristic shape, by accumulating deposits of calcium carbonate. Many corals are of compact structure and look like more or less large kidney stones; others have a bushy form, and still others look like antlers or take the shape of shallow dishes or plates heads of lettuce, or stems bearing Brussels sprouts. Each of these arise from a single larva, but in the course of its growth it develops into a great many polyps, in most cases only a few millimeters long, which are interconnected and together secrete the hard skeleton that gives the coral its shape.

Corals growing under strong light in shallow water usually have some distinct color. But the tropical reefs are not really docked out in glowing hues, as many of the early scientist/explorers overenthusiastically described

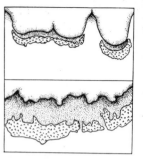

Fig. 17-23. View from above of a fringing reef (top) and a barrier reef (bottom). Coarse stippling: reefs; fine stippling: lagoon dark line: coast.

Fig. 17-24. Addu Atoll, the southernmost atoll of the Maldives in the Indian Ocean. Black region: islands on the reef.

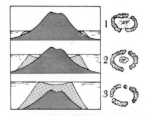

Fig. 17-25. Sinking theory according to Darwin.

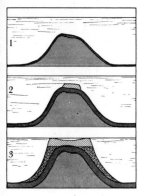

Fig. 17-26. Lifting theory.

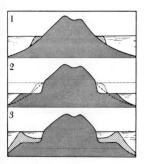

Fig. 17-27. Origin of a reef during Ice-Age sea-level changes.

Fig. 17-28. Cross section through an atoll reef. A few isolated miniature reefs have grown up in the lagoon.

them, and one is certainly not justified in calling them—as Ernst Haeckel did—"gardens of the Hesperides." In fact, greenish and brownish tones predominate, with occasional spots of bluish or reddish pastel colors. This coloration is due entirely to algae, green algae and especially the unicellular brown algae called zooxanthellae, which exist as symbionts both in the living tissue and in the skeleton of the corals.

Between these algae and the corals which house them there is a close, mutually advantageous relationship. The algae receive a certain amount of protection (from protozoans, for example, which might eat them) and utilize certain end products of the coelenterates' metabolism. The most important of these is carbon dioxide, which the algae fix by photosynthesis, but they also take up nutrient salts, especially nitrates, phosphates, and ammonium salts. On the other hand, the coral polyps obtain large amounts of oxygen from the algae, as well as a supplementary food supply. Moreover, the algae remove the toxic secretions of the corals and keep them from poisoning themselves, for the polyps have no excretory organs. Finally, the symbiotic algae actually seem to accelerate the formation of the coral skeleton.

The interdependence between algae and corals is so great that the algae are evidently no longer able to live apart from their partners, and polyps without algae lose vigor and soon die. The interdependence in fact is such that one can consider the association between coral and alga as autotrophic—that is, the partnership is capable of supplying itself with all the organic nutrients it needs—although the coral polyps do take additional food in the form of minute planktonic organisms. American reef specialists have determined that a head of coral contains three times as much plant as animal tissue. Most of the plant tissue comes from the small green algae within the calcareous skeleton, and the lesser part consists of the zooxanthellae in the tissues of the polyps.

Even apart from these, plants are common on the coral reef. These are certain red and green algae called calcareous algae because they secrete calcium carbonate in and around their cell walls. In so doing, they form thick crusts on the upper side of the reef which are more stable than the coral skeletons and more able to resist damage by the surf. The significance of the algae as reinforcing elements among the corals had been noted by Charles Darwin. In the part of the reef exposed to the heaviest surf, calcareous algae are essentially the only visible structures, for they are invulnerable to the grinding action of the waves.

The calcium carbonate required to build a reef must be taken out of the water by the coral polyps. A coral reef can be formed only where the concentration of dissolved calcium carbonate is very high, much greater than is usually found in sea water.

Moreover, a number of other conditions are absolute prerequisites for reef formation. For example, the bottom under shallow waters must offer a firm foundation, a solid substrate upon which the swimming larvae of reef-building corals can settle and develop buds to secrete the skeleton. Suitable foundations are usually solid rock, an underwater outcrop of plutonic rock or well compacted marine sediment, the hardened lava of a submerged volcano or even an earlier, now dead coral reef. Sunken ships or parts of them can also serve as a substrate for the growth of coral. But a reef has no chance to develop on pure sand, for it is constantly shifting under the waves and currents.

Another determining factor in reef formation is the temperature of the water. The average for the year should be between 23° and 28°C. If it should fall below 18°C for any protracted period the corals would soon die, and this in fact happens from time to time during the winter months in the northern Red Sea. In addition, the corals—especially their symbiotic algae—and calcareous algae need large amounts of light. The most luxuriant growth of coral is always close to the water surface; relatively few reef-builders are adapted to the twilight of somewhat deeper water.

The oxygen requirement of corals is also high. The stronger the water currents, and the greater the oxygen content, the larger the reef becomes. In this case, though, the function of the oxygen is not so much related to the respiration of the coral polyps, which are supplied with oxygen directly by their algal symbionts, but rather to increase the concentration of dissolved calcium carbonate in the sea water.

The salinity of the water plays an important role; the range of tolerance of the corals is between 3% and 4%. Should the salinity exceed these limits, the corals suffer, and brackish water can kill reef-building corals. The coral polyps are very sensitive to turbidity of the water. In places where a river brings a fine suspension of mud from the land into the sea, or where the water constantly whirls up fine grains of sand, corals cannot live permanently; the mud and sand settle on them and asphyxiate the polyps.

The most recent danger to the corals is the water pollution caused by man. Oil that sinks to the bottom, fine films of floating oil that sticks to the polyps exposed at low tide, the poisons in industrial wastes and many other unbiological side effects of modern life are unfortunately already making themselves felt on the most distant islands, and they mean death for the delicately balanced coral-reef community. In future, the more the oceans, and especially the coastal waters of tropical oceans, are loaded with the poisons we produce, the more certain we can be of the eventual death of the coral reefs.

If one takes a closer look at a head of living coral from a reef, one finds not only coral polyps but also a lively crowd of other animals. The oceanographer Sebastian Gerlach, during the Xarifa Expedition in the Maldive region, studied a prime example of such a coral community. The highly branched, bushy corals offer many potential hiding places and thus have an especially great variety of animals among their branches.

aa Window
bb bb BB Weights
c Air hose
d Water level inside bell
e Boat

Fig. 17-29. Baron Eugen v. Ransonnet-Villez of Vienna travelled over the Red Sea and Ceylon some time before Ernst Haeckel did, and reported on his journey. In his book on Ceylon (1868) are color pictures of underwater landscapes, painted while in a diving bell. But Haeckel thought the colors of these "coral seascapes" were much too dull and tried similar pictures himself; in an excess of enthusiasm, he made them too bright.

Communities in heads of coral

There are fish like the coral goby *Gobiodon* and similar forms, which emerge from their shelter only at twilight, to feed on the plankton that drifts by. Reef perch, in particular *Dascyllus aruanus*, which is always found close to such corals, hide there when in danger. Various crustaceans, chiefly snapping shrimps of the genus *Alpheus* and coral crabs (*Trapezia*) sit among the branches; sea-lilies, brittle stars, polychaetes and numerous other animals adapted to life in rock crevices find conditions suitable in such a head of coral.

Inside the branches, in the living part of the head, one discovers not only the channels containing the polyps, but also the holes of boring clams, sessile gastropods and barnacles, and a number of other animals. The lower part of the head, in which there are usually no more living polyps, is inhabited both outside and inside the skeleton by a great number of sponges, bryozoans, tunicates, small sea anemones, and many other animals, mostly sessile. In the larger crevices and holes of the lower part, and under the outspread branches, live sea urchins, sea stars, cleaner shrimp and other crustaceans and an array of fish species, which either retire here to rest or, like moray eels and certain perches, lie hidden in wait for prey. Squirrel fish and small *Tanichthys* spend the daylight hours here, and as night approaches swim out onto the reef in search of food. Altogether, a single head of coral amounts to a microcosm—a little world of its own.

American scientists who have studied the communities living on different reefs have recently proposed new terms to describe the organisms closely associated with corals. "Peribionts" are those animals which characteristically live in the near vicinity of a reef but display no morphological adaptations to this habitat. Chief among these are the "coral fish"—a term which lumps members of a great variety of taxonomic groups, such as surgeon fishes, trigger fishes, wrasses, trunk fishes and others. "Parabionts," on the other hand, have a significantly closer relationship to the reef, living among the branches at least part of the time, and they show corresponding adaptations. There are a number of crustaceans in this category, but the best examples are again fish, such as *Dascyllus*, the hairy-looking caracanthids, and similar forms. "Epibionts" are organisms that have become permanently attached to the surfaces of dead branches of coral or to crusts of calcareous algae—for example, sponges tunicates, and small sea anemones. "Hypobionts" sit deep in clefts, in the dark gap between narrowly separated branches, and in other deep, shadowy parts of the reef. These include certain gastropods, crustaceans, brittle stars and other twilight animals. The "cryptobionts" are a variety of animals which bore into the corals—barnacles, bivalves, worms and other animals equipped for making holes in a calcareous substrate. "Endobionts," finally, are the algae living in the tissues of the polyps and within the calcareous skeleton, which perform the task of photosynthesis.

Fish fauna of the reef   But the reef as a whole is a distinct community, as one can easily show by reference to the fish fauna. No other marine habitat harbors so great a number of fish species, or of individual fish. It is true that many of these are not really specialized for life on the reef, but nowhere else can they find such good opportunities for feeding, resting and hiding as are offered by a living, complexly organized coral reef. And there are a great number of other species which eat polyps or coral, live exclusively in or near the coral heads, or feed upon animals which live only in reef areas.

The fish fauna does not have the same composition everywhere in the reef; the kinds and proportions of species differ as greatly as do the various subdivisions of the reef itself. There are a number of fish species which live only in the strong surf on the outer edge of a reef; others prefer quiet waters, and are to be found only on the protected inner side.

The coral reef is of course not an entirely isolated biotope, but has clear relationships to the open ocean and to the coastal zone; similarly, the fish fauna of the coral reef is not an isolated unit. There are a number of oceanic fish—for example, certain gray sharks and horse mackerel—which make regular forays onto the reefs in order to hunt the numerous small fish living there. On the other hand, many sand-zone fish of the lagoon, such as rays, flatfish, flatheads or goatfish, are regularly found in the reef wherever sand has accumulated between the heads of coral. These occasional visitors, however, make no fundamental difference to the general aspect of the fish fauna in the region of the coral reef.

As mentioned above, growth of the coral polyps depends upon sunlight, cleanness of the water, degree of water motion and many other environmental factors. All of these also affect the fauna and the reef community as a whole. The most important element is the plankton, which at night rises from the depths to the surface of the sea and thus into the vicinity of the reef. Whereas most of the polyps are retracted during the day, at night their circlets of tentacles open widely. Then, perhaps, the display of color and the graceful undulations of the countless outstretched tentacles might indeed justify the expression "gardens of the Hesperides."

But no garden is entirely peaceful, and the polyps and the animals living in the coral are always threatened by predators. Sea stars creep about feeding upon the smaller sea anemones and sponges as well as upon the coral polyps. Brightly colored gastropods nibble their share of the anemones, and their more predatory relatives hunt a variety of coral-dwellers. A number of butterfly fish (*Chaetodon*), young *Chaetodontoplus*, *Oxymonacanthus* and other species specialize in eating polyps. *Oxymonacanthus* presses the firmly closed ring of its specially adapted mouth against the pore containing a living polyp, and by sucking pulls the animal out easily. Such a fish spends the whole day sucking one polyp after another out of its apparently invulnerable shelter.

Certain puffers, porcupine fish and parrotfish use less refined methods to attack the coral; with the beaklike, strongly developed mouth and

Relationships between the reef and its inhabitants

teeth they bite off pieces and entire branches of coral, and swallow them whole. Surgeon fish, trunk fish and trigger fish concentrate their attentions upon the other inhabitants of the coral heads, and no crustacean, anemone, worm or sponge is safe from them.

Until recently it was an encouraging finding that in spite of the many animals acting to destroy the coral, the reef as a whole was invulnerable; the regenerative capacity of the billions and billions of coral polyps, and of the other animals, was so great and the number of predators so small in comparison that the biological equilibrium was unimpaired and no permanent damage was done to the reef-builders. And with the corals safe, the community they sheltered was in no serious danger. But lately, in some places, the situation seems to have changed.

The sea star *Acanthaster planci*, called the "crown-of-thorns," is red-brown in color and bizarre in structure, with a round central disk and more than twelve arms; it can be as large as sixty centimeters in diameter. It bears spines over its entire surface, and these are coated with poisonous mucus. It has long been known that these sea stars feed on the polyps of the stone corals, but they were always found only in limited numbers and presented no real danger to the reef. Since 1962, however, *A. planci* has been multiplying at an explosive rate in certain places, and in a few years it has destroyed whole sections of reef. The threat is particularly severe in the case of the Great Barrier Reef, the corals of the Marshall Islands, Hawaii, and Guam, and a number of other reefs. Examination of a map showing the affected areas suggests that masses of the coral-killing sea stars appear whereever humans are particularly active. The cause of the plague is not yet known; some environmental factor may be greatly increasing the chances of survival of the larvae of this species.

There is hardly any doubt that man—involuntarily—has upset the ecological balance of the coral reefs, by some sort of influence on or damage to the natural habitat (for example, by accumulation in the sea of certain wastes from drainage water). The catastrophic population explosion of the crown-of-thorns sea star might thus be the consequence of such an ecological disequilibrium. But it could be simply a matter of a natural fluctuation in population density, which will vanish as rapidly as it appeared. One can still hope—and related studies around the Great Barrier Reef suggest that the hope is justified—that despite this massive attack the walls of killed coral will not gradually disintegrate, but will be recolonized by corals so that the reef is eventually restored. In any case, the appearance of this destructive creature gives a strong incentive for further thorough investigations of the coral community, the physiology and behavior of the sea star and its natural enemies, and the factors responsible for the apparent loss of ecological balance in certain coral reefs.

Beyond the shallow neritic waters, at the point where the slopes of the continental land masses fall off much more sharply toward the abyssal plain, begin the high seas—the oceanic province. Usually the water here

Are the reefs in mortal danger?

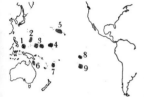

Fig. 17-30. Map of the Pacific Ocean showing the regions where the "crown-of-thorns" sea star, *Acanthaster planci*, is concentrated: 1. Palau; 2. Guam; 3. the Carolines; 4. Gilbert Islands; 5. Hawaiian Islands; 6. Great Barrier Reef; 7. Fiji Islands; 8. Marquesas; 9. Tuamotu Islands.

is a clear blue, because of the lack of inorganic suspensions and especially because of the considerably smaller numbers of microscopic phytoplankton and zooplankton. Some parts of the ocean, such as the Sargasso Sea in the western North Atlantic, have a particularly strong blue color; they might be called the "deserts" of the ocean. Here sensitive measuring devices have detected traces of sunlight as far down as about 1000 meters, though only in the blue-green part of the spectrum. A characteristic property of the oceanic region is the complete lack of bottom animals in the zooplankton; in the waters over the continental slope the number of echinoderms, bottom-dwelling crustaceans, gastropods, bivalves and other animals declines rapidly with distance from the shore. Only in places where currents flow seaward from the continents can such larvae occasionally be an appreciable component of the plankton.

In contrast to the shallow waters, those of the oceanic province are uniform in salinity and temperature over wide areas. On the average, the salt concentration is about 3.5%, though in tropical regions where the rate of evaporation is high it can reach 3.7%. In such places temperatures up to 27°C have been measured, whereas at high latitudes the temperature drops to about 4°C. In both the tropics and the polar regions, the temperature fluctuates by less than two degrees in the course of a year. Only in the temperate zone are there greater fluctuations, over as much as ten degrees, and these are essentially limited to the upper 100–150 meters of water. In the tropical and subtropical regions the water near the surface is strongly heated by radiation from the sun. This superficial layer of warm, lighter water is about 50–100 meters thick; it rests upon the denser mass of cold deep water. Between the two layers is a transition zone, where the sharp gradient of temperature, and to some extent of salinity, constitutes a considerable barrier to many planktonic organisms. This thermocline also severely impairs the exchange of nutrients and oxygen between the two layers.

As in the neritic province, in the open ocean sunlight is the almost exclusive source of energy for all living beings. In the presence of light, the phytoplankton uses chlorophyll to synthesize organic matter from water and carbon dioxide; photosynthesis can be carried on down to depths of 100 meters, or at most 200 meters, in the clear oceanic water. Below this euphotic zone is a region of dim light, insufficient for photosynthesis, which extends to about 800 meters.

By far the larger fraction of the marine phytoplankton consists of a multitude of different forms of siliceous algae or diatoms (class Bacillariophyceae) and shelled flagellate algae including coccolithophores and dinoflagellates. Their rates of growth and reproduction depend not only on the distribution of light, but also to a great extent upon the presence of certain nutrient salts. Chief among these are phosphates and nitrates, but iron, manganese and certain vitamins (Vitamin B_{12}, among others) are important as well. In addition, the diatoms need silicates for the

Fig. 17-31. Characteristic members of the oceanic phytoplankton:

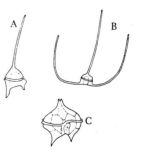

Shelled flagellates: A and B. *Ceratium*; C. *Peridinium*.

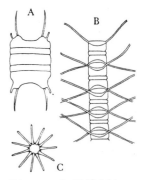

Diatoms: A. *Biddulphia*; B. *Chaetoceros*; C. *Asterionella*.

The oceanic province, by J. Kinzer

construction of their shells. Most of these substances are very nonuniformly distributed in the ocean. Only at depths of more than 1000 meters are there rich reserves of phosphate, and there it cannot be used by any living organism.

At latitudes where the day length changes with the seasons, the spring increase in light is associated with rapid reproduction of the plankton, which soon uses up all the nutrient salts available in the euphotic zone. Only in areas of upwelling near the coasts, such as the waters off western Africa and Peru, do currents steadily replenish the surface zone with nutrient-rich water from the depths. In such regions there is a luxuriant growth of plankton almost all the year round. Similarly, in the equatorial region of some oceans the divergence of surface currents brings about an upwelling of the deeper water, and here photosynthesis by the phyto-plankton is also enhanced. Productivity is greatest in the regions of cold climate, where a pronounced vertical exchange of water prevails, and in the above-mentioned regions of upwelling. In contrast, large parts of the high seas are relatively unproductive. Because of this, the total productivity of organic matter by the world's oceans is only about one half that of the land. Especially in view of the fact that the oceans occupy 71% of the area of the planet, we must regard their primary productivity as low. Mean net primary productivity in the open oceans is only about 125 grams of dry organic matter per square meter per year, contrasted with product-ivities of 1000 to 2500 g/m²/yr in many forests, and a mean for land vegetation of about 780 g/m²/yr. In all the oceans together, net primary production is about 55 billion metric tons of dry matter (25×10^9 t of carbon) in organic matter annually. Current estimates of net primary

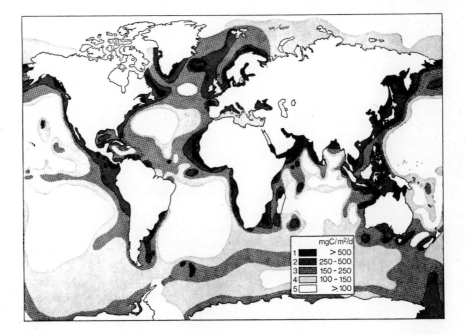

Fig. 17-32. Primary production of organic matter by phytoplankton in the world's oceans (in mg carbon per square meter per day).

production on land, in contrast, are 105 to 125 billion metric tons of dry organic matter annually.

The organic matter synthesized by the algae is passed directly or indirectly, through a food chain, to all the other organisms living in the sea. The second link of the chain consists of filter-feeders. Plant plankton is microscopically small, measuring between 0.002 and one millimeter; it does often form colonies, but even these are rarely larger than five millimeters. To subsist on such food, an animal needs a suitable filtration apparatus. Many species of copepod (for example, members of the genus *Calanus*) have sievelike mouthparts bearing fine feathery processes; with these they can carry on a continuous filtration of the surrounding water. Salps (tunicates of the class Thaliacea) and the "tailed" tunicates of the class Larvacea are typical filter-feeders; they strain the water through an apparatus so efficient that it catches planktonic organisms which slip through even the finest plankton nets (with a mesh of only 0.05 mm). Species of fish which appear in large schools, such as the South American sardine *Engraulis ringens*, can feed on phytoplankton; they let the water flow in the opened mouth and out through the gill chamber, and the little algae are caught on the gills. In addition to phytoplankton, the filter-feeding oceanic animals also eat the detritus (products of the decomposition of organisms) floating in the water. Detritus, together with the attached bacteria, can even be more important in the nutrition of the filter-feeders of certain regions than the living plankton.

The third link in the food chain is formed by carnivorous animals that prey on the filter-feeders. Like the neritic waters, those of the oceanic province are inhabited by a great variety of such species—for example, medusae, ctenophores, siphonophores, arrow-worms, copepods, euphausids, and gastropods. The herring, another secondary consumer, is itself a filter-feeder; its chief food is copepods, of which there are large populations in the northern seas.

In fact, the largest of all the animals that have ever lived on earth, the gravely endangered baleen whales (suborder Mystacoceti), feed exclusively upon plankton. In the arctic oceans especially, they sieve out huge swarms of the small crustaceans called "krill" (*Euphausia superba*). It has been estimated that in former times the baleen whales consumed 50-80 million tons of krill each year. Now that man has reduced the stocks of baleen whales so greatly and much of the krill is uneaten, he is faced with the problem of inventing methods to catch these little animals as food for himself and his cattle.

A final, fourth link in the food chain is characteristic of the oceanic community; this consists primarily of the larger predatory fish. Some of them, such as the cod, rosefish, and several species of tuna, are very important to fishery on the high seas. Cephalopods, sea birds and odontocete whales are also among the terminal consumers.

As organic substances pass from one link of the food chain to another,

The food chain in the open ocean

▷
Above left: Hydromedusa. —Below it: young squid. As an adaptation to life in open water, the animal is almost transparent; only eyes and liver are pigmented.
Above middle: Ctenophore.—Below it: Cubomedusa (*Cyanea lamarcki*).
Above right: The turbellarian *Youngia aurantiaca* from the rocky shore of the Mediterranean.
Below: The sternoptychid fish *Argyropelecus* with luminescent organs on the ventral surface, photographed during the expedition of the research ship *Meteor* in the Indian Ocean 1964/65.

Oceanic filter-feeders

The large predatory fish

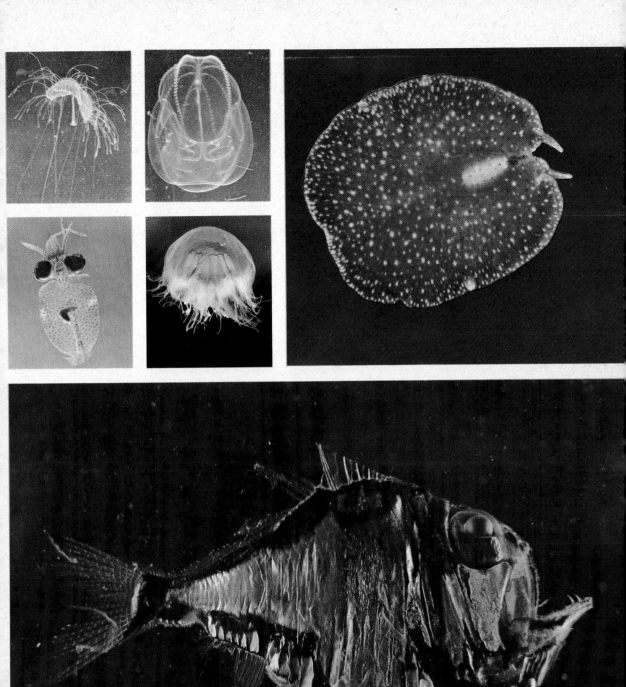

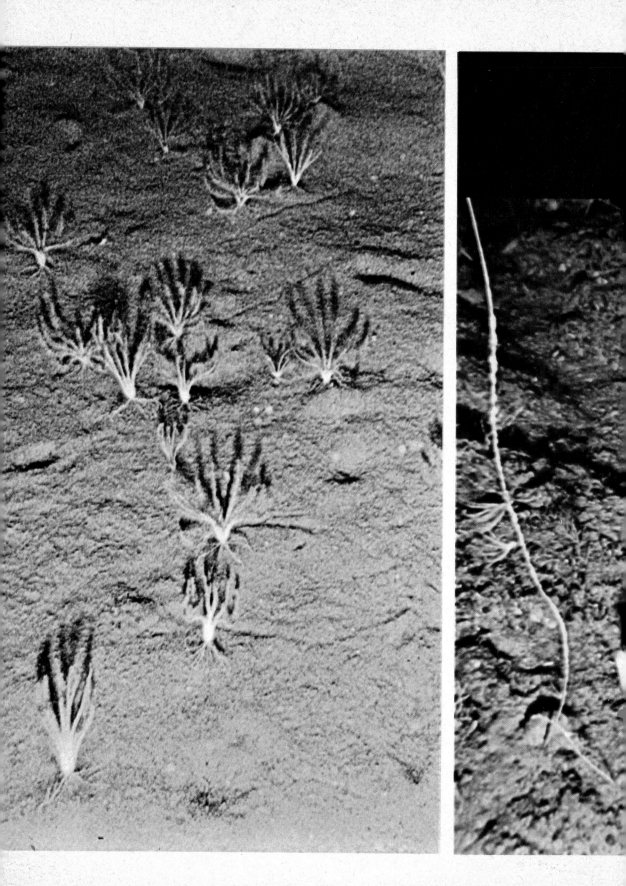

there is a considerable loss of energy, since most of the energy in the food at each stage is used up in metabolism; only about 10% can be used to form new tissue. This explains why the anchovies and sardines, which subsist on filtered algae and are thus near the beginning of the chain, can manage to develop such huge schools as are found in the cold Peruvian Current. The fishery built up here in the past years is among the largest such industries in the world, with annual catches amounting to eight or nine million tons of sardines. Furthermore, there are enormous populations of birds—gannets, pelicans and cormorants—in the same area which compete with men for the fish, and they catch 2.5–3 million tons of sardines per year.

The active vertical migrations of zooplankton and some species of fish accelerate the transport of food from the euphotic zone to the twilight zone and into the darkness below. The animals move to different depths, depending on the time of day. Some copepods, despite their small size (4–6 mm), descend every day to depths of 100 or even 200 meters. Large crustaceans, like the euphausid *Meganyctiphanes norvegica*, swim with an average velocity of ninety meters per hour, and when swimming downward they can reach 130–200 meters per hour. From catches in nets that can be closed at different depths, it has been determined that these crustaceans stay at 400–600 meters during the day and at night rise into the upper hundred meters, where they find most of their food.

The study of the upward and downward migration of invertebrates and fishes has been greatly facilitated by the development of automatic echo-sounding equipment. These devices, which continually record the depth at which emitted ultrasound (at frequencies from 15 to 30 khz) is reflected, soon became an indispensable aid to navigation. During the day, in addition to the bottom profile, they indicate a remarkable "phantom bottom" or deep-scattering layer at depths of about 400–600 meters. In the evening twilight, within two or three hours, this moves into the upper hundred meters, and around dawn the echo-sounder record shows a descent to the original depth. In the last thirty years these deep-scattering layers have been observed in oceanic regions around the world; only in arctic and antarctic waters are they restricted—if they are present at all—to depths between 50 and 100 meters.

When the scattering layers were first discovered it was suggested that they were probably caused by marine animals, for their daily upward and downward shifts are associated with the distribution of sunlight in the water. These animals must have some property which enables them to reflect ultrasound. In fact, as we now know, the scattering layers are inhabited by lantern-fish (suborder Myctophoidei), deep-sea hatchet-fish (family Sternoptychidae), and shrimp of the order Euphausiacea. Many of these crustaceans and fish possess well-developed luminescent organs. The fish are also equipped with large swim-bladders, which reflect the ultrasonic pulse sent out by the ship. Some siphonophore species also have

◁
Right: Feather stars sit close together on alcyonarian corals, with sponge and polyp colonies next to them. A snipe fish sucks water into its beaklike, elongated mouth, looking for food between the stones. Josephine Bank, 188 m deep.
Left: In the upper parts of the deep-sea bottom there is a dense population of feather stars. They feed on particles drifting in the water. Off Portugal, 270 m deep.

enclosed air-bubbles, and these act similarly to produce an echo layer in the ocean. Among the crustaceans in the deep-scattering layer there are often, in addition to many species of euphausids, large swarms of shrimp-like decapods of the genus *Acanthophyra*. Neither the luminescent fish *Maurolicus muelleri* nor the deep-sea hatchet-fish are known to occur in antarctic waters, and there are no deep-scattering layers in these regions.

The daily rhythm of the vertical migrations is brought about mainly by the variation in light in the water. Measurements with sensitive photo-metric devices at depths down to 1000 meters have confirmed this sugges-tion. Many planktonic animals, and larger ones as well, stay all day at depths where the light is of a certain intensity. During the periods of twi-light in the morning and evening, they move along with this region of preferred light intensity, gathering at night in the upper 50–100 meters of the water.

In the clear oceanic water vertical migrations occur over several hundred meters, and require a considerable expenditure of energy on the part of the animals. The reason for these daily movements is not yet known; probably they move down in the morning to escape from the light, and stop in the depths where the intensity is low enough to conceal them. In well illuminated waters—except for the Sargasso Sea with its bunches of floating seaweed—there is nowhere to hide; only almost complete transparency, such as is found in numerous planktonic species, affords a degree of protection. During the evening twilight conditions in the warmer upper waters again become such that the animals can rise to feed, by filtering or predation.

Surprisingly, the "urge" to descend to the deeper twilight region is so strong that even the oxygen-depleted zone at a depth of 200–500 meters, which extends through the tropical and subtropical oceans, presents no obstacle. At the low temperatures (only 5–10°C) prevailing in the twilight region, the metabolism of even poikilotherms is considerably slowed, so that the animals respire at a more economical rate and to some extent compensate for the expenditure of energy during the upward and down-ward migrations. Vertical migrations occur on an annual as well as a daily basis; for example, certain arrow-worms and copepods of the genus *Calanus* move to different depths at different seasons.

The Sargasso Sea, which has been mentioned several times, lies in the western North Atlantic, within the circle of the great Atlantic currents. Its name comes from the seaweed *Sargassum*, which is very common here. Highly branched bunches of this weed float free under the surface of the water and offer many animals with a strong tendency to live in seclusion a habitat unique in the oceanic province. As it increases in size, the seaweed fails to develop large enough air-bladders to keep it afloat, and pieces of it sink slowly down to great depths. The different animals on this seaweed constitute a distinct community. So far a total of sixty-seven free-moving species have been described as inhabitants of the *Sargassum* weed, though

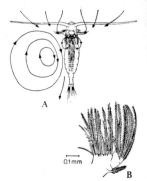

Fig. 17-33. Filtration apparatus of a copepod (*Calanus*). A: the arrows show the direction of flow during swimming and filtering. B: left mouthpart with captured phytoplank-ton.

The Sargasso Sea

some of these are only guests in transit. The crustaceans, gastropods and fish that live there permanently are usually a brownish-yellow color and are thus very hard to see among the weed.

Pleuston and neuston

The upper centimeters or decimeters of the oceans, which in the tropics, especially, seem almost inimical to life because of the intensity of the sunlight, harbor a fauna of their own—the pleuston on the surface of the water and the neuston just below. Animals of the pleuston have structures that serve as floats, so that they are always at the very surface. One of the best-known examples is a siphonophore, the Portuguese man-of-war (*Physalia physalis*). The float here is a large air-filled bladder called the pneumatophore, which stands like a sail above the water. Another jelly-fish, *Vellela spirans*, sails similarly before the wind, while the violet snail (*Janthina janthina*) uses a foamy float to stay on the water surface. In tropical oceanic regions there is even an insect that lives on the surface—a bug, the oceanic water-strider *Halobates*. This is the only insect to have conquered the ocean. All the pleuston animals live as predators.

Research on the fauna living just under the water surface, the neuston, has been assisted in recent years by the development of a special neuston net which strains only the uppermost centimeters of water. True neuston animals are characterized by blue or red pigments, which presumably serve to camouflage them and also protect them from ultraviolet and infrared radiation; typical of the neuston are copepods of the family Pontellidae, the shrimp *Parapeneus longipes*, and the isopod *Idotea metallica*. In the subtropical Atlantic samples of neuston consisted of 94% invertebrates, mostly crustaceans; half of these were copepods and a third were ostracods, whereas crab larvae and amphipods were less common. For many fish species of the oceanic province and for quite a few bottom-dwellers as well, especially in the shelf region, the uppermost centimeters of the water are a sort of nursery where the young stages develop. As adults, these animals live at greater depths and come to the surface only occasionally, generally at night.

Since the phytoplankton avoids these upper centimeters by day, the food supply here is limited. There are bacteria on the surface film, but this "bacterioneuston" is probably used as food only by young copepods, some pteropod species, and a few other organisms. On the other hand, in waters near the coasts the drifting bodies of insects can make a considerable contribution to the food of the neuston. Night, by comparison, is a time of feasting for the neuston animals, for many planktonic organisms rise to the surface from the deeper water. Heteropods, isopods and the sardine *Maurolicus* have large eyes and can hunt their prey even in twilight.

Only a few species, including the above-mentioned isopod *Idotea metallica* and certain copepods such as *Pontella atlantica*, stay directly below the surface all day long; these are called the "euneuston." Most of the other invertebrates and the fish occupy this habitat only at night, and at daybreak they return to depths of 30 meters or more. And there are

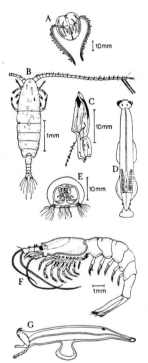

Fig. 17-34. Predatory planktonic animals of the oceanic province.
A Ctenophore (*Pleuro-brachia pileus*)
B Copepod (*Calanus finmarchicus*)
C Siphonophore (*Cheloph-yes appendiculata*).
D Arrow-worm (*Sagitta enflata*)
E Medusa (*Bougainvillia principes*)
F Euphausid (*Meganycti-phanes norvegicus*)
G Heteropod (*Firoloida*).

animals with daily migrations in the opposite directions; these include the young stages of certain neuston fishes—for example, the flying fish (suborder Exocoetoidei) and the long-spine snipe fish (*Macrorhamphosus scolopax*)—and the pteropod *Creseis acicula*, which moves somewhat deeper in the evening and stays close to the surface during the day.

In addition to plankton of various sizes, the oceanic province is the home of numerous species of cephalopod and vertebrate. In contrast to the plankton, these are capable of moving over long distances under their own power, even against a horizontal current. This is why they are called nekton (from the Greek word for "swim"). They are able to make long-distance migrations, a characteristic of many oceanic animals. Of all the vertebrates of the nekton, the greatest number of species are fish. Reptiles are represented only by a few marine turtle and snake species, which temporarily enter the oceanic province; the marine turtles must return to the beaches to lay their eggs. Penguins and seals are also amphibious, alternating between water and land. Among the mammals the cetaceans—especially the dolphins—are the most skilful swimmers and have gone furthest in their adaptation to life in the water. A newborn whale dolphin is already large and independent enough to be a full-fledged member of the nekton, and the same is true of the young of certain viviparous species of shark. On the other hand, most of the larval or young stages of fish belong to the plankton for considerable periods, before they develop sufficiently to swim like their parents. The best-known example of a long developmental period is given by the European river eel (*Anguilla anguilla*); its slender, leaf-shaped leptocephalus larva drifts all the way from the Sargasso Sea to the coasts of western Europe, carried by the prevailing currents. Not until it has completed its development in the rivers there, and is ready to return to the Sargasso Sea to spawn, can the eel cross the ocean under its own power.

Most of the migrations of oceanic animals are from relatively warm spawning regions to colder regions with a more abundant food supply. In some cases it has been possible to follow their routes by marking the animals. It has been shown that fish often cover remarkable distances. The Atlantic salmon (*Salmo salar*), for example, proceeds from the coasts of Europe and of eastern North America to the waters of Greenland, while the Atlantic herring (*Clupea harengus*; see Fig. 17-35) travels from the southern Norwegian Sea into the waters of Spitzbergen and Iceland. Many tuna undertake even longer trips, straight across the ocean. Marking experiments have demonstrated that an individual blue-fin tuna (*Thunus thymnus orientalis*) from the vicinity of the island Guadalupe (Mexico) covered a distance of 5800 miles, to reach the southern coast of Japan. Another characteristic of many fish of the high seas is that they can swim rapidly for long periods without rest. Tuna swim an average of eighty, and bonitos (*Katsuwonus* and *Sarda*) as much as 200 nautical miles in a day. Among the fastest and at the same time most elegant swimmers are with-

Nekton

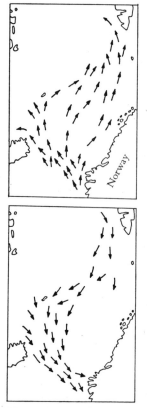

Fig. 17.35. Migratory routes of the Atlantic herring (*Clupea harengus*) in the eastern North Atlantic.

out doubt the decabrachiate cephalopods. Relatively little research has been done on their migrations, since the large species in particular are very hard to catch in nets. The largest members of the group are the giant squid of the genus *Architeuthis*; specimens as much as 17 meters long, including the arms, have been found, though never alive—they had either been stranded on a beach or were floating on the surface of the water. No one knows what they eat. Investigations of the stomach contents of sperm whales have revealed cephalopod suckers as much as 25 cm across, and cephalopod eyes up to 40 cm in diameter. One may thus conclude that some giant squid can reach even more astonishing sizes than have yet been seen.

The deep sea, by H. Thiel

The home of such marine monsters was thought to be in the deep sea, at a time when that region was largely unexplored. "Abyssos" in classical antiquity was the name for the underworld, and the name "abyssal region" is still used for the part of the ocean at depths between 3000 and 11,000 meters. People who refused to believe in the existence of legendary marine monsters (Fig. 17-36) in the oceanic realm also believed, until well into the 19th Century, that no animals could live in the darkness of the deep sea.

At the beginning of the 19th Century animals had already been pulled up from depths of about 2000 meters, but the results of these catches were not widely known for a long time. Not until 1860, when a deep-sea cable between Sardinia and North Africa was taken up, was it proved that animals could live below 500 meters. The first great deep-sea expedition was made between 1872 and 1876 by the English research vessel *Challenger*. It was followed from 1898 to 1899 by the German trader *Valdivia*, which drew up a large number of animals from depths down to 5000 meters and more, in the Atlantic, Indian and Antarctic Oceans. More recently, a great deal of biological deep-sea research has been done, with the *Galathea* of Denmark, the *Vitiaz* and other ships of the Soviet Union, Germany's *Meteor* (Fig. 17-38), and several ships from the USA, including the *Eltanian*, the *Anton Bruun*, and the *Atlantis*.

Fig. 17-36. In earlier centuries people believed that monsters lived in the still unexplored deeps. Giant octopus, with tentacles 15 m long or more, were called sea monsters.

Although there has been a considerable increase in exploration of the deep sea in the years since 1950, there is still no general agreement as to the upper limit of this zone. Various possibilities have been suggested. One is the average depth of the point which separates the continental shelf from the steeper continental slope; this would set the upper limit of the deep sea at 200 meters. Temperature can be used to characterize the deep sea only in certain regions; for example, in the tropics the deep sea could correspond to the water mass below 4°C. But toward the poles this temperature line rises, until in the arctic and antarctic regions it reaches the surface. If the daily vertical migration of the plankton were taken as an indicator, the deep-sea boundary could be set at a depth of 400–600 meters. Finally, there is an especially pronounced change in the species composition of the benthos at a depth of about 3800 meters.

As mentioned previously, the transitions between the zones on the floor of the ocean and the open-water regions are always gradual. Here we shall ignore the transition zone, in order to describe the characteristics of the actual deep sea more clearly. Moreover, the discussion will be limited, apart from the deep trenches, to the zone between 3000 and 6000 meters, which represents 76% of the ocean floor and is thus the largest habitat on earth. Within the abyssal zone three regions are distinguished: the abyssal plain, which begins at the foot of the continental slope, the hill regions, and the mid-ocean ridges. In all three regions the slopes are very gradual, so that the vertical dimensions must be exaggerated in diagrams. Certain islands and groups of islands (for example, the Azores and St. Helena in the Atlantic), as well as submarine mountains like the Great Meteor Bank and Josephine Bank (both also in the Atlantic), just high up from the ocean floor, though the peaks of the mountains do not reach the surface of the water. The term "trench" is used for those deep-sea valleys extending to depths greater than 6000 meters. They occupy only 1.2% of the ocean floor; they are no wider than 120 km, but in some cases they are over 11,000 meters deep. Most of the deep-sea trenches are in the Pacific, just off the continents and groups of islands.

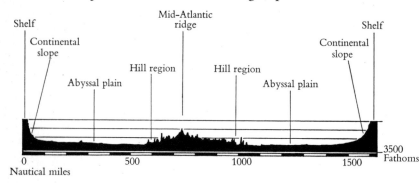

Fig. 17-37. Depth profile of the Atlantic Ocean, from western Africa to northern South America.

The floor of the deep sea

The sediments on the floor of this zone almost completely lack those components of sediments nearer land that are washed down from the continents by rivers or blown over the water by wind. The bottom here consists of the calcareous and siliceous shells of protozoans of the euphotic and twilight zones. When they die, the living matter is decomposed by bacteria, and only the shells sink to the depths. By far the largest area of the bottom is covered by so-called globigerina ooze, consisting mainly of the shells of the foraminiferan *Globigerina*. At a depth of 4500–5000 meters the solubility of calcium carbonate increases so greatly, under the influence of the hydrostatic pressure, the temperature, and the carbon dioxide concentration, that the calcareous shells dissolve. Siliceous shells of radiolarians and diatoms then are the chief components of the sediment (Fig. 17-39). In the deepest waters reddish and brownish oozes of particles of inorganic sources (notably volcanic dust) occur, and these are called the "red clay."

Conditions in the
depths

As a habitat, the deep sea is distinguished by a high degree of uniformity. The water temperature is always less than 4°C, and over broad regions it varies by only a few tenths of a degree; it is as low as −1.2°C in the oceans at the North and South Poles. On the floor of the Iberian Basin and over large expanses of the North Atlantic the temperature is about 2°C. The Mediterranean is exceptional, in that 13°C has been measured here at depths greater than 4700 meters. But even in such special cases the temperature is always constant. The salinity, too, varies within such a narrow range that, at least as far as we can tell at present, it has no influence upon the life in the deep sea.

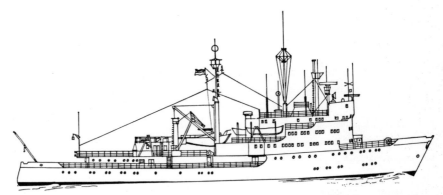

Fig. 17-38. The German research ship *Meteor*, put in service in 1964, like its predecessor in 1925–1927 contributed a great deal to research on deep-sea biology. The overall length of the new *Meteor* is 82 m, width 13.5 m, displacement about 2740 tons.

Currents have been demonstrated in almost all regions of the deep sea. The water flowing over the deep-sea floor in the western South Atlantic comes from the surface of the ocean off Antarctica, while the deep water of the North Atlantic comes in large part from the region of ocean between Greenland and Spitzbergen. The rate of flow involved in this movement of water masses is only a few centimeters a second; it can be raised or lowered under the influence of the tides. But it is evident that the velocity seldom becomes so high that particles swirl up from the bottom and are carried to other regions. The currents distribute oxygen so thoroughly that there is enough to support life at all depths; the slow decrease in oxygen concentration in the five to ten meters of water nearest the bottom indicates the physiological activity of organisms there. Other indications of such activity are the increase of dissolved inorganic nutrients, which are set free in the ocean floor, and the increased acidity of the water.

Among the influences determining the chemicophysical environment of organisms here, hydrostatic pressure deserves first mention. This increases with depth at the rate of one atmosphere pressure per ten meters. This means that animals living at 5000 meters are under a constant pressure 500 atmospheres greater than those at the surface. This has no effect upon their shape, since there is no air-filled space in their bodies—if there were one, it would be compressed to nothing at this depth. Liquids, on the other hand, have extremely low compressibility, so that physically the animals can withstand the high pressure quite well. Chemical reactions, however, are affected by pressure, and it must be expected that such processes as digestion and respiration are influenced. How the animals cope with this difficulty is still a mystery; to solve it, devices would be required with which deep-sea organisms could be caught and studied without changing the pressure in their surroundings. So far there are no data on the effects of pressure on deep-sea organisms, but it is certain that many bacteria and metazoans are unable to survive under less pressure.

Hydrostatic pressure also prevents researchers from determining the number of bacteria and protozoans in the deep sea. Only by keeping the animals in culture can their population density be determined. But because of the low pressure in the laboratories many of them die before they can be counted. So far only minimum values have been obtained, and with these it is difficult to achieve any understanding of the food-chain relationships in the deep sea. But an explanation of this aspect of the communities there is one of the most important goals of contemporary marine biology.

In recent years Soviet, American and German scientists have tried to estimate biomass and productivity in the deep sea. The abyssal organisms, like those of terrestrial soils, can be classified in three large groups, independently of their systematic position. The macrofauna includes metazoans of over a millimeter in size, such as sea cucumbers, sea stars, sea urchins, polychaete worms, bivalves, snails, sea anemones and crustaceans. The meiofauna comprises metazoans smaller than a millimeter—for example, nematodes, ostracods, copepods and the juvenile forms of the macrofauna. Bacteria, fungi, ciliates and other one-celled organisms constitute the microfauna. Although nothing can as yet be said about the possible existence of fungi and ciliates in the abyssal zone, for the other groups it is possible to estimate at least the order of magnitude of production in grams of organisms per square meter. From the amount present at the time the sample was taken and the number of generations in a year, the increase of living material per year is computed.

Accordingly, the following values can be given for the deep sea: microfauna, 8 grams live weight per square meter per year; meiofauna, 1 gram live weight per square meter per year; macrofauna, 0.2–0.5 gram live weight per square meter per year.

From the point of view of the food chain, the relative sizes of these order-or-magnitude estimates are reasonable. One would expect the microfauna to be taken as food by the meiofauna, and these in turn to be eaten by the macrofauna. The decrease in weight from one link to the next that is evident in the above figures makes clear that most of the food is used for vital processes such as respiration, movement and reproduction. But this simple picture leads to a difficult question that has come up again and again in the hundred years since the discovery of the deep-sea fauna by the *Challenger*: What is the food of the abyssal bacteria, the first link in this food chain? All animals are ultimately dependent for food upon the

Fig. 17-39. The deposits on the deep bottoms consist chiefly of the shells of protozoans, with Foraminifera, Radiolaria, and diatoms predominating:

A third of the present-day ocean floor is covered by "globigerina ooze," consisting of the shells of the foraminiferan *Globigerina*.

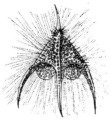

"Radiolarian ooze" is the bottom sediment consisting of the skeletons, often very beautifully shaped, of Radiolaria.

Remains of diatoms ("diatomaceous ooze") and found in the oceans of the South Pole, in the northern Pacific, and elsewhere.

organic matter synthesized by plants, which in the ocean are represented by the large algae in the neritic province and by the microscopic algae in the euphotic oceanic zone. It used to be thought that organic food reached the abyssal regions in the "rain of detritus," the organisms which die in the surface waters and sink toward the bottom. But this explanation does not suffice. It is true that the dead organisms sink, but the velocity of the bodies of the small organisms, which are by far the greatest fraction by weight of the surface flora and fauna, is very low. Moreover, the breakdown of the organic matter chemically and by bacteria begins immediately after death. This means that by the time the organisms have fallen through the first thousand meters almost all the organic matter has been decomposed and cannot reach the ocean floor. The abyssal animals must obtain food in some other way.

Vertical migrations

One possible explanation is offered by the vertical migrations, mentioned above, which large numbers of organisms perform daily. Fish, crustaceans and siphonophores rise in the evening, from depths as low as 600 meters, to take advantage of the abundant food in the upper waters. With the dawn they move down again, taking organic substances with them in their gastrointestinal tracts; these are excreted in the deeper water. Often such excretions still are highly nutritious and could serve as food for organisms at greater depths. Other animals also make vertical migrations, between deeper water levels. There results a sort of "ladder of migration," by which food is brought to the deep sea step by step. Incompletely digested materials are frequently excreted as fecal balls which sink at a higher velocity than the small particles that were initially eaten.

Another idea about the food supply of abyssal animals involves the fact that organic substances such as sugar and amino acids are dissolved in the water throughout the ocean and are continually being produced by physiological processes in the organisms—in digestion, excretion, and bacterial decomposition. These dissolved substances can accumulate at the surfaces of organic particles and be taken along as the particles sink to the depths. In addition, dissolved substances in the water near the bottom become attached to the countless protozoan shells on the sea floor, and hence can serve as food for the deep-sea animals.

Fig. 17-40 gives a much simplified diagram of these relationships. In fact, of course, the food chain in every habitat is really a food web; the bacteria utilize not only the organic matter brought in from other parts of the ocean but that from the decaying bodies of the local meio- and macrofauna. In both the meiofauna and the macrofauna there are organisms which can take up dissolved organic substances through the general body surface. However, they feed primarily on living and dead organic matter in the sediment.

In a modified form, these feeding relationships also hold for the open waters of the deep sea. Microscopic animals, copepods, ostracods and other forms filter the sinking particles out of the water, including the "olive-

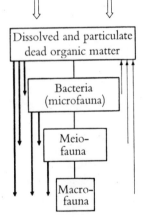

Fig. 17-40. Diagram of the food chain on the ocean floor.

green cells" discovered during the expedition of the first *Meteor* (1925–1927) in the South Atlantic. Even today it is not clear whether these cells are alive or dead. In any case, they transport organic substances which can be used as food by filter-feeding organisms. The filter-feeders in turn serve as prey for larger species.

The food supply in the deep sea was a factor in the evolution of the abyssal community, as comparison with the communities at the upper edge of the deep-sea region makes clear. In the open water between 200 and 400 meters there is abundant food; hence the community on the ocean floor at this depth is composed mainly of animals that catch prey floating in the water. Chief among these are the sponges, various coelenterates, and feather stars. In contrast, the abyssal plains at 4000 to 5000 meters are inhabited primarily by animals that live on and in the bottom and take in sediment and other bottom animals as food: worms of various groups, bivalves, snails and especially sea cucumbers. Animals which catch floating food particles are rare in this habitat; a few, such as the sea anemones, can probably also take up the small organisms of the meiofauna from the surface of the ooze.

This outline of the "food web" is based mainly on the results of investigation of organisms in the neritic zone. Since it has not been possible to experiment with abyssal animals under high pressure, their physiological adaptations to life in the deep sea—which may involve rate of growth, rate of utilization of food, and the rate of succession of generations—have not yet been studied. On the other hand, there are clear morphological and behavioral adaptations. In a bivalve genus found over a wide range of depths, the gut in the species of deeper regions is longer than that of shallow-water species; as a result, the nutritional value of the food is more thoroughly exploited, which compensates for the smaller amount of food available. Other adaptations are associated with the way in which food is obtained, with mutual recognition and with reproduction. Since the amount of food in the deep sea is limited, many animals are specially equipped with organs to facilitate the capture of prey. For example, various crustaceans, such as copepods and shrimps, at great depths have a particularly well-developed filtration apparatus. It is important for them to filter out and eat food particles of all sizes, whereas related species in shallower regions with more abundant food can afford to specialize in certain sizes.

Some deep-sea fish have evolved quite striking modifications to assist prey capture. The slender saccopharyngoid fish *Eupharynx pelecanoides* has wide jaws that can be spread so far apart that it can grasp animals as large as itself or even larger. And the black swallower (*Chiasmodon niger*), the stomach and skin of which can expand to form a huge sack, can also swallow very large prey. Often the teeth of deep-sea fish are long and sharp, so that food once seized is not lost again. The evermannellid fish are further modified for prey capture in having a flexible cartilaginous

Fig. 17-41. A young saccopharyngoid fish (*Eupharynx pelecanoides*).

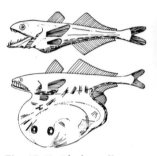

Fig. 17-42. Black swallower (*Chiasmodon niger*) before feeding (above) and with a large prey fish in its stomach (below).

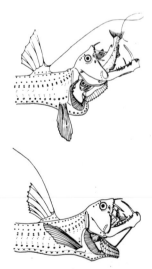

Fig. 17-43. The evermannellid fish (*Chauliodus sloanei*) swallows a luminescent sardine (*Maurolicus*).

Fig. 17-44. *Borophryne apogon* has a "lantern" over its mouth, and long teeth.

Fig. 17-45. Deep-sea crustacean (*Cystosoma neptuni*) with especially large eyes.

Fig. 17-46. Deep-sea squid (*Sandalops melancholicus*) with stalked eyes.

Fig. 17-47. Deep-sea shrimp (*Sergestes corniculum*) with long antennae.

connection between skull and vertebral column. When prey comes within reach of one of these fish it throws the head back while pushing the jaws far forward, so that the mouth opening becomes extraordinarily large and the prey is more certain to be caught in it. Still another adaptation is found in species of the genus *Malacosteus*; they have no skin or muscles joining the two sides of the lower jaw at the bottom of the mouth. When the mouth springs open the lower jaw shoots forward to snap up the prey. If the bottom of the mouth were closed it would seriously slow the movement of the lower jaw through the water.

Angler fish are also found in the deep sea. In these, the first ray of the dorsal fin, which is located well forward, in front of the eyes or just over the mouth, can be more or less long, branched or tufted at the end, and may even bear a luminescent organ. The motion of this threadlike structure, or the glow of the light, serves to attract smaller animals. In the darkness of the deep water they do not detect the angler fish, and they mistake the thread, the tuft at its end, or the light for a bite of food. Before they have a chance to snap at the lure, they are themselves snapped up by the angler and held in its large, toothy jaws.

The development of large and stalked eyes in certain fish, crustaceans and cephalopods of the deep sea can be ascribed to the fact that in the permanent darkness of their home there are many animals with luminescent organs. These eyes are specialized for dark vision and for movement detection; color vision would be of no use here. On the other hand, there are also crustacean and fish species with small, weak or even nonfunctional eyes, but with an especially well-developed tactile sense. In crustaceans the tactile organs and sensory hairs are frequently located on long legs and antennae; they serve to detect feeble water currents and pressure waves which can betray the presence of enemies or food. In deep-sea fish, tactile sensors are concentrated either in the barbels, which are often branched, or in the elongated rays of the dorsal, ventral and tail fins. The fin rays of *Bathypterois bigelowi* (Fig. 17-49), for example, are extremely long and are used to feel about for food on the ocean floor.

Because of the limited food supply, the population density of the deep-sea animals is small. As an adaptation to this, certain deep-sea angler fish have evolved a pronounced sexual dimorphism. The females are of normal size and structure, whereas the males are very small and live as parasites on the females. As a juvenile, a male attaches to a female with his teeth, and thereafter his tissues fuse with hers so completely that the two circulatory systems are joined. The advantage of this "parasitic marriage," in which the male becomes in effect an organ of the female, is clear; the two partners need not seek one another out when they are ready to mate, for they are already joined together and reproduction is assured.

Another type of adaptation already mentioned in another context, the luminescent organs, can also be of use in recognition of sexual partners, conspecifics in a group of animals, or prey, as well as in frightening away enemies. Luminescent organs develop from mucus glands in the skin and in many cases are complicated structures resembling eyes. The light is produced by chemical processes; in some species bacteria living as symbionts in certain cells of the luminescent organ are also involved.

Of all the environmental factors in the deep-sea habitat it seems clear, from the structural adaptations of many animals and from the nature, as far as it is known, of the food web in the abyssal open-water and bottom communities, that food is the most important.

Fig. 17-48. "Parasitic marriage": female deep-sea angler fish (*Edriolychnus schmidti*) with three males permanently fused to her body.

Fig. 17-49. *Bathypterois bigelowi*, feeling along the bottom for food with its elongated fin rays.

18   Inland Waters

Introduction, by
J. Illies

Lakes and streams cover only a small fraction of the area of the continents. But continental bodies of water are closely involved in the overall circulation of water—upon which, in the last analysis, all life on earth depends. According to the most recent calculations, the earth's inland water supply is made up as follows: soil moisture, 21,000 cubic kilometers; lakes and streams, 116,000 cubic kilometers; and ground water, 4,000,000 cubic kilometers. For comparison, the world's oceans contain 1.37 billion cubic kilometers, and the polar ice caps twenty-seven million cubic kilometers of water. Fresh water, then, represents a very small part of the total water on earth, but it is indispensable; it is drunk by almost all animals that live on land, and it is the habitat of a multitude of aquatic animals.

Life originated in the ocean, and cells still contain salt solutions resembling sea water. Accordingly, the body fluids of all animals are quite salty. Since fresh water contains only small quantities of salt, special adaptations of the internal organs are necessary in order for animals to live in fresh water at all. Osmotic pressure, which tends to drive water into the animals' bodies, must be compensated by mechanisms for the elimination of water. Some groups of animals have never developed such mechanisms, and therefore are not to be found in fresh water; these are the radiolarians, foraminiferans, corals, echinoderms, and many gastropod and fish families. Other groups, in the course of their evolution, have become so completely adapted to life in fresh water that they cannot live in the ocean; examples of these are the amphibians and the insects. As a result, fresh-water communities have a special, characteristic composition quite different from that of marine communities. Animals that can live in both fresh and sea water are rare exceptions.

The inland waters became the focus of special attention at an early stage in the development of the science of ecology. The branch of ecology originally called "hydrobiology" was split into limnology (fresh-water biology) and marine biology during the last century, the profound

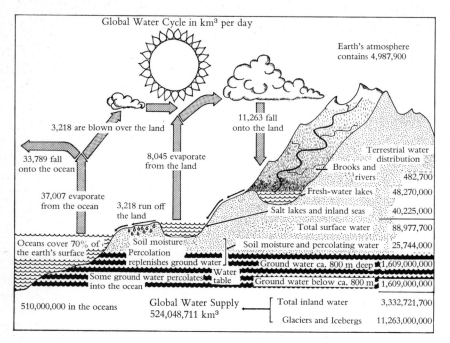

Global Water Cycle in km³ per day

Earth's atmosphere
contains 4,987,900

3,218 are blown over the land

11,263 fall
onto the land

33,789 fall
onto the ocean

8,045 evaporate
from the land

37,007 evaporate
from the ocean

3,218 run off
the land

Oceans cover 70% of
the earth's surface

Soil moisture
Percolation
replenishes ground water
Some ground water percolates
into the ocean

Water
table

510,000,000 in the oceans

Global Water Supply
524,048,711 km³

Terrestrial water distribution	
Brooks and rivers	482,700
Fresh-water lakes	48,270,000
Salt lakes and inland seas	40,225,000
Total surface water	88,977,700
Soil moisture and percolating water	25,744,000
Ground water ca. 800 m deep	1,609,000,000
Ground water below ca. 800 m	1,609,000,000
Total inland water	3,332,721,700
Glaciers and Icebergs	11,263,000,000

Fig. 18-1. Schematic representation of the total water reserves on earth and the circulation of water.

Only a small fraction of the planet's water is fresh water, and a considerably smaller fraction of this is involved in the daily cycle of evaporation, precipitation and drainage. Nevertheless, these stores of fresh water—the inland lakes, streams and ground water —are the first prerequisite for any organic life on land.

differences between the two habitats having already been recognized. Today limnology, though it deals with a relatively small fraction of all the habitats on earth, is the branch of ecology which has provided the most precise investigations and produced the greatest insight into the interaction among various factors. With the founding in 1887 of a limnological commission by the Swiss zoologist August Forel (1841–1912), and with the publication from 1892 to 1904 of his three-volume treatise on Lake Geneva, limnology began to progress as an independent discipline; since then it has contributed a great deal toward establishing ecology as a quantitative science. The work of August Thienemann (1882–1960) made Germany one of the main centers of limnological research. The fundamental knowledge acquired during those many years has now found crucially important application in the effort to avert the dangers threatening the inland water systems.

Bodies of fresh water are particularly well suited to ecological studies. The lakes, especially, are closed, clearly delimited ecosystems in which many cyclic processes are almost independent of the surroundings and thus more readily observed and measured. Nor is it difficult to set up model fresh-water habitats in the laboratory, which permit controlled experiments on the physiology and behavior of the communities there. As home aquarium enthusiasts know, such segments of nature can be kept in equilibrium with little effort. Sea-water aquariums and terrariums, on the other hand, can be maintained only with much more complicated apparatus and techniques.

In the inland waters, then, ecological research has made especially

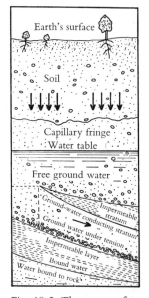

Fig. 18-2. The routes of percolation and flow of water underground.

great advances; most of the ecological principles now recognized were first observed here. Limnology is currently receiving an impetus to still more intensive research by the increasing global problem of disposing of the wastes of our advanced civilization. Numerous laboratories throughout the world are now carrying on limnological research with the most modern tools and methods. Some universities already have sections or departments for limnology and even for waste-water biology. The amount of data that has been accumulated about individual fresh-water habitats throughout the world is impressive; the results fill many libraries. Considerations of space, however, demand that the following discussions present only a general, much abbreviated selection from this wealth of information.

Ground water, by S. Husmann

Ground water, as defined by the limnologist August Thienemann, is all the water in the outermost part of the earth's crust, under the surface of the ground. Continually replenished by rain and melting snow, it flows through gaps and crevices in the subterranean rock and eventually joins the surface water, when it emerges as a spring or at the bottom of a lake or stream.

When rain percolates through the soil, a thin film of water clings to the soil particles and the rest sinks deeper, filling the spaces between the particles more and more until the water table is reached. The water below this level exists as a continuous phase and is called ground water. The cavities in which it is stored and through which it passes extend down to the stratum of impermeable rock; over this there flows a more or less broad subterranean stream. Sometimes permeable and impermeable strata are stacked one above the other, so that there are layers of ground water. Where a higher ground-water layer is connected with a lower, the upper one exerts pressure upon the one below; it is this water under pressure which can come to the surface through deep drill-holes as a so-called artesian well.

The deposits of loose stone left by streams and glaciers offer routes for flow of the subterranean water which differ considerably in permeability. The distribution of grain sizes in sand, gravel and loose stones determines the size range of the interstices; in an accumulation of such materials there may be adjacent and interconnected systems of spaces with quite different resistances to the flow of water. As underground water flows through clefts, cracks and cavities in rock, originally produced as the crust of the earth was forming, it enlarges them to form secondary cavities of various sizes. Where the rock consists of especially water-soluble substances—calcium carbonate, calcium sulfate, and the double carbonate of calcium and magnesium called dolomite—the joint effect of solution and the movement of drainage water from the surface is to produce widely branching systems of underground caves and tunnels. Through these flow subterranean rivers and streams; the water table is uniform throughout such a formation, and can vary by several tens of meters in the course of a year.

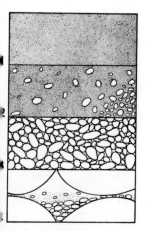

Fig. 18-3. The loose substrates conducting ground water can vary widely in grain size.

Systems of ground water flowing through sand and gravel or through the gaps in rock masses can be inhabited by very distinctive animals, without eyes or pigmentation. The flow of subterranean water is a crucial prerequisite for the existence of aquatic communities here, for it is only by movement of the water that a steady, adequate supply of nutrients is assured. This constant influx of fresh water must also provide a certain amount of dissolved oxygen, and it must be free of harmful substances such as hydrogen sulfide.

But the most critical factor in the maintenance of subterranean aquatic communities is food. As food is consumed, it can be continually replaced by circulation of the ground water. Bits of decomposed organic matter from the surface enter the ground water and serve as the first link in a food chain which, here as elsewhere, continues with the consumers of such substances and the ground-water animals that prey upon them. Ground-water habitats, like the deep sea, are characterized by permanent darkness, and hence require input of basic food substances from the surface; there are no multicellular plants here to serve as primary producers. Wherever there is not a constant or at least occasional current to turn the wheels of life, the ground water is a barren desert. However, ground-water animals are quite capable of surviving the temporary disappearance of water from the cavities in which they live—the humid hollows still provide them with a reserve of food, and the oxygen in the air, which these animals can absorb through the whole body surface, is sufficient to support adequate respiration.

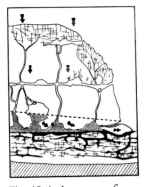

Fig. 18-4. A system of cavities in limestone. Arrows: paths of percolating water; cross-hatching: range of fluctuation of the water table.

For example, examination of 1000 cubic centimeters of sand which was almost dry, so that it could easily be scattered, revealed nematodes, annelids and hundreds of living ground-water copepods of the genus *Parastenocaris*. Moreover, a number of soil animals are known which can live temporarily in water. In fact, many species (especially among nematodes and annelids) cannot definitely be classified as either soil or water animals. Within the range over which the water table fluctuates live both ground-water and soil animals, each capable of adopting the alternative mode of life when necessary.

In this ecologically variable zone, then, the concepts "ground water" and "soil" really are descriptions of two unstable states of a single habitat, each of which changes gradually into the other as the water table rises and falls. As habitats, ground water and soil are intimately related, the only basic difference between them being the proportion of water in their overall structure. The ground-water habitat includes not only the water in relatively large cavities but also that in the interstices of loose stone and the crevices in rock, as well as the products of the breakdown of rock and the fragments of plants that form the basis of the food chain. And these are exactly the same things to which a geologist refers when defining "soil." Soil (in contrast to rock) is always a biotope, whereas ground water is a biotope only where elements of soil are also present.

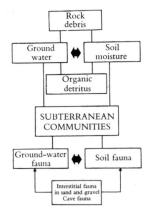

Fig. 18-5. The ecological relationships between ground water and soil.

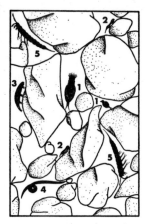

Fig. 18-6. The interstitial fauna in sand: 1. Rotifers; 2. Gastrotrichs; 3. Tardigrades; 4. Nematodes; 5. Copepods.

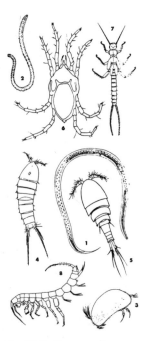

Fig. 18-7. Community from the ground water in the gravel bed of a subalpine brook: 1. Nematodes; 2. Oligochaetes; 3. Ostracods; 4 and 5. Copepods; 6. Hydrachnids; 7. Insect larvae; 8. Freshwater gammarid.

Ground-water biotopes include pools in large mountain caves, water-conducting cracks in rock, the spaces between the stone in piles of rock debris, and the interstitial systems in the sand or gravel underlying terraces and river valleys. In the gravel beds of streams there is an important ecological interface zone between ground and surface water—a sort of "ecological gate," which permits a transition between the two realms.

Here ground and surface water mix. From far under the river bed and the adjoining meadows, blind, milky-white ground-water animals move through the water-filled spaces between sand grains and bits of stone until they are near the open water; there they encounter those members of the benthos (the bottom-dwelling organisms) which find suitable conditions in the same interstitial system. The "true" ground-water animals and the "guests" that have come from the surface of the stream bed join to form a single community. Though one can in principle distinguish the "stygobionts" (the eyeless and colorless "true" ground-water animals) from the "stygophilous" animals that have moved into the habitat as guests, both are permanent inhabitants of the gravelly beds of streams. Such communities may also be found in certain subterranean locations far from the riverbanks or in certain parts of the surface water. But among the hydrachnids there are certain species entirely restricted to the ground water close to rivers or brooks. Some insect larvae live in the interstitial water of sandy-gravelly stream beds only during the first stages of their development.

With increasing distance from such stream beds, in the ground water under the stream and the adjacent land, the number of species also capable of living in surface waters gradually declines, until finally the ground-water communities consist exclusively of blind animals. That is to say, once the influences of the surface waters are excluded, under favorable conditions there is an essentially closed biotope populated by species entirely or to a great extent limited to subterranean waters.

It is a rather remarkable fact that the closest relatives of many of these true or "stygobiotic" ground-water animals live not in the gravel beds of rivers but rather in the interstitial water of sandy or gravelly seacoasts. All these fresh-water animals derived from the fauna of the coastal ground water indicate the existence of another transition zone; where sand and loose rock are deposited along the coasts, they provide a route along which animals with the appropriate characteristics can move down the salinity gradient from sea water to the inland ground water. For example, the archiannelid *Troglochaetus beranecki* is widely distributed in the ground water of Europe; one of its closest relatives, *Thalassochaetus palpifoliaceus*, lives in the ground water in loose sand and gravel in the Kieler Bucht in the Baltic Sea. Early in the 1930's the zoologist Karaman, investigating the ground water in the city of Skopje (Yugoslavia), discovered isopods of the genera *Microcerberus*, *Microparasellus* and *Microcharon*, the closest relatives of which have since been shown to exist at various places in the coastal ground water. The genus *Ingolfiella* ranges even further into the ocean; it inhabits the inland interstitial ground water, the coastal ground water, and even the deep sea.

The animals which came from the ground water of the seacoast or the beds of streams were already endowed with a suitable body shape, which permitted the necessary freedom of movement within the system of narrow spaces in sand and gravel. Characteristics of a considerable number of ground-water animals are a small size or an extremely elongated body of small diameter.

Habitats of the interstitial type have been available for colonization by suitable animals for long periods of geological time. As a consequence, communities of ground-water animals are composed of members differing greatly in phylogenetic age, depending upon the time in the earth's history when their ancestors adopted the habitat. There are even "living fossils"—primitive, phylogenetically ancient types—in the ground-water fauna; their ancestors found an appropriate habitat here, and the extremely cramped quarters had the effect of an evolutionary "strait jacket." The primitive ground-water animals from earlier geological eras show that that once the habitat had been adopted, there was no going back. This is particularly true of a group probably containing the most ancient members of the sand-gravel habitat, the primitive crustacean *Bathynella* (Fig. 18-10) and its relatives.

These singular blind and unpigmented ground-water crustaceans are living relicts of the Syncarida (a nearly extinct superorder of the Malacostraca); apart from a few species in the surface waters of Australia and Tasmania the Syncarida are known only as fossils, most of which were found in bituminous coal. The body of *Bathynella*, only a little over a millimeter long, appears so primitive because of an odd mixture of the characteristics of thoracostracans and arthrostracans. The possession of a furca at the hind end puts them in a special systematic position and indicates an origin very early in crustacean evolution. On the other hand, the fact that a flattened tail segment, the pleotelson, is already present indicates a more recent branching off from the crustacean evolutionary line. The two characteristics constitute, so to speak, a phylogenetic bridge between crustaceans with a furca and those with a telson, and this at least hints at a connection between the Entomostraca and the Malacostraca (for example, the copepods, which possess a furca, and the amphipods with a telson).

Taking all this into consideration, it has been decided to put these "living fossils" next to the extinct crustaceans of the order Palaeocaridacea. The comparison in Fig. 18-10 between an extinct genus (*Acanthotelson*) and *Bathynella*, which still lives in the ground water, clearly shows how closely their structures are related. The zoologist Vejdovsky, who in 1882 brought up from a well in Prague the first two—and for a long time the only known—specimens of these ancient crustaceans, realized

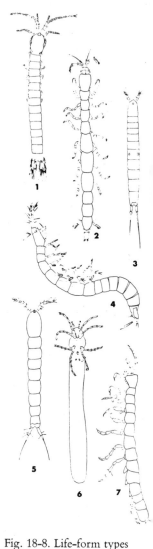

Fig. 18-8. Life-form types among the interstitial fauna of sand and gravel: 1. Syncarid (*Parastygocaris*); 2. Isopod (*Microcerberus*); 3. Harpacticoid copepod; 4. Syncarid (*Leptobathynella*); 5. Copepod (*Parastenocaris*); 6. Hydrachnid (*Wandesia*); 7. Amphipod (*Ingolfiella*). 2, 3 and 7 are immigrants from the coastal ground water.

the situation. But dubious zoologists regarded *Bathynella* as a figment of his imagination, and according to the zoologist Vinzenz Brehm one loud critic was so far carried away as to remark, "Now all we need is for somebody to fish up living trilobites from the Hradschin!"

But when Chappuis rediscovered *Bathynella* in 1915, the search began in earnest. Since then many more living specimens of related ground-water crustaceans have been found in Europe, Asia, Australia, Africa and South America, so that now there are nine genera in the *Bathynella* group, with over 70 species and subspecies—a vindication of the "well professor" of Prague. The worldwide distribution of the group can only be explained by an extraordinarily long history of colonization; it is remarkable in view of the fact that these interstitial animals have a very limited capacity for dispersal. Altogether, the various peculiarities of these primeval crustaceans are fundamentally interrelated; the geologically ancient habitat, the great phylogenetic age of the animals, the long history of colonization and the worldwide distribution are all reciprocally explanatory, and together emphasize the importance of the time factor. The crux of the matter then is the means by which a habitat could persist for so long, despite all the changes that have occurred in the history of the earth.

Water-filled interstitial systems in the sandy-gravelly beds of streams have existed for as long as water has been flowing in brooks and rivers, for one of the characteristics of running water is that it moves sand and gravel along with it. But the spaces between the loose stones and grains could not become a habitat until, in the course of the earth's evolution, food materials in the form of plant fragments had accumulated there. This means that multicellular plants first had to evolve on the earth's surface.

It is evident that for a long period of geological history the ground-water fauna in loose stone had all that it needed to maintain itself. It could never have been destroyed by the global processes that changed the face of the earth, since the changes in sea level never flooded the old, permanent continental areas, and even the younger parts of the continents that became fused to these were spread from submersion at least in some places and at some times. All these undisturbed regions of the earth's crust, which elsewhere was so unsettled, became refuges for certain animals and plants.

These organisms could move out from the old protected regions and the younger marginal zones during the periods when the floods subsided, and then they gradually colonized the newly exposed areas of land. Similarly, ground-water animals could follow the receding edges of the inland ice between and after the glacial epochs. As they did so, currents of ground water in the gravel beds of brooks and rivers and the sandy-gravelly deposits the glaciers left behind offered then suitable habitats and routes for migration. And even more important, this "Noah's Ark"

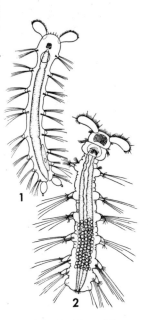

Fig. 18-9. Archiannelids: *Thalassochaetus* (1) and *Troglochaetus* (2).

The "Noah's Ark" effect in interstitial ground water

effect operated vertically as well as horizontally; the animals escaped into deeper zones of the ground water, which were not unfavorably affected by the climate.

It is equally safe to assume that marine animals have been able to migrate from interstitial ground-water systems on the seacoast to those inland since early in geological time. The abovementioned rise and fall of the sea level assisted in the establishment and expansion of regions of immigration; the gradually moving coast zone in the flooded regions during the Tertiary, which left more and more of the continent exposed, can be thought of as such an immigration region. This is indicated by the places where continental ground-water animals descended from the marine fauna have been found. Finds have been made, for example, on old coast lines of the Mediterranean and on sites previously occupied (before the formation of the Alps displaced it) by an arm of the ocean which in the Middle Miocene extended through the Rhone valley, the Bosporus and Mesopotamia to the Persian Gulf; when this ocean withdrew, it left behind Lake Balaton, the Black Sea, the Caspian Sea, and the Aral Sea.

We can be sure, then, that for long periods in the earth's history the subterranean fresh water in sandy-gravelly stone deposits offered all that was required for marine and fresh-water animals to form joint communities. The ground-water animals had an extraordinarily long time in which to adapt to the special aspects of their habitat, the confinement and the absence of light. Mutation and selection brought about the worm-like shape, sometimes almost grotesquely overemphasized, the loss of eyes and the lack of pigment; the process involved many groups of animals and is still operating today. Hydrachnids of the genera *Ljana* and *Atractides*, which live in gravelly stream beds, came to have extended bodies, and in *Atractides* the eyes also regressed. It is particularly interesting to find different stages of eye regression existing side by side in different individuals of the subterranean cave-dwelling aquatic isopod *Asellus aquaticus cavernicolus*; these hereditary modifications eventually end in blindness. The inheritance of pigment loss has also been demonstrated in these animals.

The reason for these apparently directed hereditary modifications, which lead finally to the loss of eyes and pigment, is certainly the fact that in the underground darkness eyes and pigment are entirely insignificant. Under such circumstances it may even be an advantage not to have them, since the body then spends no energy in forming useless structures and can use its reserves for other, more important tasks. As the zoologist De Lattin realized, the inheritance of eyelessness can also be explained simply by the ecological isolation that occurs naturally, by chance, in subterranean waters.

Neither the animals originating in the ocean nor those originating in fresh water have become appreciably less restricted to the interstitial

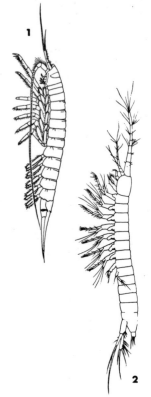

Fig. 18-10. Syncarid crustaceans: 1. *Acanthotelson* (fossil); 2. *Bathynella* (ground water).

Interstitial systems in sand and gravel: the real habitats of the ground-water fauna

system as members of the ground-water fauna. Even though the ground water in sand and gravel may be continuous with that in rock cracks and caves, so that it is in principle readily colonizable by animals of suitable shape, essentially no interstitial species has shifted its chief range of distribution into the water in cracks or into cave pools. In the Harz-Weser region, all thirty-eight of the local stygobiont species live in the interstices of sand and gravel; only four of these are also found in the more spacious crevice waters and caves. These more widespread species are the amphipods *Niphargus aquilex*, *Niphargus schellenbergi*, and *Crangonyx subterraneus*, and the isopod *Proasellus cavaticus*.

These four species represent departures from a general ecological principle that governs the choice of habitat by the ground-water fauna. According to this principle, the body shape of the ground-water animals, and in particular the largest cross-sectional measurement, is an important factor determining habitat choice; the extreme confinement of the smallest interstitial spaces is advantageous in that it keeps away larger predators. Very thin and elongated animals living in the spaces between sand grains, such as *Parastenocaris* (Fig. 18-8) and *Bathynella* (Fig. 18-10), accompanied by a fauna distinguished by small overall size (for example, the polychaete *Troglochaetus beranecki*, Fig. 18-9), are so well protected in their habitat that predatory species in the fauna of gravel interstitial systems cannot reach them. The animals of the gravel ground water, in turn, are sheltered from still larger animals that cannot fit into the spaces between the fine stones.

Cracks in rock that contain ground water can also afford protection. Recently, in fact, it has been discovered that the well-known urodele *Proteus anguineus* lives chiefly in undisturbed clefts, which meet its needs better than the caves in which it was first found. There are even a few elongated, blind fish that preferentially occupy the ground water in rock crevices that "fit" them, and certain forms of shrimp ordinarily found in wells and caves have proved to inhabit such crevices.

In contrast to crevices and interstitial systems, the inhabitants of which are protected by their enforced uniformity of size, the water in spacious cave pools is potentially dangerous for minute animals which make their way into it. But certain species of the typical interstitial fauna do manage to colonize cave pools in considerable numbers. Such pools can offer favorable conditions if they maintain no aquatic predators of superior strength—that is, if the small animals are effectively as secluded as in their ordinary habitat. In caves, wells and similar habitats, as in the interstitial ground water, the development of communities depends upon a steady or at least sufficiently frequent influx of water. Of course, the inflowing water can bring not only food and oxygen but various pollutants from the surface, which render the communities incapable of keeping a proper balance between input and breakdown of the substances that are washed in. Toxic materials thus not only poison the water directly, but by

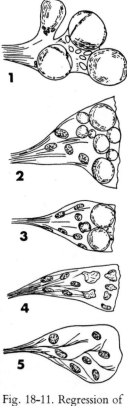

Fig. 18-11. Regression of the eyes in *Asellus aquaticus cavernicolus*, a cave form of aquatic isopod: 1. Four fully developed ocelli at the end of the optic nerve; 2-4. Progressive loss of the ocelli and nerve cells; 5. Complete regression, with only fibers and cell nuclei remaining.

harming the animals they seriously impair the natural processes by which the water is kept clean.

The ground water filling the spaces in sand and gravel is not only a habitat for microfauna, but also an important source of drinking water. In places it is in imminent danger, since sand and gravel offer little resistance to the percolation of impurities. Protection of the ground water from such substances is an urgent task for ecologists and those concerned with the management of water resources.

Although the depressions containing lakes appear to be filled with a uniform mass of water, the animals living there form characteristic communities reflecting the special aspects of different habitats, each with a typical plant community. The animal communities are not entirely separate; there are always a number of animals able to live equally well in either of two adjacent habitats.

Lakes, by J. Schwoerbel

A lake has three main regions: the littoral zone near the shore, which is well-lighted and in some cases has luxuriant vegetation, the well-illuminated upper levels in the open water (the limnetic zone), and the deeper water beyond the range of effective penetration of light (the profundal zone). The surface film of the water is counted as a fourth habitat, used either permanently or transiently by a few characteristic aerial or aquatic animals.

The community comprising the most species is that of the littoral zone. Its members live in the bottom or on more solid substrates, particularly those offered by the many partially or completely submerged water plants. Aquatic insects can swim well, but from time to time they must stop on some solid surface; moreover, many use the plants and the bottom detritus as food. Predatory insects also find adequate food in the littoral zone. Many of them lay their eggs in or on the plant tissues, so that in this and other ways even they are dependent on the vegetation here.

The littoral zone

The most conspicuous members of the littoral community are insects and their larvae. But molluscs are also quite prevalent; on the plants, especially, one finds lymnaeid snails, with their shells twisted to a point, and planorbid snails with low-spiralled shells. On the bottom are freshwater clams such as *Anodonta*, *Unio*, *Dreissena*, the small rounded bivalves of the family Sphaeriidae, and the even smaller *Pisidium*. Some of the smaller animals are nevertheless quite striking. Among them are the hydrachnids, many of which are brightly colored; these are the only chelicerates which have become entirely adapted to life in the water. A true spider commonly found in the littoral zone of swampy lakes is *Arygoneta aquatica*, but it must go to the surface from time to time to renew its air supply. The many worms of the littoral zone, which live on plants and in the soil, are inconspicuous (except for the leeches) and can be found only by careful investigation. Large numbers of crustaceans—phyllopods, copepods, ostracods and amphipods—as well as isopods, rotifers and protozoans live in the open water between the plants.

The littoral fauna

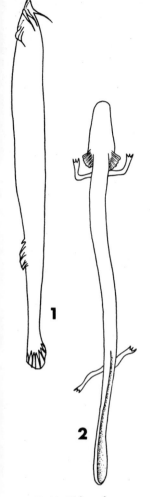

1

2

Fig. 18-12. Fish and amphibian colonists of the ground water in narrow spaces: 1. *Pygidianops eigenmanni*, of the interstitial system in the bank of the Amazon; 2. Amphibian *Proteus anguineus*, the chief habitat of which is the water in crevices in Dinaric limestone (Yugoslavia).

The profundal benthos

The insects of the littoral community include water bugs (suborder Hydrocorisa), diving beetles (Dytiscidae) and water beetles (Hydraenidae and Hydrophilidae), and the larvae of Mayflies, dragonflies, damselflies, caddis flies, midges and mosquitoes. The behavior of all of them is similar, in that they are all air-breathers. Whereas the larvae usually stay underwater, all of the imagos that live in the water must come to the surface to obtain air; like the water spider, they have remained fundamentally land animals. For this reason they are restricted to the shallow littoral zone, since the air they take with them to the bottom permits them to breathe only for a short time—sometimes just a few minutes. They avoid going too deep by detecting the increasing water pressure, and they can turn back immediately when it passes a certain limiting value. The water scorpions (Nepidae) have a caudal breathing tube which keeps them in almost permanent communication with the air; they tend to move uphill along the bottom, toward shallower water. They detect the direction of slope with an abdominal sense organ that operates like a carpenter's level. The pulmonate snails mentioned above are also air-breathers.

Moreover, most of the fish species in a lake are to be found near the shore. Roach and rudd, tench, carp and stickleback as well as the predatory pike and perch swim here and spawn in the thickets of water plants. In many lakes the littoral zone also houses whitefish and other salmonid fish of the subfamily Coregoninae. Finally, the littoral fauna includes salamanders, frogs and certain toads as well as the many birds that breed or look for food at the water's edge.

In littoral regions where there is pronounced wave action, so that plant growth is minimal, the fauna is unusual in many respects. Here the habits of the animals resemble those of species living in running water, which of course is also in constant motion. But in contrast to the situation in streams, the direction of flow of the water on lake shores is quite complex, and as a result the organisms in the wave zone cannot adapt to it by such simple means. Either they withdraw from the region of water movement by burrowing into the bottom, as many midge larvae do, or they resist the current by attaching firmly to stones or other solid surfaces in the manner of certain snails and caddis-fly larvae. Those animals that lie on the surface of the sand have very broad cases or shells so that they are less likely to be rolled over by the water. An especially good example of this tactic is given by the larva of the caddis fly *Molanna*, which is often encountered on sandy shores exposed to waves.

On deeper parts of the lake bottom hardly any of these littoral animals are to be found, and the plants too disappear at increasing depths. The reasons for this marked change in the community are light, water temperature, and under certain circumstances the oxygen content of the water.

At greater depths the light grows steadily dimmer and changes in spectral composition; just above the region of complete darkness it is blue-green. But all animals, even those that prefer twilight or darkness, depend on light for their existence. Animal communities are more profoundly altered, the deeper the part of the lake they inhabit. Light provides the energy by which plant matter is synthesized from the nutrients dissolved in the water, and the plants are the direct or indiret food source for all the animals. In the deeper water, where there is not enough light for photosynthesis, there is a fundamental change in the food chain; the animals living here eat the remains of dead plants and other animals from higher parts of the water. Most of them, then, are omnivorous, and only a few predators inhabit the profundal lake bottom.

Another significant factor in the composition of lake communities is the oxygen supply, which is closely related to the temperature and the productivity of the lake. In many deeper temperate-zone lakes, the profundal water has a temperature of about 4°C all year, whereas the mass of water above it warms up in summer and cools off in winter. The fluctuation in temperature during a year is especially pronounced in the top few meters of a lake. This highly variable layer is separated from the constant-temperature deeper waters by the thermocline, a boundary region in which the water rapidly becomes colder with increasing depth. In a lake with a summer temperature profile of this sort, the surface water (the epilimnion) does not mix with that below the thermocline (the hypolimnion) because of the difference in density, even when strong winds are blowing across the surface. Such layering can persist for several months.

For profundal animals this means that the oxygen they use during these months is not replenished by circulation from above; they must manage with the oxygen dissolved in the deep water at the time the layering is established. This would be quite sufficient for the larger animals in this zone, if they were its only inhabitants. But this is not always the case; there are also microorganisms which can use up oxygen in decomposing the remains of other organisms. Much of the organic detritus is already broken down in the epilimnion, so that the critical factor determining the oxygen supply in the hypolimnion is the quantity that fails to be decomposed above. The organic residue that reaches the bottom is less, the deeper the lake (i.e., the greater the distance a dead organism has to fall) and the lower the velocity of sinking. In deep lakes there is less organic detritus on the bottom and hence a better oxygen supply for the profundal animals.

The population densities on the bottom of a deep, well-oxygenated lake are small, but there are a large number of different species. The low density is brought about by the meager food supply. The main bottom-dwellers here are chironomid larvae (*Tanytarsus* and others), the snail *Bithynia tentaculata*, some species of the clam *Pisidium*, and small crustaceans and hydrachnids. In the profundal zones of lakes in northern Europe and North America there are crustaceans like *Pontoporeia affinis*, *Mysis relicta* and *Saduria entomon*, all relics from the late Ice Age. On the bottoms of

Fig. 18-13. The three most important lake habitats: the shore or littoral zone, the profundal benthic zone, and the profundal and limnetic open water.

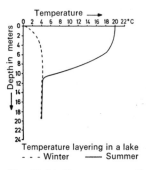

Fig. 18-14. Temperature of lake water at different depths in summer and in winter.

▷
Some examples of organisms living in the littoral zone or at the surface of a lake.
Top, left to right: Water strider (*Gerris lacustris*) on the water surface.—Larva of a mosquito (*Culex*), hanging by its respiratory tube from the surface.—Predaceous diving beetle (*Dytiscus*), which breaks through the water surface with the tip of the abdomen to renew its supply of air.
Middle, left to right: Water flea (*Daphnia*).—Spherical algae (*Volvox*).—Copepod (*Cyclops*) with egg sacks.—Rotifer (*Brachionus*) with eggs.
Bottom left: The freshwater polyp *Hydra* with buds (young polyps).
Bottom right: Hydrachnid.

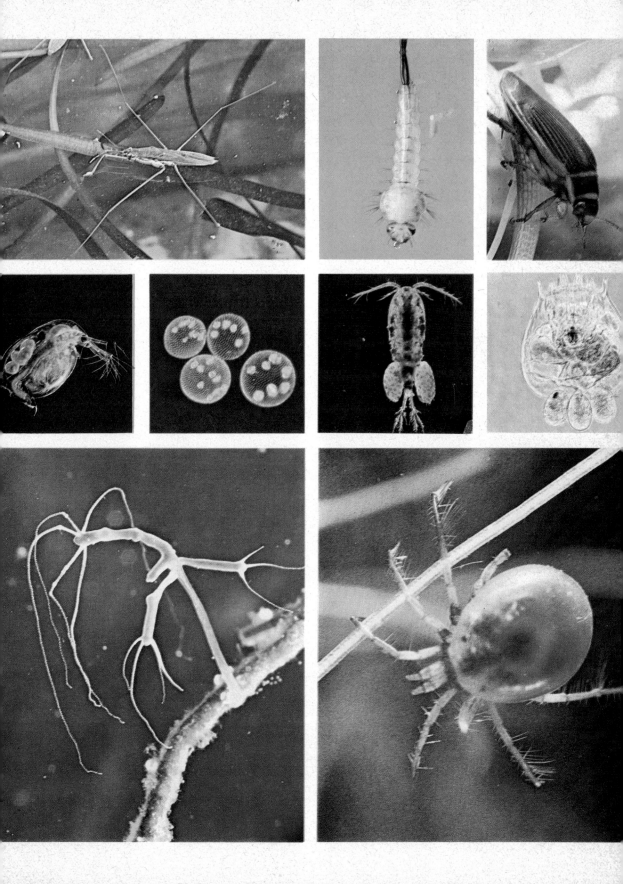

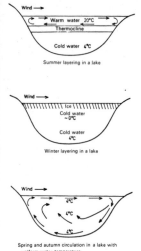

Fig. 18-15. Layering and circulation in a lake in regions of warm summers and cold winters.

◁

Running waters at different altitudes:
Top left: Water from the melting edge of a glacier (Svartisen glacier, northern Norway).—Right: Alpine brook (New Zealand) fed by cold rivulets from glaciers.
Middle left: Foothill river at an altitude over 1000 m, with little water because of high evaporation loss in the dry climate (Peru).—Right: Foothill river at the same altitude with a high volume-flow rate.
Bottom left: Foothill river with low water level (high evaporative loss in dry climate; Patagonia).—Right: Shallow lowland river (Scandinavia) with high volume-flow rate.

particularly deep lakes there also live cave animals such as the crustacean *Niphargus* and certain nematodes. The profundal benthos of the oldest lakes on earth forms a community descended from an ancient Tertiary fauna. Where the oxygen supply in the depths is especially good there are certain bottom-dwelling fish, like the burbot (*Lota lota*), which feed on the other bottom animals.

There is a great difference between thsee and the profundal communities in lakes where there is a lack of oxygen. In the latter case, the number of species is small but each is very abundant. Most typical are larvae of the midge *Chironomus* and various species of mud worms (*Tubifex*, *Limnodrilus*). As predators, there are often huge swarms of larvae of the alder fly *Sialis lutaria*.

In most cases the layering of a lake is not permanent. As the surface layer cools off mixing of the water becomes more extensive, until eventually there is circulation throughout the lake, driven by the friction of the wind on the surface. During this period the oxygen content in the depths is restored to its maximum level. In the winter that follows a reverse layering can develop, with cold water above and warmer below; again, the restricted circulation brings about a reduction in oxygen in the depths. In the spring there is another "overturn," or period of thorough circulation, and this is followed by reestablishment of the summer stratification. This alternation between layering and circulation is a vital factor for the profundal communities; food produced in the epilimnion during the summer months is brought to them by the fall overturn, and both periods of circulation renew the supply of oxygen. Without these periodic overturns there could probably be no life in the depths.

Profundal animals, like those of the littoral zone, tend to keep to the bottom or some other firm substrate. The limnetic zone, on the other hand, offers no such supports, and all the organisms living there must have some way of keeping themselves from sinking, in order to stay where the light is bright enough. The most important and diverse limnetic community is that composed of the delicate, small to microscopic plants and animals which are only slightly heavier than the water. These comprise the "plankton"; they include algae, bacteria and a great variety of small animals.

It is particularly important for the algae to float near the surface, for they have a direct requirement for light and are to a great extent incapable of independent motion. The fact that they are small permits them, like dust particles, to remain suspended or to sink only slowly. Some species compensate for their negative buoyancy by the inclusion of oil droplets and gas bubbles; sinking is also slowed because their various complicated shapes have a "parachute" effect. The fact that the algae are passively suspended in this way is important to the planktonic animals—protozoans, rotifers and countless small crustaceans—that feed upon them, for they sweep them into filtering devices along with the water and strain them out.

The planktonic animals, of course, can also keep themselves from sinking and can move through the water to some extent. Many species follow the daily alternation between light and darkness by vertical migrations; in the evening they move toward the surface and in the early morning they withdraw to greater depths. These migrations are primarily controlled by light, as the animals "chase" it up to the surface at nightfall and flee from it in the morning; but we do not ket know just what is the function of these regular changes of position.

The zooplankton community includes chiefly rotifers (Rotatoria), water fleas (Cladocera) and copepod crustaceans, particulary those of the order Gymnoplea and the family Cyclopidae. Whereas most of these feed on bacteria and algae, some also swallow other planktonic animals. Among these predators are the large rotifer *Asplanchna*, the wonderfully transparent crustacean *Leptodora kindtii*, which is about a centimeter long, and the equally striking water flea *Bythotrephes longimanus*, with its long spine for a tail. Other predators are certain copepods and the only planktonic insect, the larva of the midge *Corethra* or *Chaoborus*. The latter is transparent, like *Leptodora*, but at both the front and back of its body it has a small air bubble, so that it can float horizontally in the water without moving, practically invisible to its prey.

The amount of plankton in a lake can be extraordinarily large, depending upon the concentration in the water of the nutrients the algae need for synthesis. When planktonic organisms have died, they sink to the depths and feed the bottom-dwellers; the quantity of plankton also affects the oxygen balance in the depths. Sewage cleaned insufficiently or not at all often provides an excess of nutrients and produces the phenomenon of "eutrophication," which affects the communities and in fact all the biological processes in the lake.

The fauna of the limnetic zone

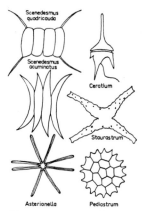

Fig. 18-16. Some algae of the so-called "net plankton," so shaped as to slow their rate of sinking.

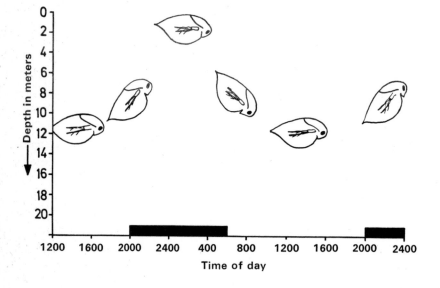

Fig. 18-17. Daily migration of zooplankton between the surface (at night: dark bar) and the depths (during the day). The diagram represents the movement of a water flea (*Daphnia*).

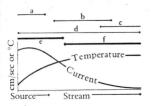

Fig. 18-18. Schematic diagram of the ranges colonized by various animal species in a river.

Animals at the inter-face between water and air

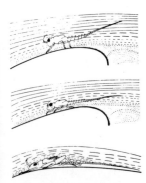

Fig. 18-19. Technique by which a Mayfly larva (*Baetis*) keeps its hold in a stream at different veloci-ties.

The limnetic community comprises not only plankton, but all the swimming animals (the nekton), which in fresh-water lakes consist of only a few species of fish. The most important of these are the whitefish and other members of the subfamily Coregoninae, mentioned above, which feed upon the zooplankton. In addition there is the lake trout (*Salmo trutta lacustris*), a predator which eats other fish. The fish of the nekton are all dependent upon the plankton—even the predators, for they eat the plank-ton eaters. In this sense one could include almost all the fish in a lake in the nekton, for even the carnivorous fish that tend to stay near the shore feed upon plankton as juveniles.

The whitefish *Coregonus albula* and *Coregonus wartmanni* are distinctly adapted to plankton-feeding even after reaching sexual maturity. When *C. wartmanni* hatches from its egg, it has not exhausted its nutrient supply, but retains enough to live for days. These first days, during which it makes its initial attempts to hunt planktonic crustaceans, are critical; at first it is successful only about three times out of a hundred, and it must be in-cessantly active if it is to obtain sufficient food. But all the behavioral traits it needs for a successful hunt are inborn, and its performance soon improves with practice. After only a few days the young fish succeeds 20% of the time.

Just at the interface between water and air, directly on and under the surface of the water, are associated a number of animals; for these the thin film of superficial water under surface tension is a vital factor. Animals from the two adjacent habitats, water and air, meet here. The aerial animals are the most conspicuous, those which spend the greater part of their lives on the water surface and are superbly adapted to this way of life. Water striders (Gerridae), water treaders (Mesoveliidae) and other water bugs, short-winged beetles of the genus *Stenus*, and certain spiders such as *Dolomedes* hunt here. The surface film provides all these animals with a firm enough substrate that they can move about without difficulty. Water striders of the genus *Gerris* can even jump on the surface, first making a little depression gainst which they push themselves off. For such an animal, the water surface is as safe as solid ground is for us. But if household detergents or other chemicals lower the surface tension, all of them—even the smallest species—sink and drown. Zoologists were there-fore most astonished to discover that the small beetle *Stenus* itself sprays detergent chemicals onto the water surface; as a result of the lowered sur-face tension it is propelled across the water without sinking. In this way it can get out of an uncomfortable situation much more rapidly than by walking.

The whirligig beetles (family Gyrinidae) are really interface animals, for they swim at the water surface in such a way that their horizontally divided eyes can scan their surroundings both above and below the water. Obstacles projecting above the water surface are detected not with the eyes but with the antennae, which lie partially on the surface and feel the slightest elevation of the surface film in the vicinity of an object. Chief among the water animals which, in a sense, cling to the surface from below are the water bugs called backswimmers (Notonectidae). The preferred orientation of their bodies suits this way of life, for they turn their "faces" to the water surface (the region that most concerns them) and anchor themselves there with the tarsi of the anterior and middle legs and the tip of the abdomen; in this position they can also take in air. When in danger they instantly dive to the depths, and the whirligig beetles adopt this method of escape as well.

All the members of this surface-film community share one characteristic: they feed on animals which fall onto the water surface. They are predators that detect their prey by the surface vibrations it produces.

In springs, the ground water emerges from below ground and runs off on the surface. In so doing, it washes out a more or less uniformly deep bed, depending upon the velocity of the current (which in turn depends upon the slope of the terrain) and the amount of water (emerging from the spring itself and added by tributaries). Over this bed flows a brook or creek at first, and eventually, after several brooks have merged, the stream becomes a river. The courses of streams change only slowly; they are characteristic features of a landscape and themselves contribute, by continual erosion and sedimentation, to shaping the terrain. Cutting out valleys, they subdivide chains of mountains; in the flatland they deposit their load of sediment and at their mouths they can build up deltas that extend far into the sea.

As animal habitats, streams are characterized primarily by the regular variation of two vital factors. One of these critical quantities is temperature. The water that emerges in a spring is at the temperature of ground water, which is the same all the year round and corresponds to the average temperature for the year in that location. But only a few meters away from the spring the summer warming or winter cooling of the running water becomes appreciable, and with increasing distance the amplitude of the annual temperature fluctuation increases rapidly. Starting from zero amplitude at the spring itself, at a distance of 3000 meters it can be as much as 15°C (Fig. 18-20), and at still greater distances the temperature approaches that of lake surfaces, which vary between 0°C (ice) and about 20°C. Many other properties of the water are a function of temperature, in particular oxygen content, rate of chemical reactions, density and viscosity. Thus all these factors fluctuate in parallel with temperature, over a steadily increasing range from the upper reaches of the stream to the lower.

The second critical factor in the running-water (lotic) habitat is the current velocity. In the discussion of currents and oxygen (see Chapter 3) we have already given some idea of its significance in the environment of aquatic animals. The current, too, changes in a predictable way with distance from the source. But the current in open water is of direct importance only to the fish; all the animals of the benthos or bottom community,

Running water, by J. Illies

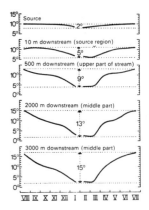

Fig. 18-20. Schematic diagram of the annual temperature fluctuation in a stream at increasing distances from the source.

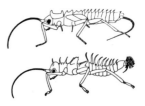

Fig. 18-21. Convergent evolution of spines on the dorsal surface in moss-dwelling stonefly larvae. Above, *Taeniopteryx hubaulti*. Below, a corresponding species of the family Gripopterygidae.

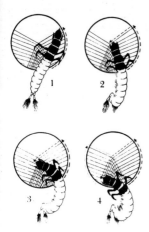

Fig. 18-22. Caddis-fly larva (*Hydropsyche*) spinning the net with which it catches prey.

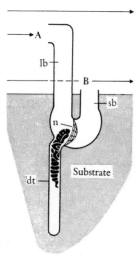

Fig. 18-23. Diagram of the case of the tropical caddis-fly larva *Macronema*. A-B, incurrent and excurrent openings, respectively, for water to flow through; lb and sb, long and short branches, respectively, of the case; dt, dwelling tube containing larva; n, net.

those living on the mud bottom, on plants, or on the surfaces of stones are affected only by the velocity of flow just next to the bottom or the stone. This is considerably less than that of the open water, and it decreases steadily at points further downstream, as is evident in the lower capacity to transport materials. In the mountains loose stones bigger than one's fist can be rolled along and carried with the water; in the more slowly flowing hill streams even quite fine grains sink to the bottom, forming a bed of gravel and sand. In the large rivers, finally, even the finest mud particles lie on the bottom for long periods of time, and mud banks housing a distinctive fauna may develop.

The gradual change of these two factors along the course of a stream produces a longitudinal zonation, so that sections at different distances from the source have different "climatic" peculiarities which must affect the lives of the animals and plants living there. As Fig. 18-18 shows, various species of animal (indicated there by the letters *a* through *f*) find specific optimal regions along the two gradients; their distributions are limited to the parts of the stream with conditions to which they are particularly well adapted.

In the water of the spring lives a community adapted to the chemical characteristics of newly emerged ground water and to slight or non-existent temperature fluctuations. In our latitudes, this constant temperature lies between about 6°C and 10°; for many animals which are unsuited to cold conditions and were widely distributed during the warm inter-glacial periods in central Europe, these springs are a last refuge. Among such relicts from earlier ages in cool sub-alpine mountain springs are the gastropods *Lauria cylindracea* and *Azeka menkeana*, which here have found the only place in the region that does not freeze even during the harshest winter. On the other hand, even in the warmest summer months the temperature of the spring hardly rises appreciably, so that we also find relicts of the glacial epochs, which were widespread when ice covered much of Europe but now can live only in these springs or in the high mountains and far north. The alpine turbellarian *Planaria alpina* is one of the best known of these "Ice Age animals" in sub-alpine springs.

In the brook (rhithral) region the limiting factors are the low temperatures and the force of the rapid current. The latter in particular, which can carry objects at more than a meter per second, represents a considerable departure in this habitat from the "norm," the conditions optimal for life. Animals must have special modifications in body structure and in behavior, if they are to maintain themselves despite the flowing water and not be washed away.

And in fact the typical brook-dwellers (which may be collectively termed the "rhithrium") have evolved many such adaptations. Very often these take the form of suckers, which attach the body firmly to the surfaces of rocks. Frog larvae in tropical mountain brooks have suckers on the lower lip, the larvae of net-winged midges (Blepharoceridae) have six round suckers on the underside of the body, and those of black flies (Simuliidae) have one at the hind end. Some Mayfly larvae (*Rhithrogena*) form an attachment surface with the abdominal gills, laid over one another like a fan. Isopodlike water-beetle larvae of the family Psephenidae have made their whole bodies into single suckers, which old them firmly to the substrate. The same method was used by the now-extinct Rhine Mayfly *Prosopistoma foliaceum* to attach to rocks in the stream, so successfully that it could not be removed even by a violent effort. Hooks and bristles on the body also help to anchor animals between stones and branches of moss; the larvae of certain mountain stoneflies, not necessarily closely related, are similarly adapted in this way (Fig. 18-21). The long-toed beetles of the family Dryopidae are so called because of the much elongated claws at the tips of the tarsi, which anchor them in cracks in the rock; the legs and abdominal feet of many caddis-fly larvae (for example, the genus *Rhyacophila*) are also equipped with effective "crampons," with which they can brace themselves against any current. Finally, many rhithral animals have evolved the ability to glue themselves to stone surfaces by sticky secretions and threads; they rope themselves in place rather like mountain climbers, and even in the strongest currents are not torn from their places. If a black-fly larva of the genus *Simulium* loses its hold in the current despite its sucker, it can still save itself; it has a thread of silk as an emergency "life-line," and can pull itself slowly back along it to the original position.

Even the non-motile stages of many brook-dwelling species, the eggs and pupal cases, are anchored by gelatinous or silky masses so that they are not washed away. In some water insects the individual eggs are actually provided with bristles, anchor threads, sticky rings and other mechanical attachment devices, so that they automatically remain between sand grains and on irregularities of the brook bed.

Some rhithral animals depend on streamlining and appropriate behavioral mechanisms to counteract the current. Mayflies of the genus *Baetis* respond to the current prevailing in their habitat at any particular time by holding themselves more or less close to the substrate (Fig. 18-19), so that they can stand upright when the current is weak and yet not be swept away when it becomes stronger. But they do not always succeed in keeping their hold on the stones as they move about; then the drift downstream for some meters before they again find a foothold.

But the current is not entirely a disadvantage to the brook dwellers. Having succeeded in anchoring themselves or otherwise maintaining a favorable position in the flowing water, they can make use of the steady stream of food it carries to them. There are many nutritious fragments there: insects that have fallen or been washed into the water, half-decomposed bits of leaves carried down from the higher parts of the brook, and in particular the drifting organisms of the stream itself, algae and small animals that have been torn loose by the current. This drifting debris is the food of all the brook-dwellers which have developed means of catch-

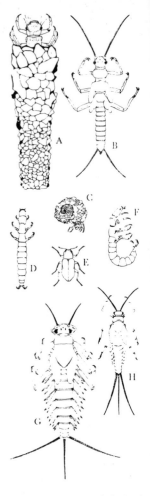

Fig. 18-24. Typical rhithral insects. Slender body form, gills poorly developed or absent.
A, C. Caddis-fly larvae in cases of stone; B. Stonefly larvae; D, F. Predatory, free-moving caddis-fly larvae; E. Dryopid beetle; G, H. Mayfly larvae.
All these animals live in a high mountain tributary of the Amazon; but the same life-form types are found in the mountain brooks on all continents.

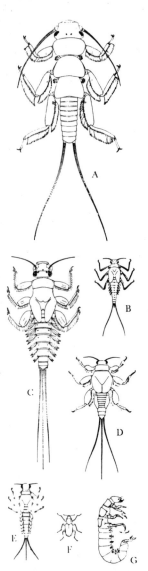

Fig. 18-25. Typical pota-
mal insects. Body and legs
appear broadened; the gills
are better developed, and
often there are accessory
gills as well.
A. Stonefly larva; B-E.
Mayfly larvae; F. Dryopid
beetle; G. Free-living,
predatory caddis-fly larva.
All these animals live in a
tributary of the Amazon
in Peru; but the same life-
form types are found in the
rivers on all continents.

ing and separating out food particles from the water. The animals called
"filter-feeders" (an ecological rather than systematic category) are masters
of this approach. Among them are the fresh-water sponges, which feed on
microscopically small elements in the stream. The black-fly larvae are an
impressive sight, with their "tentacles" stretched out into the current;
these are actually mouthparts, and they fish out of the water all the useful
bits of food. These larvae are so completely adapted to feeding in this way
that they would starve in still water.

The method "invented" by black-fly larvae of the genus *Hydropsyche*
(Fig. 18-22) is astonishing. This larva spins a fine-meshed net through
which the current flows, and then lurks like a spider in its hiding place,
waiting for a drifting animal to be caught in the net; then it is seized and
eaten. The most fantastic—almost unbelievable—development of this
method is found in tropical relatives of *Hydropsyche* which were discovered
recently by the zoologist Werner Sattler in the Amazon region. In the
gravel of the jungle brooks they construct automatic filtration arrangements so efficient that the most minute clumps of organic molecules, only
a few thousandths of a millimeter in diameter, can be caught. The net
spun by these insect larvae has a mesh of five by twenty thousandth of a
millimeter, and is this considerably finer than any that can be produced by
industry.

Another advantage of life in rapidly flowing water is that there is a
constant fresh supply of oxygen to breathe. In fact, there is more than
enough, so that the animals need only small gills, and many insect larvae
in mountain brooks manage without any gills at all, breathing through
the soft membranes joining the segments of their bodies. The low temperature of the brook water acts in the same direction; that is, cold water
can hold a greater concentration of dissolved oxygen than warmer water.
Brook animals are not only tolerant of, but actually dependent upon, this
very high oxygen concentration. If the water warms up or the current
stops, such an animal will suffocate in a short time; both of these can
happen, for example, if such an animal is removed from its natural habitat
and put in an aquarium for observation. The species most thoroughly
adapted to high oxygen concentration, such as larvae of the Mayfly
Epeorus, die after only a few minutes when placed in still water. Other
species have evolved a sort of "emergency respiration" to deal with such
events; they can move their gills through the water.

In summary, it is apparent that in the brook region of streams there
live only communities of animals with extreme adaptations to the great
water velocity and particular temperature relations in their environment.
These animals are of characteristic "life-form types," which unmistakably
stamp brook communities as such in the mountain brooks all over the
world. Figure 18-24 shows insects—most of them in the larval stages—
from a high mountain brook in South America (a tributary of the Amazon
at an altitude of 3000 m); at first glance, mountain-brook insects in

Europe or Australia look quite similar. The slender body with a rigid, bristly appearance and large claws, the small size or absence of gills, and the heavy stone cases of the caddis flies are typical features of all such communities.

Comparison of rhithral animals with those characteristic of the river region (the potamium; Fig. 18-25) immediately reveals the difference in their adaptations. Since the temperature in the rivers is higher, and thus the oxygen concentration may be lower, the potamal animals have larger gills, and in many species there are even accessory gills on other parts of the body. The body is distinctly flattened; long fringes of hair on the back edges of the legs enhance this flattening, which helps the animals to press themselves close to the substrate and divert the current. It is true that the current velocity near a river bed is usually less than that in a brook, but when the water is high the brook bed offers better shelter; the river dwellers have no place to hide, and can keep from being swept away only by flattening themselves against the river bottom.

A streamlined shape offers the least resistance to the current. Fish, as well as the animals of the benthos, have matched their body form to the particular conditions of their brook or river habitats. Animals living in rapidly flowing water are more or less circular in cross section, and have a highly developed body musculature. In order to hold a steady position with respect to the river bank, a trout may have to swim against the current with a speed of more than a meter per second; in fact, trout are able to keep up such rapid swimming for hours, staying in one place and snapping up the food that drifts past. In more slowly flowing or standing waters the fish need considerably less muscular strength, and accordingly their body form is more flattened and "narrow-chested."

Curiously enough, the fish of fast-flowing water, which are good enough swimmers to station themselves wherever they like in a stream and would be capable of swimming upstream from the mouth to the source, are strictly adapted to narrow regions of the current-velocity and temperature range. In Fig. 18-18 the ranges marked a through c correspond to the preferred regions of certain fish species: a = trout (*Salmo trutta*), b = grayling (*Thymallus thymallus*), and c = barbel (*Barbus barbus*). Fisheries biologists have long recognized this principle of fish distribution and have used the names of the typical fish to designate the different longitudinal sections of streams. In Europe these sections, from the source to the mouth of the stream, used to be as follows: trout region, grayling region, barbel region, bream region, and perch/flounder region (Fig. 18-28). Now these regions are usually lumped, according to the groups to which the fish belong, so that streams are divided into a salmonid region and a cyprinid region; trout and grayling belong to the Salmonidae, and barbel and bream to the Cyprinidae.

These fish regions also delimit different ranges of distribution of the benthos—the insect larvae, crustaceans, molluscs and hydrachnids. All

▷
These photographs indicate the vast extent of tropical rivers:
Above: bank of the Rio Negro, one of the tributaries of the Amazon.
Below: Native women in piroges on the Congo. Some characteristic animals of tropical-river habitats.

these, like the fish, choose to stay in particular ranges of the gradients of environmental factors, and as a result there are typical benthic animals in each of the longitudinal zones of the streams. The fish regions, like the terms rhithral and potamal region, denote the habitats of "true" communities—the rhithrium and the potamium—in the sense of Moebius' definition (see the Introduction to Section III). As the Belgian limnologist Marcel Huet has pointed out, these habitats are also distinguished by more externally obvious characteristics, so that an expert can pick them out just by looking at a map. The slope of the terrain plays an especially important role, and the shape of the valley through which the stream flows is also decisive. The course of a mountain brook is quite straight, whereas in the grayling region the stream begins to wind in "meanders" and in the potamal (cyprinid) region there are dead-end branches of the river and "ox-bow" ponds formed by meanders isolated from the main stream (Fig. 18-28).

Since the different ecosystems in running waters are determined by ranges of temperature and current velocity, it is understandable that the same regions are to be found at corresponding altitudes throughout the world. Toward the equator, of course, the limiting altitude shifts upward, so that the brook region is limited to higher mountain regions and eventually is found only above 3000 meters; toward the poles, the potamal region is displaced steadily further down into the flatland. Figure 18-26 summarizes these relationships in a diagram. But the division of running water into two great habitats really does not do justice to the diversity of animal types that appear there. Smaller animal communities can be distinguished in patches of moss and in the deposits of sand and mud in a brook. In the river region we find a variety of quite different communities side by side, in a mosaic arranged according to the local conditions of water flow and the nature of the stream bed. In particular, the regions near the banks are clearly distinct from the more central part of the bed.

In the lower reaches of the rivers, which flow into the sea, the effect of the tides and the associated occasional rise in salinity becomes apparent. A zone of brackish water is formed, where life-forms of the ocean and of fresh water meet. There is essentially no special fauna of brackish running water; a few fresh-water species, such as the perch *Acerina cernua* and various European and North American sticklebacks, are robust enough to withstand brackish water, while some marine fish like flounders, salmon and sturgeon can swim upriver—usually in order to spawn there.

Running waters are old habitats, in which conditions have remained uniform for long periods of time (see the third ecological principle in the Introduction to this Section); hence their communities are mature and stable. It is true that current and temperature in the brooks and rivers have changed profoundly several times during the last million years of the earth's history (for example, during the Ice Age), but in rivers extending for considerable distances the brook community always had the oppor-

◁
Top left: Herons and other birds on the shore of a marginal lake in the "varzea" of Amazonia.
Top right: Jacanas (here the African species) live on the floating leaves of water plants.
Middle: Hippopotamus (left) and crocodile (right) in the White Nile.
Bottom left: The catfish *Farlowella*, one of the typical animals of Amazonian clearwater brooks.
Bottom right: Tapir, the only large animal in the Amazonian jungle, by the blackwater of the Rio Negro.

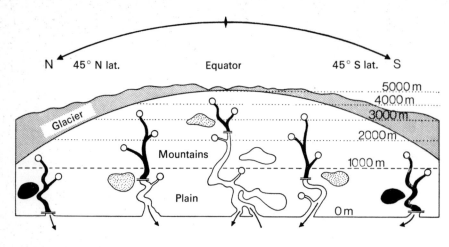

Fig. 18-26. Schematic diagram of the distribution of the brook community (black) and the river community (white) over the earth, as a function of latitude and altitude. The separate community of standing waters (dotted) appears only at temperate latitudes and in tropical high mountain lakes; at other latitudes it closely resembles the river community (in the tropics) or the brook community (polar region).

tunity to move toward the source during the warm periods and down toward the flatland when the climate became cold, so as to keep its own environment optimal. Similarly, the brook community could move downstream to warmer zones during cold periods, and return to the original position during the subsequent warm epoch. Thus wherever sufficiently extensive migrations and displacments of the fauna were possible—as was the case in North America, with the long chains of mountains running from north to south—a fauna comprising large numbers of species and forms was able to maintain itself through the ages. In North America most genera and families of the lotic fauna contain three or four times as many species as do their counterparts in Europe. On the other hand, the European high-mountain zones were so limited, and they were so strongly affected during the Ice Age, that the high-brook animals adapted to cold conditions split up into many neighboring species, each restricted to a specific mountain range (the Alps, Pyrenees, Caucasus, and the mountains of Scandinavia).

By now, thanks to thorough limnological investigations involving both experiments and field observations, the fundamental aspects of the ecological relationships in lotic communities are known. A stratum of producers, consisting of small algae (especially diatoms), fungi and bacteria, provides the basis for the circulation of nutrient substances, either by direct conversion of light energy in photosynthesis or by decomposition of the fragments of leaves and other organic matter washed into the stream. Higher aquatic plants here—in contrast to the situation in standing waters —play only a very subordinate role. This producer level supports a diverse and much subdivided chain of consumers. At the end of the chain are predatory fish and insects and other terminal consumers, including man insofar as he enters the aquatic cycle by fishing. The terminal consumers and all other members of the community which do not serve as food for a higher consumer level are recycled after death by the activity of decomposers, most of them bacteria (Fig. 18-27).

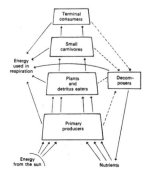

Fig. 18-27. Diagram of the flow of energy (left) and the transport of matter (right) in the ecosystem. Dashed arrows: joint operation of both phenomena.

The first person to investigate in all its detail the way that conversion of energy and the circulation of matter are woven into the overall web of interactions of a brook community near the source was the American ecologist H. J. Odum, in the late 1950's at Silver Springs, Florida. It proved possible to obtain precise data, so that we now have a scientifically exact idea of how the energy in the sun's radiation and the basic organic matter produced by the plants are passed on through the food cycle during the year, and how they are used and transformed at the different trophic levels. With such insight into the mechanisms operating in lotic communities, we may hope to escape the damage to our streams that the current environmental crisis threatens to cause—for only when one knows the causes and course of a disease can one expect to heal it.

Tropical rivers, by
R. Geisler

In the tropics of South America and Africa there are streams of enormous size. In the high tropics of the southern Asian continent there are also many rivers that far exceed the dimensions common in Europe. In central Europe rivers like the Elbe and the Rhine are considered quite large, but the amount of water that flows through them is relatively small in comparison with these tropical rivers. For example, the rate of flow in the Elbe near Hamburg, averaged over the year, is 750 cubic meters of water per second, while that in the Rhine at the border between Germany and Holland is 2200 cubic meters per second. By contrast, the corresponding value for the Orinoco at its mouth is 14,000 cubic meters, and at the mouth of the Amazon an average of 180,000 cubic meters of water per second flow into the sea. Among the tributaries of the Amazon, the Rio Madeira moves 19,100, the Rio Negro 25,000, and the Rio Tapajós 5600 cubic meters per second. In Africa, the Congo and the Niger lead the list, with 42,000 and 5700 cubic meters per second, respectively. The Nile, the longest river in Africa, flows in large part through deserts and there loses so much water that it can deliver only 2790 cubic meters per second to water the oasis bordering it in Egypt. The Nile is far surpassed by two Asian rivers—the Mekong, with 15,900, and the Irawadi, with 14,000 cubic meters per second.

Of all the rivers on earth, that with the largest volume of water is the Amazon; even among its tributaries, seventeen are longer than the Rhine. It offers the most useful example of the ecological situation in tropical streams. It is justly referred to as "Rio Mar" (Ocean River). Its enormous catchment area comprises more than five and a half million square kilometers—about a third of the whole continent of South America. Here are found all the water types that can be encountered in the large-river regions of Africa and in the southern part of Asia, influenced by monsoon winds. Characteristics of the tropical lowland climate are uninterrupted heat, with the temperature during the coldest month averaging more than 18°Cs and annual precipitation of at least 750 mm (though this is far exceeded in most regions).

In tropical rivers the water temperature lies between 27.5° and 30.5°C,

almost without exception. The variation between day and night amounts
to less than one degree. This uniform high temperature enhances and accelerates all the chemical and biological processes by which matter is cir-
culated, and thus the physiological reactions of all aquatic organisms from
the planktonic algae to the fish. The high temperature has an effect comparable to that of pressing steadily on the gas pedal of a car. It is associated
with metabolic rates about four or five times higher than those in the
rivers of central Europe. For example, egg development in tropical
characid fish requires only about forty-eight hours, whereas in the related
cyprinid fish of European waters it takes an average of six to eight days.

The temperature difference of about twenty degrees between tropical
and central European rivers, and its effect on all biological processes, make
it impossible to apply the same measures to the two. For example, if
analysis of the water reveals a phosphate content of thirty millionths of a
gram, that would be a very good supply of this nutrient in a tropical
stream but a deficiency in a cool one. The high temperatures of the tropics
ensure that nutrients are taken up and incorporated by organisms almost
as fast as they enter the water or are released by decomposition, so that
they are free in the water for only a short time and may hardly be measurable at all.

In addition to climatic, seasonal changes such as dry and rainy periods,
there are also chemicophysical properties of tropical rivers which are revealed by the quite different coloration or turbidity of the different
streams. In South America there are three types of water:

1. Rivers with very turbid water of a light brownish clay color, called
"whitewater." Among these are the Amazon, the Rio Madeira and the
Rio Purús.

2. Rivers with clear water, lacking suspended clay particles and having
a yellowish-green to olive-green color. This is called "clearwater," and
such rivers include the Rio Tapajós and Rio Xingú.

3. Rivers in which the water is also clear, with no suspended substances to make it turbid, but with dissolved humic substances which give
the water a brown color and the name "blackwater." The Rio Negro,
the "dark river," is one of these.

This sort of pronounced differentiation of the water naturally implies
ecological differences. The same classification applies outside South
America, in the humid tropics of Africa and in eastern Asia. The Congo,
for example, is a clearwater river with contributions from blackwater.
The largest rivers in continental southeastern Asia—the Irawadi in Burma,
the Menam in Thailand, and the Mekong in Vietnam—are typical whitewater rivers. What is true of Amazonia, then, has general implications for
all the streams of the tropics. The differences between the water types are
based on geological, climatic and edaphic factors.

The geologically youngest rivers—for example, the Amazon and the
Rio Madeira—are of the whitewater type. The rivers from which they

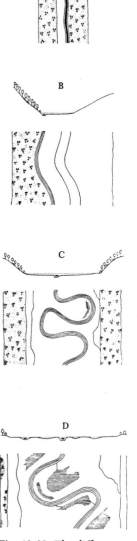

Fig. 18-28. The different
courses of a stream in its
valley correspond to the
different "fish regions"; in
each case the cross section
is above and the view from
above beneath it.
A. Trout region; B. Gray-
ling region; C. Barbel
region; D. Bream region.

take their source are in the high Andes. There the rainy periods, which bring about 2000 mm precipitation per year, cause a great amount of soil erosion. East of the Bolivian capital La Paz is the catchment area of the Rio Beni, which flows into the Rio Madeira and eventually into the Amazon; here the "lunar" mountains show the extent to which water shapes the terrain. When the brooks cut their beds several centimeters deeper each year during the rainy season, huge amounts of soil materials are carried away. In the dry seasons the brooks arising from springs to feed the white-water rivers are clear, without sediments, but during a flight over the eastern chain of the Andes and down into the lowlands one can see that even when there is little rain, the rivers in the last and just preceding mountain chains become loaded with suspended material by lateral erosion and are colored a brown-red when they enter the broad plain of Amazonia. A cubic meter of such "clay rivers," for which the term "whitewater" hardly seems appropriate, contains up to 1.5 kg of soil material; in the upper reaches of the Nile a content of 4 kg per cubic meter has been measured.

Fig. 18-29. Schematic cross section through a white-water river. 1. Actual stream bed; 2. Marginal lakes of the "varzea"; 3. Dry land which is never flooded.

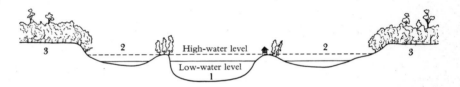

As a result, the water is so turbid that sunlight can penetrate it for only a few centimeters. A white porcelain disk dipped into the water can no longer be seen at a depth of thirty centimeters. Only a very thin layer of water near the surface, which is constantly being turned over, is well illuminated in whitewater rivers; the great mass of the water is completely dark. Consequently, there is no phytoplankton here, and there are no submerged higher plants.

In the middle and lower courses of the whitewater rivers, the beds are usually several kilometers wide, and along the edges the suspended particles are deposited in strips, depending upon the current and their grain size. When the water level falls, giant lakes—up to 100 km long and forty kilometers wide—can be isolated on either side of the river; during the next high-water season, they are again in communication with the main stream. These unstable marginal lakes in the flood region of the Amazon (the "varzea") are the most important habitats for plants and animals, and thus for the humans living in the region; because of the regular influx of quickly sedimenting substances the supply of nutrients here is adequate to support them. The Nile mud, too, a fresh layer of which is deposited every year, was for a long time the basis of life in Egypt.

In the marginal lakes along the tropical whitewater rivers the suspended particles sediment out to such an extent that sunlight can penetrate the water to depths of several meters. As a result, plants can grow there, and the establishment of a food chain extending from phytoplankton to fish is made possible. The most economically important fish—in Amazonia, for example, the osteoglossid *Arapaima gigas*, which can be as long as two meters and is thus the largest fresh-water fish—live in these marginal lakes or at least enter them and the brooks flowing into them occasionally to spawn, as do the characid *Triportheus* and other species. In relatively dry seasons strips of shoreline are exposed, and this recently flooded soil can be cultivated to produce rice, corn and jute without additional fertilization—in contrast to the extraordinarily infertile soils of the higher regions that are never flooded.

In these sediment-rich whitewater lakes there grows the well-known royal water lily (*Victoria regia*), the floating leaves of which can reach a diameter of a meter or more. Where the Amazonian whitewater flows slowly "floating meadows" can develop, growing far out from the shore into the open water and often encompassing an area over a hundred meters wide and several kilometers long. These consist of grass species such as *Paspalum* and *Echinochloa*; at their edges is often a band of true floating plants—for example, *Pistia* and the water hyacinth (*Eichhornia*), found in almost all tropical rivers. When the rate of flow suddenly increases large islands of these plants may be torn free and drift downstream.

The masses of organic matter produced in these floating meadows can be appreciated in dry seasons or when the water level is low. Then the trees along the shores are full of hanging, dried grass that grew when the water was high and could not follow as it receded. In tropical streams the floating meadows are the sites of most abundant life, highest productivity and best food supply. Up to 130,000 small animals of the sorts eaten by fish—for example, copepods, water fleas, and the larvae of Mayflies, midges and caddis flies—have been counted in a square meter. In the presence of such a feast the young characid fish grow rapidly. Between the masses of leaves and in the network of roots live the slender Gymnotid eels (Gymnotidae), particularly *Eigenmannia* and *Gymnotus*, as well as swamp eels (Synbranchidae) and catfish like *Otocinclus* and *Farlowella*, all of which eat the organisms living on the plants. Underwater plants are the basic food of the manatee (the mammalian genus *Trichechus*), which has been intensively hunted and as a result has already become quite rare; members of the Amazonian species in Brazil are appropriately given a local name meaning "fish-cattle."

The fish fauna in the region of floating meadows, *Utricularia*, and other underwater plants serves as food for the predatory fish of the open water, among them the arapaima and the notorious piranhas (Serrasalminae). Despite its ill-repute, however, of the roughly forty species of piranha only about five are dangerous to man, and then only at certain times—when they are raising their young or food is unusually scarce. In the open water and the marginal lakes they are joined by the fish-eating Amazon

Fig. 18-30. The fresh-water dolphin *Inia geoffrensis* of the Amazon.

dolphin (*Inia*). Outside the tropics, there are three other genera, each with one species, of fresh-water dolphin: the Ganges dolphin (*Platanista*) in the lower reaches of the Ganges, the La Plata dolphin (*Stenodelphis*) in southeastern South America, and the China dolphin (*Lipotes*) in the Yangtse Kiang. In the extremely murky water these mammals find their way not by vision but rather by hearing; they put out a continual sequence of sharp clicks and orient by the echo.

The main streams produce only small amounts of nutrients themselves, but the marginal lakes provide them with a variety of food in the form of washed-out plant and animal plankton and organic detritus. Hundreds of species of catfish, some of them as much as one and a half meters long, and detritus-eating characids like *Prochilodus* are typical of the whitewater fish fauna. In the dim light of the turbid water live barely pigmented catfish, whitish-gray trichomycterids, which burrow into the soft bottom mud during the day and at night swim into the open water in search of food; some species enter the gill chambers of resting large fish and suck blood from the vessels in the gills.

Fig. 18-31. Schematic cross section through a clearwater river.

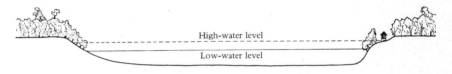

High-water level

Low-water level

The sources of clearwater rivers are usually in geologically ancient regions. There the ground is made up of hard granite and gneiss; since there are no particles that can be carried in suspension by the water, it remains transparently clear. Because they carry nothing which can sediment out, clearwater rivers do not form marginal lakes, nor do they leave fertile mud behind when their floods recede. The riverbed appears essentially the same regardless of the water level. For these reasons, clearwater rivers like the Rio Tapajós and the Rio Xingú, which can be up to thirty kilometers wide in their lower reaches, are considerably less well supplied with nutrients (one of which, in tropical waters, is calcium) than the whitewater rivers. But light passes through clearwater to depths of as much as seven meters, and in this respect conditions are much more favorable for plants; thus the phytomass here is about equal to that in whitewater. If the changes in water level during the course of a year are not too large (as is the case, for example, in tributaries of the Rio Tapajós) there develops in the clearwater a luxuriant submerged flora, in particular the nymphaeaceous *Cabomba*. This is associated with populations of small fishes of a density not to be found anywhere else; these include a great variety of characid species and cichlids.

But if the water level, following the annual climatic rhythm, changes over such a wide range as in the Rio Tapajós (as much as 7.1 meters) or the Rio Xingú (6.5 meters), higher water plants and algae cannot survive.

On the banks of such clearwater rivers, then, one finds only broad beaches covered with white sand that looks quite infertile. There are no floating meadows, since the concentration of nutrients is too low. In the broad lower reaches, if the current velocity slows to a few centimeters per second, conditions are best for the development of plankton in the well-illuminated water. Along the lower course of the Rio Tapajós there regularly occur "blooms" in which masses of blue-green algae of the genus *Anabaena* appear. In the open water of the South American clearwater rivers live swarms of delicate, transparent fresh-water herring (*Anchoa, Anchoviella*), which eat the plankton and in turn are preyed upon by the characid *Raphiodon*.

If the rain, in a permanently warm and humid climate, percolates through fairly thick layers of plant matter on the ground, and the soils are poorly aerated, the decomposition of organic matter produces dissolved or colloidal humic substances which give the water a characteristic brown color like that in the bog waters of cooler regions. Water of this sort, which in a glass looks rather like weak tea, in a large river appears deep black—hence the somewhat unfortunate term "blackwater." Examples of such rivers, apart from the Rio Negro, are certain tributaries of the Congo and various rivers in Malaysia. A cross section through the largest blackwater river on earth, the Rio Negro, shows that the real river bed is flanked on either side by a terrace which can be many kilometers wide and is flooded, during the high-water months, by up to ten meters of water. Here is one of the most peculiar plant communities in the world, the flood- or swamp-forest which in Amazonia is called "igapó." The trees and shrubs, which include *Coccoloba, Symmeria, Campsiandra, Pithecolobium* and others, have adapted remarkably well to their unusual habitat. Their roots are almost constantly under water in an extraordinarily poorly oxygenated soil. In the rainy season the trunks and even the crowns of the trees are also submerged for several months, but the plants suffer no damage; even when completely immersed they do not lose their leaves.

Blackwater offers perhaps the most uncommon environmental conditions to both animals and plants. There is an extreme lack of calcium carbonate and other electrolytes; here calcium and magnesium are really trace elements. The high concentration of colored humic substances causes rapid extinction of light with depth, as we can see from measurements in the Rio Negro; at a depth of fifty centimeters only 15% of the incident light remains, and at one meter all but 3% has been absorbed. Below 1.5 meters the water is utterly dark. In the lower reaches of the Rio Negro, which can be as much as forty-five meters deep at average water levels, only a very thin surface layer is well illuminated. In blackwater there is so little radiant energy from the sun and so low a concentration of nutrients that no higher plants, no algae, and no phytoplankton can live. Consequently the oxygen concentration is unusually low, during the high-water period only about 50% of the normal saturation value.

▷ Above: The faunal kingdoms and regions of the earth:

I. HOLARCTIC, with the Neoarctic and Palearctic Regions.

II. PALEOTROPICAL, with the Ethiopian (including the Capensian, C), Madagascan and Oriental Regions.

III. AUSTRALIC, with the Australian (A1), Oceanic (A2), Hawaiian (A3) and New Zealand (A4) Regions

IV. NEOTROPICAL

V. ARCHINOTIC

VI. TRANSITION

REGIONS: Holarctic-Paleotropical (T1, T2); Central America (T3), Australic-Archinotic (T4), Neotropical-Archinotic (T5), Wallacea (W). Below: The kingdoms and regions of the neritic animals:

SOUTHERN KINGDOM: Antarctic Region (1), Southern Australian Region (2), Southern African Region (3); Kerguelen Region (4), South American Region (5), Peruvian Region (6).

TROPICAL KINGDOM: Eastern Atlantic Region (7), Eastern Pacific Region (8), Indo-Western Pacific Region (9), Western Atlantic Region (10).

NORTHERN KINGDOM: Mediterranean-Atlantic Region (11), Sarmatic Region (12), Atlantic-Boreal Region (13), Arctic Region (14), Northern Pacific Region (15).

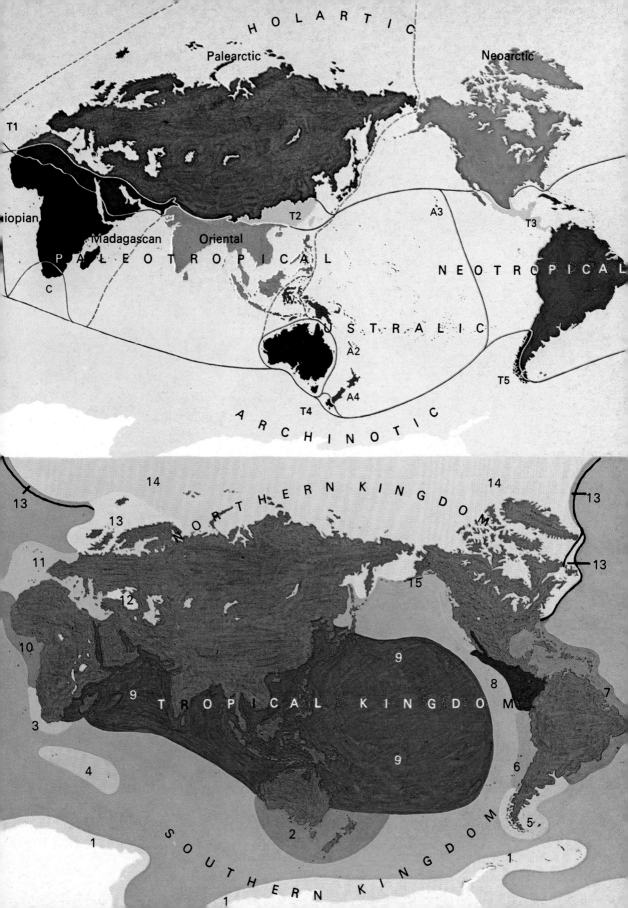

H O L A R C T I C

Palearctic

Neoarctic

T1

Ethiopian

Madagascan   Oriental   T2

A3

P A L E O T R O P I C A L

N E O T R O P I C A L

C

W

T3

A U S T R A L I C

A2

A4

T4

T5

A R C H I N O T I C

NORTHERN KINGDOM

14   14

13   13   13

13

11   15

12   13

10   9

9   8

3   T R O P I C A L   K I N G D O M   7

4   6

1   2   5

S O U T H E R N   K I N G D O M   1

1

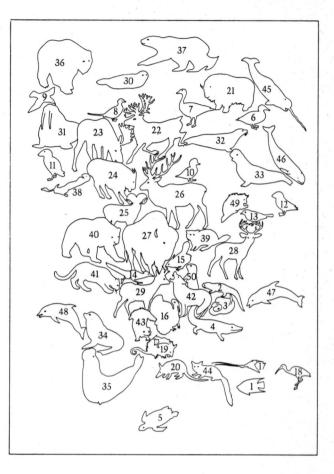

THE FAUNA OF NORTH AMERICA (HOLARCTICI).

FISH: 1. Butterfly fish (*Holacanthus ciliaris*).

AMPHIBIA: 2. Tiger salamander (*Amblystoma tigrinum*).

REPTILES: 3. Diamond-back rattlesnake (*Crotalus adamanteus*); 4. American alligator (*Alligator mississippiensis*); 5. Hawks-bill (*Eretmochelys imbricata*).

BIRDS: 6. Eider duck (*Somateria mollissima*); 7. Canada goose (*Branta canadensis*); 8. Old squaw duck (*Clangula hyemalis*); 9. Slaty-backed gull (*Larus schistisagus*); 10. Bufflehead (*Bucephala albeola*); 11. Tufted puffin (*Lunda cirrhata*); 12. Common puffin (*Fratercula arctica*); 13. Chestnut-sided warbler (*Dendroica pensylvanica*); 14. Greater roadrunner (*Geococcyx californianus*); 15. Greater prairie chicken (*Tympanuchus cupido*); 16. Turkey (*Meleagris gallopavo*); 17. Streamer-tailed humming-bird (*Trochilus polytmus*); 18. Scarlet ibis (*Eudocimus ruber*).

MAMMALS: Marsupials: 19. Opossum (*Didelphis marsupialis*).—Edentates: 20. Nine-banded armadillo (*Dasypus novemcinctus*).—Artiodactyls; 21. Musk ox (*Ovibos moschatus*); 22. Caribou (*Rangifer tarandus arcticus*); 23. Moose (*Alces alces*); 24. Rocky Mountain goat (*Oreamnos americanus*); 25. Bighorn sheep (*Ovis canadensis*); 26. Wapiti (*Cervus elaphus canadensis*); 27. Bison (*Bison bison*); 28. White-tailed deer (*Odocoileus virginianus*); 29. Pronghorn (*Antilocapra americana*).

CARNIVORES: Pinnipeds: 30. Ringed seal (*Phoca hispida*); 31. Pacific walrus (*Odobenus rosmarus divergens*); 32. Harp-seal (*Pagophilus groenlandicus*); 33. Hooded seal (*Cystophora cristata*); 34. Californian sea lion (*Zalophus californianus*); 35. Northern elephant seal (*Mirounga angustirostris*).—Land carnivores: 36. Brown bear (*Ursus arctos beringianus*); 37. Polar bear (*Thalarctos maritimus*); 38. Sea otter (*Enhydra lutris*); 39. Raccoon (*Procyon lotor*); 40. Grizzly bear (*Ursus arctos horribilis*); 41. Puma (*Puma concolor*); 42. Coyote (*Canis latrans*); 43. Striped skunk (*Mephitis mephitis*); 44. Ring-tailed cat (*Bassariscus sumichrasti*).—Cetaceans: 45. Narwhal (*Monodon monoceros*); 46. White whale (*Delphinapterus leucas*); 47. Bottle-nosed dolphin (*Tursiops truncatus*); 48. White-sided dolphin (*Lagenorhynchus acutus*).—Rodents: 49. North American porcupine (*Erethizon dorsatum*); 50. Black-tail prairie dog (*Cynomys ludovicianus*).

Because the humic acids are not buffered by calcium and magnesium salts, the pH (see Chapter 5) of tropical blackwater is very low. In the Rio Negro it is about 5.0, and in some places as low as 3.9. pH values down to 3.6 have been measured in the river region of the Congo and in Malaysian rivers; this corresponds to the acidity of weak vinegar.

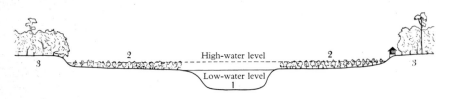

Fig. 18-32. Schematic cross section through a black-water river. 1. River bed; 2. Periodically flooded igapó forest; 3. Tall forest on land which is not flooded.

As a result of the deficiency of minerals, the high acidity, and the poor illumination there is essentially no photosynthesis in tropical blackwater, and thus the first link in the food chain is missing. Accordingly, black-water is poorly populated with animals, in comparison to the other river types. Even for man, blackwater rivers count as famine areas. In a real blackwater river, such as the several-kilometers-wide Rio Negro, one encounters hardly any fish; only rarely do even small fresh-water herrings appear. In the igapó and the blackwater brooks there is more plentiful food for fish, since here ants, termites, beetles, and other land insects, as well as pollen from flowers, fall into the water. Certain fish species of various subfamilies, such as *Gnathocharax*, *Carnegiella* and *Pyrrhulina*, live just under the water surface and take advantage of this gift from the land.

It has not yet been settled whether there are fish species endemic to blackwater. The brightly colored tetras—for example, the neon tetra (*Paracheirodon innesi*) and the cardinal tetra (*Cheirodon axelrodi*)—are well-known aquarium fish throughout the world; their glowing blue-red coloration makes it possible for schools of these fish to stay together. It is commonly thought that they are inhabitants of typical blackwater, but this is not so. Their real habitats are in clearwater, though there may be a certain admixture of blackwater there.

A decisive element of the tropical lake and stream environment is the alternation of dry and rainy seasons. Usually the onset of the rainy period is sudden and the water level rises rapidly, flooding dry surfaces. The soil is thus the more readily leached, and nutrients are taken into the water. This abundance of nutrients in the first weeks of the rainy season allows extremely rapid development of the plankton and the best possible food supply for young fish. Therefore, most tropical fish spawn at the beginning of the rainy season. A few weeks beforehand, huge schools of fish in Amazonia move upriver or from the marginal lakes into the brooks that flow into them. The spawning migrations of the characid *Prochilodus insignis* are well known, for these fish—in Brazil called "jaraci"—make loud sounds as they travel.

We do not yet know what factors elicit and affect such spawning migrations. In the spawning regions the water temperature is two or three degrees lower, because of the altitude and the relatively cool rain water. Moreover, the heavy tropical rains lower the concentration of electrolytes in the water, as has been observed in the Congo region. It has been possible experimentally to bring about spawning of tropical catfish by using rain water to lower the temperature of the water in which they were kept. In blackwater, the heavy rainfall causes an increase in the oxygen concentration. Even though the waters of the tropics are uniformly warm all year and thus seem to many to have a monotonous climate, rainy periods bring about a considerable change in the ecological relationships. These seasonal climatic changes may appear to be a small part of the total picture, but plants and animals respond to them in ways that show their decisive biological importance.

19   The Ranges of Animal Distribution

Zoogeography is the science of the distribution of animals throughout the world and the local ranges of populations within the regions they inhabit. The presence of an animal or plant in a certain region is determined by ecological and historical factors, and there is a close reciprocal relationship between the occurrence of animals and that of man. Populations of organisms can become established in a region only if the range of conditions under which the species or individual can thrive (its ecological valence) is consistent with the sum of the conditions prevailing there. Animals and plants, then, are living indicators of the characteristics of their environment; their ranges mark the places in which environmental conditions are the same or similar. At the same time, the evolution and distribution of species casts light upon the geological evolution of various parts of the earth, and upon the course of global changes in climate and vegetation. The results of zoogeographical research can make considerable contributions toward a deeper understanding of the current state of the earth's surface and of our own environment.

In industrial areas, the distribution of animals and plants can be used to determine the degree of local pollution. The saprobionts in bodies of water are real "pollution indicators." Similarly, lichens are particularly sensitive to sulfur dioxide; in the "lichen deserts," where these plants do not grow or have ceased to grow, man is also beginning to find conditions intolerable. The distribution of other organisms may also directly affect that of man; many disease pathogens and "pests" have influenced and even determined the fate of human cultures. For example, it is thought that the massive migration of the Mayas from Guatemala to Yucatan around 1000 A.D., which preceded the foundation of the "new kingdom," was brought about by a pest that destroyed their cornfields in the old kingdom.

To interpret the range of species properly it is necessary to know in detail the conditions required for the species to live and thrive. The science of zoogeography has both ecological and historical aspects; the two are

By P. Müller

intimately interwoven, and each helps to elucidate the other. Everything we now regard as the history of organisms concerns, to a great extent, the environments of earlier times. One can usefully consider zoogeography as being subdivided into three approaches—descriptive, analytical and applied.

To descriptive zoogeography falls the task of examining and organising the bewildering diversity of organisms in the different parts of the earth. Scientists in this field attempt to describe ranges of distribution as completely and precisely as possible and to discover which species are represented in each region, taking into account their systematic relationships. Some specialize in the study of distribution and modification of communities. A community is the biotic part of an ecosystem, which with its biotope forms a unit in which each member plays its role. Individual animals can come and go, but once a state of equilibrium has been reached between the system of populations and the environmental conditions, the characteristic species composition of the community remains stable.

The effect of environmental conditions on animal distribution is the concern of analytical zoogeography, the object being to determine the causes underlying the distributions we observe. In its ecological aspect, the field treats of the dynamics of present-day communities—their formation and modulation, the stresses to which they are exposed and their responses to these. The historical approach, on the other hand, focuses upon the long-term processes by which communities and environments were formed and evolved, so as to clarify the effect of past events upon the distributions found today. The field also has an experimental side, in which conditions are artificially imposed to test directly hypotheses about their involvement in certain aspects of animal distribution. The most neglected subdivision of animal geography is the applied branch, in which ways are sought of turning the findings of analytical zoogeography to the advantage of man.

Life is found in three major regions of the earth—the land, the fresh water, and the ocean, and zoogeographers tend to specialize in one of these three regions. The first step in any program of zoogeographical research is to discover the exact spatial extent of the range of distribution under study. This is no simple task; even in regions as thoroughly studied as Europe and North America, the limits of ranges have been only approximately established for vertebrates. Only where there are natural obstacles such as water, mountains, and competitors can fixed boundaries be drawn; where such barriers are lacking, one can only determine the ranges of species and subspecies with a certain degree of probability. Boundaries can be estimated more closely in the case of subspecies, which for phylogenetic reasons are mutually exclusive. Such subspecies (or species), occupying separate ranges, are said to be allopatric. If we find subspecies A on the east bank of a river and subspecies B on its west bank, there is a high probability that the river is the boundary limiting the distribution of the two subspecies. It is more difficult in the case of sympatric species, which have overlapping or superimposed ranges but do not lose their individuality by cross-breeding. Moreover, the natural ranges are today in the process of profound modification as a result of human activities. It is thus more urgent than ever that they be defined as soon as possible.

Not until we know all the pertinent facts about a distribution can we proceed with investigations to clarify the current trends in the area inhabited. A zoogeographical datum that consists simply in confirmation of the occurrence of a certain species in a certain country is of only limited value; in many cases—for example, where parasites are concerned—such information may be of relatively minor importance. The data required in the study of animal distributions are exact descriptions of the habitats and the nature of the environments in which the animals of given countries live.

The actual range of an animal species is first specified by the region in which the species can continue indefinetely to reproduce and maintain itself without immigration from outside the area. Apart from these reproduction ranges there are ranges in which the animals can live and through which they move, and it is necessary to distinguish clearly among these. Many species quite capable of successful crossing in the laboratory maintain their individuality in nature by reproducing in the same region, but at different times. They are isolated not geographically, but temporally. **The reproduction range**

The extent of an animal's range can vary widely among the different groups; it depends upon the animal's general habits, capacity for locomotion or being transported (vagility) and history of dispersal, and upon the geographical area of origin of the species. On the other hand, it is rare to find a general relationship between the size of a range and the phylogenetic age of a species. Many genera and species are to be found all over the earth, but their age varies widely. These cosmopolitans, because of their great adaptability and vagility, are not resticted to any zoogeographic realm. Also members of this group are the animals man has taken with him into all parts of the earth he inhabits—his domestic animals, pests, and parasites. On the other hand, no species is found simultaneously in the ocean and in the inland waters or on land. **Cosmopolitans**

Examples of species with essentially worldwide distribution are the barn owl (*Tyto alba*), the osprey (*Pandion haliaëtus*), the common heron (*Ardea cinerea*), the peregrine falcon (*Falco pereginus*), though this has recently become rare, and the painted lady butterfly *Vanessa cardui*, which however is not found in South America. Others are the diamond-backed moth (*Plutella maculipennis*), the butterfly *Nonnophila noctuella*, the tardigrade *Macrobiotus hufelandi* (the encysted stage of which can survive the most extreme conditions), and numerous species of plant, such as annual meadow grass (*Poa annua*), ratstail plantain (*Plantago major*), dandelion (*Taraxacum officinale*), the goosefoot *Chenopodium album*, the common reed (*Phragmites communsi*), and the stinging nettle *Urtica dioica*.

Even though cosmopolitans are so widely distributed, most of them (except for a few ubiquitous species which are able to live and reproduce even under unfavorable conditions) do place certain requirements upon their habitat. At the opposite end of the scale are the species which at present are to be found only in one restricted location. These are organisms formerly more widely distributed, which as environmental conditions changed in the course of time experienced a shrinking or shifting of their habitat; now they can survive only as "relics" in places where conditions are especially suited to their needs.

Of particular interest to historical zoogeographers are those ranges which have separated into several subdivisions. For some past or present reasons, the populations in these areas are not found in the regions dividing them. The spatial separation of populations which once formed a unit is one fundamental way in which new species come into being ("allopatric speciation"). A complete description of a range must take into account all the temporal variations, such as migration or transport of animals.

Animal migrations

When animal populations change their habitat, the process is called migration. Vertical migrations are carried out in a regular rhythm by planktonic organisms, many of which rise to the ocean surface at night and in the morning return to the depths (see Chapter 17). The migrations of the palolo worms (*Eunice viridis* and *Eunice furcata*; see Chapter 4) are associated with the phases of the moon. Mountain animals, such as the North American white-tailed deer, the chamois of the Alps and the hummingbirds of the Andes, move between the valleys and the upper slopes depending on the season. In the search for suitable feeding grounds, savanna animals like gnus and zebras, steppe animals like bison, and tundra animals like reindeer travel over long distances. The springbuck of South Africa used to make particularly notable migrations.

There are also numerous fish, including herring, tuna, haddock and cod, which carry out migrations. The European river eel grows to maturity in the inland waters and travels to the Sargasso Sea at spawning time (see Chapter 5)—it is a "catadromous" fish. "Anadromous" fish show the reverse behavior; for example, salmon move from the ocean into the rivers to spawn. Using its sense of smell, a salmon can find the very river in which it hatched from the egg.

Migrations can also involve a change between aquatic and terrestrial life. Seals, penguins and marine turtles move onto the beaches to reproduce, whereas certain species of land crab, such as *Birgus latro* and *Gecarcinus*, enter the ocean for the purpose. Amphibians are especially characterized by their movement to bodies of fresh water during the spawning season. Toads have been shown always to migrate to the same pools to spawn. North American newts of the genus *Taricha* manage to return year after year to the part of a brook in which they were born. Bird migrations are especially famous, but some lepidopteran species are also capable of covering long distances in their seasonal migrations. To mention only one, the monarch butterfly (*Danaus plexippus*) reproduces

EASTERN PALEARCTIC VERTEBRATES (HOLARCTIC II)

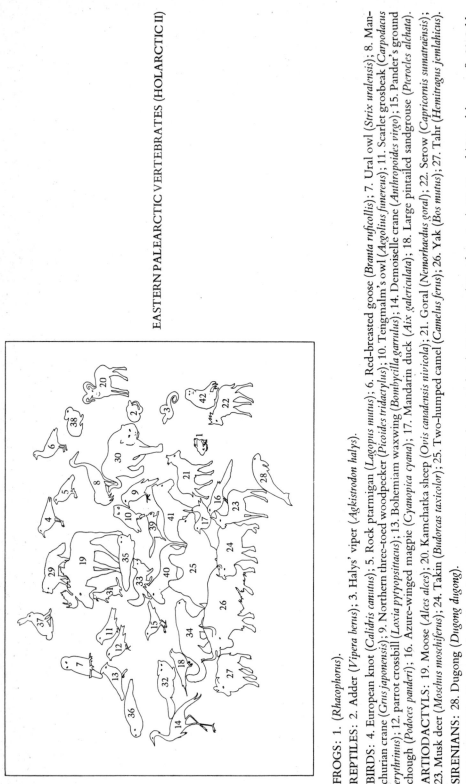

FROGS: 1. (*Rhacophorus*).

REPTILES: 2. Adder (*Vipera berus*); 3. Halys' viper (*Agkistrodon halys*).

BIRDS: 4. European knot (*Calidris canutus*); 5. Rock ptarmigan (*Lagopus mutus*); 6. Red-breasted goose (*Branta ruficollis*); 7. Ural owl (*Strix uralensis*); 8. Manchurian crane (*Grus japonensis*); 9. Northern three-toed woodpecker (*Picoides tridactylus*); 10. Tengmalm's owl (*Aegolius funereus*); 11. Scarlet grosbeak (*Carpodacus erythrinus*); 12. parrot crossbill (*Loxia pytyopsittacus*); 13. Bohemian waxwing (*Bombycilla garrulus*); 14. Demoiselle crane (*Anthropoides virgo*); 15. Pander's ground chough (*Podoces panderi*); 16. Azure-winged magpie (*Cyanopica cyana*); 17. Mandarin duck (*Aix galericulata*); 18. Large pintailed sandgrouse (*Pterocles alchata*).

ARTIODACTYLS: 19. Moose (*Alces alces*); 20. Kamchatka sheep (*Ovis canadensis nivicola*); 21. Goral (*Nemorhaedus goral*); 22. Serow (*Capricornis sumatraënsis*); 23. Musk deer (*Moschus moschiferus*); 24. Takin (*Budorcas taxicolor*); 25. Two-humped camel (*Camelus ferus*); 26. Yak (*Bos mutus*); 27. Tahr (*Hemitragus jemlahicus*).

SIRENIANS: 28. Dugong (*Dugong dugong*).

CARNIVORES: 29. Arctic fox (*Alopex lagopus*); 30. Siberian tiger (*Panthera tigris altaica*); 31. Ermine (*Mustela erminea*); 32. Manul (*Octocolobus manul*); 33. Sable (*Martes zibellina*); 34. Snow leopard (*Uncia uncia*).

PINNIPEDS: 35. Seal (*Phoca sibrica*); 36. Caspian seal (*Phoca caspia*).

HARES: 37. Arctic hare (*Lepus timidus*); 38. Altai pika (*Ochotona alpina*).

RODENTS: 39. European flying squirrel (*Pteromys volans*).

PERISSODACTYLS: 40. Asiatic wild ass (*Equus hemionus*); 41. Wild horse (*Equus przewalskii*).

MONKEYS: 42. Japanese macaque (*Macaca fuscata*).

VERTEBRATES OF THE WESTERN PALEARCTIC (HOLARCTIC III)

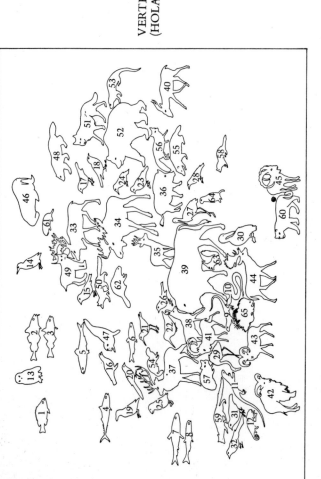

FISH: 1. Rosefish (*Sebastes marinus*); 2. Cod (*Gadus morrhua*); 3. Haddock (*Melanogrammus aeglefinus*); 4. Atlantic mackerel (*Scomber scombrus*); 5, 6, 7. Atlantic herring (*Clupea harengus*); 8. Pilchard (*Sardina pilchardus*).

REPTILES: 9. Lizard (*Lacerta sicula*); 10. Sand viper (*Vipera ammodytes*); 11. Eyed lizard (*Lacerta lepida*); 12. European chamelon (*Chamaeleo chamaeleon*).

BIRDS: 13. Snowy owl (*Nyctea scandiaca*); 14. Atlantic murre (*Uria aalge*); 15. Brambling (*Fringilla montifringilla*); 16. Red grouse (*Lagopus scoticus*); 17. Siberian tit. (*Parus cinctus*); 18. Redwing (*Turdus iliacus*); 19. Razor-billed auk (*Alca torda*); 20. Magpie (*Pica pica*); 21. Oystercatcher (*Haematopus ostralegus*); 22. European woodcock (*Scolopax rusticola*); 23. Common jay (*Garrulus glandarius*); 24. Greater spotted woodpecker (*Dendrocopus major*); 25. Puffin (*Fratercula arctica*); 26. Hedge sparrow (*Prunella modularis*); 27. Black stork (*Ciconia nigra*); 28. Common roller (*Coracias garrulus*); 29. Greater flamingo (*Phoenicopterus ruber*); 30. Eastern white pelican (*Pelecanus onocrotalus*); 31. Red-legged partridge (*Alectoris rufa*); 32. Azure-winged magpie (*Cyanopica cyana cooki*).

MAMMALS: Artiodactyls: 33. Reindeer (*Rangifer tarandus*); 34. Moose (*Alces alces*); 35. Roe deer (*Capreolus capreolus*); 36. Wild boar (*Sus scrofa*); 37. Red deer (*Cervus elaphus*); 38. Chamois (*Rupicapra rupicapra*); 39. European bison (*Bison bonasus*); 40. Saiga (*Saiga tatarica*); 41. Ibex (*Capra ibex*); 42. Barbary sheep (*Ammotragus lervia*); 43. Wild sheep (*Ovis ammon*); 44. Fallow deer (*Dama dama*); 45. Wild goat (*Capra aegagrus*).

CARNIVORES: Pinnipeds: 46. Walrus (*Obodenus rosmarus*); 47. Harbor seal (*Phoca vitulina*).—Land carnivores: 48. Wolverine (*Gulo gulo*); 49. Lynx (*Lynx lynx*); 50. Pine marten (*Martes martes*); 51. Wolf (*Canis lupus*); 52. Brown bear (*Ursus arctos*); 53. Eurasian river otter (*Lutra lutra*); 54. European polecat (*Mustela putorius*); 55. Old World badger (*Meles meles*); 56. Red fox (*Vulpes vulpes*); 57. Central European wildcat (*Felis silvestris*); 58. Marbled polecat (*Vormela peregusna*); 59. Common genet (*Genetta genetta*); 60. Leopard (*Panthera pardus*).—Rodents 61. Norway lemming (*Lemmus lemmus*); 62. Beaver (*Castor fiber*); 63. Red squirrel (*Sciurus vulgaris*); 64. Spotted souslik (*Citellus suslicus*); 65. Crested porcupine (*Hystrix cristata*).

in nothern North America in the spring and travels in huge swarms in the fall to its winter territory on the Gulf of Mexico. In certain states there are laws to protect the trees these butterflies regularly choose as resting places during each journey. The next spring, the monarch butterflies fly north again to mate and lay their eggs.

The migrations of European butterflies usually involve more than one generation. This is the case among the painted lady butterflies, red admirals, common silver Y moths, ringlets, and death's-head and convolvulus hawkmoths. Odonata (for example, *Sympetrum fonscolombei* and *Aeschna affinis*) and Myriapoda also migrate, but these migrations are irregular and can be induced by a great variety of factors. At various intervals Scandinavian lemmings (*Lemmus lemmus*) undertake the mass migrations described in Chapter 10. The nutcracker (*Nucifraga caryocatactes*) and crossbill (*Loxia*) of the far north travel as far as central Europe. The mass outbreaks of migratory locusts in the steppes and savannas (see Chapter 15) are ascribed to the irregularity of precipitation there.

In general it is true of such migrations that the actual reproduction area is rarely expanded to any appreciable degree. But the situation is quite different in the case of the transport of animals by man. Usually this process of animal dispersal is associated with the history of expansion of certain human populations or with the opening up of major transportation routes. House rats, mice and sparrows have become cosmopolitans in part by the unintentional assistance of man. Man has also introduced large numbers of reptile and amphibian species to new parts of the world. The giant toad (*Bufo marinus*) of South America was introduced to Cuba, Haiti, eastern Australia and New Guinea as a countermeasure against insects. The small house gecko *Hemidactylus mabouia* was accidentally carried from Africa to South America in the first slave ships, and it has become a real member of human communities in its new home.

Because of its economic value the rainbow trout (*Salmo gairdneri*), originally restricted to western North America, has been used to stock streams in Eurasia, Chile, Argentina, southern and eastern Africa, Madagascar, Australia and New Zealand. For the same reason man has distributed the oyster (*Ostrea edulis*) far beyond the original limits of its range. European species such as the wild boar, brown hare and starling were shipped to North America; conversely, men contributed to the establishment of North American species such as the potato beetle, muskrat, gray squirrel and raccoon in parts of Europe. The native fauna of New Zealand has been swamped with introduced aliens. Once there were no mammals there apart from bats, but now the country is inhabited by marsupials like the kusu, a native of Australia, various European and Asian deer species, the wild boar, brown hare, polecat, ermine, weasel and hedgehog. Some of these, such as the red deer, have long since come to have economic value, but others must be subjected to severe control measures if damage to the countryside and the native fauna is to be prevented.

Passive dispersal mechanisms

In most cases, in fact, the introduction of alien species causes marked disturbance of the original communities, and often the result is catastrophic. The muskrat and potato beetle are instructive examples of this. The snail *Achatina fulica* has expanded its range during the last two centuries from eastern Africa to the agricultural areas of Asia, the Pacific islands, California and Florida; because of its high rate of reproduction and food consumption, and because of the plant diseases it transmits, it has become a dreaded pest in these newly colonized regions. Since it has no effective natural antagonists there, efforts are made to control it with viruses, poison bait and in particular by organized stocking of the areas with the antagonist gastropod genera *Gonaxis* and *Eugladina*.

Faunal kingdoms

In the last century the biosphere was classified zoogeographically in terms of so-called "faunal kingdoms." As our understanding of the diversity and the different historical development of regions inhabited by various species has increased, the idea that such clearly delimitable kingdoms exist has often been questioned. Places are now known where flatland rainforests, montane forests, savannas and plateaus intermingle within a very small space; the animal species adapted to this environment present such a complex picture that the difficulty of making a simple subdivision of the world is apparent. Nevertheless, although the boundaries between zoogeographical kingdoms are commonly broken by one animal group or another, one can at least refer to generally accepted large zoogeographical units in the case of such well-studied vertebrate classes as the reptiles, birds and mammals.

Originally the cofounders of zoogeography, Philip Lutley Sclater (1825–1913) and Alfred Russel Wallace (1823–1913), divided the earth into three large kingdoms: 1. Megagaea (or Arctogaea), including North America, Eurasia, Africa, the Arabian peninsula, India and Indochina; 2. Notogaea, including Australia, Oceania and New Zealand; and 3. Neogaea, including South and Central America together with the Antilles.

The subdivision used today also takes into account the flora and the invertebrate fauna, and in particular the systematic relationships between the groups of animals living in the different ranges. Accordingly, the faunal kingdoms of the earth can be represented as follows:

Kingdom	Region	Areas
1. Holarctic	a) Neoarctic	North America and Greenland (but in floristic terms Florida, Southern California and the Mexican Highlands belong to the Neotropical Kingdom).
	b) Palearctic	Eurasia without India but

Kingdom	Region	Areas
		with Iceland, the Canary Islands, Korea, Japan and Northern Africa.
2. Paleotropical	a) Ethiopian	Africa south of the Sahara.
	b) Madagascan	Madagascar and the offshore islands.
	c) Oriental	India and Indochina as far as the Wallace Line, which runs through the Strait of Macassar between Borneo and Celebes and the Lombok Strait between Bali and Lombok.
3. Australic	a) Australian	Australia, New Guinea and islands east of the line named for Richard Lydekker.
	b) Oceanic	Oceania, New Caledonia.
	c) New Zealandic	New Zealand except for the southwestern part.
	d) Hawaiian	Hawaiian Islands.
4. Neotropical		South and Central America, including the Antilles.
5. Archinotic		Antarctica, southwestern South America and south-western New Zealand.

This organization includes the Solomon and Hawaiian Islands and central and northern New Zealand in the Australic Kingdom. However, these island groups have so many special characteristics and such close relationships with the Paleotropical Kingdom that the above classification does not hold for all groups of animals.

The boundaries between the kingdoms listed here are not in general very distinct, but rather represent broad transition zones which in many cases—for example, in Central America—have a geological history of their own. Here recent immigrants have moved in on top of an old, established fauna. For these reasons the zoogeographers regard some transition zones as kingdoms in themselves. One can regard kingdoms as having clearly defined borders only where intermingling is prevented by high mountains, wide arms of the ocean, or ice deserts.

The boundary lines in the Indo-Australian transition zone, called Wallacea in honor of Alfred Russel Wallace, have become famous. They mean little with respect to plants and some groups of animals, but for other animal forms they are of considerable significance. Wallacea extends from the Lesser Sunda Islands, Celebes and Lombok in the west to the

Wallacea

Fig. 19-1. Biogeographic-
ally important "bounda-
ries" in the southeastern
Asian-Australian area. 1.
Wallace line (from Huxley,
1868); la, Wallace Line
(from Mayr, 1944); 2.
Müller Line (1846); 3.
Weber Line (1902); 4.
Lydekker Line (1896);
5. Limit of marsupial range.

Boundaries on the
continents

Molucca, Kai and Aru Islands in the east. It is separated from the Australic
Kingdom by the Lydekker Line, and from the Oriental Region of the
Palaeotropic Kingdom by the Wallace Line. Although the fauna here is
essentially mixed, being of Oriental and Australian origin, Wallacea is
inhabited by certain remarkable animal forms found only here. Among
them are the various subspecies of the Celebes macaque (*Macaca maura*),
the closely related monkey *Cynopithecus niger*, and an ancient representative of the Suidae, *Babyrousa babyrussa* of Celebes, Buru and the neighboring Sula Islands.

Through Wallacea runs the Weber Line, established in 1902 by the
zoologist Max Weber; it falls between Celebes and the Moluccas, then
proceeds further south between the Lesser Sunda Islands and Timor.
Oriental and Australian animal groups are about equally common in this
transition zone. The Weber Line does not apply to invertebrates in the
same way as to vertebrates, but it does coincide with the limits of distribution of various species of malaria mosquitoes (*Anopheles*). The Wallace
Line, mentioned above, was recognized as a barrier to dispersal as early as
1846 by the explorer/scientist Salomon Müller (1804–1894); according to
Müller, however, the islands Lombok and Sumbawa belonged to the
Oriental Region. Moreover, Müller disagreed with Wallace in defending
the view that the barrier effect was a function of environmental influences.
Australian marsupials are found as far as the Müller or Wallace Line, but
are absent in the south to the west of the islands Wetar and Timor. The
boundaries of Wallacea otherwise coincide to a great extent with the
two-hundred-meter depth line, down to which the ocean floor was left
dry when the sea level fell during the Ice Age.

In contrast to this important mixed-fauna region in eastern Indonesia,
the boundaries on the continents are considerably less meaningful. The
Reinig Line is ascribable to geological processes, having been formed
during the Ice Age; it runs from the eastern banks of the rivers Lena and
Aldan along the Stanovoi and Yablonovoi Ranges as far as the Tien Shan
Mountains. At the Johansen Line, which runs from Severnaya Zemlya
Island and the Taimyr Peninsula in the north along the eastern side of the
Yenisey River to the Altai Mountains, animal groups of the western and
eastern parts of the Old World north meet. Since western animals are
adapted to life in the lowlands, the central Siberian plateau to the east of
this line prevents all but a few of them from expanding their ranges to the
east. Similarly, among the eastern highland species on the western edge of
the central Siberian plateau, only those that are unusually adaptable can
reach the flatland to the west of the Johansen Line. The line marks the
western limit for eastern bird species such as the thrushes *Turdus sibiricus*,
T. obscurus, and *T. naumanni*, and the ducks *Anas formosa* and *A. falcata*;
and it marks the eastern limit for western species like the red-backed shrike
(*Lanius collurio*), the sedge warbler (*Acrocephalus schoenbaenus*), the spotted
crake (*Porzana porzana*) and the velvet scoter (*Melanitta fusca*).

The boundaries between the Neotropical Paleotropical and Holarctic Kingdoms have been questioned repeatedly. Whereas most biogeographers assign Central America to the Neotropical Kingdom, others regard it as a transition zone between the Neotropical and Neoarctic, in which South American animal groups predominate. Some researchers, like Robert Mertens, would even make Central America a kingdom in itself. To some extent, these disparate views result from the differential dispersal capacity of certain animal groups. For example, mammals and birds obscure the individuality of the Central American fauna, whereas reptiles, amphibians, millipedes (Diplopoda), centipedes (Chilopoda), and gastropods offer evidence in favor of its independent status.

The Central American transition zone

Regardless of the differences of opinion about the classification of Central America, all zoogeographers agree that in the tropical rainforests there the proportion of species originating in South America is astonishingly large. Nevertheless, some North American species not only have penetrated the Central American highlands but have advanced much further toward South America, to the region of the Andes. Animals entirely restricted to Central America include numerous species of frog of the genera *Eleutherodactylus* and *Hyla*, several snake species (among them the primitive subfamily Loxoceminae), and more than 100 bird and 40 mammal species.

There is an equally broad transition zone between the Paleotropical Kingdom (Ethiopian and Oriental Regions) and the Holarctic. The Sahara, for example, is not a uniform area of desert; in the dry heart of the desert are scattered groups of mountains—the Tibesti, Hoggar and Air Mountains. Here holarctic forms can extend their ranges far to the south. Moreover, the desert fauna of Africa is composed of many species found also in the dry regions of India. Among the plants, the proportion of species growing both in the Sahara and in India amounts to as much as 70%. In view of all this, it is justified to lump the Oriental and Ethopian Regions together in the Paleotropical Kingdom, especially since the correspondence between the faunas of Africa and southern Asia are more marked than those between these two regions on the one hand and the Holarctic on the other. In both regions, for example, live representatives of several mammalian families—the chevrotains, rhinoceroses, elephants, hyenas, porcupines, scaly anteaters, anthropoid apes, baboons and lorises —as well as sunbirds, bulbuls, pittas, honey-guides and hornbills; of the reptiles, chameleons are represented in both regions, and of the amphibians, the rhacophorid frogs. Only four bird families are entirely restricted to the Ethiopian Region, and the only family restricted to the Oriental Region is the fairy bluebirds (Irenidae.)

The Saharan transition zone

The transition zone between Paleotropical and Holarctic Kingdoms is just as broad on the Chinese side. Here the original subtropical forests have been largely destroyed by man, and as a result species adapted to open country have to some extent taken the place of the former forest

The Chinese transition zone

animals. The fauna of Taiwan, which was connected to the continent during the Ice Age, displays a marked intermingling of oriental and palearctic species.

The "ancient south"

At the southern tips of South America and New Zealand, finally, there are transition zones leading to the Archinotic Kingdom, the "ancient south" which, before Antartica was covered by ice, was one physically continuous kingdom. Whereas the vertebrates now found in these zones are closely related to the more northern inhabitants of the two land masses, numerous groups of more ancient invertebrates, such as the stoneflies (Plecoptera), chironomid midges and certain crustacean families that have existed since the early Tertiary, indicate that the transition zones do belong to the Archinotic Kingdom.

The Holarctic Kingdom

Of all the kingdoms, the Holarctic has been the most thoroughly studied. Characteristic mammals here are the moles, beavers, jumping mice, pikas and bison; among the amphibians, one finds salamandrids, proteids and the giant cryptobranchid salamanders of eastern Asia and North America, and typical fish are the pikes (*Esocidae*) and cyprinid minnows of the subfamily Leucisinae. The invertebrates most notable in this kingdom are crayfish (Astacidae), clouded yellow butterflies (*Colias*), and the bumblebee genus *Cullumanobombus*. The close relationship between the animals in the northern parts of the Old and New Worlds is associated both with the historical development of these regions and with their similarity in habits. Northern Eurasia and northern North America are both spanned by a continuous belt of tundra and taiga. As late as the Würm glaciation, there was a land bridge across the Bering Strait, which made possible the last exchange overland between the faunas of North America and Eurasia.

Typical Eurasian species of the tundra (e.g., reindeer), taiga (three-toed woodpecker) and winter-deciduous forest (red deer) are replaced in North America by closely related species or subspecies. Altogether, the northern parts of the continents correspond much more closely in their faunas than do the southern parts. Nevertheless, in both the Neoarctic and the Palearctic there are a number of remarkable species living in only that one region; these show that the faunas in these regions have become more individualized than the floras.

The Neoarctic Region

Mammals restricted to the Neoarctic are the mountain beaver, pocket gopher, pocket mouse and pronghorn antelope. Endemic reptiles are anniellid lizards, the venomous helodermatic lizards of the dry regions in Mexico and the southwestern USA, and the alligator lizards, which advance far toward the south in the mountains of Central America. Endemic amphibians are the bell toads (family Ascaphidae), with a small range near the Pacific coast, and the urodele families Ambystoidea, Sirenidae, and Amphiumidae. The turkeys of North and Central America were once also considered to be a neoarctic group, but they may be immigrants from the Neotropical Kingdom.

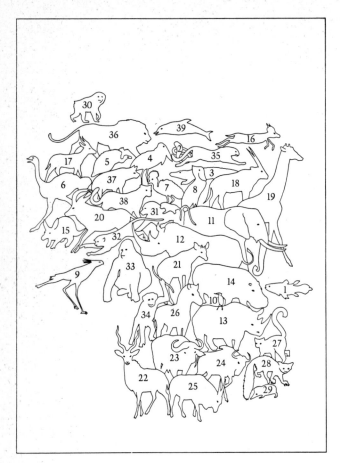

VERTEBRATES OF AFRICA AND
MADAGASCAR (PALEOTROPICAL I)

FISH: 1. Lolee-fin (*Latimeria chalumnae*).

REPTILES: 2. Egyptian cobra (*Naja haje*); 3. Nile crocodile (*Crocodylus niloticus*).

BIRDS: 4. Marabou (*Leptoptilos crumeniferus*); 5. Griffon vulture (*Gyps fulvus*); 6. Ostrich (*Struthio camelus*); 7. Crowned crane (*Balearica pavonina*); 8. Shoebill (*Balaeniceps rex*); 9. Secretary bird (*Sagittarius serpentarius*); 10. Cattle egret (*Ardeola ibis*).

MAMMALS: Proboscideans: 11. African elephant (*Loxodonta africana*).—Rhinocerotids: 12. Square-lipped rhinoceros (*Ceratotherium simum*); 13. Black rhinoceros (*Diceros bicornis*).—Hippopotamids: 14. Hippopotamus (*Hippopotamus amphibius*)—Tubulidentates: 15. Aardvark (*Orycteropus afer*).—Artiodactyls: 16. Mountain gazelle (*Gazella gazella*); 17. Dorcas gazelle (*Gazella dorcas*); 18. Oryx (*Oryx gazella*); 19. Giraffe (*Giraffa camelopardalis*); 20. Roan antelope (*Hippotragus equinus*); 21. Okapi (*Okapia johnstoni*); 22. Greater kudu (*Tragelaphus strepsiceros*); 23. Cape buffalo (*Syncerus caffer*); 24. Brindled gnu (*Connochae testaurinus*); 25. Eland (*Taurotragus oryx*).—Perissodactyls: 26. Plains zebra. (*Equus quagga*).

PROSIMIANS: 27. Ring-tailed lemur (*Lemur catta*); 28. Aye-aye (*Daubentonia madagascariensis*).

INSECTIVORES: 29. Streaked tenrec (*Hemicentetes semispinosus*).

SIMIANS: 30. Barbary ape (*Macaca sylvana*); 31. Anubis baboon (*Papio anubis*); 32. Grass monkey (*Cercopithecus aethiops*).

ANTHROPOID APES: 33. Gorilla (*Gorilla gorilla*); 34. Chimpanzee (*Pan troglodytes*).

CARNIVORES: 35. Cheetah (*Acinonyx jubatus*); 36. Lion (*Panthera leo*); 37. Striped hyaena (*Hyaena hyaena*); 38. Leopard (*Panthera pardus*).

CETACEANS: 39. Common dolphin (*Delphinus delphis*).

THE FAUNA OF THE ORIENTAL REGION
(PALEOTROPICAL II)

FISH: 1. Mindanao barbel (*Barbel* sp.).

FROGS: 2. Borneo flying frog (*Rhacophorus pardalis*).

REPTILES: 3. Asian lancehead snake (*Trimeresurus* sp.); 4. Indian gavial (*Gavialis gangeticus*); 5. Flying dragon (*Draco volans*); 6. King cobra (*Ophiophagus hannah*).

BIRDS: 7. Laughing thrush (*Garrulax* sp.); 8. Himalayan monal pheasant (*Lophophorus impejanus*); 9. Peacock (*Pavo cristatus*); 10. Red jungle fowl (*Gallus gallus*); 11. Shama (*Copsychus malabaricus*); 12. Pekin robin (*Leiothrix lutea*); 13. Monkey-eating eagle (*Pithecophaga jefferyi*); 14. Great Indian hornbill (*Buceros bicornis*); 15. Great argus pheasant (*Argusianus argus*); 16. Blue-backed fairy bluebird (*Irena puella*).

MAMMALS: Proboscideans: 17. Indian elephant (*Elephas maximus*). Tapirids: 18. Malayan tapir (*Tapirus indicus*).—Rhinocerotids: 19. Great Indian rhinoceros (*Rhinoceros unicornis*); 20. Sumatran rhinoceros (*Dicerorhinus sumatrensis*); 21. Javan rhinoceros (*Rhinoceros sondaicus*).

ARTIODACTYLS: 22. Axis deer (*Axis axis*); 23. Nilgai (*Boselaphus tragocamelus*); 24. Arna (*Bubalus arnee*); 25. Babirusa (*Babyrousa babyrussa*); 26. Anoa (*Bubalus depressicornis*); 27. Borneo banteng (*Bos javanicus*); 28. Blackbuck (*Antilope cervicapra*); 29. Gaur (*Bos gaurus*).

CARNIVORES: 30. Giant panda (*Ailuropoda melanoleuca*); 31. Lesser panda (*Ailurus fulgens*); 32. Leopard (*Panthera pardus*); 33. Large Indian civet (*Viverra zibetha*); 34. Clouded leopard (*Neofelis nebulosa*); 35. Bengal tiger (*Panthera tigris tigris*); 36. Common palm civet (*Paradoxurus hermaphroditus*); 37. Indian gray mongoose (*Herpestes edwardsi*).

PROSIMIANS: 38. Philippine tarsier (*Tarsius syrichta*); 39. Tree shrew (*Tupaia glis*); 40. Slender loris (*Loris tardigradus*).

SIMIANS: 41. Rhesus monkey (*Macaca mulatta*); 42. Entellus langur (*Presbytis entellus*).

ANTHROPOID APES: 43. Orang-utan (*Pongo pygmaeus*); 44. White-handed gibbon (*Hylobates lar*.)

The Palearctic Region is characterized by certain animal groups not found in the Neoarctic. Among them are mammals—the dormice (Glirinae), mole rats (Spalacidae), desert dormice (Seleviniidae) and pandas (Ailuridae)—as well as the bird family Prunellidae, the lizard subfamily Anguinae, and amphibians of the families Hynobiidae and Discoglossidae, the latter being represented (by the frog *Barbourula busuangensis*) as far as the Philippines.

The Palearctic Region

The Neotropical Kingdom essentially comprises South America, the Antilles, and large parts of tropical Central America. Its characteristic fauna includes an extraordinary number of species. Typical members are the opossums (family Didelphidae), one of which (the common opossum) has been able to colonize large parts of North America within historical time, as well as the rat opossums and larger groups of mammals such as the edentates, caviomorphs, New World monkeys, peccaries and no fewer than five families of bat, including the leaf-nosed and true vampire bats. Only on the Antilles are found the insectivore family Solenodontidae and the rodent family Capromyidae. The northern boundary for many groups is the Sierra Madre do Sul in Mexico; among these are are the marsupials (except for *Didelphis virginiana*), the New World monkeys and the anteaters. These "ancient South Americans" were joined in the Pliocene/Pleistocene by members of a great variety of carnivore families, ancestors of the cats, dogs, martens, racoons and spectacled bear (*Tremarctos ornatus*), as well as artiodactyls such as certain deer species which migrated down from the north when the Panama bridge became passable.

The Neotropical Kingdom

The number of birds restricted to South and Central America is particularly surprising. Two whole orders—the rheas (Rheiformes) and tinamous (Tinamiformes)—are found only in the Neotropical Kingdom. Within the other bird orders, no fewer than twenty-nine families are endemic to this kingdom; these are the boat-billed herons, screamers curassows, hoatzins, seriemas, trumpeters, limpkins, sunbitterns, seed, snipes, potoos, oilbirds, puffbirds, jacamars, toucans, fourteen families of Passeriformes, and, finally, the todies, a small family limited to the Antilles. Altogether there are 2906 South American bird species. The hummingbirds (order Trochiliformes) may also have originated in this kingdom, although some of their species have become distributed even in the northern parts of North America. No less than 242 hummingbird species are endemic to South America; there they occupy all habitats from the highest slopes of the Andes to the Amazonian lowlands but, remarkably, are not to be found on the Galapagos Islands.

The number of reptile species native to South and Central America is also surprisingly large. The snake-necked turtles (family Chelidae), otherwise found only in New Guinea and in Australia, are very much in evidence, as are the iguanas (family Iguaindae); a few species of the latter live in Madagascar, Fiji and Tonga, but a great variety have emigrated to North America. Other characteristic neotropical reptiles are the erotalid

Fig. 19-2. Migratory routes of the South American "savanna fauna" during epochs of drought in the Pleistocene and subsequently.

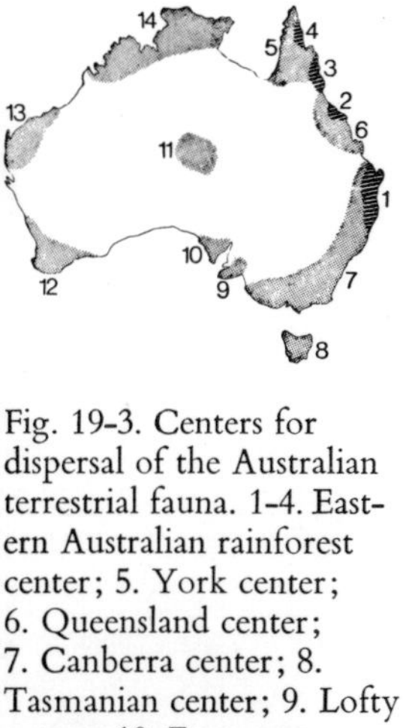

Fig. 19-3. Centers for dispersal of the Australian terrestrial fauna. 1-4. Eastern Australian rainforest center; 5. York center; 6. Queensland center; 7. Canberra center; 8. Tasmanian center; 9. Lofty center; 10. Eyre center; 11. Macdonell center; 12. Darling center; 13. Hamersley center; 14. Kimberley center.

snakes *Bothrops* and *Lachesis* and the caimans (*Caiman* and *Paleosuchus*). The coral snakes (*Micrurus*, *Micruroides* and *Leptomicrurus*) also are distributed mainly in Central and South America; only a few species also inhabit North America. A total of 694 snake species and 635 lizard species are endemic to South and Central America.

Among the amphibians, the predominant neotropical groups are the tree frogs (Hylidae), the Leptodactylidae and the Atelopodidae. By contrast, the ranid frogs are represented in South America by only one species and the lungless salamanders by twelve—of which eleven live only in Columbia. Typical South American catfish are the armored catfish of the families Callichthyidae and Loricaridae. Some of the roughly 2700 South American fish species (for example, the characids, cichlids and osteoglossids) and their parasites display remarkable relationships to Africa. The South American lungfish (*Lepidosiren paradoxa*) is also closely related to the African lungfish (genus *Protopterus*). Many invertebrate groups, including the millipedes, ostracods, chelicerates, chironomid midges, stoneflies, onychophorans and molluscs, reveal such close relationships to both Africa and New Zealand.

During the Pleistocene and into the Recent Period there were shifts of the vegetation zones in South America. Dry periods opened up swathes of savanna in the Amazonian rainforest. Such changes, which involved isolation of some groups of animals, underlie to a great extent the diversity of the species in South American habitats.

The Australic Kingdom, like the Neotropical, is distinguished by a large number of species found nowhere else. On the basis of the vertebrates living there, New Guinea clearly belongs to this kingdom. This cannot be said as certainly, however, for the Fiji and Solomon Islands or for Micronesia, eastern Polynesia (including Easter Island) and the Hawaiian Islands. On all these oceanic islands, because of their isolated positions, there was a strong tendency for evolution to proceed independently, and in places their faunas bear the stamp of the Paleotropical as much as the Australic Kingdom. In the rainforests of New Guinea, too, we find a large proportion of paleotropical forest species among the invertebrates. Australia and the surrounding islands within the 200-meter depth line were characterized by their vertebrate groups at an early stage. Egg-laying mammals (the order Monotremata) are represented here by three genera and five species and there are sixty genera, with 145 species, of marsupials, whereas the placentate mammals essentially comprise only the muroid rodents and bats and the dingo, a dog which ran wild after its introduction by man.

Australic birds include the emus, cassowaries, mound-builders, owlet-nightjars, cockatoos and numerous other parrots, and passeriform birds such as the flightless scrub-birds, bell magpies, magpie larks, lyrebirds, bower birds, and birds of paradise. Altogether, 35% of the australic bird fauna is composed of species endemic to this kingdom.

The Amphibia have a particular importance in zoogeography; in the Australic Kingdom the absence of urodeles and the predominance of tree frogs and leptodactylid frogs, which also predominate in South America, is especially striking. Among the snakes, viperids are lacking whereas elapids are very well represented. The snake-necked turtles, mentioned in the description of the South American fauna, are also found in Australia; and specimens of fossil turtles of the family Meiolaniidae have been found in both kingdoms as well. The pitted-shelled turtles (Carettochelyidae) and the lizard family Pygopodidae are limited chiefly to New Guinea. Invertebrates, too—the crustacean order Anaspidacea, which has existed since the Carboniferous, the bug family Peloridiidae, the stonefly family Gripopterygidae, and the midge family Aphrotaeniidae—indicate the ancient relationships among the fauna of the southern hemisphere.

The kagu (*Rhynochetos jubatus*) is native only to New Caledonia; this bird is the only member of its family, which occupies a special position among the Gruiformes. On this island there are sixty-eight bird species, eighteen of which colonized New Caledonia from Australia. Among the latter are the owlet-frogmouths (family Aegothelidae). Other notable animals here are six giant gecko species of the genus *Rhacodactylus*. New Caledonia

The two islands of New Zealand occupy a special position. In addition to animal groups indicating that the fauna originated in Australia (for example, gastropods of the family Athracacophoridae), there are a notable number of other groups endemic to the islands. Among these are bats (the family Mystacinidae), the kiwis (Apterygidae), the now-extinct moas (Dinornithidae), the keas (Nestorinae), and the New Zealand wrens (Xenicidae) and wattlebirds (Callaeidae); the tuatara (the lizard *Sphenodon punctatus*), famed as a "living fossil," and the ancient frogs of the family Leiopelmatidae are also endemic here. And finally, there are numerous families which demonstrate more or less close relationships to forms of the South Pacific islands and of South America. This is true in particular of the stonefly family Eustheniidae, the crustacean group Stygocaridacea and fresh-water pulmonate gastropods of the family Latiidae, the nearest relatives of which are the South American Chilinidae. The New Zealand pulmonate *Latia neritoides*, which spends most of its time in dark surroundings, is the only fresh-water animal so far known to possess luminescence. It was because of these evidences of association between the faunas of the southwestern parts of New Zealand and South America that the independent faunal Archinotic Kingdom was established; it corresponds in essence to the floral kingdom of Antarctica. New Zealand

In southern Asia, the Australic and Holarctic Kingdoms are separated by the Paleotropical, which can be subdivided into an Ethiopian, a Madagascan and an Oriental Region. For practical purposes it can be considered to comprise the tropics of the Old World.

Characteristic animal groups of the Ethiopian Region—that is, Africa south of the Sahara—include pipid frogs (*Xenopus, Hymenochirus* The Ethiopian Region and *Pseudhymenochirus*), the snakes called mambas (several species of *Dendroaspis*), and a number of birds—ostriches (Struthionidae), secretary birds (Sagittariidae), the hammerhead (Scopidae), touracos (Musophagidae), colies (Coliidae), and the shoebill storks (Balaenocipitidae). Characteristic mammals are otter shrews (Potamogalidae), golden. moles (Chrysochloridae), elephant-shrews (Macroscelididae), jumping hares (Pedetidae), African dormice (Graphiurinae), African cane rats (Thryonomyidae), rockrats (Petromyidae), aardvarks (Orycteropodidae), hyraxes (Procaviidae), hippopotamuses (Hippopotamidae) and giraffes (Giraffidae). Of the great number of African fish the most notable are those of the ancient order Polypteriformes, the Mormyridae, the electric catfish (Malapteruridae) and the African lungfish (genus *Protopterus*). There is a gastropod family found only in the Ethiopian Region, the Aillyidae.

The extensive savanna regions of Africa are inhabited by a unique fauna of large animals that live in herds (see Chapter 14). There are no deer, but in their place are many other horned animals such as the antelopes, gazelles and buffalo, and these are joined by zebras and giraffes. Whereas the plant geographers consider South Africa as a separate kingdom, the "Capensian," distinct from the Paleotropical, such a distinction is not justified on the basis of the fauna. It is true that there are a large number of species restricted to South Africa—among them the Cape fox *Vulpes chama*, the black-footed cat, and no less than ten viverrids, including the well-known slender-tailed meercat (*Suricata suricatta*)—but these simply confirm South Africa as a distinguishable subregion of the Ethiopian.

The Madagascan
Region

A quite different fauna, diverging widely from that of Africa and southern Asia in many respects, is that of the Madagascan Region, which includes not only Madagascar but the Seychelles, Comoros and Mascarenes. Certain conspicuous mammalian groups—the simians, perissodactyls, elephants and scaly anteaters—are altogether absent here. Ungulates living in Madagascar in the Pleistocene were a small hippopotamus (*Hippopotamus lemerlei*), now extinct, and one species of aardvark; the African bush-pig (*Potamochoerus porcus*) was certainly introduced by man. Moreover, there are no agamas, monitors, elapid or viperid snakes, or toads, in Madagascar.

Most laymen with an interest in animals think of Madagascar primarily as the land of the prosimians. Two prosimian families—those including the lemurs and the indris—have here produced many genera and species to take the place of the missing simians; they are joined by the peculiar aye-aye (*Daubentonia madagascariensis*), which now is on the point of becoming extinct. Many prosimian forms, including most of the indriids, have probably been killed off only since the island was colonized by man, as was the family Archaeolemuridae, ancient lemurs which with their short heads and various characteristics of brain and dentition were reminiscent of simians. There are also very primitive insectivores in the Madagascan Region, the tenrecs (Tenrecidae), which are closely related to the African otter shrews. Besides the Madagascan rats (Nesomyinae) and bats of the family Myzopodidae, the only mammals in Madagascar are three groups of primitive viverrids: four genera of Madagascar "mongoose" (Galidiinae), the falanoucs (genus *Eupleres*) and the closely related fanaloka (genus *Fossa*), and finally the confusingly named fossa (*Cryptoprocta ferox*), which perhaps is at the base of the evolutionary line of the felid and viverrid carnivores.

The bird fauna of the Madagascan Region also shows many distinctive traits. Particularly prominent are the elephant birds (Aepyornithidae), which became extinct or were killed off within historical times, as well as the thrush-sized stilt-rails (Mesitornithidae), the Couniae, cuckoo-rollers (Leptosomatinae), ground rollers (Brachypteraciinae), asitys (Philepittidae) and vangas (Vangidae). The relationship between the Madagascan and the Oriental Regions is often overemphasized; on the contrary, certain ancient plant and animal groups indicate a relationship to the Neotropical —the musaceous fan-palmlike *Ravenala*, the bolyerine snakes (closely related to the boas), the Madagascan iguanas (*Oplurus* and *Chalarodon*) and the turtle *Podocnemis madagascariensis*, a genus also represented by several species in South America.

The faunas of Africa and southern Asia match so well that the latter area cannot be classified as a kingdom, but rather must be considered a region of the Paleotropical Kingdom. Common to both Oriental and Ethiopian Regions are conspicuous mammals like the elephant, rhinoceros, bovids, antelopes and gazelles. A large part of the present-day African steppe fauna also, as fossil finds in the Siwalik strata south of the Himalayas have revealed, lived in India in the late Tertiary and into the early Pleistocene. The deer, however, which are represented by so many species in the Oriental, have not reached the Ethiopian. Animals entirely restricted to the Oriental include insects (cellar beetles, family Trictenotomidae), reptiles (the earless monitors, family Lanthanotidae and gavials, family Gavialidae), birds (the leaf-birds, family Irenidae) and mammals—the tree-shrews (Tupaiidae), tarsiers (Tarsiidae), gibbons (Hylobatidae) and rodents of the family Platacanthomyidae, closely related to the dormice.

The Oriental Region

There are a remarkably large number of carnivore species endemic to the Oriental Region. The viverrids have evolved a particular variety of forms, distributed among four subfamilies; to mention only a few, there are the linsangs (genus *Prionodon*), palm civet (genus *Paradoxurus*), three-striped palm civet (genus *Arctogalidia*), brown palm civet (genus *Macrogalidia*), binturong (*Arctictis binturong*), otter and banded palm civets (Hemigalinae), stink badgers (genera *Mydaus* and *Suillotaxus*), ferret badgers (genus *Melogale*), Indian bear, Malayan sun bear, marbled cat, bay cat and other cat species.

The kingdom which at present houses the fewest animals is the Archinotic, the "ancient south" mentioned above. Fossil finds show that

Antarctica

Antarctica was not always as inimical to life as it is now. For example, coal deposits have been found here, remains of the flora of the former Gondwana, with the fern *Glossopteris*, fossil amphibians and large carnivorous dinosaurs like the anomodontian *Lystrosaurus*. Of particular interest are the dinosaur remains first discovered in 1970/71, which document the relationship to South Africa. For example, the cotylosaurian *Procolophon trigoniceps* and several theriodonts appear to have lived simultaneously in South Africa and Antarctica. Today the antarctic flora is essentially restricted to algae and lichens; the southernmost edge of the range of higher plants lies about at 68° south latitude, where *Colobanthus crassifolius* and *Deschampsia antarctica* can still live. Invertebrates are represented in Antarctica primarily by tardigrades, mites and insects (including the springtails so characteristic of glacier areas).

Vertebrates can thrive in the region of the South Pole only if their food is provided by the ocean. A prime example is the penguin, which because of the impermeability of its plumage to water, its insulating layer of fat (2–3 cm thick), and various behavioral traits tending to increase basal metabolic rate are superbly adapted to life in the antarctic coastal regions. To be sure, there is only one species that breeds on the antarctic continent, to within about 1400 kilometers from the South Pole; this is the emperor penguin (*Aptenodytes forsteri*). In earlier periods, perhaps even as recently as the Tertiary, the antarctic was an arc of dry land, free of ice, reaching from New Zealand to South America. Certain plant communities became dispersed along this bridge, and remnants of them still survive in the forests of southern beech (*Nothofagus*) found both in Chile and New Zealand.

Faunal kingdoms of the ocean

The ocean can be divided into faunal kingdoms comparable to those on the continents. As was described in Chapter 17, there are three major realms in the ocean—the neritic province, the upper oceanic province, and the deep sea—and within each of these one can distinguish different faunal regions and subregions. The coastal fauna, restricted to the shelf and the waters above it, is subdivided more sharply than the others because of the barriers presented by the continents and the open ocean. It comprises three kingdoms: the tropical, the northern and the southern.

The Tropical Kingdom is made up of the following parts: 1, the Indo-Western Pacific Region, including the Malayan, south central Pacific, Hawaiian, southern Japanese, northern Australian and Indian districts; 2, the Eastern Pacific Region; 3, the Western Atlantic Region; 4, the Eastern Atlantic Region. This kingdom is characterized by coral reefs, described in detail in Chapter 17. Of the many species in its fauna we mention here in particular those members of various fish families collectively called "coral fish"—the butterfly fishes (Chaetodontidae), demoiselles (Pomacentridae), parrot fishes (Scaridae), wrasses (Labridae) and groupers and sea basses (Serranidae).

The Northern and Southern Kingdoms are also divided into a number

THE FAUNA OF WALLACEA AND THE AUSTRALIAN REGION

FISH: 1. Diagonal-banded sweetlips (*Plectorhynchus goldmani*); 2. Butterflyfish (*Chelmon rostratus*); 3. Angelfish (*Pomacanthus semicirculatus*); 4. Butterflyfish (*Chaetodon ephippium*); 5. Grouper (*Epinephelus cyanostigma*); 6. Striped triggerfish (*Balistapus undulatus*); 7. Leafy sea dragon (*Phyllopteryx eques*).

REPTILES: 8. Sea krait (*Laticauda semifasciata*); 9. Komodo dragon (*Varanus (komodensis*); 10. Snake-necked turtle (*Chelodina longicollis*); 11. Moloch (*Moloch horridus*); 12. Bluetongued skink (*Tiliqua rugosa*); 13. Tuatara (*Sphenodon punctatus*).

BIRDS: 14. Rose cockatoo, (*Kakatoe moluccensis*); 15. King of dauony's bird of paradise (*Pteridophora alberti*); 16. Geoffroyus geoffroyi; 17. Red bird of paradise (*Paradisaea rubra*); 18. Australian cassowary (*Casuarius casuarius*); 19. Golah (*Kakatoe roseicapilla*); 20. Kagu (*Rhynochetos jubatus*); 21. Zebra finch (*Taeniopygia guttata castanotis*); 22. Emu (*Dromaius novaehollandiae*); 23. Parakeet or budgerigar (*Melopsittacus undulatus*); 24. Little penguin (*Eudyptula minor*); 25. Takahe (*Notornis mantelli hochstetteri*); 26. Greater Owen's kiwi (*Apteryx owenii haasti*); 27. Striped bower bird (*Amblyornis subalaris*).

MONOTREMES: 28. Duck-billed platypus (*Ornithorhynchus anatinus*); 29. Bruijn long-nosed spiny anteater (*Zaglossus bruijni*); 30. Australian short-nosed spiny anteater (*Tachyglossus aculeatus*).

MARSUPIALS: 31. Spotted cuscus (*Phalanger maculatus*); 32. Yellow-bellied glider (*Petaurus australis*); 33. Koala (*Phascolarctos cinereus*); 34. Gray kangaroo. (*Macropus giganteus*); 35. Marsupial mole (*Notoryctes typhlops*); 36. Eastern Australian native cat (*Dasyurus quoll*); 37. Large rabbit bandicoot (*Macrotis lagotis*); 38. Marsupial anteater (*Myrmecobius fasciatus*); 39. Tasmanian devil (*Sarcophilus harrisi*).

ARTIODACTYLS: 40. Anoa (*Bubalus depressicornis*); 41. Babirusa (*Babyrousa babyrussa*).

THE FAUNA OF SOUTH AMERICA (NEOTROPICAL)

INVERTEBRATES: 1. Stonefly (order Plecoptera).

FISH: 2. Frogfish (*Histrio histrio*); 3. Ocean sunfish (*Mola mola*); 4. Piranha (*Serrasalmus piraya*).

REPTILES: 5. Mexican beaded lizard (*Heloderma horridum*); 6. Galapagos tortoise (*Testudo elephantopus*); 7. Marine iguana (*Amblyrhynchus cristatus*); 8. Common iguana (*Iguana iguana*); 9. Anaconda (*Eunectes murinus*); 10. Bushmaster (*Lachesis mutus*); 11. Smooth-throated lizard (*Liolaemus magellanicus*).

BIRDS: 12. Buff-bellied hummingbird (*Amazilia yucatanensis*); 13. Quetzal (*Pharomachrus mocino*); 14. American flamingo (*Phoenicopterus ruber ruber*); 15. White-necked jacobin (*Florisuga mellivora*); 16. Brown pelican (*Pelicanus occidentalis*); 17. *Phalacrocorax harrisi*; 18. Galapagos penguin (*Spheniscus mendiculus*); 19. King vulture (*Sarcoramphus papa*); 20. Scarlet macaw (*Ara macao*); 21. Red-breasted toucan (*Ramphastos dicolorus*); 22. Orange-winged amazon (*Amazona amazonica*); 23. Andean condor (*Vultur gryphus*); 24. Peruvian booby (*Sula variegata*); 25. Guanay cormorant (*Phalacrocorax bougainville*); 26. Paradise tanager (*Tangara chilensis*); 27. Common rhea (*Rhea americana*); 28. Slender-billed parakeet (*Enicognathus leptorhynchus*); 29. Puna tinamou (*Tinamotis pentlandii*); 30. Darwin's shea (*Pterocnemia pennata*); 31. Magellanic penguin (*Spheniscus magellanicus*).

MARSUPIALS: 32. Yapok (*Chironectes minimus*).

INSECTIVORES: 33. Haitian solenodon (*Solenodon paradoxus*).

BATS: 34. Vampire bat (*Desmodus rotundus*).

EDENTATES: 35. Three-fingered sloth (*Bradypus tridactylus*); 36. Giant anteater (*Myrmecophaga tridactyla*); 37. La Plata three-banded armadillo (*Tolypeutes matacus*).

SIMIANS: 38. Red howler monkey (*Alouatta seniculis*); 39. Emperor tamarin (*Saguinus imperator*).

TAPIRS: 40. Lowland tapir (*Tapirus terrestris*).

ARTIODACTYLS: 41. Vicuna (*Lama vicugna*); 42. Guanaco (*Lama guanicoë*).

CARNIVORES: 43. Jaguar. (*Panthera onca*); 44. Red coati (*Nasua nasua*); 45. South American fur seal (*Arctocephalus australis*).

RODENTS: 46. Orange-sumped agouti (*Dasyprocta aguti*); 47. Chinchilla (*Chinchilla laniger*); 48. Capybara (*Hydrochoerus hydrochaeris*); 49. Guinea pig (*Cavia aperea*); 50. Viscacha (*Lagostomus maximus*); 51. Mara (*Dolichotis patagonum*).

CETACEANS: 52. Amazon dolphin (*Inia geoffrensis*).

of regions. In the north these are the Mediterranean-Atlantic, the Sarmatic, the Boreal Atlantic, the Baltic, the Northern Pacific and the Arctic Regions, and in the south the South African, South Australian, Peruvian, South American and Kerguelen Regions. The distribution of the fauna adapted to the upper oceanic province is much more strongly affected by temperature and other environmental influences than that in the neritic regions. The abyssal fauna, together with that in the deep trenches, is separated into regions associated with geographical aspects of the deep ocean floor; these regions are termed the Arctic, Atlantic, Indo-Pacific and Antarctic.

The faunal kingdoms of the continents and the ocean, a rough outline of which has been presented here, basically represent only the framework for a much more detailed zoogeographic organization. Animals are dependent upon their environment—the vegetation, other animals, man and abiotic influences which together make up the habitat. Animals occupying the same habitat, reproducing there and living in mutual dependence, form a community. Community and habitat together form a unit with a dynamic behavior of its own. Individual organisms within this unit can replace one another without damaging the system as a whole. The more diverse the niches available in a habitat, the greater the number of species making up the animal community there; its diversity is limited by competition among its members. Where the environmental conditions are relatively uniform throughout fewer species can live side by side than where conditions change more rapidly in space or time.

Communities and habitats

The classification of communities meshes with that of the great climatic and vegetation belts of the earth. The basic level of classification is determined by plant community types such as the tropical rainforest, montane forest, savanna, tundra, taiga and desert. Plant communities at this level, together with the animals adapted to them, can be called biomes; they represent the largest community unit. The arid-savanna biome, for example, is composed of the plant community "arid savanna" and the savanna fauna characteristic of it. Biomes are arranged on the earth in a regular manner corresponding to the climatic zones. A biome comprises all the smaller communities in the area it covers, in all their developmental stages; all the communities evolving toward the same climax stage belong to the same biome. Since a biome is essentially determined by the climate, it can be modified only by fundamental climatic changes.

Biomes

The concept of a biome, based largely on plant communities, allows for the inclusion of several smaller ecosystems. There are ecosystems not based on living plants, which instead obtain a large part of the food at the lowest level of the chain from outside the system. This is true, for example, of the many cave communities and for the fauna of the deep-sea trenches. The decisive factor is that in an ecosystem there is a cycling of matter and energy. It may be relatively independent of its surroundings, as are tropical rainforests and coral reefs, or it may be dependent upon the provision

Ecosystems

of matter and energy from other ecosystems. Even a modern industrial city is an example of an ecosystem.

Numerous animals that live in certain biomes display characteristic adaptations to them. These life-form types may have evolved convergently in different systematic groups and in biomes widely separated in space. For example, many desert snakes—including the sidewinder (*Crotalus cerastes*), the common sand viper (*Cerastes vipera*) and the dwarf puff adder (*Bitis peringueyi*)—have evolved a sidewinding form of locomotion as an adaptation to open terrain. Other very interesting forms of adaptation are the ability to bury themselves in the sand, the migration of the eyes toward the top of the head, and the adoption of a warning signal that consists in rubbing the scales together, rather than hissing.

There are as many biomes as there are major plant formations. Their diversity has been indicated in the preceding chapters on terrestrial and aquatic habitats and their faunas. Those descriptions introduced us to the dynamic relationships between the plants and animals currently inhabiting the earth, the ecological dependence of animal species and their spatial and temporal distribution. Now that we have become familiar with these contemporary aspects, it is appropriate to consider the historical aspect of zoogeography.

Historical zoogeography

Historical zoogeography attempts to clarify the way ranges of distribution have evolved together with the organisms. There are areas on earth that have remained largely unchanged for a long time, and other enormously dynamic areas that have continued to change until most recently. The length of time a species has inhabited a given place on earth is only very rarely associated with the geographic age of that place. The fact that a species or genus is now distributed in South America by no means implies that it originated there. To carry out a precise investigation of the history of an animal's range, one must know all the facts affecting and determining the present-day environment as well as the evolutionary development of the terrain and the species itself.

If one wished to ascribe the presence of closely related animal groups in different parts of the world simply to the existence at some time in the past of land or water bridges, without taking into account evolution and the possibilities for dispersal currently available, there would be no place on earth where such an explanation could not in principle apply. Many such bridges are known to have existed, but their existence is not necessarily corroborated by the occurrence of related animals in the two areas so connected. In fact, ill-founded "bridge building" has been done often enough to damage the field of zoogeography considerably. But it is worth mentioning a few of the suggested bridges of earlier eras.

Schuchert Land

Schuchert Land, in the view of Schuchert and Ihering, was a North American-Pacific mountain chain which in the Cretaceous joined North America and South America, between the Pacific coast in the west and the Missouri Basin (which was occupied by the Tethys Sea) in the east.

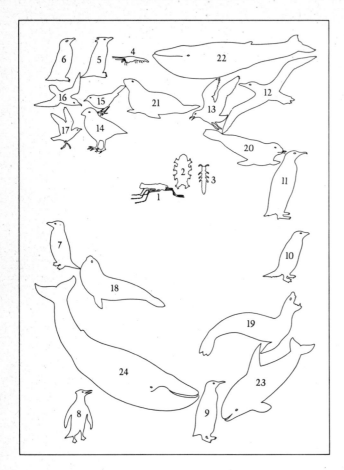

THE FAUNA OF THE ANTARCTIC
(ARCHINOTIC)

INVERTEBRATES: 1. Midge (Chironomidae); 2. Tardigrade (*Macrobiotus hufelandi*); 3. Springtail (Collembola); 4. "Krill" shrimp (*Euphausia superba*).

BIRDS: 5. Macaroni penguin (*Eudyptes chrysolophus*); 6. Magellanic penguin (*Spheniscus magellanicus*); 7. Chinstrap penguin (*Pygoscelis antarctica*); 8. Yellow-eyed penguin (*Megadyptes antipodes*); 9. King penguin (*Aptenodytes patagonica*); 10. Adelie penguin (*Pygoscelis adeliae*); 11. Emperor penguin (*Aptenodytes forsteri*); 12. Wandering albatross (*Diomedea exulans*); 13. Skua (*Stercorarius skua*); 14. Snowy sheathbill (*Chionis alba*); 15. Antarctic pipit (*Anthus antarctica*); 16. Magellan diving petrel (*Pelecanoides magellani*); 17. Wilson's storm petrel (*Oceanites oceanicus*).

PINNIPEDS: 18. Ross seal (*Ommatophoca rossi*); 19. Leopard seal (*Hydrurga leptonyx*); 20. Crab-eater seal (*Lobodon carcinophagus*); 21. Weddell seal (*Leptonychotes weddelli*).

WHALES: 22. Common rorqual (*Balaenoptera physalus*); 23. Killer whale or orca (*Orcinus orca*); 24. Blue whale (*Balaenoptera musculus*).

Lemuria

Lemuria was constructed on paper by Sclater and Ihering as a land bridge connecting Madagascar and India, in order to explain the present distribution of the Madagascan and Indian prosimians. More recent biogeographical investigations, however, have demonstrated the individuality of the Madagascan fauna; moreover, it has been possible to show that many of the Madagascan animals immigrated by way of the ocean.

Beringia

◁

THE MAJOR BIOMES
OF THE WORLD
1 Desert and semidesert biomes
2 Antarctic biome
3 Steppe biome
4 Arctic biome
5 Tundra biome
6 Montane forest biomes
7 Winter deciduous forest biomes
8 Boreal coniferous forest biome
9 Subtropical forest biomes
10 Mediterranean biomes
11 Savanna biomes
12 Rainforest biome
13 Montane forest biome
14 Mangrove biome
15 *Nothofagus* biome

As early as the time of Count Buffon (1707–1788) it was supposed that a Beringia bridge had once existed between Eurasia and North America. According to more recent paleontological, geological and biogeographical findings, this Beringia formed several times during the Tertiary and the glacial epochs of the Pleistocene. Across it proceeded an exchange of animals that was of great significance to both the Old World and the New. Successive strata of marine and terrestrial deposits in the Bering-Chuckchee platform, with giant redwoods and other plants, indicate that in the early Tertiary there were various land connections across the Bering Strait. But at the beginning of the Quaternary these were submerged under sea water and the bridge was broken; the extent of the flooding can be determined by an ancient coastal reef that runs from the Arctic coast as far as the Yukon River. The gastropod genus *Neptunea*, which during the Tertiary was still restricted to the Pacific Ocean, begins to appear in Atlantic sediments formed after this period of flooding. During the subsequent Ice Age Beringia formed anew, as a result of the lowered sea level. Pollen investigations, core samples and C^{14}-dating, however, show that the bridge was submerged repeatedly during the interglacial epochs and finally vanished at the end of the Pleistocene.

Archiplata

Archiplata, according to Ihering, is a connection that was formed during the Cretaceous from a South Pacific land bridge (Archinotica) to the part of Schuchert Land where the Andes of South America now stand. During the Tertiary North and South America exchanged animals across Archiplata.

Archiguiana

An island assumed to have existed during the Cretaceous in the region of Venezuela and the former Guianas is called Archiguiana. The island is thought to have convered an area identical to the present-day range of numerous monospecific genera, such as the vulturine parrot (*Gypopsitta vulturina*), the cotingids *Perissocephalus tricolor* and *Haematoderus militaris*, and the tyrant-flycatcher *Microcochlearis josephinae*. More recent biogeographical investigations have revealed, however, that this distribution was brought about by very recent shifts in the rainforest.

Archhelenica

The mesozoic Archhelenica is a suggested land bridge joining eastern South America with southwestern Africa by way of the island Tristan da Cunha. It was intended to help explain the similarities between the old African and South American faunas. As Kosswig showed in 1944, however, the relationships of South American animals to African ones can also be elucidated on the basis of other considerations. This applies to the millipede family Spirostreptidae, the bivalve family Mutelidae and numerous parasites such as *Nesoelecithus*, as well as characid and cichlid fish, pipid frogs and the mesosaurid reptiles, now known only as fossils. The ranges of all these animals include both South America and considerable parts of Africa.

A Cretaceous land bridge supposed to have connected the Antilles and Florida to northern Africa and southern Spain, and to have included the Azores, Canaries and Cape Verde Islands, is called Archatlantica. It was meant to explain, among other things, the distribution of the manatee (genus *Trichechus*), which appears on both sides of the Atlantic.

As early as the 19th Century biogeographers were beginning to guess that the Archinotic Kingdom mentioned above once—in the Cretaceous and early Tertiary—served as a land bridge from southern South America across the antarctic and the South Pacific islands to New Zealand and Australia. This is still considered a valid assumption today, for there is no other reasonable way to explain the close relationship between the plant and animal groups distributed on either side of the South Pacific. This relationship is exemplified by the beech *Nothofagus*, the fresh-water crustacean family Parastacidae, stoneflies of the family Eustheniidae, chironomid midges, terrestrial gastropods of the family Bulimulidae, and snake-necked turtles (Chelidae).

As we can see from all the precedings, in most cases the former presence of such land bridges is called into question by considerations of geology and the known history of animal dispersal. Currently, geologists have compiled an array of crucial facts which support the view held by Alfred Wegener in 1929 concerning movements of the continents. The idea of Gondwana has once again become highly significant.

Gondwana is the name given to a continent existing in the southern hemisphere in the Paleozoic and comprising what are now South America Africa, Madagascar, India and Australia; according to Wegener, this ancient continent disintegrated when the continents shifted apart. The inferred position of Gondwana offers a key to the distribution of numerous animal and plant species of the Mesozoic—the fern *Glossopteris* and the mesosaurian reptiles, to mention but two. To the northwest of Gondwana lay the ancient continent Laurasia, which comprised present-day North America, Greenland, Scandinavia and parts of Siberia. In Wegener's opinion, Laurasia continued into the Cenozoic to consist of two continental blocks cut off by the Tethys Sea; one of these, Laurentia, was composed of the northern parts of North America, and the other, Angaria, was a forerunner of Eurasia. The phylogeny of Permian and Mesozoic reptiles can be related to the assumed degree of separation between Gondwana and Laurasia during these eras. The evolution and division into branches of the Cotylosauria, Testudines, Eosuchia, Rhynchocephalia and ornithischian dinosaurs took place in Gondwana, while the saurischian dinosaurs evolved in Laurasia.

Archatlantica

The South Pacific land bridge

Gondwana and Laurasia

The notion of the existence of Gondwana and Laurasia was debated for a long time, as were their implications with respect to animal evolution. But in recent years the fundamental work of Hennig, Brundin and Illies has demonstrated that the results of geophysical studies by the Wegener school are extremely well corroborated by zoogeography. Edwin Hennig has shown that the evolutionary history of animal species also illuminates the evolution of land masses and local terrain. Of course, species and individuals can be passively dispersed around the world, so that one must be well aware of the means of dispersal a species has at its disposal in order to make valid zoogeographical inferences.

Biogeography of islands

The study of islands, in particular, has brought about a deeper understanding of the possible ways in which individual species can be dispersed. Island faunas have elucidated fundamental processes such as the colonization of new areas, expansion of range, competition, adaptation to difficult environments, crowding out and eventual extinction. In so doing, they have provided important documentation for research into phylogeny. Island animals can help to explain the dynamics of the distribution of related continental species; they can shed light upon earlier geological and climatic conditions and thus increase our comprehension of the relationships in present-day environments.

According to the equilibrium theory developed by Preston, Mac-Arthur and Wilson, the species coming as new immigrants to an island and those becoming extinct there are numerically in balance. The success of the original colonization of an island depends upon its size as well as upon its distance from the site of origin of the colonists. The curve representing rate of colonization can rise with very different slopes, but eventually —after a time depending upon the size of the island and the sort of environment it offers—it reaches a maximum. After this additional species can become established only to the extent that existing species disappear.

Surtsey

In certain islands of known age the rate of colonization can be investigated directly. A very good example here is Surtsey, an island of 2.7 square kilometers thirty kilometers south of Iceland, which was formed on November 14, 1963 as a result of an undersea volcanic eruption. At first it was without life; the process of natural colonization has since been studied by many biologists. The first insect observed on the island, on May 14, 1964, was a chironomid midge, *Diamesa zernyi*. In the fall of 1964 an owlet moth, *Agrotis ypsilon*, was caught there. By 1968 seventy species of living arthropods had been collected on Surtsey; the dipterans predominated, with forty-three species. In contrast to the arthropods, most of which immigrated by air, the five species of higher plant found there by 1968— *Cakile edentula, Cakile maritima, Elymus arenarius, Honckenya peploides* and *Mertensia maritima*—came to Surtsey across the ocean. No lichen species had reached the island by that time, but numerous terrestrial algae could be demonstrated. Surtsey is an impressive illustration of the conditions under which a new ecosystem can be built up on an originally infertile island.

Another example, the 832-m-high volcanic island Krakataó to the west of Java, has achieved worldwide fame. It was covered by forest up to the peak of the volcano. On August 26 and 27, 1883, an eruption destroyed its plant and animal life and reduced the size of the island from the original 32.5 square kilometers to 10.64 square kilometers. Only three years later it was shown that twenty-seven higher plants were growing on the island that remained; in 1897 the number had grown to sixty-two, and by 1906 there were a total of 114 species. Most of these had been carried there through the air. In 1898 Krakataó was inhabited by forty species of arthropod, two species of reptile and sixteen species of bird; a count of species in 1923 revealed 500 arthropods, seven land gastropods, three reptiles (one of them a snake), twenty-six birds with breeding grounds on the island, two bats and one rat. Krakatao

In their species composition, both Krakataó and Surtsey show that organisms differ greatly in their ability to extend their ranges at different stages of development of a community. These islands also indicate that the "ecological valence" of a species has a decisive effect upon its dispersal. Although some species are able to fly or cross great distances by other means, they make no use of this capacity to colonize such new areas, whereas other species evidently are routinely represented among the "aerial plankton." Above all, the examples of Krakataó and Surtsey make it possible to understand the development of other island faunas which have frequently presented problems to zoogeographers attempting to establish a temporal organization. Here we shall mention two oceanic (i.e., beyond the continental shelf) islands—Hawaii and the Galapagos.

On the basis of its fauna, which is particularly rich in endemic forms, some scientists have regarded the Hawaiian Islands as a faunal kingdom in its own right. This Pacific island group is of Pliocene origin; it was created by volcanic activity and was never joined to a continental land mass. All the animals living there immigrated by sea, and the early immigrants subsequently evolved into new species. This is true, for example, of the honeycreepers (the bird family Drepanidae), found only in Hawaii, and the gastropod families Achatinellidae and Amastridae. Other native birds deserving mention are the nene goose *Branta sandvicensis*, a distant relative of the Canada goose, and five species of honey eaters (of the genera *Moho* and *Chaetoptila*); populations of the nene goose have now declined ominously, and four of the five honeycreeper species have probably been completely exterminated. Fresh-water fish, amphibians and numerous invertebrates, including the large snail *Achatina fulica*, were introduced by man. Hawaii

The geological status of the Galapagos is similar. Its unique fauna stimulated Charles Darwin to develop his theory of evolution. It was in the Galapagos that Darwin recognized the significance of spatial isolation in the development of new species. Vertebrates notably lacking here are fresh-water fish and amphibians; the vertebrates that are native to the The Galapagos

Galapagos indicate very intimate relationships with the area between the Andes and the Pacific, with Central America and, though to a much smaller extent, with the Antilles.

The marine iguana *Amblyrhynchus cristatus* is represented by several closely related subspecies on the islands of Narborough, Albemarle and Indefatigable, which lie within the 200-m-depth line, whereas the subspecies found on James Island (*A. cristatus mertensi*) diverges more markedly. There is also another iguanid genus, *Conolophus*, with two species, living only on the Galapagos. The closest relatives of *Amblyrhynchus* and *Conolophus*—the common iguana and the black iguana—are distributed in Central and Southern America.

None of the remaining reptiles of the Galapagos can be assigned to genera different from those on the mainland; they are related to forms living in the coastal regions of the Andean countries. Among them are the lizard *Tropidurus galapagoensis* and the three species of Galapagos snake (*Dromicus biserialis*, *Dromicus dorsalis* and *Dromicus slevini*), which can be derived from *Dromicus chamissonis* of western South America; all four species of snake are distinguished by similar scale structure. It is striking that the species are not uniformly distributed; on the eastern island, Chatham, there are three species, whereas all the other islands are inhabited by only one species.

The giant tortoise of the Galapagos, *Testudo elephantopus*, is also derived from ancestral forms on the South American continent; they are put together with the South American land tortoises in the subgenus *Geochelone* and thus are not particularly closely related to the giant tortoises of the Seychelles, which belong to the subgenus *Aldabrachelys*. In this regard it is worth mentioning the occurrence of a giant tortoise (*Testudo cubensis*) during the Pleistocene in Cuba; the resemblance between this ancient tortoise and the Galapagos tortoise is strong. Another tortoise, *Testudo praestans*, has been found as a Pleistocene fossil in Argentina; it has characteristics of both the present-day South American tortoises and the extinct Cuban giant tortoise, and deserves consideration as an ancestral form. There are many indications that the Galapagos giant tortoise reached this island group no earlier than the beginning of the Pleistocene, either by swimming or by riding on floating tree trunks.

Other immigrants that came over the sea are the eighty-nine species of bird which breed on the Galapagos. Among them are the flightless cormorant *Nannopterum harrisi*, the Galapagos penguin (*Spheniscus mendiculus*), the swallow-tailed gull (*Creagrus furcatus*), the dusky gull (*Larus fuliginosus*), the Galapagos mockingbird (*Nesomimus parvulus*) and, above all, the now-famous Darwin finch (tribe Geospizini; thirteen species of which inhabit the Galapagos and one, the island of Cocos off Costa Rica, about 800 kilometers away to the northeast. Probably the Darwin finches have ancestors in common with the Cuba finches (genus *Tiaris*). A family conspicuous by its absence from the Galapagos is that of the hummingbirds.

Apart from the Galapagos fur seal (*Arctocephalus galapagoensis*) and a subspecies of the California sea lion (*Zalophus californianus wollebaeki*), the mammalian fauna of these islands is composed of only small forms. Among them are the bat *Lasiurus brachyotis* and the hoary bat (*Lasiurus cinereus*), the rice rats *Oryzomys galapagoensis* and *O. bauri*, and other rodents, including *Megalornys curioi, Nesoryzomys indefessus, N. darwini, N. swarthi* and *N. narboroughi*. These have been joined by animals introduced by man—mice, rats and many domestic animals that have gone wild, all of which now do considerable damage to the native fauna and flora.

The ecology and phylogeny of animals and the developmental history of their habitats can illuminate one another if the centers from which the animals became dispersed are clarified and pinpointed geographically. By centers of dispersal are meant the places where the animals and plants were able to survive even the most unfavorable periods in their history—ages of drought, glacial epochs, unusually intense competition from other species, and so on. In such places the complex of environmental conditions was such as to allow permanent viability of the communities present in them. These centers basically arose as places of refuge to which animal populations retreated as conditions elsewhere changed for the worse; here they lived in isolation from other regions and populations. This, of course—the geographical separation of sections of an originally uniform population—is one of the most important factors leading to the evolution of new species and subspecies.

Centers of dispersal

Everything that we can learn about these centers is important not only to zoogeography but as an aid in understanding the evolution of organisms. They can illuminate features of the earth's geological and climatic history, which naturally affected the course of phylogenetic development, and can expand our knowledge of the processes shaping the land today. One such center in the pampa of Argentina, for example, is inhabited by an independent population of animals adapted to open, unforested terrain; this fact argues against the view that the pampa was woodland before the arrival of man. Of course, it must first be demonstrated that for the animal groups concerned such a region actually is the center where they have survived through past ages. This can be difficult, if they are not represented by special subspecies in the region.

It is quite conceivable for a species to come into being in some particular place and later, because of a number of chance events, to become extinct in that place although continuing to survive in one or more other, recently colonized regions. In fact, the present range of a species by no means necessarily corresponds to the center of origin of the species, and may not even include that center. Particular study of present-day ranges is required to discover their relationships to the centers of origin. To decide such questions for genera, families and higher taxa, it is necessary to have a complete picture of their phylogenetic history, but there are only a

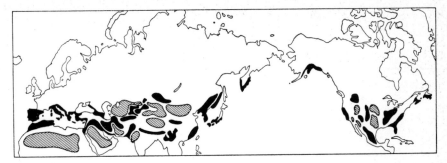

Fig. 19-4. Centers of dispersal of the holarctic forest and steppe fauna.
Black zones: forest areas; cross-hatched: steppe areas.

Subspecies, species and superspecies

few such animal groups for which a satisfactory evolutionary account exists. Initially, then, it is most practical to limit the study of centers of origin to species, superspecies and geographical subspecies.

Subspecies are defined as populations of a species which are geographically restricted to a certain area, often quite small, and which differ consistently from other populations of the same species with respect to at least one distinguishing characteristic. Subspecies are capable of cross-breeding, so that if the barriers originally separating them are removed zones of hybridization develop. The term superspecies, on the other hand, is used to designate a group of allopatric species of the same ancestry, which are very closely related but differ sufficiently in certain characteristics and are so little capable of fertile crossing that they are not considered a single species. One third of the Australian bird fauna belongs to such superspecies. Subspecies and superspecies have one thing in common: their ranges, apart from a few exceptions, are located in the vicinity of their centers of origin.

The above definition of "subspecies" should be qualified in one respect; the geographical isolation of parts of an originally uniform population is not the only way in which subspecies can evolve. They may come into being, for example, when animal groups migrate into habitats where certain conditions differ widely from those in the former habitat. Types already present in the original population but by chance better adapted to the new conditions than the others soon come to dominate in the new habitat, and in a short time the population as a whole is modified accordingly. Such a rapid evolution of subspecies is known to have occurred, for example, among the house sparrows introduced to North America toward the end of the 19th Century. Distributional centers can be determined by charting the smallest ranges of species, superspecies and subspecies on the map of a continent, faunal kingdom or smaller region. The different ranges do not, except in rare cases, correspond at their boundaries, but they do have common properties in the area where they overlap, the nucleus. Nuclei so determined are not necessarily centers of dispersal, but simply centers of the current distribution. Whether plant and animal groups can survive there when unfavorable environmental conditions prevail can be determined only by examining the systematic relationships of the organisms associated with these centers.

Fig. 19-5. Centers of dispersal of the South American land fauna.
Dotted: lowland rainforests black: montane forest centers; cross-hatched: centers in open country; white: alpine centers.

Every species has at least one center of dispersal—its center of origin. Since in the course of its evolution the species' range may move far from its center of origin, if conditions should worsen the range may contract to a new center of dispersal different from its center of origin. The centers of dispersal we observe now are thus simply the places in which the plant or animal groups have survived the most recent period of environmental stress. Today there are areas of refuge throughout the world to which plants and animals are withdrawing in order to survive despite the influences man, to an extent never before experienced, is exerting upon the environment.

Many of the the centers of dispersal that have been studied so far came into being during the Ice Age and in the postglacial period. In the northern parts of the Old and New World they form a continuous band along the southern margin of the region which was free of ice during the Würm glaciation. Here plant and animal species of Eurasia and North America found protection from the masses of ice moving down from the north and from the mountains. During the numerous glacial epochs in the last two million years, however, the cooler climate was not the only determining factor; in many places various aspects of the precipitation changed as well. The exact nature and effect of such changes within small areas is still not sufficiently well known. In any case, the climate in the tropics during the Ice Age was by no means constant; prolonged seasons of drought and rain alternated during the Pleistocene in South America, Africa, New Guinea and Australia.

The result of this, as seen for example in tropical Africa, was large-scale shifts in the pattern of vegetation which had a decisive effect upon speciation in the African fauna. In the Australian fauna, too, the evolution of species and subspecies is to a great extent ascribable to the isolation of populations during a period of dry climate along the edge of the continent; time estimates for this epoch of drought which determined the centers of dispersal in Australia, however, range from 4000 to 20,000 years. Pollen studies and geological investigations confirm these inferences in both Africa and Australia.

The same processes of isolation, evidently also associated with dry periods and shifts in the vegetation, operated in South America. Here, though, there was expansion of the savanna in various places (the so-called campos) even in postglacial times, in the course of which animals of the relatively densely wooded savannas (the campos cerrados) migrated to Amazonia. This expansion of the savanna occurred 8000 to 4400 years ago; at that time the open terrain extended from Cabo Frio to Rio Grande do Sul, and there was a period of drought in northeastern Brazil. Then, 4400 years ago, there began a reexpansion of the forest which still continues today; this interrupted almost all the routes of migration of the animals adapted to open country.

Within the Amazonian rainforests there are islands of campo, which

Range displacements

▷
A prehistoric drama, captured on a cave wall in Lascaux (France) 12,000–15,000 years ago. A wounded wisent, its entrails hanging out, attacks a man—perhaps the magician of a rival totem group, as the staff with a bird at its tip would indicate.

Range displacements in South America

have a characteristic flora and fauna and are joined to one another by a bridge of savanna-climate. They must be regarded as relics of these drought epochs of the very recent past. The positions of the South American centers of dispersal, especially those of the forest regions, were decisively affected by the epochs of drought. In the region of the campo migration routes, which the forest has reclaimed only in the last 4000 years, there are strips where forest populations intermingle with those of the open country. The beginning and the end of the Quaternary period of dryness are characterized by a humid climate and expansion of the rainforest. Consequently, the populations of animals adapted to open country became isolated. The campo cerrado mentioned above, which from the beginning of the Quaternary drought epoch until the present has hampered or entirely prevented genetic exchange between the rainforest forms of the Brazilian coastal forests and those of the Amazonian forests, must have been considerably more densely forested in certain places 9000 years ago than it is today.

Not until the late Tertiary did the Andes reach their present altitude. In the Würm glaciation they, like the highest mountains of New Guinea and Africa, were covered by glaciers in many regions from Patagonia to Columbia. Afterward, as the climate became steadily warmer, various groups of animals began an accelerated process of separation into isolated populations by moving to higher altitudes; the animals now living in the montane forests and on the high plateaus once—as little as 13,000 years ago—preferred habitats in the flatland. For example, fossil finds have shown that the vicuna, now restricted to the high Andes, at that time lived in the broad pampas regions around Buenos Aires.

The number of centers of dispersal in the New World tropics can be compared with the enormous species diversity of South American biomes. Zoogeographers have demonstrated that the large number of species in the South American rainforest can to a considerable extent be ascribed to the fluctuating degree of isolation of sections of the forest during the periods of drought.

Centers of dispersal, too, can be subdivided according to their history. For example, within the Mediterranean center at least nine smaller centers can be distinguished. Selecting from these nine centers a single one—the Adriato-Mediterranean center, which includes Italy and Sicily—we find, upon investigating the refuge areas for heat- and cold-loving species, that still another level of subdivision is necessary. Heat-loving reptiles were distributed in small refuge areas near the coast during the Würm glaciation, because of the glaciers covering the Apennines. These former refuge areas are revealed by the evolution of subspecies among Italian lizards such as *Lacerta sicula*, *Podarcis*, *Archaeolacerta* and the emerald lizard.

The totality of communities to be assigned to given centers of dispersal thus is composed of many strata, with groups differing widely in age. We can understand this organization only by taking into account much

◁
Above: One of the most famous African rock paintings is the five-meter-long frieze in the Leopard Gorge of the Brandberg (South West Africa), in which bushmen and game animals surround a mysterious central figure, the "White Lady of Tsissab." Presumably the "White Lady" was really a male, the chieftain of an unknown hunting tribe. Below: In some primitive populations hunting is supplemented by the catching of small animals: a man of the Kaluli language group on Mount Bosavi in New Guinea shows off a bush rat he has captured. The Kaluli live in the tropical rainforest by gathering, hunting and cultivating small plots of land.

more ancient processes in the evolution of organisms and their habitats. And in so doing, we are involved with the evolutionary history of whole continents, and of the earth itself.

IV. MAN AS A FACTOR IN THE ENVIRONMENT OF ANIMALS

20 Man as Hunter and Gatherer

By H. Wendt

The history of man is also the history of his relationship to the earth and his biotic environment, the plants and animals. Man is the only organism to have made profound changes in the natural relationships that took millions of years to evolve; his influence has been disruptive and to a great extent destructive. Now his fate depends largely upon whether he can succeed in achieving a new equilibrium between the natural surroundings he has conquered and the civilization he has created.

Darwin's fundamental works on the origin of species and the descent of man have had a marked influence on the science of ethnology. They established a conceptual bond between the notion of evolution and the prehistory of humanity—the periods during which man's relationships to his environment changed and developed. As a result, a much more objective study of primitive tribes was begun, and their cultures came to be regarded as earlier stages in the process of evolution of more highly developed cultures. The hunting and gathering tribes themselves benefited from this interpretation of the theory of evolution. From the age of exploration until into the 19th Century members of civilized nations had thought nothing of slaughtering such "primitive" peoples or selling them as slaves and destroying their croplands. But now these "natural men" and all aspects of their lives became the focus of ethnological research. Primitive man was recognized as part of a harmonic natural order, in which he could exist without destroying its equilibrium.

Even today, of course, the scattered remnants of the primitive races suffer to some extent from the effects of civilization. Since the time of Darwin, however, an attempt has been made to follow the development of cultural relationships as far back into the past as possible and to obtain, from the study of the life and behavior of present-day primitive peoples, insight into the condition of humanity near its origin. Two important questions were immediately evident: What is the precise denotation of the term "man?" And in what sort of habitat was it possible for early man to evolve from the ancient anthropoid apes?

The answer to the question of the definition of man today seems self-evident. The first aspect that comes to mind is mental achievement—the development of the brain. But our highly developed brain, as the numerous fossil finds of manlike apes and early man testify, is a quite recent acquisition; the direct ancestors of the genus *Homo*, the australopithecines, had a brain volume of 400–680 cubic centimeters and thus surpassed the present-day anthropoid apes only slightly in this respect. The boundary between man and the great apes is so fluid that some anthropologists actually speak of an animal/man transition field. One must draw upon other indications, besides anatomical characteristics. But which ones? Speech and insightful action (for example, the use of fire) have been cited here by some researchers, but it is thought that the earliest humanids, the ramapithecines, and the australopithecines neither had the gift of speech nor had they recognized the value of fire.

Another characteristic which seems to provide a clearer distinction between man and the great apes is the making of tools. Indeed, it is quite easy to imagine that the accidental use of natural objects could mark the beginning of a line of development leading to the intentional application of these as tools, to improving and refining them, and eventually to the invention and production of specially designed tools. But even in this respect man is not unique among living beings. Very recent observations of free-living chimpanzees have revealed that these primates, our closest biological relatives, fish for termites with stalks of grass, bite twigs into a better shape for use as "tools," and use branches as weapons to fight off enemies such as leopards. The uncertainty anthropologists feel in defining "man" is also reflected in the fact that many fossil ramapithecines and australopithecines were classified as apes just after their discovery, before their manlike nature was recognized.

Even before the fossil australopithecines had been found, Darwin (in 1871) had set down in quite useful terms what the notion of man involves. ". . . for many actions," he wrote, "it is indispensable that the arms and whole upper part of the body should be free; and he must for this end stand firmly on his feet." In another place he wrote, "Man could never have attained his present dominant position in the world without the use of his hands, which are so admirably adapted to act in obedience to his will." The uniqueness of man, according to Darwin, thus involves primarily his bipedal gait and the freeing of his hands for the use of self-produced tools.

Such a "toolmaker" with upright posture could not have evolved in the jungle, as had been assumed in the early period of the study of evolution. Conditions in tropical rainforests are most unfavorable for ground-dwellers. The trees filter out almost all light, and above all there is no food suitable for the ancestors of man. Apart from a few "food specialists" most primates are naturally omnivorous, and the number of prey animals on the rainforest floor is not sufficient to support them. The human digestive system is not adjusted to a steady diet of nutrient-poor plants; the swollen bellies of the pygmies, and of other primitive peoples that have secondarily returned to the jungle, give evidence of this. This new anthropoid creature, walking upright on two legs, does not become a real man until he has a more open range than the jungle affords, and the opportunity to experience consciously a larger environment. Only then can he face nature and subordinate it to himself. Such considerations had already led to the conclusion that the ancestors of man must have lived in the steppe, even before the savanna-dwelling australopithecines were discovered.

According to the more recent excavations and datings, the ramapithecines lived about twelve million years ago, and the australopithecines five to one million years ago. Only scant remains of the ramapithecines have been found, so that we can say nothing about their appearance and behavior. Anthropologists like Gerhard Heberer assume, however, that the ramapithecines were savanna dwellers and may already have been able to use quite simple natural objects as tools. This is hardly sufficient, however, to justify defining them as "men" in the sense of cultural development.

We are much better acquainted with the environment and the culture of the australopithecines, evidence of which has been found chiefly in eastern and southern Africa. One of their discoverers, Raymond A. Dart, in the central Transvaal valley called Makapansgat, found not only numerous remains of australopithecines of the A Type (characterized by short stature) but also—along with them—partially crushed baboon skulls and a surprisingly large number of thigh bones of large and medium-sized antelopes. The knee joints of these femurs fit exactly into the marks in the damaged skulls. At the same sites Dart also collected many lower jaws of small antelopes, still retaining complete sets of teeth.

From all this Dart concluded that the australopithecines had lived not only as collectors of roots, fruits, berries and other vegetable food. They must have been hunters, and have been capable of bringing down even fairly large animals with their clubs of bone. Moreover, the lower jaws of the antelopes found by Dart would have served a primitive human very well as a rough sort of saw. Associated with these finds were many quartz tools about as large as one's hand, hammered at one end so as to form a sharp point or blade. Some even displayed as many as fourteen surfaces where their makers had chipped off splinters of stone to improve the shape. Later so-called "pebble tools" were found in association with the geologically older hominids discovered in eastern Africa. These too were very simple stone tools which might have been used to skin game after it had been killed. The ecological role of the australopithecines, then, was presumably that of well-armed predators which lived by hunting as well as by gathering.

The gathering of fruits, young shoots, and various roots, tubers and bulbs is just as ancient a primate inheritance as the supplementation of the vegetarian diet with insects, worms, bird eggs and small mammals. The

South American marmosets, tamarins, and titi monkeys, like the Asian gibbons, are extremely skilled at catching birds. Steppe baboons not only snatch up small mammals here and there, but when a favorable opportunity presents itself can even catch other monkeys (*Cercopithecus*). Evidence of hunting and meat-eating, then, among ramapithecines and australopithecines is not surprising.

In fact, the primate most closely related to us, the chimpanzee, according to the ethologist Jane van Lawick-Goodall, now and then displays distinct predator behavior. In the course of the many years she spent in the Gombe reserve of Tanzania she observed the chimpanzees that live there hunting and eating both juvenile and adult colobus monkeys, *Cercopithecus* and even young bushbuck and bush-pigs. Sometimes they catch their prey almost by accident. A little bush-pig runs across the path in front of a chimpanzee, and with little more than one snatch the victim is captured and killed. In other cases, however the chimpanzees hunt in a much more organized manner; the different animals in a group cooperate amazingly well, several chimpanzees positioning themselves so as to cut off all possibility of escape once the prey has been driven into a corner. Moreover, when eating meat the chimpanzees behave not much differently from members of primitive tribes which are still at the hunting level. Usually they chew each mouthful together with a few leaves; they consume their meat and vegetables simultaneously.

"Predator behavior" of chimpanzees

Carnivorous animals play an extremely important role in the balance of nature. They prevent population explosions among the herbivores; this contributes to maintenance of the vegetation and keeps the whole system in equilibrium. When omnivores, in the course of evolution, become more committed to hunting, this modification is often preceded by a change in the environment. This is especially true in the case of the ramapithecines and australopithecines. Environmental alterations can have a marked effect upon the activities of organisms that are only slightly specialized—those that are phylogenetically young and therefore still plastic. At first they adapt only a little, and are not noticeably changed by the new conditions, but as time passes natural selection ensures increasing dominance of those mutants best suited to the current environment; the latter reproduce more effectively than the "conservative" individuals. During the early Tertiary in Africa (especially in the north and south) there was a gradual shrinking of the rainforests, beginning in the Miocene and continuing through the Pliocene and into the first part of the Pleistocene. Again and again forest was replaced by savannas with fairly large trees and subsequently by nearly treeless steppes which offered insufficient food to strictly vegetarian primates.

Steppe formation and the development of hunting

It can be assumed that the ancestors of the australopithecines, and perhaps those of the chimpanzees as well, initially became accustomed to life at the edge of the jungle. Even today there are populations of chimpanzees that live in savannas or at least on the margins of savannas. As the conversion to steppe proceeded, the way of life of the ancestral "prehumans" had to change fundamentally. Another likely result of this change was that the ramapithecines, stronger both biologically and in their "weapons technology," drove the chimpanzees back into the forest. The upright gait suitable for life in the steppes resulted in progressive differentiation of the limbs. Since their hands were free, the australopithecines were better able to grasp useful objects and to manipulate and adapt them for defence against enemies or the killing of prey. They made up for the lack of vegetable food by turning more and more to meat-eating, and since the medium-sized and larger mammals of the steppes and savannas could not be brought down by one or just a few australopithecines, it became necessary for the men to join forces and hunt in groups.

The hunting/gathering level, simplest form of human economy

It is remarkable that, to judge by the finds made so far, the australopithecines hunted chiefly baboons, which were their main competitors for food. In addition they fed on spring hares and other rodents, and they could even overcome gazelles and antelopes. As a supplement to their diet they gathered roots and fruit. In contrast to the predatory animals, among the australopithecines it was presumably only the men that went out on hunts, for the women were tied to fixed camping places by pregnancy, giving birth, and the responsibilities of child care which lasted for years. In later hunting and gathering tribes, too, it has been primarily the men who provide the group with meat, while the women collect vegetable food and animals. Accordingly, the australopithecines had already reached the hunting and gathering level, the simplest form of human economy. Since they probably did not appear in great numbers in any particular place, it is unlikely that they disturbed the balance of nature any more than another of the carnivorous animal species with which they shared their habitat.

In the course of human evolution both hunting and gathering methods were continually refined. Among the early humans of Asia, Africa and Europe (*Homo erectus*), to whom a geological age of around half a million years is ascribed, Peking man in particular left behind whole storehouses of fossilized fruit and berries, as well as bones of deer, gazelles and wild horses, remains of ashes and stone tools. At this early-human stage fire was already in use; to make his fires Peking man chose primarily the wood of the Judas tree (*Cercis siliquastrum*). Not only did these men warm themselves by their campfires, but they roasted meat over them, as the large numbers of charred bones demonstrate.

Advances in the making of weapons and tools

Among the somewhat more recent pre-sapiens men a new weapon was introduced, which enabled the hunter to overcome even large game—a wooden spear hardened in the fire. The prey of these pre-sapiens people was probably similar to that of *Homo erectus*, but spear tips and stone tools originating in their culture have also been found together with the remains of bones of ancient elephants.

Further great advances in the art of making tools, weapons and traps were made by pre-Neanderthal and Neanderthal man. Depending on their specific environments they emphasized hunting, fishing or the gathering of wild plants. In the course of their gradual dispersal over the earth men adapted to a great variety of local situations and ecological conditions. As weapons technology was perfected the range of animals that Stone Age man could kill became ever greater.

At the Neanderthal stage the preferred game animal, the cave bear, began to appear as part of the cultural heritage, which already had reached a high degree of development. This ponderous, relatively large herbivore, which spent a third of its life in hibernation, was an ideal prey for the Neanderthal people—a living pantry, so to speak. Bear meat and bear fat were most palatable; bear skins provided protection from rain and cold, and bear bones could be made into weapons and other devices. When they were hungry in winter, these men wandered through the subterranean labyrinths, searching until they had found a niche in which a bear was slumbering; then they beat it to death with their clubs, dressed it and dragged it away with them.

In order to kill cave bears, the Neanderthal man of Mousterian times invented a stone axe-blade. To cut up their corpses and process their skins, he developed a new technique of manufacturing objects of flint and quartz. He fastened roughly shaped sharp fragments of stone to wooden shafts, and with these lances could kill bears even in inaccessible corners. Marks on certain cave walls, probably made by the blows of large paws and the scratching of claws, permit the inference that Neanderthal men even tried to catch the cave bears in traps or nooses.

The moment in history when man first succeeded in overpowering an animal ten times stronger and heavier than himself was a turning point; it marked a revolution not only in technology but in mental attitudes. The first magicians appeared; man set himself above nature and believed in the assistance of supernatural powers. In certain caves strange accumulations of bear bones have been discovered—for example, in the Drachenloch, above Vättis (Switzerland). There were rectangular boxes lined with stones and covered carefully with flat slabs; each such box contained several cave bear skulls with large limb bones stuck through the eye and mouth holes. The Neanderthal men had beheaded the bears and arranged the skulls in this special way. In the Petershöhle (in the region of Nürnberg, Germany) niches in the walls of the cave were filled with neatly prepared skulls and bones of cave bears. Other caves give evidence that the Neanderthal men inpaled the heads of bears they had killed on stakes and danced around them.

Even today there are certain primitive tribes with a similar bear cult— the Ainu in northern Japan and the Gilyaks at the mouth of the Amur in Russia, near the island of Sakhalin. Among these people the bear is regarded as a higher, holy being. They eat its flesh and dress in its skin, but at the same time they revere it like a divinity. The skulls of the bears are

Bear hunting and bear cults

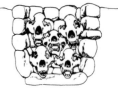

Fig. 20-1. In the Drachenloch of Switzerland a stone box with the skulls of cave bears was found.

Fig. 20-2. The skull and leg bones of several cave bears appear to be arranged according to a cult ritual (Drachenloch).

hung in the tops of tall trees, so that the bear god can recreate live animals from them; captured bears are treated with ceremony and supplication and finally, at a great festival, solemnly sacrificed.

The sacrifice of bears was presumably the first cult activity of humanity. Since in Neanderthal times bear hunts were carried on so extensively in many regions, the question arises whether this might have been the first instance of man's changing his environment to the extent that an animal species became extinct. It is now thought that that was not the case. The number of men was too small in those times, and their weapons were too little developed, for them to have endangered any species. Yet the cave bear disappeared, either because it was vulnerable to man or because of its poor adaptation to changing environment.

Extinction of the cave bear

As a species, the cave bear was in full bloom during the mild Riss-Würm glacial epoch, when it evolved into the largest of predatory land mammals. Conditions were more favorable then than ever before; the summers were long, and there was enough grass and other food. The bear needed no extensive period of hibernation, and it had hardly any enemies. Since it was no longer engaged in a struggle for existence, natural selection could not have its full effect. When conditions began to worsen again, in this case because of the long winters of the Würmian glaciation, the bears were no longer able to adjust to the changes in their environment and became extinct. This huge animal, having carried its evolution too far in one direction, and become very vulnerable to human hunting, was replaced by its smaller cousin, the much more versatile brown bear.

For the prey of Cro-Magnon man, who lived during the late Ice Age and has now disappeared from the earth, the situation was probably much the same, although the opinions of certain renowned scientists differ on this point (see the Introduction to Part Two). For example, the American Paul S. Martin contends that even then, thanks to his long-range weapons or even to the employment of fire, man had begun to exterminate many genera of large mammals. In this view, with the invention of spear, slingshot, harpoon, and bow and arrow toward the end of the Pleistocene the stocks of wild animls declined so severely that man—now for the first time as a thinking and planning being—moved out on large-scale migrations and eventually conquered the earth. Toward the end of the Pleistocene and shortly thereafter a not inconsiderable number of large animals did in fact become extinct—for example, the mammoth, woolly rhinoceros and giant deer of the Old World. But the extent to which the hunters of the early Stone Age contributed to their extermination is still under discussion.

The mammoth

As the paleontologist Othenio Abel has demonstrated, even the mammoths of the last glacial epoch displayed evidences of genetic decline. Whereas the steppe mammoth (*Mammonteus trogontherii*) of the middle Pleistocene had really "mammoth" dimensions (the bulls in the Mindelian epoch were about four and a half meters tall, and in the Rissian still four meters), the average height of the cold-steppe mammoths (*Mammonteus primigenius*) of the Würmian was only about three meters and thus less than that of the African elephant. In the loess of Krems on the Danube and in northern Siberia forms of a decidedly stunted appearance have been found. One can well imagine that these smaller animals were unable to cope with the changes in climate and other environmental conditions toward the end of the Würmian. They may have died out gradually, as a result of climatic stress and accidents or diseases rather than because of human hunting pressure.

Fig. 20-3. Rhinoceros hunt: a rock engraving from the dry river valley In Habeter, in a part of the Sahara still inhabited by many kinds of steppe animals in the late Stone Age.

It is not known whether the same processes led to the extinction of the woolly rhinoceros and the giant deer. These inhabitants of open country disappeared toward the end of the Ice Age, as the steppes again became forested. Large-scale environmental changes could have been responsible for their disappearance. We should not exclude, however, the possibility that hunting by man forced the populations of many of these large and slowly reproducing animals to decline to extinction.

Paleolithic hunters, during the late Pleistocene, revealed their relationships to their environment, and above all to the animals they hunted, with their own hands. Their magnificent cave drawings, figures scratched in stone, and carvings are the earliest known artistic creations of man. At the same time they are among the most gripping and impressive art objects humanity has ever produced. Art as a whole can be assumed to have its roots among the hunting tribes, not among those primitive people that lived as gatherers and later evolved agricultural societies. The hunter has an entirely different attitude to his environment than do those tribes that live by harvesting their food. He must take what he can find in nature; he harvests without having sown. Hunting peoples produce nothing, but simply kill the animals they need and leave their replacement to nature. The hunter is in harmony with nature and takes his place as one of the natural predators in his environment. Planters, on the other hand, change nature; they take a stand against it and as a result have no incentive to include natural objects—especially animals—in their cult activities and art. The art of the hunting peoples is "zoomorphic," whereas the later-blooming art of the agricultural peoples is anthropomorphic.

This is clearly evident in the Scandinavian, eastern European and Siberian rock pictures, which were made much later than the cave drawings and carved pictures and statues of early Stone Age man—in Scandinavia about eight thousand years ago, and in Siberia about four thousand years

Hunting tribes as creators of the first works of art

Rock pictures in northern and eastern Europe

ago. At that time these northern people were already going to sea in boats; they were beginning to cultivate the soil and in addition lived by fishing, killing seals, and gathering clams, or, like certain present-day Siberian peoples, existed as hunters and trappers of wild animals. Their art was rather somber; it froze into the form of ornaments. In the rock drawings man and his domestic animals are the central figures. If wild animals were, represented at all, they were depicted in nothing like the lively and naturalistic style of the late Ice Age rock artists. The animals were usually drawn only in rough outline. The "X-ray" style of many of these post-Pleistocene pictures is quite interesting; the vertebrae, arteries, heart and other internal organs can be seen as though in an X-ray picture. To invoke fertility and a successful hunt the people in the isolation of the arctic regions apparently needed no realistic pictures; it was enough to give a schematic representation of the events with which they were concerned.

Fig. 20-4. A painting in bright red of an ibex hunt, from the Gasulla Gorge in the province of Castallon, eastern Spain. This sort of painting, about 6000 years later than the Paleolithic cave art, is in an impressionistic style that appears quite modern. Despite the force with which men and animal are hurtling toward one another, the picture displays an appealing lightness and elegance.

Paleolithic realism

In contrast to the symbolism and the X-ray style of the Mesolithic and Neolithic artists, the much older works of art made by the hunters in the Paleolithic strike modern man as extraordinarily lively; it is hard to imagine their having been drawn in the dim prehistoric past. This freshness and vitality is associated with the sharp perception of the hunting peoples. The fragments of the hunting culture which remain today, the bushmen in the Kalahari and the Australian aborigines, understand their game animals intimately; they know how and when the animals reproduce, and they keep certain closed seasons to protect them. All such tribes have not only a decided talent for drawing animals, but also a comprehensive and precise knowledge of the plants in their surroundings and the ways they can be used as food, medicine and poison. For example, the bushmen are familiar with fifty different plant genera, which they put to use in one way or another. It may be that even the Paleolithic people had discovered healing herbs and plants that could serve as stimulants. On the other hand, counting was a matter of great difficulty for the hunting peoples. They seem incapable of anticipating things far in advance, and live as it were from hand to mouth, exploiting the animals in the regions where they live or following the animal's migrations.

The animals characteristic of cave paintings, apart from the mammoth, woolly rhinoceros and giant deer, are either species still more or less widely distributed (ibex, chamois, red deer, reindeer and wild boar, for example) or species like the aurochs, wisent (European bison) and primitive wild horse, which became extinct only later, as a result of excessive hunting by modern man or the encroachment of civilization. Many cave pictures are distinguished by the fact that they depict not only the kill, but other aspects of the animals' lives, particularly mating and pregnancy; and the same can be said of the later bushman and Indian drawings. Pictures of female animals carrying young are thought to ensure fecundity among the game—an aspect of primitive beliefs that was probably shared by the hunting peoples even in the early Stone Age.

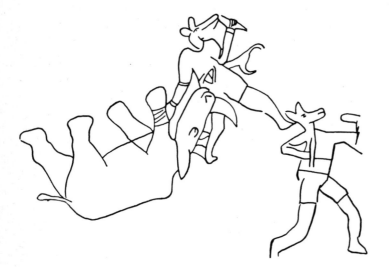

Fig. 20-5. From the Mesolithic on, hunters disguised as animals appear in African pictures. Here two men wearing jackal masks have killed a rhinoceros and are dragging it away. A rock engraving from In Habeter (Sahara).

Similarly, Paleolithic men (like many later primitive tribes that have remained at the hunting level) developed a great variety of special customs associated with the hunt. For example, they draped themselves in furs and in this disguise crept toward their prey. The caves decorated with paintings, which were often secluded and difficult to reach, became hallowed places where young men, groups of hunters, or the founders of families hoping for fertility among their women would gather and, under the leadership of the magician, perform dances before the supernaturally potent paintings in order to conjure forth the desired results. Figures of "enchanters," disguised as animals to perform rituals related to the hunt, are

Fig. 20-6. The great magician, from the cave Les Trois Frères in Ariège, France (Paleolithic).

found most notably in the caves of Tuc d'Audoubert and Les Trois Frères in the French department Ariège.

An animal, then, did not only represent food; it was much closer to the men of the early Stone Age than to modern man—a mighty partner in their overall existence, which could be mastered only with extreme cleverness and skill. The eyes of the hunters of this age were sharp, and their memories were excellent. They took in their environment with all their senses. As a result, once they had discovered how to represent color and perspective, they succeeded not only in creating uniquely effective animal portraits but in capturing the spatial and temporal movements of a herd of animals almost as though on film. There are even some carved pictures from the last culture of the late Ice Age, the Magdalenian, in which man and animal are brought together in a remarkable way. As in a puzzle where a figure is hidden within another picture, here the outlines of the bodies of a pair of lovers or a pregnant woman are intermingled with those of bears, deer or other powerful animals. The intent was probably like that in drawings of present-day hunting tribes, magically to compel a transfer of power from the depicted animals to the humans.

The cult underlying these works of art, traces of which are still to be found in the attitudes of present-day hunting peoples, is called shamanism. The ancient spells, dances and so on concerned with hunting, in fact the whole significance of animal-related magic, is based on symbolically conjuring up and captivating the souls of animals in order to obtain power over the actual animals. Pictorial images secure power over their archetypes—that is the secret of the shaman's art. A successful hunt is anticipated and represented so convincingly that when the hunters set out they are psychologically affected and in fact are able to find and kill the game they seek.

Another aspect of shamanism is the belief that the souls of the hunted animals are bound to certain parts of the body, bones, or pieces of hide. By keeping such a part a person can bind the soul of that animal to himself. According to these magical concepts, it is even possible to cause the animal souls to become incarnate and once again be hunted as living beasts. In many hunting tribes the shaman cult gave rise to totemism. A totem, in the original sense, is an animal with which a group feels a close association and which it represents in pictures. Often the group calls itself after its totem and prohibits, completely or for certain times, killing and eating of the animal. Both shamanism and totemism are based on the notion that certain animals are closely related to certain groups of humans.

The first known epoch in the history of human art began about 40,000 years ago and continued into the postglacial period. This is termed Franco-Cantabrian cave art, since most of the pictures were discovered in France and northern Spain. Subsequently, and continuing into the Mesolithic, there developed a second art style. This was also dominated by the hunt and the capture of wild animals, but differed in that animals were not shown alone; rather, men and animals appeared together in hunting scenes and engaged in other activities, a combination very rarely encountered before. Men with bows and arrows chase their quarry, animals rear up in terror under a hail of arrows, a honey collector climbs a tree, warriors hurl themselves upon one another, a hunter with a bow waits in great suspense for an animal to pass along a trail. Sometimes the forms of animals and men become quite abstract. This "Levant style," which can also be found in paintings in Sicily, displays an astonishing parallelism to rock pictures in mountain gorges in the Sahara as well as in Nubia and eastern and southern Africa. The last remaining evidence of this "Eurafrican hunting culture" is considered to be the animal paintings of the bushmen—pictures, often surprisingly true to life, of wild animals, particularly those of the African steppe.

The characteristic animal-art style of the hunting tribes is found in almost all parts of the world where human societies at the hunter level existed—in old Anatolia, in central India and Australia as well as in the places inhabited by those pre-Columbian Indians who were not farmers and founders of cities and states. It characterizes a type of economy in which there was no form of either animal husbandry or agriculture. With their weapons, the men ensured a supply of meat, while the women gathered wild plants and occasionally caught small animals. Probably even in Paleolithic times it was customary for several families to form a group with fixed hunting and gathering territories. The larger these clans became, and the more they joined forces to form tribes, the fewer wild animals were available in their territories; even the plants they preferred became relatively scarce. They had a superabundance of food only during the mildest seasons, for in summer, when it was easiest to catch the animals, the meat spoiled quickly. Thus the first step toward a more highly developed economy was very likely learning to prepare dried meat. Smoking and drying of meat was useful even in winter, since it warmed the people

Fig. 20-7. Examples of the postglacial "second hunter style" in eastern Spain (about 6000–2000 B.C.):

Marksman with a bow from Cueva Viéja (Albacete province).

This archer from the Cueva del Civil in the Valltorta Gorge in eastern Spain marks a change in style to pure expressionism.

A deer hunt, Cueva Viéja (Albacete province). This picture was once considered the first representation of a "hunting dog"; but today this interpretation is challenged.

themselves; their resting and camping places were the same as their fire sites.

A first step in the transition from gathering to agriculture was taken

From gatherer to farmer

by the harvesting tribes; they collected certain wild plants according to a definite schedule, and it was a natural development to begin actually cultivating the plants. Since gathering had been the task of the women among hunting peoples, matriarchy predominated among the early agricultural groups. The planting of tubers and grain certainly developed from the food-gathering that the women had always done while the men were out on a hunt. Similarly, animal husbandry may have arisen from the custom of accompanying certain herds of animals, which was practiced by some hunting tribes and is still done with reindeer by Lapps and Siberians, or of driving them into isolated valleys and keeping them there. This form of economy, which tended to be more patriarchal, gradually led to the planned breeding of the more useful animal species.

Cultivation of the soil and breeding of cattle established a relationship between man and his environment quite different from any that had existed before. His interest in game animals and useful wild plants declined progressively; instead, he was occupied with the fertility of the soil and of his animals. Accordingly, the close bonds between man and the natural communities were broken. Wild animals lost their significance as the basis of his existence; he had become independent of them. Now, in fact, carnivorous animals became his enemies because they could kill his cattle, and herbivores grazed on his pastures or damaged his crops. Except for a few special cases, it was at the cultural level where farming began that there first emerged a real threat to the environment, which led increasingly to disturbances of the natural order of things.

The special development of Australia

One of these special cases is the Australian continent, which was colonized in the postglacial period by various waves of immigration from the Indonesian Papuan area. In Australia there lived no higher mammals, but only monotremes and marsupials, and these were not able to withstand superior enemies like human hunters, armed with spear and boomerang, and the dog he brought with him (the dingo, which later returned to the wild). Man and dingo crowded the marsupial wolf (*Thylacinus cynocephalus*) off the Australian continent onto the island of Tasmania; but this largest of carnivorous marsupials did not become extinct until recent decades, when it was exterminated by men of our civilization. It is quite possible, however, that the aboriginal Australians contributed to the disappearance of some species of large marsupials which we are certain still existed at the time of the Tartanga culture, six and a half thousand years ago. *Diprotodon optatum*, an animal about the size of a rhinoceros, could have been the victim of a change in climate that made large parts of Australia arid. Nevertheless, the aboriginal hunters probably at least caused a sharp decline in the numbers of these giant animals, which of course yielded more meat and were easier to hunt than the agile kangaroos.

Eurasians penetrate the American continent

Toward the end of the Pleistocene the first men moved onto the American continent—hunting people from Eurasia who in subsequent millennia pushed the frontier forward gradually until they had reached the southern tip of South America. In America, too, a number of mammal species became extinct only after this invasion, but long before the discovery of the continent by Columbus. These included proboscideans—the Alaska mammoth (*Mammonteus columbi*) and the mastodon *Zygolophodon americanus*—and the giant sloth *Mylodon*, as well as the primitive camel *Camelops* and ancient horses (*Parahipparion, Equus andium*, and *Equus neogaeus*). The latter were side branches, rather than ancestors, of the perissodactyl line. It remains a mystery whether the Indians hunted while riding these extinct New World camels and horses. Drawings of proboscideans, either mammoths or mastodons, have been found, as well as mastodon bones in the refuse of ancient Indian campsites; bones, bits of hide and fecal balls of the giant sloth *Mylodon* were discovered in a cave in Patagonia. From this we know that the Indians were familiar at least with one North American proboscidean and with the giant sloth. The *Mylodon* finds in Ultima Esperanza (Patagonia) appear to indicate that the people then not only hunted these animals but even tried to smoke them out of the caves to which they fled.

Altogether about a hundred mammal species disappeared during and after the last glacial epoch in America. In contrast to this mass extinction (if hunting by the Indians was responsible for it), was the relation of the Plains Indians to the animals that supported them. The Indians in the Great Plains of North America were, because of their cult attitudes to their surroundings, especially well able to maintain a state of equilibrium with their environment. There has probably been no other people in which harmony between primitive hunting methods, a simple way of life, and strong association with nature was so successfully established as among the Indians. Lorus and Margery Milne have described this situation as follows: Indirectly, the prairie Indians were fed, clothed and warmed by the grasses. They hunted the bison for its meat and its skin, and they fueled their various campfires with dried bison dung, since the broad grasslands offered little else that burned well. But the Indians could do no serious damage, either to the grazing land or to the animals upon which they depended.

The double island of New Zealand was not reached by man until the 13th Century. There he found no mammals; the largest animals that could be hunted for meat were the moas, several genera and about nineteen species of which inhabited the islands. Among them were gigantic birds of the genera *Dinornis* and *Pachyornis*, which weighed up to 250 kg, as well as medium-sized and small forms (*Eurapteryx, Megalapteryx, Anomalopteryx* and *Emeus*). The fact that these flightless birds could evolve to become the dominant herbivores of New Zealand is associated with the absence of large land mammals here, prior to the appearance of man. The very first immigrants, the Moriori, who probably came from the Chatham Islands, exterminated most of the moa species. Then, around 1350, the Maori from the Society Islands area reached New Zealand and des-

Annihilation of the moas in New Zealand

troyed both the Moriori and the rest of the moas. The white explorers and colonists never had a chance to see these birds. It is possible that the progressive extermination of the moas was the indirect cause of cannibalism in New Zealand. For apart from the small relatives of the moas, the kiwis (genus *Apteryx*), and certain other birds there were no animals on either island that could provide enough meat to support an increasing population. New Zealand, in this case, would be one of the few places where cannibalism developed not as a cult ritual but for sheer lack of meat.

Extinction of species in Madagascar

The third largest island in the world, Madagascar, was also colonized by several waves of seafaring Polynesians and Malayans, perhaps beginning as early as the first century A.D. These colonists, like the Maori, were sailors and had passed the hunting and gathering level of economy; the last immigrants even used their seaworthy vessels to bring domestic animals and crop plants to the island. But they, too, encountered a strange fauna not adjusted to the presence of man. It is thought that the Madagascans, even before the first Europeans appeared on the scene, had caused quite a few species to become extinct, either directly by hunting or indirectly by the progressive transformation of the countryside. These animals were the giant elephant birds *Aepyornis maximus* and *Aepyornis hildebrandti*, and no less than fourteen species of prosimians; the latter included certain very large lemurs such as *Megaladapis*, *Palaeopropithecus*, *Mesopropithecus*, *Neopropithecus* and *Archaeoindris*, some of which were as large as anthropoid apes.

In hunting and gathering societies, man remained a member of a natural community, and his actions were in balance with those of other community members. Not until the gathering/hunting level had been passed, and man began to interfere with aspects of his environment which had previously been undisturbed, was he capable—as we have seen in the examples of New Zealand and Madagascar—of upsetting the natural equilibrium in his own favor and to the disadvantage of other organisms. As long as the number of other organisms was large enough and that of the men stayed small, there were no injurious effects of such activities. It was only with the rise in the human population that serious consequences resulted; the equilibrium of the soil was disturbed and its fertility was reduced, a process now going on all over the earth.

The eradication of animal species and plant communities must necessarily have affected the subsequent development of mankind, for when any creature vanishes forever, so does its influence upon man. The environmental problems of our time, discussed in the second part of this volume, show us how greatly the natural order everywhere on earth has been displaced by human demands—largely parasitic demands, which in destroying nature as it has evolved may well eventually present the same danger to ourselves.

21   The Environment of Domestic Animals

Domestic animals are usually given a special position in the animal kingdom, since they live in close association with man. In the process of domestication, members of wild species were removed from their old systems of ecological relationships and placed in new environmental conditions, shaped and continually changed by man. Domestic animals lead lives quite different from those of their wild relatives; they have acquired special physical and behavioral characteristics. Many of these are not common among wild animals, and some of them actually appear in a similar form in domestic species of various origins. For this reason domestic animals are often dismissed as "unnatural" and left out of discussions about the evolution of the animal kingdom.

But such judgments miss a crucial point. Domestic animals should be considered as organisms that have been capable of long-term adaptation, involving hereditary modifications, to new conditions and ecological relationships. Their physical traits and biological peculiarities show us how parts of animal species can respond to transformations of their environment. In the case of domestic animals, man is the biologically effective, shaping and selecting force. In sum, domestic animals can be regarded as the result of a vast human experiment; they provide a graphic illustration of the fact that there are many capacities inherent in wild animals which remain hidden as long as one observes only the ecological relationships that have evolved in nature. An understanding of these capacities can be of considerable importance.

Domestic animals are one of the fundamental elements of human econ-

By W. Herre and
M. Röhrs

Are domestic animals
"normal"?

Fig. 21-1. The sheep is the oldest domestic animal. The drawing shows sheep in ancient Egypt being driven over the fields after sowing to trample the seeds into the soil.

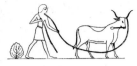

Fig. 21-2. This ancient Egyptian relief shows an escaped steer being caught with a lasso.

omy; they first enabled man to achieve a degree of regularity in his food supply. The development of animal-keeping and plant cultivation liberated man from the necessity of gathering and the unpredictability of the hunt. As a result, he had more time and opportunity to develop his mental abilities, and he did so at a greater rate than ever before. Thus domestic animals have contributed to the evolution of cultures and civilizations; our present-day manner of life and the steady increase of the human population would be unthinkable without domestic animals. Conversely, the advances in human mental abilities affected the animals and their environment in many ways. The first animal to come under the care of man, over twelve thousand years ago, was the sheep. In the course of this long association the relationships between man and his animals have been modified repeatedly. As domestication progressed, animals came to resemble their parent species less and less, and their environment departed ever further from the habitats of the wild species. This process of change, of course, is still going on.

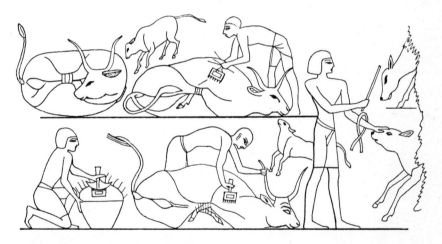

Fig. 21-3. Even in ancient Egypt cattle were branded to designate ownership.

Man never transformed all the respresentatives of a wild species into animals of his own; he separated out small groups, prevented them from mingling and interbreeding with the wild species, and tried to achieve the highest possible rate of reproduction in his stocks; with these chosen animals, he not only selected those most useful to him, but also made some effort to care for them. Animals so domesticated in some cases display a certain attachment to their protectors—they become tame. We now know that there are also tame wild animals, and that many domestic animals are not tame at all. The relationship between man and his animals can by no means be called a symbiosis—an association for the good of both partners. Man, of course, benefits from his animals, since they work for him and provide him with food. In this relationship, man is a constant agent of change, for it is in his interest to increase the performance of his servants. In so doing, he makes the domesticated species more and more dependent on him; and to the same extent he becomes dependent upon them, for he must guard and care for them.

But it is doubtful that an animal species obtains any benefit itself from this rather selfish protection it receives. By changing their environment, man has brought out such marked modifications in domestic animals that they can no longer exist under the conditions in the wild, unless special provision is made for them. They need to be part of a household, or at least to have equivalent surroundings. Domestication can be regarded as a special biological condition associated with the mental abilities of humans, since there is no other animal species that has created **true** domestic animals.

Fig. 21-4. Ancient Egyptian illustration of plowing with a team of oxen.

Originally, domestic animals were kept to meet the needs of small groups of people. Probably all the classical domestic animals, including horse and dog, were at first simply providers of meat. They were kept in herds which were larger than the natural family groups but held in a more restricted space, which affected the quality of the food. Gradually people became more demanding; the herds grew larger, and other ways of using the animals were discovered and exploited. For example, men increased the reproductive performance of the animals—the number of offspring, the rate at which one litter followed another, and the quantity of milk. To achieve this, the animal-keeper separated the young from their mothers

Fig. 21-5. This herd of goats is engraved on an ancient Greek drinking mug; it is driven by a herdsman with two dogs.

at a very early stage, shortening the time between successive births; in the wild, this result of loss of the young was biologically advantageous, and in the human economy it provided higher yields. Finally, by selection of suitable animals, it proved possible to do away with the seasonal aspect of reproduction in the ancestral forms. The "internal clock" present in wild species, which ordered the sequence of biological events, was reset or reconstructed. Selection also converted domestic animals to beasts of burden, carriers of loads and pullers of carts and plows. In some cases changes in the hairy coat of domestic animals could be enhanced, eventually producing wool that man learned to spin and weave.

It is certain that the first domestic animals continued to live in relative freedom, almost in a natural state. Their herders demanded and received only a small tribute from them. Even in our time there are such primitive animal-keepers—for example, among the nomads in Africa, who consider themselves superior to the groups that cultivate the soil. But in seasons of drought these herders too have work to do; they spend much time driving their animals to better grazing land and adequate water holes. However, they do not regard caring for their animals in this way as work, because of the bond that exists between themselves and their charges.

Occasionally the conclusion has been drawn that the environment of such "primitive" domestic animals was little affected. Certainly simple nomadic herdsmen make no particular efforts to obtain high yields from their animals, even though pride of ownership is a motivating factor. Large herds are desirable, but excessively large herds would involve full-time employment, a prospect by no means regarded as desirable by their owners. Despite a certain primitive quality in the way they are kept, the environment of such domestic animals is still notably different from that of the wild species. In the herds the animals live closer together and with a different proportionality between the sexes, which has an influence upon the natural social relationships. Grazing by dense populations of animals makes the vegetation more uniform; many plants preferred by the wild species, which in some cases are very important for proper digestion, disappear.

Such modifications of the environment are of course even more significant in highly developed animal husbandry. Their extent is affected by the level of the culture and by the attitude of the people toward productivity. Initially men usually kept domestic animals apart from their settlements, in pastures a considerable distance away. Gradually as the history of domestic animals unfolded, and especially rapidly in recent times, they brought the animals into the areas of human settlement.

The development of cities and centers of industry made animal husbandry a necessity and endowed it with a special significance. Individual animal owners, with their small free herds, were replaced by animal breeders whose task it was to supply the growing, ever denser masses of humanity. Yields have been increased steadily to meet the increasing demand. Breeding has been directed entirely toward enhanced performance. But such extremely productive animals require greater efforts on the part of their keepers. Fodder is grown in large stands of a single crop, and

Fig. 21-6. In this Egyptian picture veterinarians are treating domestic animals: 1. Feeding sick geese; 2 and 3. Treating two tame oryx; 4 and 5. Treating sick goats; 6 and 7. Sick cattle receive medicine.

special preservative methods are used in storing it; its composition and intake is controlled. As a protection against the weather barns are built, which isolate the animals more and more from the natural climate. Animals kept in the open must often be covered with blankets. In such ways, detrimental effects on productivity can be reduced. But these measures also affect the possibilities for selective breeding of suitable genetic strains, and the direction in which such breeding leads.

Moreover, the relationship between man and animal has changed. The first thoughts of herdsmen and other primitive animal keepers were probably not of themselves and their working hours but of the care of the herds; they felt a personal bond to their charges, to which the animals no doubt often responded. The contrast between this relationship and the one which city dwellers today have with the animals that supply their food is a striking one indeed.

Fig. 21-7. The Assyrian king Assurnasirpal (668-630 B.C.) on an aurochs hunt. One aurochs has been killed and another caught alive. This animal (*Bos primigenius*) is the ancestor of the domestic cow.

But cattle farming has shown that such relationships can be significant. Cows usually give more milk when the milker is someone they know and favor. But in our modern age the domestic animal is becoming nothing more than a means of production. This implies a very profound environmental change, to which the animal often responds with a decrease in production. Man, however, has meanwhile become so skilled at animal management that he can make organizational alterations, adopt procedures for the prevention of disease, and employ selective breeding toward less sensitive strains. As compared with the parent forms, domestic animals have become stunted beings, with a smaller realm of experience. This is one result of man's changing the environment of animals and then breeding the animals to suit it. But men rely on animals not only as producers of goods, but as "comrades" in their own realm of experience.

Therefore, for some domesticated animals, environmental conditions were created that differed from those of the purely utilitarian beasts. These

From utilitarian animal to pet

are the animals that he treats with special respect and love. The wild horse, for example, was once an important game animal. Domesticated horses originally provided meat, but later they were harnessed to the plow and wagon, replacing the cattle that had done this job. Horse-drawn vehicles could be used in warfare and were developed into a weapon of the greatest importance. With their help great kingdoms of the world have been destroyed and new kingdoms established. Later the horse was used as a mount—and again as a weapon of war. Mounted warriors for centuries decided the outcomes of battles. America was to a considerable extent conquered by men on horseback. Because of its historical role the horse came to occupy a special position among domestic animals. It became a personal companion, upon whose speed and adroitness people often depended for their lives. It earned a special sort of care—a special environment.

Agricultural peoples elevated the horse to a symbol of strength and dependability. Now the tractor has robbed the horse of its economic importance; neither does it play any role in war. Nevertheless, in many industrialized lands, it continues to be preserved and treasured as the bearer of a proud tradition. City dwellers find in the horse a source of power, an extension and reminder of their own strength. The former utilitarian domestic animal has become a favorite sport animal and pet.

The dog, too, has had a varied history and has been used in many capacities. It once was regarded by many groups of people as nothing more than a source of meat, and even today some tribes fatten dogs for the table. Some of the characteristics of certain breeds of dog can be interpreted on the basis of this history. As later cultures developed, dogs were employed as helpers in the hunt; in the inhospitable north they became important draft animals, and among certain other peoples they served as guard dogs. As a result of these different functions, there were notable differences in the ways dogs were kept and the environmental modifications they experienced. Selection of dogs suitably adapted to the very different tasks they were called on to perform generated a number of different breeds.

In our time the domestic dog is important chiefly as a pet over large parts of the earth, especially in the cities. Such dogs are there simply to be "loved"; they offer their owners a diversion and free them from feelings of loneliness, neglect, and not being understood. In this role they are surrounded by a very special environment, and the breeds that are developed are often quite bizarre, expressing not only ideals of beauty but the caprices of the human milieu. A highly diversified industry encourages people to buy things that make the environmental conditions of their dogs more "human." What once were useful dogs became spoiled and pampered pets to be dressed, barbered and pedicured; man puts them in an environment that in his view has all conveniences and comforts, but in many respects does not do justice to the animals' real requirements for exercise, proper food and partnership—man is using his own criteria and not those of the dog.

Fig. 21-8. A number of forms of dog are known to have lived in Egypt. This white-painted piece of ceramic from the grave of Mereruka (6th dynasty, 5th Century B.C.) shows a man leading two dogs with tightly curled tails—a trait highly prized in domestic dogs by the ancient Egyptians.

Fig. 21-9. This statue comes from the Chien-Lung period (China, 1736–1795); it is considered a "lion symbol," but presumably represents a Pekinese dog.

Nevertheless, there are still dogs that perform more utilitarian services; some are kept in stalls to serve as food and others are companions in work which share food and shelter with their owners. Still others live in packs of their own kind but help men in the hunt. The range of environmental conditions affecting the species as a whole—from the wild members, the wolves, to the various breeds of domestic dog—has been enormously expanded.

Domestic chickens also live in a great variety of surroundings. The ancestral species, the red jungle fowl, forms small family groups in dense jungle and the clearings there. For centuries domestic fowl lived in rather larger family associations in the vicinity of human houses. They spent the night in trees or simple shelters and, by scratching in the dirt, found a large part of their food for themselves. Man used primarily their eggs, at that time still few in number, and their meat. More recently, especially in this century, there has been a division between the several functions of chickens, with an extraordinary effect on the shaping of the animals' environment. Many people, especially in cities, satisfy their need to care for living animals by keeping chickens. As a result, so-called ornamental breeds of fowl have been developed, most of which are distinguished by beautiful colors or unusual shapes. Such ornamental fowl live in small families and, like the wild species, have nests in dark places. They receive a varied diet, though usually they lay only a few eggs.

From wild fowl to battery chicken

But the triumph of utilitarian attitudes, the necessity of efficient production, has spared the chicken no more than the other domestic animals. To feed growing masses of people there must be more eggs and more meat, delivered on the most regular schedule possible. Thus, on economic grounds, chickens have been made more uniform in color, form, productivity, feeding and in the conditions they require. Very large numbers of them are kept in a small space; their physiological rhythms are controlled by artificial lighting and they are fed with a special food mixture to encourage laying. The red jungle fowl and primitive breeds of domestic fowl could never perform so well at egg-laying, but by selection man has produced breeds with the appropriate hereditary characteristics. Selective breeding has made it possible to keep the birds in masses, under conditions such that the individual has no room for a large territory and there is practically no opportunity for family groups to form.

The genetic basis of these characteristics is complicated, and some aspects of the original behavior are retained even under modern environmental conditions. Even in hens that must live in batteries one can detect remnants of social behavior. Essentially, however, the individual animal disappears in the crowd and must fit into it. The changes observed in the animals are not all direct responses to the current state of their man-made environment; genetic modifications are also produced, so that the requirements of the animals actually become different from those of wild animals, and differ even among the various breeds of domestic animals.

Peaceful conquest using domestic animals

Domestic animals have helped men to penetrate regions of the earth previously inaccessible. Man has conquered the far north of Eurasia with the help of the reindeer, the upper slopes of the Himalayas with the yak, and various desert regions with the camel. In all these places life is hard and food, at least part of the time, is scarce; by himself man could never survive permanently there. In tropical and swampy areas, to which domestic cattle were not suited, man introduced better adapted animals—in India the water buffalo was bred from the arna, in Indochina the gayal was bred from the gaur, and in Indonesia the Bali cow was bred from the banteng. These three forms are important as domestic animals only in narrowly restricted areas, where the environment is similar to that of the parent species. Only the domestic buffalo has been introduced into more extensive regions, as far as China in one direction and southern Europe in the other.

Fig. 21-10. Assyrian fighting troops ride two to a camel, one urging the beast on while the other acts as an archer. The picture is from the northern palace of the Assyrian king Assurbanipal in Nineveh.

In general, men took their animals with them on their migrations and when they were conquering new parts of the earth, and with the help of the animals they were better able to exploit their new surroundings. The adaptability inherent in domestic animals even under such conditions is astonishing; a good example is that of the domestic sheep. The wild species lives mainly in sub-alpine mountains. Man has brought the domestic sheep into cold alpine regions, hot steppes with seasons of relative barrenness, and humid, cool coastal zones. Herds of domestic sheep can be left to wander quite freely over wide ranges, as in the expanses of the South American pampa or the enormous range areas of Australia, but they can also be kept in relatively crowded conditions, grazing on small enclosed pastures and herded into folds. In the course of such different treatment various breeds were formed, with quite different environmental requirements.

The ancestral form of domestic cattle, the aurochs, inhabited parklike grassland with scattered trees. Man has taken his cattle to quite different environments, to which they have adapted. In the far north domestic cattle are kept for many months in narrow, dark stalls. In contrast, the beef cattle of the South American pampa and the North American prairie live practically unattended in the open; they can hardly be called tame, nor can the herds of cattle in the hot, dry savannas of Africa, most of which are breeds of zebu. Dairy cattle, specially bred to produce large amounts of milk and readily accept the care of men, are found on lush pastures in the temperate zone even in the vicinity of large cities.

All of these examples illustrate how greatly man has expanded the range of habitats of his domestic animals as compared to that of the parent species. Again, it is clear that man has not only changed the environment of his animals but, as a selective breeder, has recognized and enhanced certain desirable traits.

On the other hand, there are also cases in which man has adapted himself to his animals. For example, the domestic reindeer lives under conditions so close to those of the wild species that it is often—though wrongly —said even by recognized scientists that they do not differ at all. Like the wild form, domestic reindeer make long migrations, and the people follow their herds. Thus the tribes that keep reindeer, from the Lapps in the west to the Tunguas and Korjäks in the east, became nomads; ethnologists have argued that the domestic reindeer has affected the environmental conditions of man more strongly than man has influenced those of the reindeer.

Fig. 21-11. Pictures of wild reindeer carved into a fragment of bone; from the Abri de La Madeleine in Dordogne, France. By the end of the Pleistocene men were already following their herds.

But research by zoologists reveals quite a different picture. Although the environment of the reindeer appears to have been influenced only slightly, man has nevertheless managed to make profound transformations. Wild reindeer live in small family groups for most of the year; a strong stag gathers a number of females about himself and defends this harem and his territory against other deer as well as predators. Only during the great migrations, when the reindeer travel to the coast, with its refreshing winds, and then return to the better pastures, do they join to form impressive herds. Domestic reindeer have retained the habit of migration, but even when they are not travelling they are kept in large herds; considerable numbers are needed to provide subsistence for a human family. Their owner can slaughter only as many animals as are replaced by young deer; in a sense, he must live on the interest from his capital, the herd, and is interested in keeping his herd as large as possible. Domestic reindeer, then, always live under much more crowded conditions than wild reindeer.

This increased herd density, imposed by man, has a variety of consequences. When so many animals graze in a relatively small space the quality of the food is affected. In recent years research has shown clearly that herbivorous wild species choose among the plants available to them; they prefer certain plant species and, for various reasons, require special mixtures of plants. When grazing so close together the animals must accept other plants in their place, and since not all the members of a species can withstand even such apparently slight changes equally well, an initial process of selection comes into play.

Since the middle of the last century the human population has been rising more and more rapidly; the movement into the cities has created problems in the distribution of food, and the stocks of domestic animals have been increased. Then the problem of feeding the animals became steadily more serious, and man was compelled to find new forms of fodder. Natural meadows were replaced with stands of single crops, and hay was harvested in increasing amounts, though its quality could vary considerably. New fodder plants were tested, and methods were developed for preserving it in new ways, such as by making silage. All these man-made changes in the food have caused adaptations of the animals' digestive processes. Animals better able to digest and incorporate their food could reproduce more successfully, and their descendants soon predominated in the herds. By now, genetic differences in ability to utilize food are very pronounced among the economically important domestic species. Even domesticated dogs—for example, poodles—need about fifty percent less food than the ancestral form, the wolf.

Pigs are omnivorous; nevertheless, even wild pigs search out special preferred foods, and choose a diet consisting mainly of bulbs, tubers and fruit supplemented by insects and small mammals. Pig-keeping in Europe, until the end of the Middle Ages, to a great extent involved letting the animals graze in the woods, where they could still find food similar to that of the wild boar. Once it had been recognized that industrial wastes could be fed to domestic pigs, there was a marked increase in pig-farming. Now pigs are kept in narrow stalls and fed largely on industrially produced fodder with a balanced mixture of nutrients designed to encourage rapid growth. Strains have been selected that are particularly good at utilizing such food. And the same is true in the case of chickens. The high laying rate of specially bred hens, an unheard-of and unpredictable achievement of the animal body, from the point of view of the wild species, would not be possible without special highly nutritious food. But even with such fodder, wild chickens would not be capable of the same performance. Here again, there is a close coupling between man's manipulation of the environment and selective breeding.

Progressive confinement as a factor

Even at early stages in domestication the freedom of movement of the animals was restricted so that they might be kept in herds. In the course of time, this restriction became more significant in the development of many domestic animals. Wild animals range over a large territory to find enough of the plants they prefer or, if they are predators, to find sufficient prey. Man, by contrast, herds his animals together in a small space and fences them in to keep them apart from the wild species. Even primitive herdsmen counteract the tendency for animals to wander away, by giving preference to the more docile, quiet individuals. In this way man has finally developed animals that he can keep in confined pens or barns, in batteries or other shelters where he can control the climatic conditions, by artificial heating and lighting. For the ancestors of the domestic animals, these artificial habitats would be unbearable.

Some domestic animals—for example, canaries and certain breeds of pig and dog—live in such confined quarters that they "waste" no energy in moving about (which of course a wild animal must do if it is to stay alive), but use essentially all their food to build up and maintain their bodies. The difference is particularly striking when the dog's requirement and capacity for rest is compared with that of the wolf. Correspondingly, domestic animals should eat less than the wild forms, unless fattening is desired.

Many of the aspects of the environment which endanger wild animals are eliminated or greatly reduced for domesticated animals. Man protects them from their predators and even reduces the danger from parasites. Another potentially serious threat, competition with other species, is in most cases entirely removed.

Almost all domestic animals originated from gregarious species, so that they have a certain " redisposition" for domestic life. Nevertheless, there are profound effects upon intraspecific interactions and the relationship between the sexes when animals are kept in herds. Once again the reindeer serves as an example. In the wild, as mentioned above, the stag vigorously defends his family. Young stags and the weaker old stags form loose "bachelor" associations, and it is these which usually fall victim to predators. In general, these stags have no chance to reproduce. Therefore wild stags battle violently for the females, and the victors demand a not inconsiderable territory for themselves and their harems. Such strong, pugnacious territorial stags do not allow the formation of large herds. Naturally, this behavior is contrary to the interest of the men who must maintain their families with the products they obtain from the reindeer.

Changes in reindeer social behavior with domestication

For this reason it has become customary for owners of domestic reindeer to castrate all stags when they reach their fourth year. Since male reindeer do not become sexually mature until the third year, this practice eliminates the harsh, disruptive battles and the territorial disputes. The three-year-old stags are entirely responsible for reproduction. This form of human intervention may at first appear to be of little consequence, since continuation of the species is assured. But it changes many aspects of intraspecific relationships, from behavior patterns to distribution of the genetic material. The rank ordering common among wild reindeer is affected, since the reindeer that would ordinarily be the leaders are deprived of that status. The influence of experienced reindeer cows is also diminished. The clear delegation of leadership, of great biological importance to wild deer, is no longer fully effective in domestic herds. But since the animals have inherent gregarious inclinations, the herdsman finds it easier to manage the animals under these conditions. Refractory animals, those with "strong personalities," can easily disturb the cohesion-of the herd; therefore the herdsman does not use them for breeding purposes. This kind of selection, in the long run, can generate remarkable changes in the herd's behavior.

Modification of social order in the dog

Another interesting example of the way man influences the social interactions of his animals is his domestication of the dog. Its parent species, the wolf, has a pronounced and highly developed social behavior; this is not the least of the reasons that man could form the dog into such a pleasant household animal. Wolves live in packs with a clear rank order. But this rank order is not stable; the wolves fight time and again for the position of leader. In contrast to the domestic dog, wolves mate on a permanent basis. In unfavorable years not all couples reproduce, but all the members of a social group contribute to raising the young. In developing the domestic dog, man has modified this social organization. He has taken the role of leader for himself; in groups of dogs occupying the same household, fixed rank orderings have also become the rule. Subordination to man has been substituted for coordination in the group. Man has also contributed to loosening the firm attachments between couples. Pairing for life is practically unknown among domestic dogs, and this further strengthens the position of their masters. Whereas wolves are decidedly social in their feeding behavior and give precedence to the young, the dog no longer displays such consideration.

Similar observations have been made with domestic animals other than the dog. For example, the man-made changes in their environment have a comparable effect upon the two domestic forms of the guanaco, the llama and the alpaca. Domestic horses and geese also display alterations in social and reproductive behavior.

Physical adaptations

Even physical characteristics associated with behavior, such as the structure and function of the nervous system and sense organs, become adapted to the domestic environment. The brains of domestic animals are about 30% lighter in proportion to body size than those of the parent species. There are signs of a decline in performance of sense organs like the eye and ear. Such physical changes have probably made it easier for man to maintain his superiority over his animals. According to the most recent findings, the ways in which nervous system and sense organs of domestic animals depart from those of their parent forms reflect actual genetic changes. From this it may be concluded that in domesticating his animals man gave preference to those differing from their conspecifics in terms of reduced aggression and enhanced subordination and gentleness.

Domestic animals as cult figures

As man devoted so much thought to devising new ways of protecting and keeping his domestic animals, associations with his religious ideas naturally formed. For example, consider the sacred cows of India. There is no doubt that they live in a special environment and in an unusual relationship to man. The scanty vegetation in India and the rarity of woodland have something to do with the special cult that has developed around these animals. The vegetation provides just enough food for cattle of modest appetite to stay alive. The animals are of practical importance in that their dung can be used as fuel and the strength of the young bulls is an indispensable help in drawing loads. But the religious association is more influential in keeping cattle from being slaughtered in a country so close to famine and so densely populated as India; this association probably had its roots in the need to guarantee that the numbers of such useful animals did not increase. There have been similar developments in other countries. For example, reluctance to eat horse meat can be ascribed to the fact that among many groups of people the horse has been a main source of economical and military power. And the current widespread prejudice against eating dog meat may well have its origin in the special comradeship existing between man and the domestic dog.

In trying to design an appropriate environment for domestic animals, one must not consider only the needs and preferences of the wild species. Since these animals have become genetically modified so as to perceive and respond to the world in a different way, their environment must be suited to their own peculiarities. Nor can man's own relationships and attitudes to his environment be a deciding factor; careful study is required to determine the degree of adaptation of domestic animals to their surroundings.

Matching the environment to the animals' needs

Despite these changes in domestic animals, in which many of their physical and mental traits appear stunted or dulled as compared with the wild species, remnants of their original behavior persist. Even when kept in dense herds or flocks they seek out areas and companions of their own. In shaping the environment of his pets, man often neglects this need for personal bonds. Dogs and parakeets are often left alone for long periods; during this time pent-up emotions accumulate, to be released when their owners return. The display that occurs then is certainly an expression of "joy," but it is also a sign of a long-term deficiency which deserves consideration.

In summary, domestic animals are subjected to an interplay between environment and genetic makeup that is entirely parallel to the processes occurring in the wild, except that man participates as a special force in the web of interactions. Man's intellect is forever at work, seeking new ways of improving the life of his own species by modifying his animals. From wild species he develops groups of individuals best suited to thrive under the conditions he creates; he continually "improves" these environments to obtain better performance from his animals. To this the animal responds by adaptation and by hereditary change, since again and again chance combinations of the genetic material prove more suited to the new conditions. The shaping of the environments of domestic animals can indeed be called a massive biological experiment.

22   Animals as Food for Man

By J. Illies

A central problem in the relationship of man to animal lies in the fact that to provide food, the animals must often be killed. This fundamental conflict is of long standing. The Ethiopian hunters called out to the hippopotamus, "Forgive us, dear father, for killing you, but your meat is so good !"; but we enlightened humans overcome the same problem differently—we shut our minds to it and obscure the connection between keeping domestic animals and slaughtering them. Lambs and calves romp on the pages of our children's picture books, while sheep, cattle and pigs are pushed away behind the thick walls of the slaughterhouses, and we open our eyes to them again only when the delicious chops are lying on a plate before us.

And yet every parent knows that there comes a time when the screen falls apart and the child's questioning forces the admission: yes, it is true, chicken and duck, lamb and cow, pig and sheep are sooner or later killed so that we can eat them. "This is the reason we keep the animals, that's just the way things are, and after all until the end they have a very good life with us"; with words like this we console our children and ourselves. In the last analysis we are left with the melancholy yet resigned attitude formulated by Wilhelm Busch when he said, "I must kill in order to live —but it is too bad."

Other respected personalities—without, of course, rejecting their slice of roast beef—have fumed in powerless rage against a human existence that burdens us with such inhuman necessities. The words of Voltaire thundered over his contemporaries, a bitter accusation to shake them out of their indifference: "It is certainly true that this horrible blood-bath going on incessantly in our slaughterhouses and kitchens no longer appears to us an evil; on the contrary, we regard this atrocity as a blessing from the Lord and thank him in our prayers for our murderous deeds." Psychological suppression of the unpleasantness offers a comfortable way out, as Voltaire himself recognized: "... I find among us no moral teacher who has made the slightest objection to this shameful custom that has now become part of our nature !"

Two hundred years later Albert Schweitzer lamented the same state of affairs, writing that the European thinkers were anxious to make sure "no animals were running about in their ethical systems." There is hardly any philosophy that advocates conscious rejection of meat; we have only the practical example of a few vegetarians who have drawn the evident conclusion and determinedly broken through the deadly circle of keeping animals in order to kill them—and in so doing they make the problem more acute for all other people. For their actions show that even the fundamental rationalization of all meat-eating, its nutritional indispensability, is questionable.

In order to understand the present situation, let us first look back into the past. In earlier epochs of prehistory man had a much more intimate relationship with his animals; there was a prevailing consciousness of a bond between the two, as we have already indicated in describing man at the hunting level of society. In those times of magical/mythical consciousness the necessity of killing must have appeared much more threatening and been felt more painfully than it is today. In the study of totemism and its partial identification of man and animal, one encounters strict prohibitions with respect to killing and eating, which early human groups imposed upon themselves in order to spare a certain animal species. Absolution with respect to the remaining animals, which were hunted, and with respect to the divinities associated with them was achieved by special rites; these survive today among hunting tribes and remnants are found even among civilized men who hunt for sport.

At the beginning of the history of many cultures the ritual of animal sacrifice merged with the eating of meat in a special cult festival. This was most clearly evident in ancient Egypt; on one hand, as a residue of the old cult of atonement to hunted animals, the "animals of the desert"—wild gazelles and antelopes—for millennia were preferred for sacrifice by fire. On the other, the problems associated with killing animals one had bred and cherished were eliminated by a sort of religious "trick." "Before they were killed and eaten," writes Erik Hornung, "they had to be ritually declared enemies; the burning of pieces of meat then symbolized the complete annihilation of the enemy."

Magically endowed by priests with this new role as "enemies," the animals—even the sacred cows of Isis—could be killed without scruples. To consume meat within the framework of the cult even became a positive, moral act, reestablishing a world order threatened by foes. But for all their religious inventiveness, which permeated their everyday life, the ancient Egyptians were still realistic enough to pay attention to palatability; asses and snakes, which in fact represented especially important incarnations of "enemies," were sacrificed but not eaten.

We encounter similar notions in the regulations covering food and sacrifices in ancient Israel. Moses declared a great number of animal species "unclean," thus excluding them as sacrifices and also as food for man.

Relieving the guilt of killing

Fig. 22-1. An Egyptian hunter with two hunting dogs, carrying over his shoulders an oryx he has killed.

Among these were toads, salamanders, slow-worms, hedgehogs, moles and mice. Nowadays we may well ask why it was even necessary to set up special prohibitions against eating these animals; but the fact that they were set up, like the repeated warnings against consumption of carrion, shows that nomadic people at that time evidently had fewer reservations about how things should taste than we do. Even palatable animals were forbidden, since according to the strict classification system in early Israelite zoology they did not fit in with the required "cleaving of hoof and chewing of cud."

That special juice
Indeed, the writings handed down from the Israelites display a definite preoccupation with the moral problem of using animals as food for humans. In the Old Testament, one can find phases of an entire cultural history of association with animals, which are continued in the New Testament. At the beginning is the recollection, full of longing, of an original paradisical state when God tells man to eat all plants yielding seeds and all seed-bearing fruit, and in which even the animals are peaceful and eat "every green plant." Then the fall from grace brings about the first enmity between man and animal but still nothing is said about food other than bread and the "plants of the field." Not until after the Flood does a new world begin, in which Noah's descendants are set up as masters over the animals they saved—all the animal species—and it is expressly stated: "Every moving thing that lives shall be food for you; and as I gave you the green plants, I give you everything."

But even at this stage there is a qualification: ". . . you shall not eat flesh with its life, that is, its blood." Later, when Moses added the many further restrictions mentioned above, the strict prohibition of blood-eating was repeated more emphatically, with the threat of punishment, and explained as follows: "You shall not eat the blood of any creature, for the life of every creature is its blood; whoever eats it shall be cut off!"

Here, then, to express it in psychological terms, we again encounter a mechanism for suppressing the reality of animal slaughter while ensuring the enjoyment of meat, by common agreement: the blood of the animals is declared to be the real seat of their lives—the "soul." In letting blood flow onto the altar, one speeds the animal soul onward to God in a sacrificial fire, and is content to eat only the remaining part that is not soul, the meat. In fact, through all antiquity blood was "a very special juice"; it signified the real vital principle. Blood brotherhood as a symbol of spiritual commingling is a concept familiar even to modern man, and in our thought and speech are countless reflections of the attitude that blood is the soul, the innermost seat of life, heredity, relatedness, passion and character. Only a few decades ago European medicine, at least in the teachings of the surgeon August Bier (1861–1949), regarded the "blood-soul" as a matter for scientific discussion.

"Thou shalt not kill"
In all the religions based on a relationship to nature—from America to Polynesia, from Africa to Australia—there were restrictive laws, strict

taboos, temporal, spatial or social rules concerning "clean" and "unclean" foods; accordingly, we can be sure that the spiritual and moral problems associated with killing animals have always played a fundamental role. The highly developed religions—especially Buddhism—have taken up this tradition and extended it. Christianity introduced still another facet of the relationship between man and animal. The general Christian commandment to love one's neighbor, if interpreted broadly, must also arrive at a repudiation of animal slaughter. The original Christian community in Jerusalem under Jacob the Just rejected the Mosaic law concerning food and lived entirely as vegetarians; Hieronymus, who created the Latin Bible, in the 4th Century provided a theological basis for vegetarianism. Through Christ, he wrote, the end of history had been linked with the beginning in Paradise, "so that it is no longer permitted to us to eat the flesh of animals."

His great contemporary Augustine surpassed him, however, by stating that he would rather give up all the fame the world can offer than kill a fly. At this point the path was clearly marked to a moral development away from any sort of killing and toward a new, peaceful coexistence of man and animal.

But this signpost remained an isolated phenomenon in the Christian world—as isolated as those few in our society who are vegetarians by conviction. Love of one's neighbor, the advancement of humanity, was so very central to occidental moral philosophy that animals—not being regarded as neighbors—were ignored in this respect. Only from time to time in the following centuries—especially in the case of Francis of Assissi —was neighborly love directed toward our non-human fellow creatures. Finally, science and philosophy deepened the theoretical gap separating man and animal, so that the bond between the two gave way to the philosopher Descartes' (1596–1650) view of the "brute as an automaton," a piece of machinery without soul or the ability to reason; only stupid sentimentality could support any objection to the killing of a machine.

Apart from all these emotional attitudes, however, there has been another important difficulty raised by meat-eating since the end of the hunting period early in man's history. Domestic animals, especially cattle, were expensive and were valuable as draft animals; the time and resources required to raise cattle made it impossible for a large part of the population to use them as food. Early in the development of Roman civilization, according to Cicero, peasants were forbidden on pain of death to slaughter cattle. Later, when the farmers were eventually allowed to bring their cattle to market, meat was still so expensive that only the rich could enjoy it; the poorer levels of society lived on bread, perhaps improving the menu occasionally with fish and small animals. Never in the history of humanity have the stocks of cattle been adequate to enable all the inhabitants of the earth's large cities to eat meat every day, nor are they adequate now. The meat of domestic animals, like fowl and venison,

The animal automaton

Gluttons and gourmets

Fig. 22-2. Fowl for sale in an ancient Egyptian shop. Fattened geese are hanging on the wall.

Fig. 22-3. Roasting geese in ancient Egypt.

Emotional value judgments

remains a prize available only to those who have risen in society, an expression of prosperity achieved.

In ancient Rome, where herds of cattle were "capital" and pigs were sacrificed in the temples daily, we can recognize the first appearance in occidental history of a cult of eating, which has been embodied for all time in the figure of General Lucius Licinius Lucullus. Animals which were uncommon, troublesome to find and often delivered over long distances attained the status of delicacies; serving these at his table, this contemporary of Julius Caesar soon became much admired. Other rich Romans hastened to imitate him; expeditions were sent out to the most distant parts of the Roman Empire and beyond, to bring back new, rarer species of game, fowl and sea animals. All of these found their way into the kitchens of the prosperous Romans, and did service to the Lucullan cult at large dinners.

These lavish entertainments marked a new attitude toward meat animals; quite apart from any nutritional needs, people capriciously used rare animals to raise their own standing in each others' eyes. This attitude is well illustrated by the story that the most highly prized moray eels were fed with slaves—though there is probably no truth in it. However, even the killing of "only" a few hundred songbirds in order to make a meal of larks' tongues is sufficiently revolting to emphasize the unnatural waste and the degeneracy of Lucullan gastronomy. A similar antagonism is aroused by present-day customs as well; every year protests are raised against the murder of songbirds by the descendants of the ancient Romans. This bird-killing is regarded as a sheer abomination, while the no less reprehensible habit of eating frogs' legs seems, to most people, merely unappetizing.

The consumption of oysters, crustaceans, snails and caviar is our own form of Lucullan gluttony. When pies are baked of fish spawn in New Zealand, when palolo worms in Oceania or the internal organs of sea urchins in Chile are eaten raw, and when in Peru brook beetles no larger than mustard seeds are used for "chiche soup," our reactions are more of amused curiosity than of moral indignation.

Why is this? What sort of strange zoology of the inner emotions does it reveal? Why do we feel that the killing of songbirds for the sake of their tongues is a merciless and thoughtless misuse of animals as food, but accept without protest the same attitude when it is directed toward "lower" animals—the ovaries of the sturgeon, the tails of lobsters and the feet of snails? Here we meet a phenomenon baffling to every biologist: the fact that his scientific system of classification, in which he distinguishes between higher and lower classes of animal, is clearly preshadowed by the innermost value judgments of humans in general. Even people who have no idea of the theory of evolution are quite certain that mammals and birds are "closer" to us than fish, to say nothing of mollusks and arthropods, and that therefore to kill animals is "bad" in different degrees. The songbird—that small, warm, colorful and peaceful creature, symbolizing the spirit in its flight and appealing to our souls with its song—in this scale of values is the embodiment of all that is precious in life. Thus it is easy to us to be humane toward it. The fact that the present-day slaughter of songbirds is indeed to be repudiated, because it has profoundly disturbing effects upon nature, has nothing to do with this emotional reaction. To rob songbirds of their tongues, the instruments of their music, in order to serve dozens of them as tidbits at the table, appears from the emotional viewpoint as the peak of inhuman behavior. But the "unjustness" of such a view as compared with our indifference to the frog should really make us pause and consider.

In this spectrum of sympathy for animals, the fish and all the other cold, mute water creatures occupy a special position. We see them as belonging to a lower category of life. The sequence of creation in Genesis reflects this; fish and fowl were created on the fifth day, whereas it was not until the sixth and last day of creation that "cattle, creeping things and beasts of the earth" came into being. These "earlier" creatures, nearer the plants, can thus—so our sense of values decrees—be killed and eaten with less compunction than large mammals. On causal inspection they even seem to have no blood. This alleged absence of the "seat of the soul" provides culture and religion with the opportunity to claim that fish is not "really" meat at all. Within the framework of Christian symbolism, fish thus became associated with fasting, as a compromise between the need to eat and abstinence from meat. For centuries it filled the role of a Friday meat substitute. From the early Middle Ages onward there developed, above all in the monasteries, a tradition of keeping fish in ponds, as a result of which carp especially became distributed throughout most countries.

A further circumstance makes fish particularly important in the human diet. They are the only organisms in vast supply, in many bodies of water, so that they can serve as the chief food of coastal peoples and those living near rivers and lakes. A large fraction of the earth's population—even today, despite the clear decline in the stocks of fish—lives primarily on fish, and in earlier times the fraction was surely even larger. Fisherman have always pulled their nets out of the water filled with rich harvests they had no need to sow; fish is cheap, and the supply once appeared inexhaustible. Even the modern oceanic fisheries, until quite recently, could not seriously diminish this superabundance in spite of all their mechanical improvements. Fish can be dried and salted, for storage and transport—ideal properties of a basic food. For these reasons, the complex of emotional problems related to killing fish have been relatively easily repressed. Bread and fish "fed the five thousand," bread and fish continued to be accepted gratefully as a gift of God, and only the moral sensibilities of particularly open-minded men could remind people sitting down to a meal of fish of the slaughter that preceded it.

The special role of fish

Fig. 22-4. An Egyptian fisherman, from a tomb painting in Thebes.

Such conscientious opponents of the killing of animals became more numerous in the Romantic age, under the "Back to Nature" banner of Rousseau. Gradually the medieval indifference to the sufferings of animals was overcome, and in the early 19th Century in Europe people began to think in terms of protecting them. In England the first law aimed at prevention of cruelty to animals was passed in 1822. The view became increasingly widespread that it was consistent with human dignity to spare the working animals, and those intended for slaughter, at least as much suffering as could be avoided. From this proposition there has arisen again and again the related decision to ban the cause of this suffering—meat-eating itself—from the civilized world. Vegetarians acting on the strength of their rational convictions, and moved not by their own physical well-being but by the avoidability of this cruelty, are no longer such a small minority. In recent years the German clergyman Carl Anders Skriver entered the field as a particularly eloquent and uncompromising champion of this cause, denouncing the "betrayal of animals by the church." He declared, "a Christianity that lives from slaughterhouses is simply shameful," and stated that the human diet must be not only dietetically, but also ethically, irreproachable. Together with the vegetarians and those active in animal protection throughout the world, Skriver hopes for "the end of this ethical Ice Age."

His indignation is echoed increasingly in other circles, since in recent years it has become public knowledge that the sufferings of animals, from birth to the moment of slaughter, have been increased in several ways by modern automation of the production process. When Ruth Harrison published her book "Animal Machines" in 1964, she set off a shock wave comparable to that following Rachel Carson's book "Silent Spring," in protest against the environmental crisis. A broad segment of the population discovered for the first time, by reading this book, that not only behind the walls of the slaughterhouses, but even in the barns and pens of the large-scale animal farmers, frightening things were going on. Raising calves in dark, narrow cells so that they would have less red blood and thus particularly white meat, keeping laying chickens in tiny cages that prevent any sort of movement, killing animals on a conveyer belt without adequate anesthetization—these are only the most striking points of protest raised in this work, the truth of which is indisputable.

In recent years other abuses of penned-up animals have come to light, which involve alarming dangers even to man as a consumer of these manipulated organisms; in these cases the interests of animal protection and human protection coincide. To fatten calves more rapidly, they are injected with estrogen and other sexual hormones, which then enter the bodies of the unsuspecting consumer along with the meat and can produce allergies, liver damage, sexual malfunctions and even cancer. Similarly, animals are often treated with antibiotics to prevent infections, even though this practice is illegal; as a result, people eating this meat are also

Prevention of cruelty to animals

Modern "animal machines"

affected by these medications, and human disease pathogens may become more resistant. In the Manchester children's hospital in 1971 forty-one children died in a typhus epidemic; to the surprise of the doctors, antibiotics were ineffective against the disease. The typhus pathogens were immune to these medicines, because the continual exposure to small amounts of antibiotics taken in with meat had made them resistant.

The danger that humans may be flooded with antibiotics by eating meat is not limited to England. For example, a test study in Hessian slaughterhouses revealed a strong contamination of 47% of the calves and a third of the pigs with various medicines; the minister for agriculture spoke of an "acute threat to the health of the consumers."

Laws to protect us are at present still in a developmental stage; it is predictable that the rapid development of new practices by the pharmaceutical industry and the pressure of competition among producers of meat products will outpace the formulation of new laws. Word has come from France that a new method of fattening geese has been tried there; a small operation is performed to destroy the brain center limiting food intake, so that a pathological voracity results. The geese develop an enormously overstuffed liver, weighing up to a pound—an advantage to the producers of Strasbourg liver paté, but to us one more reason for thinking seriously about the moral limits of our behavior. In the raising of animals for food, as in the other aspects of the environmental crisis, one thing is clear: no fundamental change in the situation can be expected from the complicated and slow-moving machinery of the law, and the only hope is a general transformation in the consciousness of the people. To become thoroughly informed about the threat from unscrupulous, profit-motivated misuse of technology and medicine is only a first step; the next must lie in the determination with which each individual takes action against these practices, in ways suited to his own position and level of responsibility—even if it is only by a boycott of suspect meat, which changes the situation appreciably for its "producers." *The other side of the story*

According to statistics from 1975, each citizen of the United States on the average consumed 113 lbs. beef, 73 lbs. pork, 3 lbs. veal, and 3 lbs. lamb and mutton per year. This means that Americans consume 38 billion pounds of red meat a year; at that rate they are the leading meat-eaters of the world. *Statistics*

The moral problem of having to kill, disquiet over cruel treatment of animals raised for slaughter, and the realization that if all animals on earth were distributed "fairly" among the whole human population they would not suffice—these three quite different factors give rise to a central hope: that it may be possible for science to close the "protein gap" in the human diet by artificial means. Will we one day be able to produce meat synthetically in factories, and thus be freed of all our misgivings? There is a genuine protein gap; it has not just been invented in defense of meat- *The "protein gap"* eating. A purely vegetable diet which includes only carbohydrates and plant fats leads to severe protein deficiencies; there are certain so-called "essential" amino acids which our bodies cannot by themselves produce from carbohydrates and must be supplied by meat, milk products or particularly protein-rich plant products such as soybeans.

Artificial protein?

This inadequacy in our physiology may well be a heritage from the hunting life of our ancestors hundreds of millennia ago; in the long time that has passed since man began to hunt, meat has been such a regular part of his diet that the synthetic ability of the body itself has disappeared. Using eggs, milk, soybeans and oatmeal, the protein gap could indeed be closed entirely without meat; but such large quantities of these foods would be needed that the entire human population could not be nourished. There are, however, already new procedures for cultivating unicellular green algae in massive amounts, so as to obtain protein from nutrient salts, water and sunlight by photosynthesis. Algal cultures in the tropics, as calculations have shown, could give yields twenty times as great as soybean fields of the same size. Such yields are, however, expensive in the facilities that must be built and the energy that must be spent, to attain them. One main thrust of contemporary research is toward the possibility of using bacteria and yeasts to transform petroleum into a protein-rich human food. The success achieved thus far is promising; it might be possible to produce in this way large quantities of cheap protein, which could contribute to the nutrition of large numbers of people. The possibility will be limited, however, by the fact that this densely populated world is beginning to run short of petroleum, which becomes costly as a potential food source, as well as of food itself.

The taste, of course, will not be like that of a steak; but this petroleum-based protein is without taste or smell and thus can be mixed with ordinary food. The biochemist Günther Weitzel said of such research: "If it proves possible to develop synthetic protein products to such an extent that the customary meat dishes can be imitated, then the transition from the traditional meat to synthetic protein will no longer be a problem. Very probably the need to feed properly the rapidly growing population of the earth will accelerate this development."

But these substitutes for traditional foods may be costly, and there is a long way to go. Even if protein from non-animal sources were available to all people in sufficient amounts, it would be quite unrealistic to expect every inhabitant of the earth to give up his Sunday roast for the sake of such "ethically irreproachable" substitutes. Perhaps, though, biotechnology will yet succeed in relieving us of the decision for or against the killing of animals. This could happen if ways could be found to grow animal muscle in tissue culture. Then cheap meat free of the blemish of murder could be produced from artificial nutrients; slaughter could be avoided, yet all the natural properties of animal protein would be retained.

At the moment, of course, this is but an optimistic view of the future. But techniques of tissue culture are steadily developing, and there is reason to hope for such a future. If this dream could be achieved, biochemistry would have made the slaughterhouses superfluous and lifted from us the burden of an age-old problem—the necessity of killing.

23   Observation of Animals in the Field

By P. Rietschel

The science of zoology cannot be learned from books alone. Books and journals help us to an understanding of what others have learned about individual animals and communities, but nature must be experienced, must be seen with one's own eyes. Real understanding results when knowledge from books and personal experience are combined.

Does modern man actually have much chance to observe animals? In spite of the number of people who must live in centers of population and industry, and in spite of the increasing poverty of our fauna, the answer is still yes. Some animal species have indeed vanished from the neighborhood of our cities, but others have multiplied or become newly established there. Forest and field may be pushed further and further from the growing centers of population, but transport systems expand along with the cities and still permit us to reach and wander through regions less altered.

There are also islands of greenery even in the centers of the cities, where all sorts of animals live; this fauna native to our own settlements deserves special attention. We cannot, of course, expect to find "virgin" communities here, nor can they be reestablished; the original communities in city parks have been modified and in part destroyed by the changes in their environment. For this very reason, we should try to ensure that even these animals and communities, now under man's influence, are not destroyed. For the observer who has practiced his skills in such parks it is a particular pleasure to leave the city and experience an undisturbed flora and fauna in its natural, dynamic equilibrium. When we go out to observe nature, after all, we are concerned not only with individual animals but with the closely woven web of reciprocal relations among fauna, flora and the abiotic environment. Some knowledge of botany is essential, but it would be a sadly one-sided person who found this a tiresome task. Many animals are restricted to certain plants for their food; moreover, the special kinds of plant communities best define the nature of the habitat of certain animal communities.

When an animal in the field attracts our attention, we usually wonder what species it is. There is of course no zoological expert capable of identifying on sight all the species in a single country—more than forty thousand in Germany, for example—to say nothing of the well over one million named species on earth. Even a professional zoologist must go to some trouble to identify the less common species; to do this, he needs written "keys" which systematically describe the animals on the basis of a hierarchy of characteristics. Such identification is not as easy as it is for the botanist, who with a single pocket-sized book can often discover the name of every native plant. There are pocket-books with keys to the fauna (for example, P. Brohmer's "Fauna von Deutschland"), but they take the zoology student as far as species identification for only a few animal groups, while for others he can make his identification only to the level of genus or even family. Even with the help of larger works it is not always possible to determine species, especially when one is dealing with the juvenile forms of the animals.

Our attempts to "key out" animals will thus often fail to provide a complete identification, but they are still extremely profitable. Being directed to look for particular distinguishing characteristics, we often notice details that otherwise would have escaped us. The insect under the lens, the mite or rotifer under the microscope, all raise a steady stream of new questions about the relationships between the structural components and their function; and in the process we often discover unsuspected beauty. The amateur zoologist, then, should not be discouraged by the difficulties of ultimate identification. To become an expert in detailed identification in some little-studied animal group, one needs extensive literature. The following hints are not intended for such a person, but rather for those who enjoy zoology in general and want to have a clearer insight into the diversity of animal forms, behavior and community life.

How should we equip ourselves for these zoological forays? They are not expeditions, after all, but (as the Leipzig zoology professor William Marshall has put it) "strolls of a student of nature." The most important equipment is our own set of sense organs, well used. Conversation and observation are mutually exclusive. We can easily amplify the power of our eyes: a folding pocket lens that enlarges objects by a factor of ten to sixteen should be a constant companion, even on paths where we really do not expect to see any animals. Secured by a cord, it is safe from loss and can accompany us throughout our lives; mine has served me well for over six decades. Even the best lens is not too expensive for such long use. It opens up a new level of nature, an order of magnitude smaller than that we know.

The second visual aid is a pair of binoculars. This should be light and small, so that we can carry it in a pocket. Then it is always at hand at the crucial monent; a large, heavy pair with the highest magnification and light-gathering power is of no use if it has been left at home. 6×24 to

Identifying species

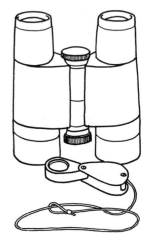

Fig. 23-1. Binoculars and pocket lens—indispensable companions on every nature walk.

The equipment

8 × 32 are perfectly adequate specifications; or a small telescope can be used instead. An important feature is the ability to focus sharply at relatively short distances, as little as six to eight meters; the binoculars should be useful in observing not only large animals at a great distance, but small ones nearby. By putting a weak convex lens in front of the objective one can shorten the focal length still more; the binoculars become a "long-distance magnifying glass."

Someone who prefers to key out small animals at home can take along a "killing bottle," a plastic container with a wide neck, screw top and a volume of about a hundred cubic centimeters, containing loosely crumpled strips of blotting paper wet with a few drops of acetic ether. A smaller bottle half filled with alcohol can receive very small, delicate animals. Take along a few small, closable plastic bags and a notebook and pencil, and the outfit is complete. But one should be careful not to kill and take home more animals than one is really going to key out; this kind of collecting is exclusively for the purpose of identifying and thus becoming familiar with the local animal species or families. It is also often useful to take a butterfly net that can be dismantled and carried easily and inconspicuously.

If water habitats are to be studied, some special items of equipment are necessary: a coarse fishing net, a fine-meshed plankton net, a few jars, a white sheet of plastic on which to observe the catch, and a thermos bottle to take the water animals home. Unless a very light portable microscope is available, plankton is better investigated at home. These organisms usually withstand transport in a thermos bottle quite well, if one does not try to take too many and leaves an air space in the bottle.

We keep notes of our observations in a diary, recording the time, place and any special circumstances; the biotope or habitat can best be described on the basis of the plant community. A photographer naturally wants to be prepared for all possibilities, but the all-purpose equipment required for good nature photographs can hardly be carried by one person. And in many cases good pictures cannot be taken on a casual basis; they demand careful preliminary observations and a great deal of time. For these reasons, excursions for observation and for photography are two different undertakings. If one wants to use a camera on an observation trip, he should keep the equipment minimal—a small camera capable of taking close-ups, the smallest possible flash attachment, and a second lens with double or triple focal length.

Nature walks are not long-distance hikes, and should be kept within a small area. The edge of a wood, with shrubbery growing along the path, includes many habitats and a rich fauna—in the foliage of the bushes and trees, under the bark of dead or felled trunks, in the leaf litter on the woodland floor, in the deeper humus, in fungi, in and under cowpats, in the corpse of an animal, in a drainage ditch, in the sand of the path, and on the flowers by the wayside. A path only a hundred meters long

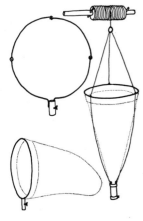

Fig. 23-2. Collecting nets: collapsible frame for an insect net (upper left); coarse fishing net (lower left); fine plankton net (right).

One small area at a time

often provides all the opportunity for observation that could be wished. The birch, for example, houses different bark beetles than the elm, and there are still others in the spruce; in a single tree, the species under the thick bark of old parts of the trunk differ from those under the delicate covering of the branches and the topmost shoots. The damp side of a trunk, green with algae, presents a different fauna than the dryer side opposite. And the body of a dead animal, in the course of decomposition, feeds a succession of different animal communities.

The meadow bordering the wood may seem comparatively sparsely populated, but a few passes with an insect net show that it is teeming with ants, small bugs, aphids, mites, spiders, small flies and midges, tiny ichneumon wasps and many other animals. But why are all these varied animals associated in a common habitat? To answer that question, we must observe the different species as they go about their activities in the meadow—a more laborious undertaking than simply catching them. To get a quantitative estimate of the many animal populations is an even harder task; this is usually beyond the scope of the amateur zoologist.

We should direct our attention not only to the animals themselves, but also to the traces they leave behind: the tunnels that scolytid, buprestid and long-horn beetles make under the bark of trees, the great variety of webs and other silken structures, the damage to foliage which appears as soon as the leaves have expanded in the spring, the caterpillar feces on the ground, and the aerial plankton caught and killed by the sticky bands painted around fruit trees. Owls spit out the indigestible parts of their food in little clumps; seeing such a mass, we not only learn that an owl was there, but we can often find well preserved mouse jaws with teeth still in place. From these we can infer which mouse species live in the area. Honeydew on leaves, ant trails, the stalked eggs of lacewings, and lady beetles all betray the presence of aphid colonies. Turning over stones, we discover still other habitats; it goes without saying that we do them no harm, but carefully replace the stones when we are finished. And we also use discretion in disturbing the bark of trees, so that these habitats too are preserved.

Animal tracks

A fascinating area of study, which involves botany as well, is the combined observation of flower-visiting insects and of the associated modifications evolved by the flowers (see Chapter 7). Here one obtains insight into the most remarkable symbiotic associations that evolution has produced.

Field observations of animals are fruitful in every season and every weather. In winter there may be fewer species to be seen, but this raises questions about where and how the animals spend the winter. Some birds and butterflies migrate to warmer regions, but the rest of the animals must still be somewhere nearby. It is enchanting to walk through new snow, with the tracks of animals crossing one another in curious patterns. To decipher these tracks is an art in itself. In the other seasons, walks should not be limited to good weather. Fine weather is better for watching insects, but rainy days are better for snails. On a cool, dewy autumn morning

Season and weather

it may be that neither snails nor insects are visible, but thousands of spider webs glitter in the sun and impress us with the dangers of life as an insect. This "spider weather," which displays the various web forms so beautifully, unfortunately lasts only a short time; when the early dew evaporates in the morning sunlight the magnificent sight disappears. Then, of course, is the time of real danger for the awakening insects.

Observation at a pond
Bodies of fresh water are also rewarding objects of study, whether they be old bomb craters or quarries now filled with ground water, small, placid woodland lakes or raging mountain brooks. The number of such habitats from which one can choose is steadily decreasing; small pools are used as dumps and filled in, and ponds and lakes are fenced round with barbed wire and staked out as private property with "No Trespassing" signs. Brooks lose the willows and alders that used to shade them, and receive instead a corset of cement and a stream of Sunday visitors who misuse them to wash their cars. Rivers today carry to the sea not just the mingled waters of natural streams but the effluent from a network of sewers. At the beginning of this century it was still common for children to discover nature in neighborhood ponds. With a big enough garden one can make such a quiet pool for himself, populated by frogs, fish and other small animals. Having found an easily accessible, not yet polluted pond or stream, one can follow the advice of W. Engelhardt: "Choose a pool or a brook and make it your pool, your brook! It will be yours only when you know all its inhabitants and all their daily activities."

This kind of exploration should not be spread out over as many bodies of water as possible, but rather should be concentrated on a few, through all seasons of the year and for many years in succession. Only then can one become familiar with the relationships between the organisms and their constantly changing environment. This is a rewarding occupation, for no other habitat displays the manifold interactions so clearly as fresh water. Study of the water habitat must also be extended to its surroundings, for the insect larvae living in the water are to be found on land as adults. From some position offering a clear view we watch the activities of dragonflies with binoculars, and we can also see damselflies going down into the water to lay their eggs. When we turn to observe life in the water itself, we can pick out a spot on the shore that allows us to peer below the surface of the water.

The home aquarium
If we do not want to be limited to such random samples of underwater life we set up an aquarium at home, a miniature copy of our pond, and bring back a few of the pond inhabitants to live in it. Care must be taken not to stock it with too many animals; in the pond, overpopulation is prevented by natural regulatory mechanisms. In the spring one can follow closely the mating behavior of salamanders and the development of frogs from eggs to tadpoles and the metamorphosis into the finished product. Aquatic insect larvae, gastropods and leeches also provide countless interesting observations in an aquarium.

Outdoors, in "our" pond, we sweep the fishing net through the water plants and tip the animals it catches onto a flat white plate for study and identification. The hand lens is of great value here. The part of the catch destined for the home aquarium is put into a thermos bottle half filled with pond water and water plants. All the other organisms are set free again. In this way, in the course of a year, we can become familiar with the larger pond-dwellers at all stages of their development.

A microscope reveals equally fascinating insights into the miniature world of the pond. We take samples of pond water with plankton caught in a net, and carry them home in a thermos bottle. Looking at this, under first low and then gradually increasing magnification, we see the first links in the food chain of the pond-dwellers—and many of them are surprisingly beautiful. To identify them costs considerable time, but is an enjoyable postlude to the collecting trip.

The microfauna

Even in the winter months, when life in our pond rests under the cove of ice, it is possible to have an abundance of material for microscopic investigations. In the fall we shake the flaky coating off of dying water plants, reed stalks and so on, collecting it in a container filled with pond water. At home, we fill several jars with the contents of the thermos, and store them in the cellar, keeping only one of them at room temperature. At first there is little to be seen under the microscope, for most of the pond organisms have become encysted or otherwise made themselves quiescent and cold-resistant for the winter. But in the warmth of the room they awaken, and soon little samples of the material that has settled on the bottom of the jar prove to be full of life. When the activity eventually slows down, and the ostracods have gained the upper hand, we can bring the next jar up from the cellar and experience the whole sequence anew, watching for what we missed the first time.

Observations of life in a mountain brook proceed quite differently Again, though, we find larvae of water insects which in the end metamorphose into flying insects that stay in the vicinity of the brook. To lay their eggs, they fly upstream. This compensates for the tendency of the larvae to drift down with the rapid current; if they did not lay the eggs further upstream, their range of distribution would shift steadily downstream. We can appreciate the rich life in the brook itself if we pick up stones from its bed. Here are found many rheophilous animals, specially adapted to strong currents and shaped in various ways so that they can stick or press themselves to the bottom. These, too, are easily observed and identified on a flat white plate. But we must be content with our field observations, for these animals need a great deal of oxygen and in most cases low temperatures; it would be very difficult to provide them with that environment in a home aquarium.

Studying a mountain brook

As the brook water flows further from the source it warms up, and its fauna changes with increasing temperature. The sequence of turbellarian worms is most characteristic of these parts of the brook. Other modifications of the fauna betray a decrease in the purity of the water. This is often detectable as soon as the brook has passed through the first human settlement; waste water from a single factory can do perceptible damage. The composition of the fauna in such waters is a more reliable indicator than the chemical testing of water samples, which might have been taken just between discharges of pollutants!

The seaside

The beach and the sea itself are also fascinating objects of nature excursions. In southern Europe, even the harbor cities offer an attraction of their own—the fish markets. Not only fishes are sold here, but all the "fruits of the sea," such as sea urchins, clams, snails, cephalopods and crustaceans. It is also rewarding to go out with the fishermen; many animals are brought up in the nets which never reach the market. Sometimes observation aquariums are set up in port cities, and these should not be missed. But for the most gripping impressions of the marine fauna, one must go into the water oneself. Self-contained underwater breathing apparatus (SCUBA) can be used only after considerable training and experience, but anyone can swim with mask and snorkel. Just below the water surface a whole new world is found. On purely sandy bottoms there are only a few animals, so that mile-long bathing beaches are of little use. But the jetties and piers in harbors often have a rich fauna, and so do rocky coasts. By staying completely motionless or moving only very slowly, one can observe the swarms of fish flitting about and study the brightly colored growths on the stones—an excellent camouflage for the equally colorful animals living there. These nature studies in the ocean have nothing in common with the "sport" of underwater hunting, which has disturbed marine life to a marked degree and threatens still further damage.

To become acquainted with the whole food chain in the shallow inshore water, one needs the same equipment as for a fresh-water pond—a plankton net and a microscope. It is extremely rewarding to take both of these along on a seaside vacation. On the microscope slide we meet not only protozoans, small medusae, slender arrow-worms, tailed tunicates and an army of copepods, but also the larvae of turbellarian, annelid and nematode worms, crustaceans, echinoderms, clams, snails, tunicates and other animals which live among the plankton only in their youth, later settling on the floor of the sea.

Moreover, there is an abundant fauna on the rocky bottoms of ocean bays. Equipped with rubber-soled shoes—as protection from the spines of sea urchins—and a pail we walk into the water to a depth of half a meter, pick up stones and study their undersides. Sea stars, brittle stars, sea urchins, polychaetes, sipunculid and echiuroid worms, limpets and chitons, tunicates and many other animals can be found here; sandy bottoms, on the other hand, are commonly inhabited by sea cucumbers and sand dollaes. On the beach we take a closer look at our finds, identify them, and return them to their home. Drying and collecting marine animals is a practice to be discouraged; in any case, it usually ends with the "souvenirs" in the trash can. Only calcareous shells and cases, from which the soft parts can be cleaned by boiling, are suitable for a permanent collection. Field studies on rocky tide flats are carried out similarly. When studying mudflats, a small shovel can be used to lift out the animals that bury themselves when the tide is out. The masses of seaweed stranded along the high-tide line also house a varied fauna. The terminal consumers in this community are the sea birds and the birds of beach and tide flats.

Though marine animals themselves should not be dried and taken home, there is a more than adequate substitute for the ardent collector. The paucity of animals in fine beach sand is compensated by the rich deposits of fine shells and other mineral remains. These may accumulate in strips, which on the Mediterranean coast are often identifiable by their red color; the color is produced by the coral-red shells of the millimeter-long foraminiferan *Miniacina miniacea*. All the small-animal remnants which are calcified and thus resist decay are accumulated here—much of the debris is fragmented, but some is still well preserved. There are foraminiferan shells (over fifty species were found in a single sample taken near Syracuse, Sicily), snail and clam shells, cases of ectoproct bryzoans, the bivalve shells of brachiopods, the spines, Aristotle's lantern, shell-plates and even whole shells of sea urchins, the vertebrae of brittle stars, tubes of polychaete worms, shells of ostracods, crab claws and much besides. Examination of the sample from the beach at Syracuse, half a kilogram of this fine calcareous debris, under magnification of ten to twenty times revealed well over a hundred animal species.

Shell-collecting on a microscale

We can collect and arrange samples like these from the Mediterranean coast in special cells for microscopic observation; this not only gives a fascinating picture of the animal life characteristic of such a beach, but under high (20–40×) magnification presents us with a little museum of "natural art forms." Moreover, in sorting through such samples we discover how greatly the seacoasts are threatened by the byproducts of civilization—many of these remnants of animal life are sticky with Diesel oil. One more habitat of the beach and lake shore deserves mention; this is simply the system of spaces between the sand grains (see Chapter 17). The exploration of its fauna has just begun and promises to be full of surprises.

Among all the many animals we meet on our nature walks, the birds occupy a special position. The great variety of behavioral patterns, often associated with calls and songs that differ from one species to another, as well as their visual appeal to our sense of beauty, have won the birds enthusiastic friends everywhere. There are more amateurs working in the field of ornithology than in any other branch of zoology. Ornithological observations, then, take up a considerable part of each of our excursions. But it only makes sense to spend time bird-watching if we know the birds well enough to call them by name.

Bird-watching

And this is easier in the case of birds than with the insects; in all central Europe there are only about 400 species and in the area an individual can reach easily from his home there are only a few dozen. In the cold months there are even fewer species, since more migratory birds leave than arrive to spend the winter there. A beginner who has the chance to accompany an experienced watcher on his outings should take advantage of it. Whether in company or alone one needs a good pair of binoculars (or a telescope) of intermediate magnification and light-gathering power (ca. 8×30), writing materials and a pocketbook for keying out the birds; the latter makes it possible to identify on the spot the sometimes rather inconspicuous distinguishing characteristics of the different species.

Once a bird has been identified and its name "checked off" in the list of species, there is still some way to go before one can claim to know it. The same species can have a different appearance at another time of year, or we may see an individual of the opposite sex or of a different age. A bird does not become an "old acquaintance" until we have observed it time and again. And as we do so, it raises a series of new questions. How long does this species stay in the area? When, where and how does it build its nest? What are its eggs like? In answering these questions we must be very careful, but a glance into the nest with the help of a pocket mirror can be permitted, when the parent birds are away. Photography of birds in the nest produces charming pictures, but it frequently endangers the brood and in such cases must on no account be done. Once the eggs are laid, another set of questions suggests itself: To what extent does the male participate in brooding and feeding the young? How often are they fed, and with what? Who cleans out the nest, and how? When are the young ready to fly? How many broods are hatched per year? When and how do the birds molt?

The voices of birds, their calls and songs, are an almost inexhaustible source of discoveries. They are difficult to describe in words or with symbols or musical notation; anyone wishing to occupy himself with them at length should tape them with a battery-operated recorder. When we find that a bird species is restricted to a special habitat, we wonder what it is that keeps it there. Sometimes birds go elsewhere, perhaps a great distance away, to sleep. By following the evening flights of starlings, one can discover their common sleeping site and witness a magnificent spectacle of nature, seen so far by very few humans.

The autumn migration is easier to see than the return of the birds in spring; the birds that remain and the arriving winter guests are more readily observed among the leafless branches. It is a charming sight when they gather around a feeder; this should be set up in the fall and supplied with food in good time—not only after everything is frozen solid. The coldest time of year offers yet another special experience. Then rivers free of ice, and other open bodies of water, are the meeting point for flocks of water birds from the far north. Here we see many a species of bird that we would have to travel far to find in summer. No nature enthusiast should miss this event, brief as it is.

The convenience of travel in modern times has opened up unfamiliar regions to the nature observer, with their unfamiliar flora and fauna. Usually he has only a few weeks of vacation to devote to them, so that he cannot hope to learn to know them as well as his home grounds. But even a short trip from an inland city to the seacoast can be rewarding. For a central European the published keys he uses at home will suffice for a visit to the north coast, but in southern Europe he will encounter animals and plants for which he will search in vain in those books. But even without knowing their scientific names one can enjoy the termites and embiids, scorpions and centipedes one finds upon turning over stones in the sunny south; and small animals that one wants to identify can be taken home and shown to an expert there.

Habitats and animals away from home

A rather different sort of nature observation is provided by excursions combining air travel to tropical countries with motorized tours through the nature preserves there. These "photo-safaris" are increasingly taking the place of the barbaric hunting safaris, but they too are concerned chiefly with the large game. The small animals get short shrift, since where game is abundant one is usually not allowed to leave the cars, for reasons of safety. In eastern Africa, for example, one can see countless termite nests but not a single termite queen.

Photo-safaris

The situation is better as far as birds are concerned, as long as there are enough people in one vehicle who are interested in watching them. It is safest to join a tour that is explicitly described as a bird-watching safari. Then we can expect to have like-minded companions, and we have all the opportunities we need to see large game as well. Those interested in photography can bring heavy equipment; in the car even a long, cumbersome telephoto lens is no burden. It is usual to take along a large supply of color film, but the connoisseur also appreciates the greater sensitivity and resolving power of certain black-and-white films. But much more important to the nature observer than all the photographic apparatus put together is a pair of binoculars or a telescope.

To become acquainted with the entirely new fauna of a foreign country, thorough preparations are required. Trips to a zoo are a considerable help here.

Zoo visits, in fact, can be rewarding excursions for amateur zoologists, even when they are not meant as travel preparations. Anyone living near a zoo should go there regularly, covering only part of it each time. Here, too, it is helpful to take binoculars, so as to study the animals in large enclosures and the water birds on the ponds. After such a visit, try to call to mind the plumage of the male mallard, the foot of a tapir, the head of a shoebill or a hippopotamus, and draw a picture of it. Then it becomes clear how little one remembers of what he has just seen. A meaningful acquaintance with animals is not obtainable by pushing down

Visits to a zoo

the shutter-release of a camera, but simply and solely with pencil and sketchbook. Even though no work of art is produced, the familiarity gained can make the local zoo one's own.

A zoo in another city cannot be visited so frequently, so that we usually wander through it all and pause only where there is something of special interest. Even in small zoos one can find rare or unfamiliar animals. Wherever we are, though, we naturally pay particular attention to the species that are now threatened with extinction—future generations may not have such an opportunity.

24   The Zoo

Today's zoos have a dual nature—they are planned for both man and animals. Through their many thousand years of history, zoos have been simply places where animals were kept, not for their own sake, but to satisfy man's need for curiosities to look at. It was not until this century that they actually developed into "homes" for animals, where the needs of the wild animals were appreciated and where they were cared for under conditions permitting health and long life. In the long run, keeping animals like this, for their own sake, also serves mankind; in this vast— and not altogether consciously intended—"biological experiment" men ensure the survival close at hand of a basic stock of animal species. This is necessary, since at the same time men are irresponsibly exterminating, directly or indirectly, the wild individuals of these species.

The Swiss zoo director Heini Hediger is probably right in comparing the current and long-range significance of these efforts of present-day zoos to the first revolutionary attempts of middle- and late-Stone-Age men to domesticate some wild animal species. However, this second world-wide experiment in keeping and caring for wild animals, as it is now carried out in the zoos, has just the opposite goal. The animals in zoos are not meant to give rise to domestic breeds, but rather to change as little as possible, retaining all the typical physical and behavioral characteristics of wild animals. In contrast to animal husbandry, then, the care of animals in zoos must be closely adjusted to the biology of their wild relatives.

Another way in which zoo technology differs from the history of domestication is that when zoos were in their infancy there was no thought of utilizing the animals except as a spectacle. They were never established in purely rural districts, but at the courts of the rulers and in cities, where wild animals occupied people's leisure time and satisfied curiosity, thirst for knowledge and need to be amused and instructed. Early in civilization zoological gardens were unknown; they have always been distinctive elements of highly developed cultures. It is understandable, then, that the

By R. Kirchshofer

Zookeeping: a global biological experiment

Why were zoos established?

rulers and the nobility in each country were the first to establish and maintain zoos. It was not until the end of the 18th Century that they were followed by the general citizenry, which by then had some voice in their own destiny.

In these days our classless society, which guarantees everyone a certain measure of free time, is responsible for the increased worldwide interest in zoos. Never have there been so many zoological gardens as there are today; never have they been visited by so many people every year. Comparison of the number of visitors to zoos with those visiting similar institutions (such as museums) shows the zoos to be in the lead. And people spend even more time enjoying nature in the open, outside the cities, than they do in the zoos. This striking interest in nature is further reflected in another leisure activity—the keeping of animals as pets. Never before have so many people surrounded themsleves with animals of no utilitarian value at all, which are meant only to give pleasure.

Fig. 24-1. Sunken deer meadow in old Bern. After the Middle Ages the trenches encircling European cities were no longer needed for defense and in many cases were converted to animal enclosures. Palisade fences divided them into sections.

The reason for this development is certainly that city-dwellers have become increasingly cut off from nature. Because of over-industrialization, the overdevelopment of technology, and the resulting population explosion, people can "afford" an existence offering spare time to everyone, but only at the price of a progressive exploitation and destruction of nature, an increasing concentration of all segments of the economy, and thus a completely unnatural way of life. Most of the grandparents of contemporary adults still lived either in the country or in small towns; woods, fields, wild animals and farm animals were as basic elements of their daily life as the changeable weather and other natural phenomena. People living in today's cities no longer experience this at first hand. They, too, however, need these natural environmental conditions for their physical and mental well-being. They show this need unmistakeably in the way they voluntarily employ their leisure hours.

But the significance of zoos as "gardens" for men and animals derives not only from civilized man's estrangement from nature, but also from the ominous fact that the wild animals are being pushed ever further into distant refuges. Hunting, trapping and destruction of their habitats threaten their very existence. Zoos offer wild animals a substitute home, where if sufficient care is taken they may be able to survive despite the danger to their original habitats. From this view of the role of zoos in the lives of men and animals, certain functions and aims automatically follow; these can be summarized under the headings recreation and entertainment, education, research, and the conservation of nature and animals.

To do justice to these functions, modern zoo-keepers must take into account the natural needs of the animals, provide for the necessary hygiene, institute the required safety procedures and offer the public a pleasing and informative display. This was not always the case, and even today these important demands are by no means met everywhere. The animal houses and pens found in modern zoos are the outcome of the particular history of each zoo. There is no standard zoo architecture, but the opinions about how wild animals should be kept that prevailed when a zoo was built are reflected in the design of the grounds and buildings.

The most ancient form of wild-animal enclosure was probably the pit or trench, which served equally to catch and to keep animals, and is still to be found today in one form or the other. An example of this is the Bear Pit in Bern, where, in keeping with old tradition, bears—the animals displayed on the city's coats of arms—are kept today as they were in the Middle Ages. But this type of enclosure satisfies the needs of neither the bears nor the visitors. It seems rather an imposition if wild animals are to be watched by their natural enemy, man, not only from all sides but from above as well. The visitor in turn finds it difficult to perceive and respect the dignity of an animal when it is literally "so far beneath him." As a showcase for animals, the pit is most unsatisfactory, if only for the fact that the observer usually sees only their backs.

Another form of animal trap has been preserved in the palisade enclosure. In India it is used now as in the past to capture elephants; they are cleverly funnelled into the giant, camouflaged trap by a chain of drivers. In Africa the salt-licks of the timid bongo antelope are surrounded by a palisade fence, with only the trail the animals ordinarily follow left open to lead them into the pen. The fenced parts of European woods designed to keep in the game are basically the same thing. In zoos palisades or picket fences are still sometimes used, but in most cases they have been replaced, in the course of time, with sturdier fences of iron rods or wire mesh.

The necessity and significance of zoos

Methods of keeping animals in a zoo

▷
From left to right and top to bottom:
Carnivores are caged in this building in the Dublin zoo (Ireland), built when the zoo was first established around 1830.—A confined outdoor cage with walls of heavy iron bars, in the zoo in Leningrad (USSR), built in 1865. It is easy to imagine how unsuitable it is for such a normally active animal as this Siberian ibex.—An imitation of exotic architecture: the bird house in the former Madrid Zoo (Spain) resembles a temple in Thailand.—This baroque sea-lion pool in Vienna's Schönbrunn Zoo (Austria) is unsuitable for such animals and today serves as an ornamental pond.—
The palisade traps used to catch animals gave rise to the wood fences still used today: the kiang enclosure in the Prague Zoo.—Later wooden rails were discarded in favor of iron pickets,

(continued on p. 507.)

(continued from p. 504.)

as used in the Bronx Zoo to fence in the tapirs.—Elephant enclosure in the Warsaw Zoo (Poland), from the 1920's. The roof is strong enough to support the animals and enlarges the area available to them. The dangerous iron stakes are now no longer in use.—The still-usable aviary for birds of prey, in the Schönbrunn Zoo; even vultures and eagles can fly in it. The artificial rock wall offers resting places and nest sites.

◁

From left to right and top to bottom:
Panorama of Africa in the Hagenbeck Tierpark, Hamburg.—A Hagenbeck-style enclosure in the zoo of Vincennes (Paris), founded in 1935: artificial rock cliff for primates, separated from the visitors by a trench and disguising the shelters behind it.— Brown-bear enclosure in the zoo of Lisbon (Portugal), in Hagenbeck style. In the background, a "classical" elephant enclosure with a shelter house of Moorish design.— Large carnivore cage in the Bristol Zoo (England), patterned after that in Basel. Wire mesh has replaced the iron bars. Open-air chimpanzee enclosure in the zoo of Chester (England), separated from the visitors only by a shallow moat (but with an electric fence for security).—In the zoo of Pretoria (South Africa) native animals (here sable and roan antelopes, water-bucks and gazelles) live in communal areas.—

(continued on p. 508.)

Fenced-in animal pens were already known in ancient Egypt, in China about three thousand years ago, in Greece in the period of classical antiquity, and from the Middle Ages to the 19th Century in Europe; they were used in three ways: as enclosures for the "peaceful" animals, as confined, secure arenas for carnivores, and as cages for birds, small mammals and monkeys. History even tells us of a major full-sized zoo—the enormous and impressive collection of the Aztec ruler Montezuma in Tenochtitlán (which is now Mexico). This zoo, with its spacious enclosures and aviaries, was so large that three hundred animal keepers were kept busy there, more than any present-day zoo can boast. When the Aztec kingdom fell before the conquering Spaniards, this zoo was destroyed.

The many menageries that were created in the Middle Ages, and subsequently in the courts of the various European rulers, resembled one another in their basic structure. Ungulates were usually kept in fenced outdoor spaces with a natural substrate; they were either rectangular or arranged like pieces of pie around a central observation building. Apart from feeding and watering sites, nothing was built into these pens for the animals; moreover, they were shut up for the night in stalls. Usually bare, dark and musty inside, these shelters were disguised externally, according to the taste of the period, as baroque pavilions, log cabins, mosques or tents. The cages of the carnivores were distinguished by their small size, hard stone floors and heavy iron bars. Often they took the form of niches set into thick walls; later, in the public zoos, they were grouped in special animal houses like fortresses. Thus the animals suffered from lack of exercise and not uncommonly from rheumatism and other disabilities, since the stone floors were damp and cold and the cages rarely were open to the light of the sun. Conditions were even worse for birds, small mammals and monkeys which, because of their tropical origins, were kept in separate animal houses with rows of cramped, barred cages, often stacked several deep; these cages could not be properly cleaned, were inadequately ventilated, and were much too dark. High mortality was unavoidable among animals kept in such places.

Despite their inadequacies, some of these animal collections played a great role in the history of zoology. The menagerie built in Sweden in 1561 still existed in the 18th Century—the time of the founder of zoological and botanical systematics, Carl von Linné; this collection may have been one of the factors that stimulated him to assign wild animals scientific names in his famous work "Systema Naturae," which was published in 1758 and remains the basis of scientific nomenclature. The former royal garden in Paris, subsequently the Jardin des Plantes, housed a number of animals and after the French Revolution became the first public zoo in recent times, serving as a site not only for scientific research but also for the entertainment and education of the public. Famous natural scientists like Count Buffon, Lamarck and Cuvier studied the exotic fauna there and established Paris as the center of zoological research at the time. Although there has long been a second large zoo in Paris, the Jardin des Plantes still survives.

The only older zoological garden is that in the grounds of the Viennese castle Schönbrunn. Its animal houses and pens have recently been rebuilt to meet the demands of modern animal-keeping, but its overall layout has retained much of the character of the former royal menagerie. It arose as a combination of two zoos of the emperor Maximilian II near Vienna, one in Ebersdorf (1552) and the other in Neugebäu (1558). In these menageries were kept, under the conditions customary at the time, large cats, elephants, perissodactyls and large ruminants; moreover, the menagerie in Neugebäu in 1736 took over many animals from the private zoo that Prince Eugen of Savoy had kept in the park of the castle Belvedere at Vienna. Sixteen years later all the animals were moved to the newly established zoo at Schönbrunn. This collection is thus the oldest surviving zoo in the world.

With the rise in prosperity of the general citizenry in the 19th Century, numerous zoos were founded in many lands, but they did not differ essentially from the old menageries; only as a result of gradual modernization have they eventually come to meet current standards. The first of these was the London Zoo, established in 1823. By 1865 there were already twenty-six other public zoos. Between the two World Wars, and especially after the Second, this number increased dramatically throughout the world. The International Zoo Yearbook for 1970 listed no less than 916 zoos and aquariums.

A revolution in zoo-keeping was brought about when Hagenbeck's Zoo in Hamburg-Stellingen was opened in 1907. Carl Hagenbeck was the first to put into practice the idea of keeping animals under nearly natural conditions in open, unfenced areas. To keep the animals in, he used trenches. The Swiss landscape architect he brought to Hamburg, Urs Eggenschwyler, designed and built the zoo according to his instructions on the former Rübenäckern in Stelling—an artificial mountain landscape with terraces of rock, waterfalls, gorges, pools and meadows. He arranged the various enclosures, separated only by moats or dry trenches, one behind the other like backdrops on a stage, so that from one vantage point the visitor could observe what was apparently a single habitat housing a freely-moving animal community.

Many people who had previously avoided zoos, because they thought of them as animal prisons, began to visit them when the animals were kept in this new way. The novelty here lay not only in the clever way the animals were put on view; Hagenbeck had in fact freed the animals from their bare, monotonous enclosures and confined cages. In his zoo they lived in community with their own species, in spacious, open areas with fresh air and sunshine. The stalls built into the hollow artificial rocks offered shelter in bad weather; the water-filled trenches were accessible to the animals and served as drinking and bathing places. All this represented

(*continued from p. 507*).

"Drive-through" open-air lion park in Longleat (England), one of the new animal exhibits through which visitors can drive in closed cars. The animals have no territory to call their own, and they are subjected to noise and exhaust fumes.—This way of keeping wild animals is unacceptable. The animals cannot claim an area as a personal territory if human visitors are present everywhere.

The Hagenbeck-style zoo

Fig. 24-2. Fortresslike bear house in the Frankfurt Zoo (demolished in 1958).

an unheard-of advance over traditional methods, which was acknowledged and imitated throughout the world.

But it remained for a subsequent generation of zookeepers to compare the methods Hagenbeck developed on the basis of intuition with the steadily growing body of knowledge about the biology of wild animals. Research on environmental factors and on behavior of animals produced many new insights into the habits of wild animals and the conditions under which they live, and these influenced the management of zoos. With his ground-breaking work "Wildtiere in Gefangenschaft" ("Wild Animals in Captivity"), H. Hediger founded a separate applied science, Zoo Biology. He was the first to realize clearly that wild animals can lead a normal, natural life even under the care of humans, if their houses and pens offer the crucial environmental conditions or at least an adequate substitute. Just as Hagenbeck did away with the notion of the zoo as a prison by discarding the fences and cages, so Hediger—supported by the results of the field biologists—refuted the sentimental idea that wild animals in their natural surroundings are entirely free, unrestrained creatures; thus captivity need not be a torment for them.

Like civilized man, even wild animals are resticted in many respects—in space, in time, and in their mental processes. They are by no means able to wander wherever they like at any time. From birth on, they are tied to a certain range, and within it to a certain habitat; there, depending on their inherent degree of gregariousness, they live either alone, in families, or in groups, within territories inherited or won by great struggles. Only in its territory, which it never leaves voluntarily, is an animal "at home." There it knows all the places where it can hide and which are most suitable for feeding, sunning itself or sheltering from the sun, bathing, wallowing, or storing food; these are joined by a network of trails made by and known only to the occupant of the territory, along which it moves from one to another in a sequence depending on its individual daily schedule. The world outside an animal's own territory is dangerous and is avoided, whereas the territory itself is defended by all the means available.

Application of the results of field research to zookeeping indicates that once animals have recovered from the initial shock of transfer to a new environment, they do not "feel" at all like prisoners as long as they are kept in appropriately designed enclosures and cared for in a way corresponding to the natural rhythm of their lives. If all their fundamental needs are provided for, they will even take possession of considerably smaller zoo enclosures and use and defend them as they did their former territories. Many species—for example, kangaroos, antelopes and wild sheep—could jump out of their open ranges at any time. But they do not do so, because they regard these areas as their territories.

Consequently, in planning new enclosures or animal houses one must know just which species are to be kept there and what their natural requirements are. For a tropical bird house, one must take into account

The biological approach in zoo-keeping

Fig. 24-3. Former bird house in the Frankfurt Zoo (demolished in 1961).

Modern zoo architecture

quite different factors than for a giraffe or monkey house. As a rule, zoo-keepers do proceed in this way when building new animal facilities. The conspicuous animal houses of past times, often made to look like temples, pagodas or other exotic architecture, satisfied the public's desire for spectacular sights but not the real needs of the animals. Nowadays the animal houses are made as inconspicuous as possible on the outside, for they are purely functional structures. The skill and artistry of their designer is expressed almost entirely by an internal construction appropriate to the animal inhabitants.

Animal enclosures are basically of two types, indoor and outdoor. Indoor enclosures are in most cases spacious shelters, more and more often bounded by glass rather than bars, and for many animals (for example, birds, small mammals, reptiles and amphibia) designed to be as natural as possible—sections of the appropriate habitat, with various niches, are included. In these it is often possible for several species to live side by side, without conflict. Care is taken to provide sufficient heat, light and humidity as well as living plants and a floor of stone, clay or sand; in these modern accommodations there are basins for swimming and diving, places where a spray of water is available, natural or artificial sunbathing areas, and suitable feeding and nesting places. Only if the animals damage such a natural arrangement, whether through curiosity or destructiveness, or if the natural surroundings cannot be provided for reasons of hygiene, are they replaced entirely or in part by artificial materials. For trees one can substitute steel climbing frames. Plastic shelves can serve instead of branches as resting places, bowls instead of ponds for bathing, and bed compartments instead of caves for sleeping. In all cases, of course, the keeper takes care to avoid harmful or poisonous materials.

In general, an effort is made to depart as far as possible from the usual unnatural rectangular outline of indoor enclosures by turning back and side walls into something like the rounded backdrops used on the stage to give an impression of depth. Glass roofs provide adequate illumination. If the floors of the enclosures are set higher than those on which the visitors stand, it is convenient to arrange heating under the enclosures; then the animals are warm, and the visitors can observe them more easily. There are ways of making indoor and outdoor enclosures equally useful; for example in many zoos plastic flaps are hung in the doorways of primate enclosures, so that the animals can move between the indoor and outdoor parts at any time of year. For tropical animals, in such cases, the ground in the outdoor enclosure is also heated at certain places during the cold season.

Depending on the space available, outdoor enclosures may be either fenced in, set off by trenches, or (as has recently become popular) surrounded by glass walls. The ground here must meet the requirements of hygiene and also be suited to the feet of the inhabitants. Mountain ungulates, with hooves that grow very quickly, absolutely require a hard rocky ground which wears down the hooves in a natural way. Cats have sensitive

▷
From left to right and top to bottom:
Open-air penguin enclosure in the London Zoo (England). The spiral cement ramps give the animals ample exercise.—The daily promenade of the penguins in the zoo of Edinburgh (Scotland) is a healthy activity for the birds.—A fresh-water aquarium in the Frankfurt Zoo, set up on ecological principles so that water composition, temperature and aeration correspond to natural conditions.—Ecological water-bird enclosure in the Frankfurt Zoo. The darters are provided with a land area and a diving pool.
It is not only for the sake of the visitors that sea-elephants (here in the Frankfurt Zoo) are made to do "tricks" for their fish. Exercise and the challenge of learning are important for their physical and mental health.—A trained killer whale performing in the San Diego Zoo. These, like dolphins, must be given enough to do if behavioral disturbances are to be avoided.—In the modern gorilla enclosure in the Frankfurt Zoo, 4-cm-thick sheets of glass were used for the first time instead of a fence. Moats are unsuitable for these animals because of the danger that they may drown.—Animal hospital (treatment room) in the Berlin Zoo.

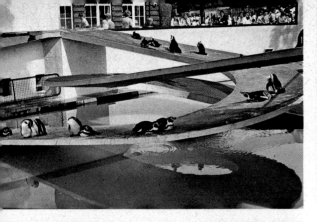

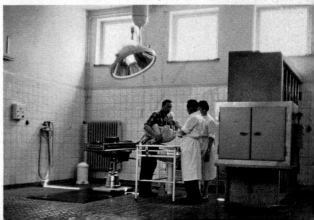

pads on their paws and need sandy soils permeable to water and air. For steppe animals the soil of choice is a mixture of clay and gravel, with a surface which is rather firm and sloped so as to drain well. The platforms the animals use as living quarters are divided into terraces as far as possible. Hills of rock or groups of bushes enable the animals to get out of sight occasionally, a necessity for certain animals. Protection from sun and rain, and places for bathing, drinking and wallowing are provided in accordance with the animals' needs, as are suitable feeding places, poles against which they can scratch themselves, sandy spots, and facilities for climbing, swimming and diving.

In the optimal situation, indoor and outdoor enclosures are arranged in such a way that the visitors have access to only a third, or at most a half, of their circumference; in this way the animals aren't disturbed from all sides, and yet the observer has a view of the entire enclosure.

In many contemporary zoos there are large aviaries, some roofed over, in which birds have room to fly and visitors can walk about with no barriers between themselves and the birds. In recent years so-called "nocturnal animal houses" are becoming more and more fashionable; here animals active mainly at night are kept in artificial twilight by day and brightly lighted at night. This brings about a reversal of their day/night rhythm, so that visitors can watch the activities of even these animals, which when kept under traditional conditions were always asleep during the day.

Not only the accommodations provided for the animals, but their care as well, must be adjusted to their natural requirements. Unlike wild animals, zoo animals have "plenty of time"; they have been released from the urgencies of avoiding their enemies and searching for food. To this extent they are free of tensions, and they visibly enjoy this state, as is made evident in the increased tendency of even adult animals to play. Of course, for the animals of more highly developed mental capacity—primates, elephants and parrots—this leisure can lead to boredom and unpleasant behavioral disturbances such as stereotyped movements reminiscent of neurotic compulsions. In view of such phenomena, an important job of the zookeeper is to provide his charges with varied opportunities for activity.

Such diversions can be presented by many different devices in the enclosures, by the presence of conspecifics, which makes possible natural social interactions, and by the keepers themselves, who are always regarded by the animals as higher-ranking members of the group and can be drawn into their social life. With highly motile and especially intelligent animals, it is even necessary to have a specifically planned program of "occupational therapy" if they are to maintain good mental health. If the possibilities for activity of wild animals under human care were to be further restricted, the result would be a slow but sure domestication—precisely what the zookeepers are trying to avoid. This is especially true of feeding

◁
Some rare zoo animals: From left to right and top to bottom: The European great bustard breeds only in the Tierpark of Berlin-Friedrichsfelde (East Germany) and in Budapest.—Certain zoos (including the one in Copenhagen) are special centers for the breeding of endangered species. The Hawaiian goose, or nene, has even been reintroduced to its homeland.—The female panda Chi-Chi in the London Zoo, which died in 1972. Futile attempts had been made to mate her with An-An, of the Moscow Zoo. In the Chinese zoos, however, pandas breed successfully.—There are okapis in only 18 zoos; the breeding herds in Rotterdam, Paris, Frankfurt and Bristol are well known.
There are a total of 44 great Indian rhinoceroses in 25 zoos; thirteen of them were born in zoos.—Only a few zoos possess bongos; they produced offspring for the first time in 1971, in the Cleveland Zoo.—In collaboration with the IUCN, groups of endangered animals with no chance of survival in their natural environment are given to zoos experienced in animal breeding. The Basel Zoo (Switzerland) received a small herd of the Somali wild ass.—Banded duikers can currently be found only in the Frankfurt Zoo.

practices. Since zoo animals need not spend many hours of the day in searching for food, as their wild relatives do, at least the ingestion and digestion of food should not be made too easy for them. Feeding with cakes or pastes having essential nutrients, vitamins and mineral salts is efficient and correct, but such foods should never make up the sole diet. If they did, the animals would become resigned to an even greater restriction of movement, which in the course of time could lead to regression of bone and muscle, especially those associated with chewing.

For this reason the food must be as natural as possible, and must force the animals to treat it in a manner typical of the species. Primates, for example, need fruit and vegetables in addition to artificial cakes and the like, and the omnivores among them also require meat; above all, however, primates need leafy twigs so that they can exercise their teeth, jaws and tongues and occupy themselves with picking off the leaves and stripping the bark. Sunflower seeds and grain are intentionally scattered over the whole floor of the enclosure, so that the animals must expend effort in gathering them up as they would have to do in the wild. Fish fed to sea lions are thrown far into the bathing pool, so that the sea lions must chase after them. Ungulates have several food racks, which act both to decrease unpleasant effects of competition in the herd and to encourage movement of the animals from one place to another. Moreover, special training—often seen among primates, elephants and large cats in a zoo—serves not only to entertain the public but to keep the animals occupied.

Fig. 24-4. It used to be customary to display large parrots chained to swings or stands. Such practices are now repudiated.

Fig. 24-5. The entrance gate to Carl Hagenbeck's "animal park" in Hamburg-Stellingen has been unchanged since the zoo was founded in 1907.

Care of the animals

Proper care of wild animals in a zoo permits them to develop a schedule of activities. In the wild, animals lead an orderly life; innate internal rhythms, together with external timing signals, determine the "large-scale space/time system"— the scheduling of mating seasons, and of migrations to different feeding grounds. The day/night rhythm, which also has innate correlates, determines the times when each species is quiet or active during a twenty-four-hour day. Each animal develops its individual spatio-temporal habits within this species-specific framework. The well-trained animal keeper knows that in going about his daily duties he disturbs an animal less, the more strictly he himself keeps to a fixed working schedule. The animal very quickly becomes accustomed to his regular reappearance and adjusts its own daily activities accordingly. In the zoo an animal does not feel really safe and settled until it is allowed to do the same things at the same time every day, in a familiar place.

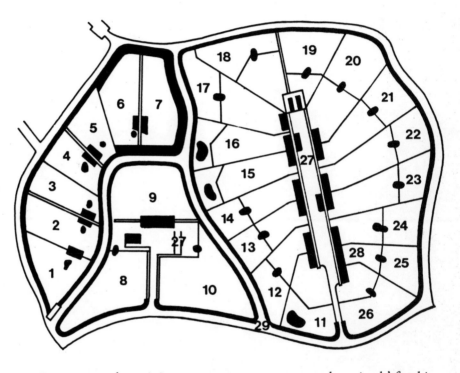

Fig. 24-6. Open-air enclosures for ungulates in the Oklahoma City Zoo: 1, 3, 4, 5. Deer; 2, 6, 7. Mountain ungulates; 8. South African steppe animals; 9. Central African steppe animals. 10. Eastern African steppe animals; 11–18. Ungulates of the forests and bush; 19–21. Savanna and steppe antelopes; 22–23. Desert antelopes; 24–25. Camels; 26. North American steppe animals; 27. Care and maintenance area; 28. Overnight shelters; 29. Paths for visitors.

Animal dietetics

In every good zoo it is now customary to prepare the animals' food in a central kitchen insofar as possible. Early in the morning the food cart is sent out. In the kitchens of the animal houses, which today can often be viewed by visitors through large panes of glass, food is mixed in a particular way for each species under the supervision of the keeper. It is a serious responsibility to prepare the food for very demanding animals such as tropical birds and some primate species, and requires considerable expertise. And even in the case of giraffes and other ungulates, particularly those that specialize in certain foods, putting together the right diet is a skill based on knowledge of the animals' natural feeding habits as well as on long years of experience. Since it is rarely possible to offer food with exactly the same vegetable and meat components the animals find in their homelands, they must generally receive a substitute diet of natural vegetables, meat, fruit, grass, hay or clover.

The person in charge of each type of animal also has the job of checking how well each individual is eating and making sure that each is being given enough. In addition, it is his duty to guard the health of the animals and report anything unusual in their appearance or behavior. Other important data include the times when the animals are in heat, copulate, become pregnant and give birth, and their success (or lack of it) in caring for the young. These data are collected by a zoo scientist in a central catalog.

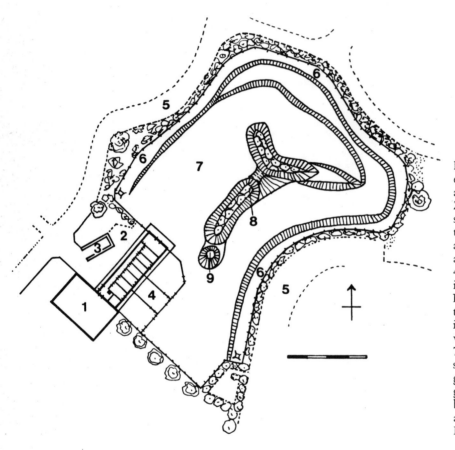

Fig. 24-7. A modern open enclosure for steppe animals in the Frankfurt Zoo: 1. Pony and donkey stalls with adjoining night-time shelters for the steppe animals; 2. Maintenance area with dungbox (3); 4. Acclimatization and isolation enclosures; 5. Paths for visitors; 6. Dry trench, with inward-sloping fence hidden from visitors by shrubbery; 7. Open-air enclosure for sable antelopes, Thomson's gazelles, African ostriches, ground hornbills and giant bustards; 8. Hill to shelter animals from sight; 9. Look-out hill.

Caring for zoo animals, then, is by no means simply a matter of cleaning the cages, though this is very important; the quality of a zoo and its animal care are evident not only in the planning of the enclosures and the health of the animals, but also in the cleanliness of the animals' accommodations and the ability of the animals to breed and take proper care of their young. Despite all this responsibility, it is only in a few countries that the job of caretaker in a zoo is considered to require professional training.

Occasionally zoo animals fall sick or have accidents and require the help of a veterinarian. Often they are not quite well when they arrive in a zoo, for capture and the subsequent changes of place and climate always are a severe physical and mental shock to a wild animal. There are metabolic disturbances, and associated with these is an increase in the numbers

Veterinary care

Fig. 24-8. Modern, naturally designed open-air enclosure for tigers in the Nürnberg Zoo. The moat also serves as a bathing pool.

of parasites. Even in the wild, animals are always infested by parasites; they suffer especially from stomach, intestinal and blood parasites. When affected by shock they are especially vulnerable to damage by these parasites, and the situation is complicated by the smaller space available in the zoo, where they may continually reinfect one another. Zoo caretakers must therefore make a special effort to control and eliminate parasites. Regular fecal examinations indicate the degree of parasite infestation and need for treatment. The parasites can be controlled indirectly by keeping the surroundings as hygienic as possible.

The basic rule "prevention is better than a cure" also holds in the field of zookeeping, but it is not much help in some cases—for example, monkeys are as likely as humans to come down with the usual colds and flu in winter, and the greatest caution cannot always keep out infectious diseases like anthrax, hoof and mouth disease, tuberculosis and infantile paralysis. Nowadays it is customary to vaccinate the animals against the most common infectious diseases such as tuberculosis and polio.

Some zoos have their own veterinary surgeon, and others even have animal hospitals. But most zoos must make do with an outside veterinarian who is under contract to visit several times a week and is on call for emergencies. Even these zoos are equipped with the necessary apparatus so that treatment can be given or operations performed on the spot. Thanks to modern anesthetics, it is now possible to spare the animals the shock associated with such manipulations. The drugs are put into a special injection device that serves as the bullet in an "anesthetic gun" and can be shot into the musculature. When the missile strikes the animal and pierces the skin its contents are released and enter the blood stream. As soon as the drug takes effect, treatment can be begun without difficulty.

When an animal develops an infectious disease or is suspected of incubating disease pathogens, it is moved to the hospital or the quarantine section of the zoo and isolated from the other animals. Not until treatment has fully restored its health is it returned to the familiar enclosure. Should an animal die, it is especially important that a professional scientist determine the cause of death; in cases of infectious disease it is then possible to take immediate steps to protect the animals still living. Moreover, discovery of the cause of death often reveals errors in the way the animals are kept.

Sources of zoo animals

There are at least six ways in which zoos acquire new animals: purchase, exchange, birth in the zoo, donation, collection by the zoo personnel, and the arrival of animals that come of their own accord. Chief among these is, as it has always been, purchase from dealers in animals, though this process is much in need of improvement. In fact, it is regrettable that it is still legal for living wild animals to be sold privately at all. This necessarily means that their value is set in terms of money and, like that of any goods, is determined by supply and demand. Worth or worthlessness so established then becomes a decisive factor in whether and how they are captured and the treatment they are given during transport. No animal dealer would crowd valuable species into containers in such a way that even slight delays in transport injure them. But in shipments of "less valuable" small animals such mistreatment still occurs. There have been horrifying reports of shipments of monkeys or birds, for example, in which three-quarters or more of the animals were dead on arrival, even though such mortality can certainly be avoided in the age of air transport, if the animals are properly accommodated and cared for. For this reason zoos under humane management buy animals only from conscientious dealers.

But even with firms highly respected by experts for ensuring good condition of the animals on arrival, it is hard to know what losses are incurred during the actual capture and transport to the point of departure. In certain cases these losses have amounted to as much as 84%. Although the highest losses occur among animals to be sold as pets, the trade in zoo animals accounts for its share as well. As Barbara Harrisson determined in investigations lasting for many years, for one orangutan that arrives in a zoo alive, four or five either have been killed in the attempt to capture them or have died en route. The logical conclusion drawn by the zookeepers several years ago was that these anthropoid apes, now in danger of becoming extinct, should no longer be purchased.

The greater the zookeepers' sense of responsibility for their animals, the more effort is made to contribute to the protection and humane treatment of animals beyond the boundaries of the zoo. The first international declaration in which this new attitude was expressed stemmed from a meeting in 1964 sponsored jointly by the IUCN (the International Union for the Conservation of Nature and Natural Resources) and the International Association of Zoo Directors; it was dedicated to "the ethics of nature conservation and animal capture, safe transportation of animals, and the trade in animals." The outcome of this meeting was a demand by the participants for legislation at the national level to make possible a workable control on animal imports, intermediate dealing, and exports. Since then, however, only the USA has taken decisive action on these recommendations, by enacting two new laws. The first, the "Endangered Species Act," was passed in 1969 and has subsequently been improved; it sets out clear regulations governing the trade in endangered wild animals. Species in danger of dying out and subject to conservation laws in their country of origin can no longer (or only by special permission) be imported and sold in the USA. The "Animal Welfare Act" of 1971 provides further controls on the keeping, sale and transporting of animals, which are intended to ensure humane treatment.

In Europe there are still no such farsighted laws; attempts to introduce them encounter all sorts of difficulties. For one thing, the fact that the individual zoos have different status prevent effective cooperation and self-regulation; some of them are private property, some are owned by corporations or scientific societies, and some are under the administration of cities or higher government agencies. The authorities responsible for all these zoos are thus quite different, and their views have a considerable influence since all zoos are dependent upon financial support. The multiplicity of states in Europe is an additional and especially severe obstacle. For the Common Market countries as a whole, only those laws are effective which are valid in all these countries. It is of the utmost urgency that European zoos redouble their efforts toward cooperation.

"The trade in animals between zoos," writes H. Hediger, "is a necessary evil which should be tolerated only insofar as it serves to establish, maintain and balance out the animal holdings of real zoos, as well as to avoid unnecessary trapping and bloodletting among the natural populations." By this he means that the zoos themselves, at least, should stop regarding the animals as goods that bring in money. In practice, however this is for the time being impossible, since nearly all zoos depend on some direct income. Nevertheless, the selling and exchange of animals from one zoo to another is distinguished by the fact that there is hardly ever any loss of life. For this reason the zoos prefer to deal with one another rather than with outside animal dealers; in addition, animals born and raised in zoos are always cheaper than equivalent imports from the countries of origin. Since most zoos regularly breed at least a few species, this means of acquiring animals is becoming more and more common.

The lions of Leipzig and Dublin are striking examples of this kind of self-support. Until the Second World War almost all the European zoos obtained their lions from the Leipzig "lion factory"; Leipzig bred and delivered a total of about 1000 lions, and Dublin more than 600. After the war other breeding centers became prominent—for example, Basel, with its pigmy hippopotamus, Prague with its herd of Przewalksi's horses and Frankfurt with its emus and rheas. Certain species, such as lions, brown bears, wolves, hippopotamus, baboons, rhesus monkeys—and some species of antelope, deer and cattle—are now bought as captured animals only occasionally, to introduce wild blood into the zoo populations; the latter have long been capable of maintaining themselves independently. Finally, we must rely entirely upon the breeding colonies in zoos for replacement of those animal species that have become extinct in the wild.

On the other hand, donations of animals to zoos are not usually appreciated. It often happens that a private citizen who is fond of animals wants to set up a "living monument" by making a present to the zoo. This can sometimes be desirable but is often embarrassing, if the zoo has neither suitable accommodations nor company for the new arrival. Single animals given by private owners can be accepted by a zoo only in very rare instances; usually they suffer from behavioral disturbances or illness, so that it would be too great a risk to the other zoo animals to take them in.

The stocks of animals in a zoo are also increased by the voluntary entry of animals such as songbirds, coots, moorhens, squirrels, and mallards.

Black-headed gulls sometimes winter in zoos and starlings spend the night there. When such animals appear in large flocks, they compete seriously with the animals in outdoor enclosures for food, and are a troublesome drain on the zoo's budget. If they seem to be getting the upper hand, the zoo must take action against them. Intensive control measures are required to keep down cockroaches, mice, rats and wild rabbits. Measures must also be taken against stray dogs and cats, foxes, martens, and other wild animals that wander into the zoo and create difficulties.

It is true that in the course of centuries essentially all wild animals that could be caught have been kept in one zoo or another, but the only species that have become real "zoo animals" are those that have proven more or less long-lived, either because of their own adaptability or because of the enormously improved conditions under which they are kept and cared for in recent decades. Advances in zoo techniques, veterinary medicine and nutritional science have also diminished the number of "problem species," though there are still some left. For example, the famous marsupial bear, the koala, at present can be kept in only one zoo outside Australia—the San Diego Zoo; this is the only zoo where a stand of eucalyptus is available. The koalas are extreme food-specialists, feeding exclusively on eucalyptus leaves. Colobid monkeys, which also feed on leaves, are likewise difficult to keep. It has so far been possible to keep fifteen of the twenty-eight species in zoos, and seven of these have succeeded in breeding, but the rest do not survive in captivity despite their close resemblance to the zoo species. Other problem animals are the various termite-eating mammals—for example, the anteaters, pangolins, aardwolves and aardvarks—and birds like the hummingbirds and sunbirds, which feed on nectar.

There are many possible reasons why wild animals cannot be kept in zoos. Sometimes it is difficult to obtain the right kind of food or to develop a suitable substitute; often diseases or parasites are not recognized. Moreover, still-undiscovered environmental factors may be critical. As J. Fisher has determined, of the 336 parrot species known in historical times, 232 have lived in a zoo at one time or another, and 127 of these were able to breed in captivity. Similarly, 43% of all primate species have so far born young in zoos. In contrast to the leaf monkeys, the less specialized long-tailed monkeys are practically ideal zoo animals; each of the thirty-seven species has not only been kept successfully in some zoo or other, but has been able to reproduce. The New World monkeys are much more particular about their food; of around seventy species so far known only about fifty have been kept in zoos, and young have been born in no more than twenty-three species. It is gratifying that all four species of the large anthropoid apes now thrive in zoos and bring offspring into the world. But the difficulties we know recognize make especially clear that the successes in animal-keeping before the turn of the century were purchased with great sacrifice of animals.

Of the many animals on display in zoos, relatively few have become

Suitability of animals for zoos

<table>
<tr><td>

What attracts people to certain animals?

</td><td>

favorites of the public. The "exhibit value" of the various species varies widely. At the top of the scale are the great apes, other ape and monkey species, and penguins; these are followed by bears, lions and elephants. The attraction of antelopes, wisents and tapirs—even if they are rare species—is relatively small. As H. Hediger has found, the exhibit value of a species can change, depending on the situation. If an animal that usually draws no crowds, such as a tapir, has just given birth and has the young by its side, its "value" as an exhibit increases considerably for a while. Feeding, play, copulation and other kinds of active behavior of the animals of course make them more interesting to visitors.

</td></tr>
</table>

Apart from these criteria, species resembling humans in appearance and behavior or having characteristics that remind us (though perhaps unconsciously) of babies have the greatest exhibit value. People instinctively respond with attention and interest to conspecific characteristics, especially if these characteristics are associated with infants or children. This is why our close relatives, the anthropoid apes, and to an even greater degree their young, with their large round heads and rounded bodies, evoke such intense interest in the public. Bears that walk upright, penguins, and in fact all animals which can adopt a manlike posture are also in this category, as are birds with large heads, forward-looking eyes and upright posture—for example, owls, parrots and shoebills. People first look for and see themselves in the animals. This innate response is the primary determinant of attraction or repulsion; it is also responsible for the entirely irrelevant judging of animals by human values.

The selection of zoo animals

Exotic animals have always been important acquisitions for any zoo, since most visitors can see them nowhere else alive. Today, since many native animals no longer can be found in the wild, even wolf, bear, lynx and wisent have become important zoo animals in Europe. Every medium-sized zoo should adopt the principle of keeping at least one species of each of the particularly characteristic mammal and bird families of its own and other countries, though this must not involve the omission of the "classical zoo animals." For example, in most zoos brown and polar bears are classically found as examples of the largest land carnivores, lions, and tigers are the most impressive big cats, wolves represent the animals that chase down their prey, sea lions are displayed as especially well adapted aquatic mammals, elephants, hippopotamus and rhinoceroses are the most weighty herbivores, zebras are striking examples of wild horses, and apes are included as the animals most closely related to man. In addition there are representatives of the many artiodactyl species—pigs, camels, deer and bovids, and of course the giraffe, the tallest of all animals. These are joined by certain small carnivores, rodents, insectivores, sloths, anteaters and one or another species of kangaroo.

Of the birds, owls and diurnal birds of prey are usually represented by two or three native and foreign species, and there are various geese and ducks on a pond and cranes, storks and herons in a pool specially built for such stilt-legged creatures. Almost every zoo has an area reserved for pheasants and other species of fowl, pigeons and native songbirds. Many keep penguins in a cooled building where they have the opportunity to swim and dive, have an open-air enclosure for ostriches and other large walking birds, and in a heated building house parrots, cotingas, sunbirds, hummingbirds and other species which give the visitor an idea of the bird fauna of the tropics.

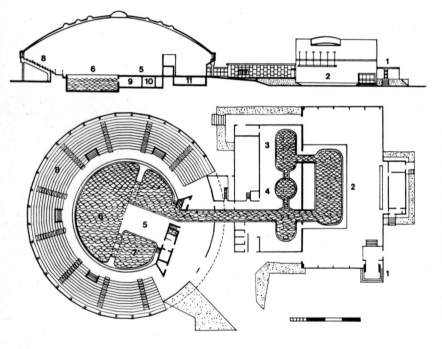

Fig. 24-9. Cross-section and floor plan of the dolphinarium in Harderwijk, Holland: 1. Main entrance; 2. Old demonstration pool; 3. Practice pool; 4. Quarantine pool; 5. Stage; 6. Pool for dolphin performances; 7. Killer-whale pool; 8. Grandstand for visitors; 9. Classroom; 10. Office of the curator and laboratory; 11. Equipment room.

Recently many zoos have also begun to specialize in certain groups, keeping and breeding large numbers of species of these animals. For example, Hanover, Naples and Rome specialize in antelopes. Prague in perissodactyls, the Berlin Tierpark in antelopes and rare subspecies of the big cats, the Berlin Zoo in rhinoceroses, cattle and deer, Frankfurt and San Diego in the large anthropoid apes and rare primate species, Whipsnade in ungulates, and New York, London and Stuttgart in nocturnal animals; the latter are kept in specially designed buildings that permit observation of their activities. Some zoos are entirely limited to certain groups; the Innsbruck Alpenzoo, for example, keeps only animals native to the Alps, the Sonora Desert Museum in Tucson, Arizona, is restricted to desert animals, and there are special bird sanctuaries; the one in Slimbridge concentrates entirely upon water birds. Moreover, there are "dolphinariums" where the emphasis is upon aquatic mammals, and aquariums or terrariums with fish, amphibia and reptiles.

There is an increasing tendency to depart from the principle that the greatest possible number of species should be kept; instead, the new direction is to offer a representative but not too diverse cross section of the animal kingdom. The former "collection of species" has been replaced by attention to keeping the animals in breeding groups that correspond to their social requirements and housing them in the most natural enclosures possible.

The functions of the zoo: recreation, entertainment and education

Even the earliest zoos and menageries provided recreation and entertainment for their owners. The modern zoo visitor has the same expectations. The observation of many different living wild animals in a well-tended garden is above all intended to bring relaxation, pleasure, astonishment and empathy with other creatures to the city-dweller plagued by crowding, noise and the demands of daily life. In this role, the zoos make a notable contribution to the mental health of man in the cities. Moreover, the encounter with wild animals in a zoo has a "socializing" effect on our society; the observer is not isolated, as he is when reading or watching television, but is stimulated to share his experiences, impressions and feelings with others.

Even if a visitor comes to the zoo without an express wish to learn something about animals, he does acquire new knowledge of nature in the course of being entertained. Anyone who often visits a zoo will eventually know a great deal about animals. Many zoos, therefore, make a conscious, directed effort to exploit the potential for education afforded by the wild animals they display. They recognize that their educational task is extraordinarily important from a sociological point of view—especially in a time when the survival of man and animals will depend not upon continual expansion of technology and industry but rather upon the recognition of the natural laws and the application of our discoveries in an effort to save and preserve biological equilibria.

Educational opportunities and methods

Simply to look at single animals, strong though the impressions obtained may be, is not an education in itself. Accessory elements—for example, suitably designed enclosures—are necessary if the observer is to gain an understanding of the animal's natural way of life and the relationships between body structure, behavior, and environment. The visitor who watches monkeys climbing or penguins diving knows without having it explained to him what the prehensile feet and hands of the monkey are good for and why the flightless penguin still has wings. An aviary so arranged that it allows kingfishers to dive through the air and catch fish from a pool of water, and in which these birds are provided with a clay wall where they can nest and raise their young, offers more biological information about the ways animals are adapted to their habitats than a bare cage with a few perches and dishes for food and water.

Signs telling something about the animals are indispensable aids to education; in the type developed by H. Hediger the common and scientific names are accompanied by a picture of the species and a map showing its range, while a short text presents information that is likely to interest the visitor. Many zoos also set up larger placards which illustrate, for example, the distribution of carnivores, the evolution of proboscideans, the intelligence of the great apes, and other themes; these can expand and deepen the basic knowledge obtained by observation of individual animals. With the help of three-dimensional models that the visitor can activate by pushing a button, it is possible to give a graphic introduction to those biologically important processes which cannot be observed directly in living animals. For example, the Steinhart Aquarium in San Francisco displays a huge model of the skeleton of a viper's head. As soon as the visitor presses the button, the jaws open and the movable fangs are shot forward, ready to bite.

Many zoos have speakers mounted near various enclosures, which the visitor can operate either with coins or with a key bought at the entrance; the recorded discussion give detailed information about the animals as the visitor watches them. In the "exotarium" of the Frankfurt Zoo it is even possible for individuals to be guided by portable radio receivers. Almost every one of the larger zoos offers printed guidebooks and trained guides who will conduct groups through the grounds.

To these general educational aids some zoos add carefully planned teaching programs, worked out and presented in special zoo schools. These chiefly take the form of courses for school classes, lectures in the classrooms of the zoo, and supervision of study groups from the schools and of students working on annual projects. These programs are generally oriented toward the overall educational program of the country concerned. But some zoo educators also collaborate in the training and further education of the teachers; the contributions of the zoos toward education does not stop at their gates. Many zoo scientists are also teachers at colleges and universities, and many of them write scientific reports and books for the general public. Others publish zoo magazines, or even have their own television programs.

Teaching programs

Nearly every large zoo offers interested adults and children the possibility of becoming a member of an association or a youth club. These support the zoo and its projects, and in return the members can participate in lecture series, special tours, and educational trips.

Zoos, in contrast to natural history museums, focus upon the living animals. To this extent they are better suited to ecological, ethological and animal-sociology observations, and can afford insights into the systems "individual-society-environment" or "body structure-behavior-habitat." This is why it is not so important for a zoo to have the largest possible collection of different animal species, but rather to house and care for the species it has in the best possible way, so that by watching and comparing them one can learn about their lives. One species, kept under biologically appropriate conditions, can be shown as a representative of many related species.

One of the foremost educational goals of the zoo is to teach people to

The goals of education

evaluate animals in an objective—and therefore fair—way. Only in so doing can people recognize and respect the dignity inherent in every living organism. Most people, though there is no justification at all for doing so, transfer their ethical and aesthetic value judgments to animals; they "humanize" the animal kingdom. The "ugly and cowardly" hyena, the "stupid and haughty" camel, and the "impudent, immoral" monkey are examples of such entirely false, humanized judgments, based on a misunderstanding of the animals. For this reason the zoos must make a special effort to counteract this unconscious, unconsidered humanization through education. They can achieve such a goal by giving people insights, as described above, into the ways animal appearance and behavior are related to the environment. This, after all, is the only way to understand their individual peculiarities. Anyone who has seen a gibbon swinging and climbing among branches will never again find its long arms grotesque or ridiculous. Not until it dives does a penguin make clear that its "comical" waddling on land is the price this group of birds has paid for its swiftness under water; such speed is made possible by the spindle-shaped body and the way the legs are set far back.

A model for pet owners

Another important educational function of the zoo is to provide an example of proper animal care to the ever increasing numbers of people who keep pets. It is true that some who raise wild animals at home are very knowledgeable and have provided an incentive for the zoos to adopt new ways of accommodating and breeding their animals. Some keepers of aquariums, terrariums, birds and small mammals have enriched the scientific literature with their observations. But in most cases the keeping of pets is a touchingly sad kind of human association with animals. Usually it consists of a mixture of loving effort, ignorance and misunderstanding that is detrimental or fatal for the animals concerned.

The third educational goal of the zoo, one which is becoming ever more prominent, is to make people aware of the threat to wild animals in their natural habitats and the consequences for man should they become extinct. In so doing, zoos contribute to the protection of the environment.

Research in zoos

Zoological gardens, from the outset, have also been research establishments. As a particularly striking example from former times, recall the Jardin des Plantes in Paris, which provided the fundamental material for the discoveries of the great zoologists at the beginning of the age of the natural sciences. Until the beginning of the 20th Century little was known of the life and requirements of wild animals; before that time the zoos had to find out for themselves how to feed and care for them. Today we can draw upon the findings of the field biologists in this area, but further specific research and considerable thought is necessary if this knowledge is to be applied properly in the zoo. Moreover, there are many questions that even the field biologist cannot always answer by studying the animals in the wild. Among these are determination of the sexual periods and the duration of pregnancy, nursing and the raising of the young. Certain forms of behavior, especially those occurring only at night or in burrows or other hiding places, are also more easily investigated with animals in captivity.

Many branches of medical science are enabled to work on a broader basis because so many species of zoo animals are available. But the zoos encourage and support only scientific work that can be done without major disturbance or danger to the animals in the zoo. As a matter of course in a modern zoo, animals that die, after the cause of death has been determined, are given to institutes or museums to be used for scientific studies.

The zoos offer opportunities for specialized scientists to carry out certain investigations, but many zoo personnel are scientists themselves. Zoo biology, according to Hediger, not only provides the scientific basis for developing the best and most appropriate ways of keeping wild animals, but it also involves examination and description of the special principles revealed when animals are held in captivity. The task is thus twofold, and the zoo biologists's attention is directed to phenomena involving man as well as animals. There are two international seriel publications which make the findings of zoo biologists available to other professionals and encourage the exchange of knowledge; these are the German-language journal "Der Zoologische Garten," founded in 1858, and the "International Zoo Yearbook," which has been published for the last twelve years.

Zoos today must also share in solving the problems of conservation. For example, they can refuse to buy species on the verge of extinction from outside sources, and at the same time devote special attention to the members of such species already in captivity, striving to breed them more successfully. For many zoo species not yet considered to be endangered, it is often necessary to find more biologically appropriate conditions, since no one knows how soon their wild relatives will be threatened with extinction. Zoos can open the eyes of their visitors to the necessity of protecting the endangered fauna and enlist public support for international conservation measures. Moreover, they can provide financial support to the conservation movement, by sponsoring fund drives.

Unlike the zoo founders of the last century and their contemporaries, we no longer think of nature as invulnerable and inexhaustible. More and more large animals have disappeared from the earth because of direct or indirect persecution by man. The loss of the wild wisent in Europe made dramatically clear the need for conservation measures, and at the same time showed how zoos could make their special contribution. The wisent was the last of the wild cattle on earth, and not long ago it was native to all the forests of central Europe; but by 1913 there remained only one wild herd of 731 animals, living in the Polish/Russian forest of Bialowieza. The events of the war and the postwar period brought about the complete destruction of this last herd; only a few animals survived in various zoos. Kurt Priemel, the director of the Frankfurt Zoo at the time, recognized the

Fig. 24-10. Houses for bison and wisent in the Berlin Zoo, which were destroyed in the war and rebuilt in the old style in 1957.

Indian wooden house, for North American bison.

Russian log house, for wisent.

unique opportunity to use these zoo animals to save the species. Today there are again more than 800 wisent, and once again a herd is living wild in the forest of Bialowieza. By carefully planned breeding, the zoos have saved the last wild bovid of Europe for future generations.

Other animals, too—Père David's deer and Przewalski's horse, the white-tailed gnu and the Arabian oryx, the Hawaiian goose and Swinhoe's pheasant—have survived only in zoos. Today studbooks are kept for many endangered animal species; these include the gorilla, orangutan, pygmy chimpanzee, maned tamarin, Goeldi's monkey, okapi, vicuna, some species of deer, wild cattle and antelopes; also included are the three species of rhinoceros kept in zoos, and other mammal and bird species, as well as endangered subspecies such as the Amur leopard and the Chinese, Siberian and Sumatran tigers. By this means the zoo directors try to keep track of the stocks of these species living in zoos and thus better organize the breeding of the animals.

Breeding programs

In addition, special-purpose breeding programs have been worked out, so that with the agreement of the IUCN certain species in particular danger can be brought to suitable zoos in an effort to save the species. Examples of such specially bred animals are the Arabian oryx in the Phoenix Zoo and the Somali wild ass in the zoo in Basel. The zoos are thus intentionally establishing breeding centers for species which in the wild face a threat at present not countered by conservation laws. But since it is often impossible to tell when a species will be endangered, it would be most appropriate to treat all the wild animals in zoos as though they were the last of their species. Unfortunately, many zoos are still a long way from adopting this attitude.

Another method of ensuring self-maintenance of the zoo stocks is the lending of individual animals by one zoo to another. This allows even single females, for which the zoo cannot purchase a partner for reasons of conservation, to mate and produce offspring. The Basel Zoo has led in this respect, for it kept a thriving herd of the endangered great Indian rhinoceros and sent their progeny to many other zoos so that further breeding could be done. The Berlin Zoo also deserves praise for sending its Indian rhinoceros bull "Arjun" to Basel after the stud bull there had died in an accident; this ensured that the Basel herd was maintained. Similar exchanges or loans have been made with gorillas. The zoo in Tel Aviv sent its female mountain gorilla all the way to Oklahoma to mate with the single male living there. The Zoological Society of London has set up a special office to help organize such cooperative breeding efforts on an international level.

In the Frankfurt Zoo there is an ape-raising center that takes in infant anthropoid apes from other zoos if they are rejected by their mothers or cannot be kept for reasons of health. Recent inhabitants of this center were an infant orangutan from the zoo in Hanover and a baby gorilla from Basel, along with the young anthropoid apes born in the Frankfurt Zoo.

The small apes thus have a chance to grow up in the company of their own kind are cared for by specially trained keepers and a pediatrician.

The zoos have still another important task in the field of conservation, which again can extend far beyond the walls of the zoo itself; in Europe this challenge was first recognized by the director of the Frankfurt Zoo, Bernhard Grzimek, and has since been taken up by many advanced zoos. The education of people in the zoo, and the use of zoo facilities to teach people outside its grounds, can and must be employed to convince the public to make personal sacrifices in the cause of conservation. In Frankfurt this is done by the Zoological Society of 1858, which supports the zoo and is dedicated to the protection of nature; it solicits donations to a conservation fund called "Help for the Endangered Fauna." This fund is used exclusively for international conservation programs in collaboration with the IUCN.

International collaboration toward conservation

Other zoos—for example those of West Berlin, Amsterdam, Basel, and London—make collections directly for the World Wildlife Fund, established to support and finance the conservation plans of the IUCN. The emblem of the WWF is the giant panda, which may soon be extinct; its picture appears in their appeals for support. Finally, zoo associations and conservation societies regularly sponsor chartered tours to nature preserves in all parts of the world. These tours also benefit the economies of the countries concerned with maintaining nature preserves, since they encourage the tourist trade. This is especially important in the case of the poorer countries of the Third World; their efforts toward conservation are thus acknowledged and rewarded.

The modern world will soon see the end of those "zoological gardens" that have not grown beyond the menagerie style of earlier centuries and have not yet found the way to a responsible, scientifically based method of keeping wild animals. Keeping wild animals in the old way, displayed singly in small, bare, monotonous cages, contributes neither to the maintenance of the species nor to the biological education of those who come to see them. To keep wild animals entirely for profit is just as outmoded and reprehensible. Modern zoos express our enlightened attitude to animals, and for many species they may represent the only possibility of salvation in the long term. At least they will not be utterly lost to future generations.

Part II

THE ENVIRONMENT
OF MAN

Introduction
The Environmental Crisis

By W. Klausewitz

In 1866 Ernst Haeckel formulated the notion of "Oecologie"; with this term he designated the science of the way animals live and their varied relationships to the biotic and abiotic environment, including both behavior and distribution. He could not then have suspected that a hundred years later the word would have taken on a much modified connotation, even socio-political overtones. During the past century, and especially in the last fifty years, ecology developed into a well established branch of science while keeping the original orientation toward the interactions of organisms and their environment. Only very recently has this science been extended in an unexpected way—as a result of the manifold effects of man upon the natural ecosystems.

Changes in the natural habitat brought about by man

For some time mankind has been changing its natural habitat without thought for the consequences. Men have turned more or less untouched landscapes into cultivated plains and cities, and converted rivers and lakes —which have a vital function in circulating the "blood of the continents" —into transportation routes, sewers and recreation sites. The air is dirtied with dust and noxious gases; the fauna has been drastically reduced, the natural plant communities have been impoverished, and artificial treatments have made the plants men use as food less nutritious, more susceptible to damage, and impregnated with poisons. Man, the most intelligent and mightiest animal on earth, is well on the way to transforming the face of the planet and its entire flora and fauna.

Of course, man's hostile attitude to nature is no recent development; it is as old as man himself. Humans have always regarded their environment as something to be exploited. They have learned to meet the once superior forces of nature and come out victorious. The first deep wounds to nature, some of them incurable, were dealt quite a bit earlier than we tend to think.

Did Ice-Age man kill off many mammal species?

For example, the American geologist Paul S. Martin believes that certain large mammals inhabiting North America and Eurasia during the Pleistocene, such as the mastodon and mammoth, several New World camel and horse species, the giant sloth, cave bear, giant deer, giant beaver, woolly rhinoceros and many another species, did not become extinct as a result of extraordinary climatic factors and changes in the vegetation, as had been generally assumed. Rather, he thinks they were exterminated by teams of hunting Ice Age men, capable of hurling missiles and using fire. This view is supported by finds of bones at fire sites in caves, as well as by the fact that it was primarily the steppe animals that disappeared, while the large forest animals survived. Moreover, many species did not become extinct until shortly after the last glacial epoch. Additional considerations are that all the smaller mammals survived, and that according to the anthropologists it was the men of the Pleistocene who underwent that mental development which finally gave rise to *Homo sapiens*, thinking man. Only a "thinking man" could have hunted with such decisive success. However this may have been, in North America alone there vanished within a thousand years after the last glacial epoch about a hundred species of large mammals; shortly prior to this, about 10,000 to 12,000 years ago, the ancestors of the Indians had reached North America, coming over the Bering Strait from eastern and northern Asia.

This view is still under discussion; other ways of looking at these events have been referred to in Chapter 20. In any case, an early effect upon the environment by man is discernible in the Mediterranean region. Here the natural features of the terrain were the chief victims. Once there was an enormous forested zone, which at the end of the last glacial epoch and in the following period surrounded the Mediterranean, extending from the western African coast far into the Near East and including the three peninsulas of southern Europe. While civilization spread throughout the Mediterranean lands, man recklessly cut down the forests and transformed them into scrub, semidesert and barren regions of limestone; the process was assisted by one of man's domestic animals, the goat, which overgrazed the land. Although climatic factors have contributed, it is striking to note that as little as 4000 years ago the Sahara did not have its present extent; less than 2000 years ago the present Libyan Desert was still the granary of Rome.

Each of these drastic campaigns to alter nature has been associated with a decisive step in human development:

1. Before the Stone Age, when men were primarily at the hunting and gathering levels, hunters (see Chapter 20) operating in groups concentrated on the herds of large mammals in the tundras and the taiga bordering the layer of ice in northern Europe and North America. There is no doubt that they used not only weapons for striking and throwing, but fire as well. Nevertheless, men at this time made no profound changes in their natural surroundings.

2. About 5000 years ago the early Stone Age agrarian society came into being, during the "Paleolithic Revolution." As conversion of woodland to cultivated fields became more and more widespread, and as wood

Margin notes:

Destruction of the natural landscape

Levels of human development

The hunting level

Agrarian society

came into use for construction, clear-cutting and burning transformed large areas of the landscape. This stage of development, which began in central and southern Asia and later spread from the Near East into Europe, was associated with a sudden acceleration of population growth.

The Industrial Revolution

3. The last cultural level of human development, the Industrial Revolution, began about 150 years ago. It combined the practical application of natural laws (technology) and the rise of the industrial society with an extensive destruction of both the agricultural areas and the remaining natural areas. "Mankind is about to forget how to deal with living systems. It applies its technomorphic habits of thought and working methods to living beings, and in so doing causes unutterable damage," as Konrad Lorenz has put it.

Today there is no longer any spot on earth that has not been affected in one way or another by man. This is true even of the ice deserts of Greenland and Antarctica. During the last 100 to 150 years the face of Europe and North America has been transformed, not only by the building up of metropolitan and industrial areas but by the drainage of expanses of land and the straightening or rivers; together, these have led to a noticeable shift toward steppe conditions. Zones of virgin forest which still appear boundless, like the Amazon region of South America, may well be cleared and cultivated to form gigantic agricultural plains in the next ten or twenty years, and within a human lifetime they will probably be vast deserts. Because of his technological achievements modern man does as he pleases with nature, for the sake of gain; he completely alters his natural surroundings, exploits water, forest and the resources of the ground, and gradually erects a mechanized artificial world.

Contamination of the environment

In the process, man not only changes his immediate environment, but also burdens the air, water, soil and all the organisms on earth with the consequences of the advance of civilization. These solid, gaseous or liquid wastes, many of them more or less poisonous, have in recent times been brought to the notice of the general public as "pollutants" of the environment.

The American Rachel Carson is generally regarded as the first to have had the courage to denounce civilized nations and economies based on the utter dominance of industry, because of the poisoning and disruption of nature and natural resources. In a manner more emotional than scientifically accurate, she aroused the country with the publication in 1961 of "Silent Spring," started a broadly based popular movement and elicited strongly opposed reactions from the industrial circles she had attacked. Her courage seems unusual, considering the situation at the time, as one can infer from just the few sentences that follow:

"The concepts and practices of applied entomology for the most part date from that Stone Age of science. It is our alarming misfortune that so primitive a science has armed itself with the most modern and terrible weapons, and that in turning them against the insects it has also turned them against the earth." With her book Rachel Carson drew down upon herself the unanimous enmity of many sectors of the economy and their lobbyists, but President Kennedy soon included the problem of pollution in the program of his government. It took almost another decade, however, for Europe's politicians to pay closer and more serious attention to the poisoning of the environment.

It is astonishing that the European consciousness of the danger to the environment awoke so slowly and hesitantly, for "Silent Spring" was soon translated. Furthermore, as early as 1954 the former director of the Bavarian Institute for Biological Research in Munich, Reinhard Demoll, had published two books "Ketten für Prometheus—Gegen die Natur oder mit ihr?" and "Bändigt den Menschen" ("Chains for Prometheus—with or against Nature?" and "Man Should Be Controlled" —literal translation of titles) in which, with persuasive language and numerous examples, he portrayed convincingly the dangers of blind exploitation, disfiguring and poisoning of our natural surroundings. He regarded technology as the great seducer of mankind, described the condition of lakes and rivers that had been turned into sewers, foretold the ground-water emergency which has in fact appeared over broad areas, and at a time when chemical insecticides were hailed on all sides as the super weapon in the battle between men and the so-called "pests," predicted that man would be the loser, since in using these methods he was not taking account of the inescapable laws of biological equilibrium.

Why, though, did these challenging books of Reinhard Demoll arouse essentially no response in Germany? Why did it remain for a Rachel Carson to emerge in the New World as the "Joan of Arc of the environment" to shake people out of their prosperous complacency and indifference? One reason was that Demoll's accusations were published at a time when the urgent warnings of a number of atomic physicists and other "dissidents" were being dismissed by influential scientists and politicians as unrealistic, anti-progress fantasies. Moreover, the people in postwar Germany were so preoccupied with their success in building up technology and the economy that anyone who questioned the established directions of modern civilized life was accused of heresy and his views were hushed up. That is why these admonitions died out without an echo. Since then, the motto "Save our environment and ourselves with it!" has become a vital contemporary concern. Nevertheless, a boundless faith in progress is still detectable in a large fraction of the population.

Rachel Carson: the environment's Joan of Arc

But how can man's alteration of the environment harm himself as well? The point of his efforts, after all, is to use technology to create an artificial environment that seems largely independent of nature, and he believes himself to have conquered the natural forces. This apparent contradiction can be very simply explained. Even as a creative being man remains a creature in the original sense of the word, a member of the natural communities and the great ecological cycles, a component of the

Man, a part of the living world

global ecosystem. His dependence on atmospheric oxygen, sunlight and water in itself shows how firmly the human creature is bound to the laws of nature. The renowned American environmentalist Barry Commoner put it as follows: "All living things including man, and all human activities on the earth's surface including every sort of technology, industry and agriculture, are dependent upon the large-scale, interwoven cyclic processes involving the four elements playing the largest role in life and the environment—carbon, oxygen, hydrogen and nitrogen."

But man is not only part of the totality of nature, so that he cannot renounce these bonds even in an artificial, mechanized world; above and beyond this, he is put directly in danger by the contamination of his environment. The chief danger does not lie simply in the few widely publicized cases of poisoning like the 1952 smog catastrophe in London which killed over 4000 people, the fatal mercury poisoning of 100 at Minamata Bay in Japan, and the recent mercury disaster in Iraq which probably accounted for several thousand deaths. A far more serious threat is presented by the small quantities of various poisons constantly acting in everyone's body, which are known to produce permanent damage and undoubtedly have other consequences as yet unknown. Every day each human body, even those not yet born, take up certain amounts of man-made poisons—dusts, gases, DDT, other chlorinated hydrocarbons and the residues of other pesticides, as well as lead, mercury and other metals in the form of dust or in solution, not to mention the gradually increasing quantities of radioactive substances.

Carcinogenic pesticides

It is true that the human capacity to adapt can moderate harmful environmental influences—a property called homeostasis. For example, the liver is capable of enzymatically breaking down poisons at an increased rate if their rate of intake is increased; but such compensatory reactions of the body are not altogether reliable. If a wine drinker regularly consumes arsenic, which used to be used in vineyards as a means of pest control, the liver does not metabolize the poison but rather, in the course of time, succumbs to a cancerlike change. Nitrites, which may be found in drinking water, can combine with amines to form nitrosamines, which are also considered to be carcinogenic. According to the 1966 pesticide report of the U.S. Department of Health, the following pesticides have been demonstrated to cause cancer: aldrin, aramite, chlorbenzilate, DDT, dieldrin, heptachlor, amitrole, avadex, PCNB and a number of other compounds. Of the amounts of these substances found in the human body, 70% is consumed along with meat, milk and eggs and only 30% with vegetable food. Other possible carcinogens are chromium, nickel and beryllium. It is certain that cancer is caused by benzopyrene, which is liberated in particularly large amounts in home furnaces and accumulates on soot, particles of mineral oil and other very fine dust, and which occurs in photochemical smog. The body takes it up in this form, by way of the lungs, but it is also to be found in sewage. Cancer can also be caused by asbestos, which is a common air-borne pollutant in cities. And these are only examples; there are a great number of other more or less poisonous substances which can infiltrate the human body and under certain circumstances cause disease.

Already there are clinical indications of the effects of environmental poisons. Cancer used to be practically unknown among children and young people, but its incidence is now clearly on the rise. The same is true of leukemia (the "cancer of the blood"), especially among children, teenagers and young adults. The number of newborns with genetic defects is also increasing steadily. Whereas only about 3% of the population in Germany died of cancer around 1900, the figure is now about 20% and the rate is rising. In East Germany alone the incidence of lung cancer has doubled in the last fifteen years, and in West Germany it increased by 150% between 1952 and 1965. About 40% of those with cancer in East Germany are still under the age of retirement; the situation is similar in the other highly industrialized countries. According to recent American findings, human life expectancy, which had been rising, is now gradually falling off among the inhabitants of the most densely populated areas.

Of course, many organisms on our planet suffer at least as much as man from the contamination of the environment. One need only think of the catastrophic decline in numbers of many bird species, as a direct or indirect effect of DDT or other chlorinated hydrocarbons. But since our society puts man in the center of things, attitudes are largely unaffected by these facts. Dirty rivers, stripped forests, a landscape converted to open plains and a gradually dying fauna do not bother most people. But a conscientious attitude to the environment can be aroused among the general populace, politicians, civil administrators—and even among representatives of industry—by pointing out the fate that will await mankind.

The new realization that man is embedded in the overall structure of nature can be termed "human ecology." To biologists, ecologists and anyone else who appreciates nature, motivation based entirely on human survival is narrow and one-sided. But this strategy must be viewed as a first and quite crucial step toward an entirely new set of attitudes. For many planners, politicians and economists it amounts to a real revolution in thought and action. In the last analysis, of course, the survival of the environment as a whole, including the neglected fauna and flora, must be regarded as decisive. But it would be unrealistic to expect such a change of heart to occur in everyone overnight, for people must be better informed in order to understand. Before an awareness of these facts is common among those capable of making decisions, throughout the world, much time will have passed; whether salvation will still be possible then is beyond our ability to predict. Environmentalist hysteria? Fanatical prophecies of doom? However others may soothe themselves, no one who knows what ecological relationships mean can look to the future with optimism.

Upsurge of cancer and genetic defects

Human ecology

1   Man, the Ruling Animal

By W. Klausewitz

The life of Stone-Age man was entirely dominated by the environment, an inimical force—particularly in the northern latitudes. The death rate before puberty was very high. Extraordinary climatic conditions, lack of food, dangerous large animals and the numerous diseases ensured that few people reached adulthood, and even these usually did not survive to a ripe old age. It has been estimated that a Neanderthal man lived at most thirty years, and the *Homo sapiens* of the late Ice Age and middle Stone Age grew very little older.

Population increase in the Stone Age

In accordance with the extremely high child mortality and the often unfavorable conditions under which these men lived, their population density over the earth was very low. American prehistorians and anthropologists estimate the world's population at the beginning of the Paleolithic, about a million years ago, at 125,000; these men inhabited only the region of Africa. In the middle part of this period, about 300,000 years ago, the population had grown to a million and had spread to Eurasia; by living in caves and making use of fire, these people had managed to improve their lot. Toward the end of the Paleolithic, about 25,000 years ago, when Neanderthal and Cro-Magnon man were both living, there were probably more than three million people on earth; the increase is attributed largely to improvements in social life.

Homo sapiens: the destroyer of other human races

But the population as a whole must have suffered considerable losses through fights between competing groups and perhaps even cannibalism. Almost all the skulls of Neanderthal men that have been found so far are smashed to pieces, and most of them are lying next to fire sites. This suggests that the more intelligent and highly developed *Homo sapiens* hunted and ate the Neanderthals, possibly in connection with skull cults or other rites. Many researchers infer that at least the "classical" Neanderthal man in the Euro-Asian region was exterminated by *Homo sapiens*, while the two forms seem to have intermingled at the same period in the Near East. The remnants of Peking Man found in Chou-kou-tien were also broken up and lay by a fire site; but the type of man to whom they fell victim is not yet known.

This defeat of various races of men at the hand—or the weapon—of that branch designated "sapiens" (i.e., wise, intelligent, insightful, understanding) may well have contributed to the fact that the population during the Mesolithic increased by only about five million people, even though the American continent had been colonized in this period by way of the Bering Strait. The first real population explosion came in the Neolithic; men who had previously roamed the earth as hunters and gatherers settled down, built houses, established villages, tamed wild animals and turned wild plants into cultivated crops. As a result, the standard of living and the general level of safety improved considerably; the consequence was that the world's human population grew within a few millennia from an estimated five million (around 8000 B.C.) to at least 130 million at the beginning of the Christian era. According to other calculations it actually rose to 250 million.

The population explosion

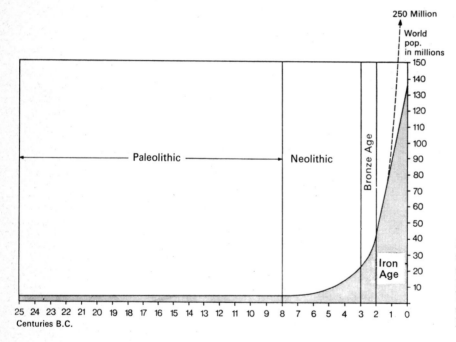

Fig. 1-1. The first population explosion followed the beginning of the Neolithic, when man began to settle and turn to farming and animal husbandry.

And in the times that followed, despite war, pestilence and high infant mortality, the growth of the population continued. If there were 250 million people on earth when Christ was born, mankind needed about 1600 more years to double its numbers to 500 million. Another doubling, to a billion people, required only about 250 years, to 1850. From this time on there was a very rapid development of industrialization in Europe and North America, which introduced a new population explosion of unprecedented size: the next doubling required only eighty years, there being two billion people by 1930, and thirty years later, in 1960, the population had already exceeded three billion. The four-billion mark

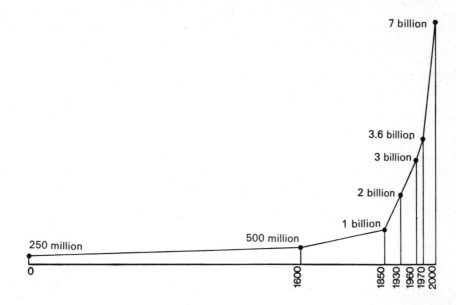

Fig. 1-2. The population increase since the year 0 A.D.

may well be passed in 1975. Since the birth of Christ the world's population has thus increased fourteenfold, and since the beginning of the Neolithic, seven hundredfold.

Whereas the marked increase between 1830 and 1930 involved primarily Europe and North America, the population today is exploding in the so-called "developing" countries, especially in South America and Asia. Since 1930 the population of Europe has increased by "only" about 100 million, but the Asians despite repeated severe famines, have grown in number by a billion.

Future life—an "Inferno"?

Based on these rates of growth, the former United States Secretary of Defense and subsequently World Bank president Robert McNamara made the following extrapolation: "In six and a half centuries, the same insignificant span of time that separates us from the poet Dante, there will be a human being standing on every square foot of ground—a horrific prospect, beside which even the 'Inferno' pales."

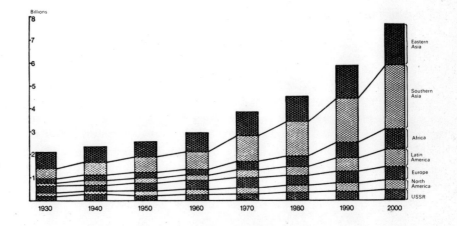

Fig. 1-3. Prior and predicted growth of the world's population, 1930-2000, subdivided geographically.

To be sure, opinions and predictions about future population growth diverge considerably. Some futurologists hold that the current trend will continue, because of further improvement in hygiene, advances in medicine, and better distribution of food resources throughout the world. They therefore predict that around the year 2000 the seven-billion level will be passed, and in 2050 at least thirteen billion people will inhabit the earth.

Other scientists, in particular a research group at Rand Corporation which several years ago took up the study of the future technological and social development of mankind, fear that it will not be possible within the next decades to improve the production and distribution of food sufficiently to prevent major famines and an increase in the death rate. And this estimate has not even taken account of the shortening of life expectancy among the inhabitants of industrialized areas as a result of the poisons that are poured into the environment. According to this group of scientists, there will be a marked slowing of population growth in the future, so that the five-billion mark may well not be reached until 2050. The truth—at least for the near future—probably lies somewhere between these two extreme extrapolations.

Nor does the American futurologist Herman Kahn believe in the continuation of the present population explosion. In his opinion, the overall rate of growth of mankind is already falling off to a notable degree, so that by his calculations no more than five or six billion people are to be expected in the year 2000. According to one of the sets of computer calculations of Professor Forrester of MIT, whose programs included forty-three factors varying in time (for example, population growth rate, raw-material supplies, level of pollution, standard of living, capital investments and so on), the world's population would have reached its peak in 2030 and thereafter, because of the whirlwind rise in pollution and other negative developments, collapse to a sixth of this value within twenty years.

In any case, it is already clear that one of the most decisive causes of environmental pollution is the rapid increase in the human population. The problem of detoxifying our environment is thus by no means simply a matter for technology, industry and the managers of the economy; it is equally the responsibility of the politicians and sociologists of all countries. Unfortunately, it is first necessary for the statesmen, military men and theologians themselves to come to the realization that populations with a declining rate of growth in the long run will be significantly happier than those producing children at the present rate. The question of the earth's population is an extraordinarily important international political problem, which can be solved only if we can succeed in outgrowing selfish nationalism and economic greed, as well as the taboos of various cultures and religions.

Hunger has always been the companion of humanity. In earlier

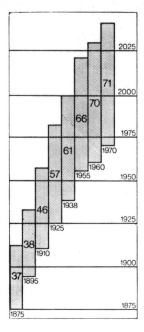

Fig. 1-4. Schematic diagram of the increase in life expectancy from 1875 to 1970.

Surplus or starvation?

millennia it was a bitter struggle to obtain even the minimum necessary for survival. Very cold winters, devastating floods and failed harvests regularly led to famine and widespread starvation. Even in the 20th Century there was a surplus of food and drink for only a relatively small privileged stratum in Europe, whereas for the great majority of the population the food supply was just sufficient or there was actual hunger. The lack of food led to unimaginable disasters wherever it was coupled with a considerable growth rate, especially in Asia. In the last century an estimated 100 million Chinese and fifty million Indians starved to death.

Overnourishment in industrial nations

In the industrial nations the situation has now changed utterly. Every employed person has far more kinds and quantities of food than even the upper levels of society had in earlier centuries. Almost a third of present-day humanity consumes more food than biological and medical considerations would recommend. Many inhabitants of the industrial nations suffer clear symptoms of overfeeding, with all its consequences to health, because during the starvation-level existence of earlier centuries and millennia there was no opportunity for a "psychological brake on appetite" to evolve. In contrast, the remaining two thirds of the world's population are incorrectly or monotonously fed, undernourished or threatened by starvation. Despite a considerable increase in the production of foodstuffs, hunger has not yet been banished. Half the human race is distinctly undernourished; a further fifteen percent actually suffers from the effects of hunger. Every year there are about 10–30 million people who die as a direct or indirect result of lack of food.

Half of mankind is undernourished

Man will not go hungry:
Colin Clark

What are the prospects of producing food in sufficient quantities? Here, again, there are widely divergent opinions. Humanity will not go hungry, claimed the English agrarian scientist Colin Clark in a polemic against the pessimistic official predictions of the United Nations' Food and Agriculture Organization. On the basis of the downhill trends in the world's food supply in 1968/1969 the FAO had come to the conclusion that the population explosion in many countries would nullify any successes in increasing food production. Clark admits that many people on earth are now hungry. But he believes that there are enough possibilities by which the present and increasing population of the world can be well fed. According to his calculations the planet, including the oceans, can supply food for 31.5 billion people—nearly ten times the current population.

There is an even more fantastic ring to the numbers derived by the Russian economist K. Malin. According to these, the continents alone could feed fifty billion people, if the vegetation consisted exclusively of crops of food for man and the edible animals. With a thoroughgoing exploitation of the ocean, especially by processing unicellular algae, in Malin's view as many as 290 billion people could eat their fill.

In the opinion of many nutritional physiologists, the food of the future will look entirely different from what we eat today; it is predicted that half of the things used as food in the year 2000 will be unfamiliar to people today. In particular, there is to be a considerable increase in easily digestible protein products, which will be made chiefly of fish and other marine animals as well as marine algae; in future the latter may play an important role. Another valuable method of obtaining protein, which has already been put into practice in supplements to animal fodder, is biosynthesis from a substrate of petroleum. In this process, microorganisms which themselves are high-quality protein sources feed on ordinary paraffin oil, a petroleum product, and reproduce with unusual rapidity. Whereas a cow weighing 250 kg synthesizes only a quarter kilogram of protein in the course of a day, 250 kg of yeast organisms are said to produce 625 kg of protein daily.

Moreover, a greater diversity in the uses of plant protein from soybeans, an approach already well developed in Japan and the USA, is likely to play a great role in feeding mankind. At the same time, efforts are being made to use chemistry in order to enhance the traditional forms of food production. One goal is to raise the annual world production of nitrogenous fertilizers from the present twenty-seven million tons to ninety or ninety-five million tons in the year 2000. These plans also provide for an increased use of chemicals (especially herbicides and pesticides) to protect crops, and of concentrated animal fodder produced mainly from petroleum and urea; finally, they call for the use of previously arid or infertile soils by artificial methods—for example, by employing a complex of urea, formaldehyde and resins which can bind moisture and is sprayed onto the soil along with water.

More plant protein from the soybean

Altogether, according to the claims of industry and some nutritional scientists, the outlook for feeding the world's population in the future is significantly better than some pessimists think. The German systems researcher H. Krauch believes that by about 2000 A.D. the field of nutrition will have achieved a paradisical state: "We shall dial a computer, type in what we want and indicate about how much money we want to spend. Taking into consideration the current state of the market, the time of day, our medical diagnosis and the demands our jobs make upon us, the computer will then make suggestions for things we can pick out of the freezer ourselves, or it can order a rapid delivery to our doors, or it may recommend restaurants in the neighborhood and show us the proposed dishes on a screen." Krauch also predicts that by the year 2000 the trend, already discernible today, to separate the intake of nutrients from the pleasure of eating—by the manufacture of tasty comestibles with an appetizing smell but no nutritional value—will be fully realized.

Paradise in the year 2000?

Such predictions sound like a modern form of Pieter Breughel's famous painting of the "land of milk and honey." Of course, we must ask ourselves whether the economists' visions and plans of turning the continents into one huge farm, and the oceans into breeding grounds for edible fish and algae, can be reconciled with ecological and economic realities.

On the basis of biosynthesis and other technical methods it will sooner or later be possible to open up new sources of protein to feed mankind. And in certain localities the catch of marine animals can be considerably increased; for example, the use of modern apparatus off the coast of Thailand made it possible to increase the catch tenfold within a few years. Moreover, there are still areas of the world now lying fallow which can be put to agricultural use. Even the culture of marine animals in large "farms," particularly in isolated bays of the ocean, is already technically feasible.

Can the human organism adapt to an artificial environment?

But it remains questionable whether these and similar measures can be carried out on such a scale that both today's hungry people and the billions that will be added during the next decades can be adequately fed. Furthermore, it has yet to be demonstrated that both the human organism and nature as a whole can adapt in the long run to such massive changes of the environment.

There are a number of medical factors which make one question the ability of the human body to adapt to such changes. Here we shall mention only one. Artificial foodstuffs consisting primarily of easily digestible proteins are already being used on a limited scale. But because of the lack of suitable roughage, which is important for proper intestinal activity, such food has led to a notable increase in intestinal diseases and a weakening of the digestive system in many people, especially in the USA. The "easily digestible" new protein preparations, then, have certain disadvantages.

Exhaustion of the agricultural land reserves

With respect to the soil available for the production of increased quantities of food, certain limits will soon be reached. If many of our remaining forests should be lost, the water balance of extensive regions may well be so severely upset that large-scale transformations to steppe or even desert could ensue. And wherever forest is converted to field one can count on erosion of the soil. The quality of the soil can thus decline despite the application of artificial fertilizers, even in areas only newly exploited for purposes of agriculture.

Agriculture in a vicious circle

Even from the viewpoint of economics, the use of artificial fertilizers and pesticides has drawbacks. These chemicals not only increase yields and protect the harvest; they lead to an accumulation in soil and water of poisons and nonbiological substances, some of which can never be removed. Moreover, the number of insects that have grown resistant to poisons is increasing; by bringing this about man has encouraged plagues of pests. Finally, as W. Haber has reported, there is an additional unexpected economic problem. In recent years the target of a 50% increase in harvest has been met at the price of a cost increase for fertilizer of 300% and expenses for pesticides that have increased by 1500%. Modern agriculture has evidently been caught in a vicious circle, in several respects.

Harvests from the sea

But what is the situation with respect to harvests from the sea? Algae are rich in protein and could be a central food source for the hungry people of the world. The Japanese have been progressing in this area for some time now. But we cannot overlook the fact that in recent times the stocks of marine algae have been harmed by various poisons, especially chlorinated hydrocarbons such as DDT. Certain algal species suffer inhibited development, and local populations of others have died out completely. It is quite possible that in the long run damage will be done not only to oxygen production in the ocean but also to the development of algae as a future food source.

The ocean is sometimes regarded as an inexhaustible reservoir of food. But estimates have indicated that no more than a hundred million tons of fish can be taken annually from the world's oceans if the stocks are to be maintained as a permanent food supply. In 1967 a total of sixty million tons of fish were caught in all the oceans of the world; the annual growth rate is currently 8%, though in 1969 a reverse trend was discernible. According to these calculations, the highest permissible catches will have been reached in 1975.

But who worries about such facts when it is a matter of profit! Since fishery is not a charitable institution for the benefit of hungry people, but a tough and serious business that has little to do with the romance of the sea, new methods of exploiting the ocean are steadily being developed. Today the fleets are made up almost entirely of modern vessels designed for the high seas and equipped with all the latest devices. Finding the schools of fish is no longer a matter of chance; they are located with echo sounders, which can also indicate the size and depth of a school. Fishing is still most commonly done by net, so that proper selection of mesh size can to a certain extent prevent fish that are too young from being caught; but the newest fishing devices, which have not yet come into general use, are based on the principles of galvanotaxis and suction, which will be much more effective than the traditional methods. The schools of fish are attracted by strong lights, enter an electrical field, are drawn to the cathode and there are sucked up and dumped on board through a hose and pump apparatus. There is no escape for any of the animals that come within range of the suction device, regardless of age or size.

New inventions to exploit the fish stocks

Such new techniques can increase the yield of fishing, but they are many times worse than all previous methods in terms of overfishing. Since even the juveniles in a school fished in this way must die, use of the electrosuction technique will decrease considerably, in only a few years, the number of mature fish able to reproduce. Economically important fish that were once caught regularly are becoming a rarity or vanishing from the severely overfished regions. Even now, just because of the modern methods of locating the swarms, certain formerly abundant fishing grounds have been essentially fished out. Some of these now-empty regions are off the California coast, others are in the waters off Scotland.

The herring, at one time the cheapest widely used food fish, declined in population so severely within a few years that recently international conservation measures—that is, limitations on catch size—have had to be introduced. Fish, crustaceans and clams living in coastal waters have in some cases become inedible because of the increased concentrations of sewage wastes in the water; in many coastal regions sewage has already made it impossible to set up "farms" of marine animals. Those who persist in thinking of the ocean as inexhaustible are quite mistaken. And the same can probably be said of the potential agricultural land the earth has in reserve. It is by no means certain that the world's population can be fed, in spite of great technical advances.

C. F. von Weizsäcker: Famine cannot be avoided

For all these reasons, the German physicist and philosopher Carl Friedrich von Weizsäcker has declared that in the next twenty years a billion people are likely to be born for whom there is actually no food available: He concludes, "It is most improbable that a catastrophic famine can be avoided." At the conference of the United Nations Food and Agriculture Organization in November, 1971, it was predicted that despite a 39% increase in agricultural yields, in 1980 there will probably be a total of about 1,400,000,000 people, in no less than forty-two underdeveloped countries, who suffer from malnutrition. In the field of nutrition, then, it also looks as though the worlds' population is proceeding directly toward a disaster of unprecedented magnitude. Some may hope that the industrialized nations can ultimately avoid partaking in this process, but there is very good reason to doubt it.

2   Changes in the Natural Landscape

For years, foresighted scientists have been talking about the danger of putting too heavy a burden on our environment; by about the end of 1969 the general public began to be fairly well informed about the forms and consequences of pollution and other types of environmental damage. Since the European Conservation Year, 1971, that continent has been flooded with pertinent publications and presentations, but in most cases it is only particular single phenomena that are described and deplored—for example, the contamination of water or the atmosphere. Only rarely have environmentalists attempted to make clear to the public the degree and extent to which all organisms depend upon the total orderliness and balance of all aspects of the environment.

A real awareness of what it means to change the environment to suit ourselves—such as E. Gassner demanded in 1972—must be based on the ecological finding that each organism is associated in a species-specific way with certain phenomena and processes in the world about it, so that its requirements for life can be met. When man, in pursuit of economic progress, interferes with nature, the fact is often overlooked that animals and plants are more or less closely tied to a certain habitat where particular conditions prevail. Soil, water, air, vegetation and fauna are the basic components making up all of the landscapes we see, from the coasts to the mountains. They are joined in an extensive, many-layered web of interrelationships—an ecosystem—so that changes made by man in individual components must necessarily affect the overall structure.

Near the beginning of his social development, man's adoption of the agrarian life modified the appearance and function of large areas of land. The way in which he established his settlements and divided up the land, the size of the individual farms, and above all the methods of cultivation —none of these was without its effect upon the natural conditions.

Since the industrial age began, there has been a much more thorough and rapid alteration of the landscape in the now populous industrialized areas. Here natural resources were consumed without the slightest

How habitats are changed, by G. Darmer

▷
Upper left: Example of agricultural subdivision adapted to the terrain: farm land in Pennsylvania.
Upper right: Permanent meadowland in the eastern Tyrol: hayricks in the Tilliach Valley.
Below: Alteration of the coastal landscape.—Left: Single-crop fields on reclaimed land (Friedrich-Wilhelm-Lübke-Koog).—Right: View over recently reclaimed marshland (Westerheversand).

Agrarian and indus-trial regions

Transformation of
natural landscapes by
man

The slash-and-burn
method

The Middle Ages;
from the clearing of
woods to the founding
of cities

restraint. Currently about 110 hectares of land are being "used up" every day for new urban and road construction and for the expansion of industry. Some of nature's reactions to this practice have been extreme: water shortages, air pollution and a disappearance of plant life. The natural plant and animal communities that have fallen victim to this "economical" line of development cannot be restored; the only organisms that can survive in the vicinity of cities and concentrations of industry are the relatively few species insensitive to such changes and those actually adapted to the man-made environment.

When man was still at the gathering level—that is, from the Paleolithic until the end of the Mesolithic—his influence in changing the virgin landscape did not exceed that of the other animals. But gradually the sphere of the environment under man's dominion was expanded. In northwestern Germany, for example, and in the loess regions of central and southern Germany (characterized by a yellowish-brown loam), the development of an agrarian economy began with the selection and cultivation of the first crop plants and the keeping and breeding of the first domestic animals. From that time on man slowly but steadily crowded out the original vegetation, the virgin forest, as he used fire and tools and set his animals to graze on the undergrowth in the woods; the exposed areas became fields which returned many times the amount sown upon them.

Agriculture of this sort followed a certain pattern. The woodlands were cut down and burned, and the ashes spread over the land as fertilizer. After a few harvests the fertility of the soil was exhausted and the land would support only grass, until eventually it was reinvaded by trees and a shrubby woodland developed. Meanwhile, in adjacent areas, new sections of forest were slashed, burned and cultivated. Another kind of primitive exploitation of the forest was the removal of leaf litter and the cutting of turf on heathland; for one hectare of fruitful fields, five to ten hectares of heather, sod, and topsoil had to be carried away, and the result of the subsequent loss of nutrients and alkaline elements was a conversion to wasteland.

In the 6th Century A.D. there was an acceleration of the development of human settlements. From this time on, man's clearing activities followed a conscious plan of attack on the forests, more and more of which became the property of local lords. The large medieval clearing operations sponsored by the nobility and the monasteries paved the way for the foundation of cities. As the size of the population steadily increased there was a need for more cleared land, and a corresponding rise in the use of wood for construction, shipbuilding and fuel. In the 16th Century the forests were invaded by men who produced beech charcoal for the iron foundries; others supplied potash to the glassmakers in the form of wood ashes. The consumption of wood by salt and other mines was very high. For a long time wood remained the most important material used by peasant and city dweller alike for fuel, industry and construction.

As a result of the extensive grazing in the mixed deciduous forests, together with the use of leaf litter as food and bedding for domestic animals, the forest soils and the stands of ash, elm, linden, hornbeam, maple and other trees suffered severe damage. Many woodlands gradually opened up, first becoming grassland with scattered trees, then weedy meadows, and finally barren wastes. Later, in an effort at "organized forestry," many of these deforested areas were replanted with trees. But the limited choice of species—the spruce being preferred for its rapid growth and the pine for its resistance to drought—caused further profound change in the local habitats and communities.

Forests used for grazing became less dense

As long as this reshaping of the natural landscape was carried out at the slow pace of past centuries, it did not have a fundamental effect on the balance between forested and open terrain. Around 1835, for example, there was still so much woodland in the farm-village region of middle Saxony that, as Käubler said, it "spread a broad cloak" over the plateaus and watersheds of the low mountains. The long, narrow villages, each household with its strip of field and pasture land behind it, were often entirely isolated by the surrounding forest. Pigs were sent out to forage in the tall beech forests and the mixed oakwoods; open stands of oak supplied the best wood for building.

When the age of technology began, about 150 years ago, the introduction of agricultural machinery brought about a basic change in the agrarian economy. Huge areas were planted with a single kind of crop; foresters replaced the mixed stands of deciduous trees, which had disappeared because of misuse, with stands of spruce and fir in which few other species were represented. No longer were there gradual transitions between the different types of vegetation; the prevailing land-management practices called for sharp boundaries between woods, crop land and pastures which have continued until the present to characterize the landscape in large regions inhabited by man. Where interference with the water balance of a region, artificial fertilization and the use of larger and larger machines was carried too far, there was a progressive enlargement of the fields to the detriment of the surrounding land and its flora.

Fig. 2-1. Farming village with scattered fields.

Even now great efforts are still being made to "clean up" agricultural land and rid it completely of all elements of the original vegetation. But we now know that even from a practical point of view this approach is wrong—that a more natural arrangement of fields intermingled with hedges and clumps of trees can in fact enhance the productivity of the soil. Moreover, the shape of the fields is important. In rural districts the land has traditionally been subdivided into rectangular plots, mainly because these were easier to measure out; but plots that follow the terrain (see Color plate, p. 547) are often more advantageous.

Depending on the population density, the ratio of population size to

Fig. 2-2. Modern arrangement of village and fields.

The modern agrarian landscape

cultivated area, and the effect that this land use has in turn upon the general economy and life style of the people, the manner in which agrarian land is utilized varies from place to place. Even in rural areas the emphasis is shifting away from the pure production of foodstuffs and raw materials and toward the housing of a population that has no role in agriculture; village and city are approaching one another both spatially and in their way of life. To a great extent, agricultural land is regarded as a reserve for eventual use in housing, industry and transportation; moreover, the open areas are increasingly being taken over as recreation grounds to occupy the leisure hours of our industrial society. Although the number of farm workers is steadily shrinking, and smaller areas are farmed, higher gross production is achieved. The alterations of habitats inevitably produced by such land use are followed by a progressive diminution in the number of species, change in the species composition, and an "indirect extermination." Where there are no large carnivores, herbivores like roe and red deer may multiply excessively and impair the regeneration of the forests.

What should be done with fallow land?

In this connection, the land currently being left fallow by changes in the agrarian structure acquires a heightened ecological significance. These are often dismissed as weed-ridden wastes, but just like forest and meadow they can have a marked effect on the overall environment. Forested land in general offers protection against wide fluctuations in the amount of water runoff and subterranean drainage, against soil erosion, the formation of cold air masses, and depletion of soil minerals; it also acts to preserve the diversity of animal species. Open meadowland, on the other hand, supports fewer species but protects the soil from erosion and water loss. In cultivated fields negative effects prevail; drainage patterns are irregular, erosion is common, the environment is encumbered with chemicals, few species are allowed to live, and the microclimate is unstable and strongly affected by the wind. The ecological conditions in fallow land reapproach those in adjacent woodland, once communities of grasses, herbs and pioneer woody plants have become established.

Fig. 2-3. Agricultural area subdivided without regard to contour of the terrain.

From the point of view of management of our natural surroundings, five possible "substitute" uses for fallow land seem appropriate: 1. Return to nature under professional supervision; this allows such "cleared out" landscapes to be enriched with heather, secondary woodland and other plant communities. 2. Forestation planned so as to restore the original woodland community, or development of a stand of economically important trees, which can also play a role as a recreation area. This approach is particularly appropriate in areas where people and industry are concentrated. 3. Keeping the land in the province of traditional agriculture, but with the collaboration of professionals concerned with management of the area as a whole. 4. The creation of new forms of extensive land utilization, again with due concern for the overall landscape. 5. Planned preservation as open terrain, with the goal of diversifying the

Fig. 2-4. The same area with field placement determined by the contour lines.

landscape and creating a variety of habitats such as dunes, heath, various types of grassland, moors, alpine meadows and so on.

In summary, it would be possible to plan the changes in the landscape which are expected to come about through agrarian reform in such a way that they simultaneously achieve an ecological "resurrection" of landscapes similar to the original natural ones.

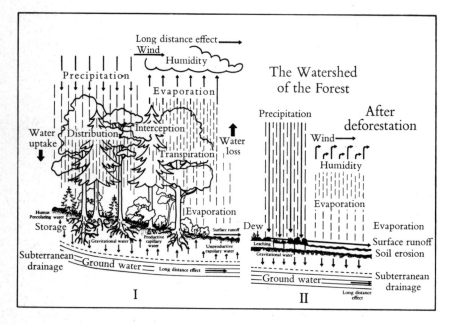

Fig. 2-5. The well-balanced water circulation in a mixed forest has a beneficial effect even on nearby agricultural land (I). By contrast, if too much of the forest is removed there is a net loss of moisture and deterioration of the soil (II).

Industrial regions

In comparison with the area required for agriculture and forestry, the space taken up by industry at first seems small. However, the fact that this branch of the economy is concentrated in industrial regions is associated with a heavy local burden on the environment, which has more general consequences. A rapid and steadily increasing takeover of land for building sites not only destroys the vegetation but also reduces the area through which water can percolate and encourages unproductive runoff of precipitation. The erection of more industrial structures and the associated housing demands more road area, more consumption of building materials, and more open space. Wherever ground is covered with buildings or dug away to allow the open-pit mining of the raw materials needed for building and industry, the destruction of the vegetation also drives away the animals. Fertile soil is lost; the soil profiles and surface relief that have evolved so slowly are changed or destroyed in short order. The water balance of the region suffers, since the water table falls and there are changes in the flow of surface water, the amount of percolating water and the rate of evaporation. The local and microclimates are also affected far into the surrounding land. There may even be considerable effects upon the macroclimate of the region.

Other factors that contribute to a change in water balance are the control of rivers and the creation of reservoirs in densely populated industrial regions. The demand for water increases and often can be met only by drawing upon distant catchment areas. An acceptable water supply involves more elaborate processing as the water becomes progressively dirtier (see Chapter 3); irreversible harm can be done if the natural capacity of bodies of water to clean themselves is disrupted. Besides the numerous chemical pollutants introduced in the drainage water from households, factories and cultivated fields, there are added physical stresses such as the warming of the rivers by water used as a coolant in industrial operations. Such a rise in temperature lowers the oxygen content of the water, damages water and shore plants and poikilothermic animals, and stimulates other organisms to excessive growth. These are not only local phenomena, but propagate into far-removed regions of the river or lake.

One of today's most worrying problems is that of disposing of solid wastes. The careless and irresponsible practices associated with traditional "dumps" are a serious threat to the environment. To mention only a few aspects, the soil and ground water are contaminated, odors and clouds of smoke are released, pieces of trash can be blown away by strong winds, germs are picked up and carried away by animals, and the spread of vermin is encouraged. Only a few of the many such dumps are so well organized that they can eventually be reshaped, planted, and put to a different use.

Air pollution

More than 300 substances given off by industry, household heating and traffic in the form of solids, gases or vapors change the quality of the air and the composition of the atmosphere. These atmospheric impurities directly or indirectly harm man, animal and plant, soil and buildings. In the cloud of vapor that typically hovers over industrial regions about 30% of the incident radiation is lost; the vital ultraviolet light is particularly strongly absorbed. Dust and gases impair the performance and the fertility of animals and plants. By way of the food chains, harmful substances such as lead and fluorine become more and more concentrated and hence more dangerous—a process that can mean death to the terminal consumer. Rain and fog bring poisons from the air into the soil and the water.

The plants standing at the beginning of the various food chains are often damaged even kilometers away from industrial sources of air pollution. Toxic substances enter their tissues by way of the stomata and disrupt metabolic processes; solid deposits on the leaves reduce light absorption and hence photosynthesis. In many cases the regenerative capacity of plants is so great that the damage can be repaired. As far as the animals are concerned, in industrial regions they are deprived of almost all the varied natural surroundings and must make do with the "technotope" as a habitat. Usually only highly adaptable animals succeed in colonizing these areas; for example, the swift, black redstart and house sparrow can adapt to such conditions.

Let us now consider a cross section of Europe, reaching inland from the coast, and some of the typical habitats and their fauna that we encounter along it. By observing the consequences of the changes made by man in each case, we shall try to establish points of departure for planning future conservation and development, and suitable methods.

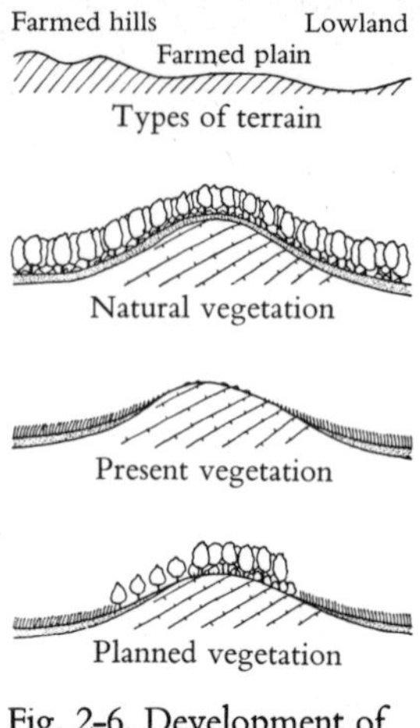

Even in the tide flats which are the furthest outposts of the land we can see how the distribution and composition of the vegetation influences the nature and development of the habitats there. As part of the process of land reclamation, soil formation by the plants naturally found in such places, such as marsh samphire (*Salicornia*) and alkali grass (*Puccinellia*), is accelerated by various techniques; consequently, there is a rapid modification of this habitat as it turns into dry land. Soil animals, which perform crucial service in soil formation and feeding other coast animals, lose part of their habitat; in its place there appear behind the dikes new agricultural fields with the uniform single-species communities of marsh and polder. In these windswept expanses trees and shrubs are sparse and slow to become established, so that a spatial organization with ecologically desirable boundaries develops only gradually, if at all.

On the other hand, the formation of open areas that can either be dry, alternate between wet and dry, or at times be completely flooded is advantageous in some respects, especially to suitably adapted species among the coast birds. There they find resting places, feeding grounds and sites where they can molt, raise their young, and spend the winter—as long as this reclaimed land has not been damaged by intensive utilization, excessive drainage, and chemicals. Recently the physical and chemical effects of inland industries are felt even in the brackish water and the open sea; they cause profound disruption of the marine food chains, extending from the masses of microorganisms to the warm-blooded terminal consumers.

On the whole, however, mud and sand flats, beaches and dunes, steep shores, lagoons and many other coastal landscape features offer an abundance of habitats even today, and can be colonized by a great diversity of plants and animals as long as they remain undisturbed. Unfortunately, here too the pressure to make use of more and more of the land—especially for recreation and for industrial installations—is increasing ominously. The sphere of action of both the native and the migratory fauna grows ever narrower; the animals encounter transformed, unnatural habitats, disappear from places they have always occupied, or suffer damage that reduces their populations. This is true especially when toxic substances derived from wastes, insecticides and other pesticides are passed along the food chain and increase their virulence in the process. Since the animals affected are highly motile and capable of dispersal, the harm extends far beyond the site of the original pollution.

Fig. 2-6. Development of the landscape in the hill country of central Germany.

Inland habitats

Further inland, the local climate and fauna are determined chiefly by the nature of the vegetation. Where there are grasses, herbs, shrubs and trees animals colonize the area; there they raise their offspring, seek shelter from storms and predators, spend the winter and find food. The kind and amount of food the plant cover affords, as well as the influence of the plants on the climate near the ground, are the major factors affecting the density of the animal populations. The more varied the different vegetation strata, the more diverse and well-balanced the fauna.

But where the inland regions are intensively cultivated, the number of habitats filling the requirements of various animal species is steadily decreasing. Continual disturbance by busy men forces the animals to change their habits (for example, to shift from daytime to nighttime activity), crowds them out of their traditional territories and not uncommonly gives rise to stress situations and unnatural massive multiplication of the animals. The eventual result is that the animals die out—or, more accurately, are killed off. In the last hundred years, among the birds and mammals, on average one species has become extinct each year; in fact, in the last fifty years, a total of seventy-six species have become extinct. Today 550 mammals and bird species are rarely to be found, and many of these are on the verge of extinction. Hunting and other forms of direct persecution of the animals have had only a slight effect; the most important factor is that in one way or another the species have been and are being deprived of the habitats to which they are adapted.

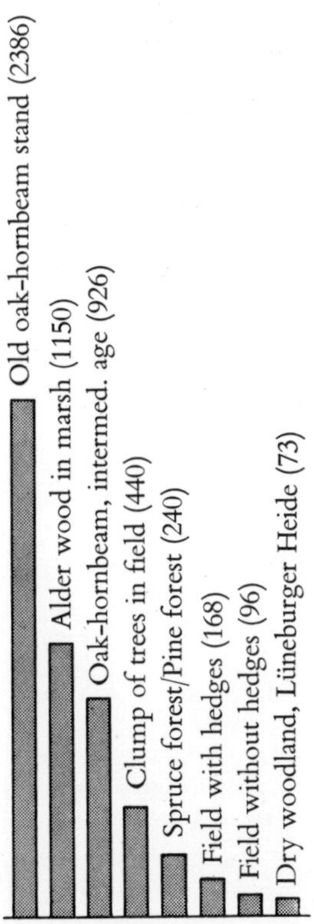

The many elements that determine the suitability of an environment to a species—light or shadow, open terrain or cover, water or land, humidity, temperature, and above all an absence of disturbance in the places the animals live and feed—are all too often overlooked, underestimated, or simply disregarded when construction or other modification of the landscape is undertaken. Profound changes are also caused when drainage projects are carried out on too large a scale, so that swamps, bogs and natural running waters are destroyed or transformed. As a result, the animals dependent on moist habitats and pure flowing water—reptiles, amphibians, fish and some birds, and mammals like the beaver and the otter—lose their homes. The frogs, toads and salamanders, useful antagonists of insects, are deprived of the ponds they need if they are to reproduce.

The conservation of natural plant communities to artificially maintained stands of plants proceeds steadily, under the pressure of economic necessity. The complex communities of the beech, oak and mixed forests (see Chapter 12, Part One) are retreating before the expanding plantations of spruce and pine. And the future is not bright for the remnants of bog and moor and the few remaining swamp regions, although they could be of great importance not only as water reservoirs but as places to which animals can retreat for survival.

In the extensive agricultural areas, where often hardly a tree is to be

Old oak-hornbeam stand (2386)
Alder wood in marsh (1150)
Oak-hornbeam, intermed. age (926)
Clump of trees in field (440)
Spruce forest/Pine forest (240)
Field with hedges (168)
Field without hedges (96)
Dry woodland, Lüneburger Heide (73)

Fig. 2-7. Bird population (breeding pairs per km²) as an indicator of structure and biological productivity of various biotopes.

seen, the rhythm of animal life is interrupted by the almost complete mechanization of agricultural operations as well as by the intensive use of pasture lands and the frequent applications of chemicals. An increase in the proportion of fallow land is not an adequate compensation, for as we have described above the ecological relationships here remain unnatural. Among the threatened, or at least severely affected, birds of open terrain are quail, white and black storks, black grouse, hazel hen, meadow lark, great bustard, hoopoe, and nightjar. Uncontrolled building, and invasion of the natural terrain by weekend cabins, further restrict the animals' territories, which may need to be quite large; a common buzzard can thrive only if about six square kilometers are available to it.

The general impoverishment of the vegetation and the habitats leads not only to a decline in species diversity, but to mass outbreaks of pests. Because of the uniformity of the man-made environment, natural predators such as the fox, badger, marten and birds of prey disappear. The resulting dominance of the ring-necked dove, magpie, jay and squirrel in turn affects the populations of small birds. Disturbance by the increasing numbers of vacationers is very noticeable among lynxes and wildcats, owls, various other birds of prey, the black stork and wood grouse; and animal photographers must share some of the blame. The peregrine falcon and certain other birds of prey are now nearly extinct because of the activities of egg collectors and amateur falconers as well as effects of DDT.

The multiplication of pests

The conditions in the habitats of the large game animals also give grounds for concern. The stocks of certain game species have become too large through overprotection (see Chapter 12, Part One) and are irreconcilable with the efficient production of timber. Even in the woods, animals are often deprived of peace and quiet. Traffic accidents take a greater toll of animal life every year, especially when territories and trails of long standing are suddenly cut through by new roads. The only solution is to fence in the woods. But all too often gaps are left in these forest boundaries by the builders of vacation cabins.

Forestry and game conservation

We are placing an ever greater burden on the inland waters, especially the ponds and lakes (see Chapter 3). Under natural circumstances these offer an abundance of ecological niches for animal life, from the shore through the littoral zone and into the open water. But now fertilizers and other pollutants are being washed into the water. Moreover, the boats and barges on the inland waters are noisy and spread oil, and swimmers and fishermen add their own kind of disturbance; all this results in a steady decline in the populations of swamp and water animals and of the birds that breed on the shores. The food chains, particularly complex in such biotopes, are destroyed. The same is true of "ox-bow" ponds and of the flat, damp meadows and woodlands fringing rivers. Particularly affected are the otter, osprey, marsh harrier, grey heron, dipper, kingfisher and swamp turtle.

The alterations of stream courses undertaken in southern Bavaria,

▷
Above: The concentration of industry in the Ruhr region (Duisburg-Kupfer-hütte) completely replaces the natural habitat. Below: Two large hotel buildings on the Geyers-berg (Bayerischer Wald, Germany), an impressive example of the way a diversified agrarian landscape can be spoiled by poorly planned architecture.

according to the report of Bezzel in 1965, had several effects: The gull-billed tern and common thick-knee ceased to breed there altogether. The populations of teal, goosander, little ringed plover, common sandpiper and common tern were diminished. There were no changes in the populations of moorhens, black-necked grebes, little grebes, and garganeys. Increases were noted—particularly after the construction of new reservoirs—in the populations of the great crested grebe, gadwall, mallard, blue-billed pintail, red-crested duck, European pochard, tufted duck, mute swan, water rail, coot, and black-headed gull.

It is evident from these data that there can be some degree of compensation, if reservoirs and other artificial lakes are provided as new homes for the animals driven from their habitats. In such cases woods along the banks, strips of beach, sand and gravel banks, hedges, and the edges of forests are important transitional habitats. Some species such as the curlew, lapwing, marsh warbler, blue-headed wagtail, whinchat and snipe, the "traditional" habitats of which are bogs, riverbanks and other places near water, are today able to survive even in agrarian countryside.

In comparison with the flatland, the hill and mountain areas still have a relatively large number of original, natural habitats. But even here the former expanses of forest are being reduced and divided up as the building of houses continues. The brown bear, wolf and lynx, golden eagle and eagle owl have given way to man; it is only recently that attempts have been made to reestablish the eagle owl in various places. Deciduous mixed forests, the best natural plant cover in many places, have for reasons of "economy" been replaced by stands of single species, chiefly conifers; on sloping ground the hedges of calcicolous shrubs adapted to warm situations are disappearing. Mountain-dwelling birds requiring large regions of forest, such as the hazel hen, Tengmalm's owl, eagle owl, peregrine falcon and grey-headed woodpecker, must bear the burden of man's interference here. Often the water balance in an area is changed so greatly that environmental conditions deteriorate for the river fishes, dippers and other animals.

According to the figures given by Geiler in 1971, the central European beechwoods are the home of about 4000 species of plants and 7000 species of animals; 1800 of these are directly dependent on the presence of the beech trees for survival. Oak forests, and mixed forests dominated by oak, with a denser undergrowth, have an even greater number of species and population density, if they are managed appropriately. If the bird-population density is taken as an indication, comparisons between natural mixed forests and the single-tree stands planted by man show clearly the relative paucity of species in the ecologically unbalanced plant communities based entirely on economical considerations. In deciduous forest and park grounds, with luxuriant vegetation and abundant undergrowth, we find 1100 to 2386 breeding pairs per square kilometer, whereas in spruce forests there are 180–240, and in dry pine woods only 96–145 breeding

◁
Open-pit lignite mining reshapes large regions of land:
Above: Power station in the lignite region of the Rhineland; the waste heap behind it has been reforested and returned to agricultural use.
Lower left: While a mine is being operated, the original habitats and their communities are destroyed.
Lower right: Later, a new landscape can be formed, with its own special value, if appropriate measures are taken; landscaping involves shaping the terrain and planting it with a variety of species.

pairs. On fields bordered by hedges one can find 112 to 168 breeding pairs of birds per square kilometer, and on fields without hedges, 40–96; in the patches of woodland among fields, the corresponding number is 400–442 pairs per square kilometer.

Mountain forests are more valuable as habitats for diverse species if they are associated with open areas in the form of meadows, moors, heaths and the like. The diversity is further increased by variability in slope of the terrain from the summits to the valleys. Accordingly, mountain habitats are impaired if valley meadows are planted with trees and no longer serve as open grassland. The disappearance of single trees, groups of trees, strips of trees and shrubbery along paths and roads, clumps of brush and brambles, hedges, or areas of closed forest can also produce an impoverishment of these habitats. Unfortunately, such types of woodland are increasingly being removed "for the good of the economy," because ski resorts and other recreational centers are likely to be profitable.

Even those large regions of the Alps still in a nearly natural state, where woods and meadows provide excellent protection for the soil and where ptarmigan, dotterel, marmot, chamois and ibex find refuge, are "overrun" by the proliferation of equipment to lift masses of visitors to the otherwise inaccessible slopes. But as we have seen before, man's intervention on behalf of the animals can also fail, when protection of game animals is carried to an extreme and the forests are damaged by the resulting overpopulation.

According to recent data, the recreation industry in the Alps causes the loss of almost eight thousand hectares of agricultural land per year. Because of the emphasis upon planting spruce, by now only every hundredth tree in the Alps is a fir, although the deep-rooting firs offer a much better deterrent to erosion. No less than eighteen bird species of the Alps are threatened by extinction because of waste gases, lack of suitable nest sites, harassment by the presence of people or poisoning by chemicals used to protect the plants. Seven others have already died out. In the Swiss Alps there are already a total of forty-two runways for small airplanes, but no more than forty nesting places for eagles remain.

Bearing all this in mind, what guidelines emerge for the planning and protection of our natural surroundings, so that as habitats are preserved or modified we may be sure of maintaining suitable conditions for the animals we have left? First, the planners must be thoroughly aware that animal and environment form a dynamic system stamped by the reciprocity of the relationship between the two components—though the influence of environment upon animal is usually greater than the reverse effect. Animals and plants are united in communities, which appear in different places with the same characteristic species composition as long as the ecological conditions are similar. Disruption of the communities occurs primarily when the vegetation is altered, whether in species composition or in growth and development of the individual plants. Where

Consequences for planning

conditions vary widely locally, species diversity is correspondingly great and the number of individuals of each species is relatively small. More uniform conditions, on the other hand, are associated with smaller numbers of species, each of which is relatively abundant.

The goals of rural planning

Following these principles, ecologically oriented planners must aim at the following: Regions in which the habitats and communities are valuable should be preserved and if necessary protected by conservation laws. Rather than the substitution of uniform stands of plants for the natural communities, there should be an effort to reestablish a varied mosaic of habitats even in highly agricultural areas. A first step in this direction is to achieve a wise distribution of different multi-species stands of plants; these can provide biological stability in countryside hard pressed by intensive agriculture. In many places "substitute" habitats and "biotope islands"—in the form of clumps of trees among fields, windbreaks, hedgerows, wet meadows, fallow land, ox-bow ponds, parks and gardens, reservoirs, and reclaimed gravel pits, quarries or slag-heaps—can be developed to serve as refuges and centers of future dispersal for the animals. A further goal would be the creation of local and even international nature reserves.

The character and amount of terrain occupied by the newly created habitats should be planned with respect to the animal populations they house; the proper maintenance and protection, and measures to assist further development must be ensured. And due consideration must be given to the land surrounding the area in question. A great variety of plant communities—fields of grass or perennial herbs, shrubbery, pioneer woodland communities and permanent forests—may be desirable, depending on the nature of the landscape as a whole and on the local fauna. It goes without saying that for any such habitats, the emphasis is on their care and preservation; harvesting, logging, hunting and fishing should serve primarily to keep the populations of the different species within an optimal range. Areas specially reserved for animals must be strictly separated from heavily used recreational areas like campgrounds and centers of water or winter sports.

Even when typical features of the landscape, such as hilltops, precipices, valleys, and river meadows, have been spoiled or are obliterated by heaps of industrial waste, they can be revived by introducing well-chosen plants. The new plant cover protects the soil by shading it, lowering the wind speed near ground, limiting evaporation and erosion, reducing temperature fluctuations and improving the retention of water. It provides animals with shelter and food.

"Formative conservation"

Finally, ecologically and biologically oriented planning must take the responsibility for "formative conservation" through planting programs designed to assist the maintenance, population increase or redispersal of endangered and rare animals. To be successful in the long run, all these measures must take into account the global ecological situation.

In summary, the target of such planning is to preserve a highly diversified, ecologically balanced landscape with zones of high natural productivity. Today, more than ever, it is vital that all man's manipulations of his surroundings should be in the greatest possible harmony with the natural laws. To achieve this, we must reach a high level of awareness and responsibility for our actions.

The forest is a large-scale community which remains closest to nature and least affected by man. Alterations in the plant composition of this community take place slowly. Only catastrophic events such as windstorms, fires, and changes in the water table, because of artificial draining of the ground water or clear-cutting, produce relatively severe consequences. Even in such cases immediate replanting can restore the forest. From an ecological point of view the forest, in contrast to cultivated fields, is a stable, permanent form of vegetation. It is true that contemporary forestry emphasizes certain species of tree, but in such a slow-growing community it takes a long time—at least a century—for a fundamental change to become established.

The "social benefits" of the forest, by E. Munzel

In central Europe the forest is in theory the climax community— that is, the final stage in the natural succession of communities (see the Introduction to Section Three, Part One)—almost everywhere except the high mountains, bogs, and certain lowlands near rivers. Depending on the soil and climate in any given place, quite different natural forest communities can develop: open oak-hornbeam forest, mixed forest of many deciduous species dominated by beech, clumps of alders by streams and in swamps, mixed deciduous forest with a large admixture of conifers, or almost pure fir-spruce forest.

As described in Chapter 12 of Part One, since man first began to settle down he directed his activities against the forest. By chopping down the trees he made available ground for cultivation. By the early Middle Ages Europeans had already realized the importance of the forest as a source of raw materials for fuel, construction and charcoal and as a grazing area for domestic animals. There were severe penalties for offenses against the conservation laws of the time. Another factor that contributed greatly to the maintenance of the forests was the local rulers' passion for hunting. After the end of the Middle Ages there were no appreciable changes in the boundaries between field and forest in Europe; not until the middle of this century (in certain places since the beginning of the century) did these boundaries begin to shift again.

Farms and towns, at the expense of forest

The reconstruction of the cities and villages that had been destroyed in the Thirty Years' War, together with the gradual increase in population brought about a decline in the still-luxuriant forests. Increased numbers of pigs and goats were driven into the woods to graze; these, and in some places large stocks of game, destroyed the natural capacity of the forest for self-renewal. There was insufficient young growth to replace the lost trees, and hence a lack of wood as a raw material. Faced with a serious wood shortage, people developed methods of planned forest management. By tending the forests and choosing particular species to cut and replant, foresters raised the yields considerably; they took great pains to ensure that the forests were not again subjected to overexploitation. These early methods of forestry were responsible for the vigorous woodlands, with their species diversity, that once characterized the central European landscape. But the steps taken later (see Chapter 12, Part One) to change the original forests into plantations of conifers amounted to a severe interference with the forest communities.

Let us consider now the "social" function of the woods, as it contributes to human mental and physical health. However strong the objections of ecologists and environmentalists to the conifer plantations may be, even this artificial forest is of great value to people in search of a change from everyday life. It has beneficial effects like those of deciduous or mixed forest, which cannot be overestimated. This social role of the forests is currently coming more and more into the foreground; they are still used for timber, but in many places this function has become secondary. The benefit of time spent wandering in the woods cannot be expressed in numbers, but it is certain that the small cost of the enlightened approach to forestry that permits such public use is far outweighed by its contribution to the general welfare.

The amount and type of forest cover has a great deal to do with an area's acceptability or unsuitability for recreation. The accessibility of woodland is a much more important criterion of recreational value than the species of trees it contains, even though from an ecological point of view the scale of values would be different. People using woods for recreation show a clear preference for the marginal region between open country and the interior of the woods, and foresters in charge of such woodland must take this into account. Where there are large uninterrupted expanses of forest the local clear-cutting and intermingling of different kinds of communities done by the foresters provides for extra boundary regions. Clear-cut areas are especially important in flat terrain as a substitute for open fields, and even in the mountains they are useful look-out areas from which to view the surrounding landscape.

The traditional sub-alpine mountain landscape of forest, fields and meadows is currently undergoing profound changes, because former agricultural land is allowed to lie fallow. A significant fraction of this fallow land is being reforested. Such expansion of the forest is not in itself harmful, and its effect on water balance is actually beneficial. But it causes a marked reduction of variety in the landscape. As long as reforestation is done not only with a view toward obtaining a profit from the trees, but also follows a plan that takes into account the need for ecologically desirable species, the conversion of fallow land to woodland need not cause an impoverishment of the landscape as a whole.

As far as water balance is concerned, forest land is of prime significance everywhere on earth. This is evident wherever forests have been destroyed without planned reforestation. The decline of the highly developed cultures on the Euphrates and Tigris and in the Mediterranean countries in classical antiquity is partially ascribable to a shortage of water; the destruction of the forests as well as floods resulted in erosion of the topsoil and consequent undermining of the basic food supply. At present many such countries are reforesting their leached-out, barren mountainsides. In central Europe, thanks to the temperate climate and the early development of forestry, the damage did not reach such dimensions.

Forests act to retain water, despite their own large consumption of water via transpiration, because they control the runoff and percolation of rain and melted snow. The roots of the trees open up passages deep into the ground; the storage spaces they create are preserved, since no plow tears through this soil. Precipitation collects in these cavities and slowly percolates through the soil, eventually to return to the light of day in springs. The quality of water from forested regions is excellent; it is very pure, since fertilizers and pesticides are rarely used in forestry.

Atmospheric hygiene

The quality of the air we breathe is also strongly affected by woodland, not only the large forests but the strips and clumps of trees in agricultural areas as well. Since the air masses over large forests heat up less than those over cultivated fields and built-up regions, there can be at least a slight circulation of the air masses between the different types of terrain even on windless days. The groups of trees among fields break up the open terrain and thus also enhance the movement of air near the ground.

Near human habitations, forests are extremely valuable, especially in densely populated areas. In building cities and planning for the surrounding regions care should be taken to provide recreational forests which people can reach either on foot or by public transport. Forests accessible only by private car are less desirable for a number of reasons. The forest provides a bit of open space where a person can feel very close to nature. Only when such open spaces are provided can densely populated towns and cities be a healthy habitat. It is ideal if strips of forest can reach into the city center or are continued within the city limits as parks and gardens.

Expansion—or preservation?

The conversion of mixed woodland to conifer plantations is not the only danger currently facing the forests. Many planners and politicians regard them primarily as land held in reserve for the expansion of towns and industries. Since in many places forest land is in the public domain, it can be had cheaply for such purposes. The income from timber is often lower than the cost of maintaining the forests, and the social benefits are difficult to assess in financial terms. But since the significance of forests to the human habitat has become so well established, and since their effects on the physical and mental well-being of mankind are so obvious, there ought really to be no more clearing of woodland in the vicinity of cities.

Nevertheless, since the beginning of this century the forests have gradually succumbed to human interference; they have been pushed further and further back by the centers of population, and new highways slice through those that survive. And this attrition continues, although it violates our own best interests. Even with minimal consideration of the long-term consequences city planning must now include the preservation and protection of our forests.

3   The Threat to the Inland Waters

The term "inland waters" (see Chaper 18, Part One) includes both the ground water and all the bodies of fresh water on the surface of the earth—springs, brooks, rivers, lakes, ponds, and swamps. There are many sorts of reciprocal relationships among the beds of streams (or the bottoms of lakes), the water itself with all its physical and chemical properties, and the communities living in both habitats. These interactions also involve the immediate surroundings, the plants and animals on the banks and the shores.

By D. König

The danger to these inland waters lies in the changes man has brought about in defiance of nature. To understand their implications, we must first consider what the inland waters are like as natural features of the landscape, in an ecologically "healthy" state. The condition, appearance and composition of a body of water is determined by several factors. The characteristics of the terrain in which it is located determine, for example, the shape of a lake or the course and gradient of a stream. The altitude has an effect upon the water temperature. Depending upon whether the substrate is solid rock, loose sand, clay or peat, the water will modify its banks or shores in various ways. The most important climatic factors are temperature, rainfall and humidity. The number of organisms present is determined by the substrate—whether it is soil formed by weathering of rock rich in nutrients, sand and stone poor in nutrients and lime, or moor, bog or fen soil with an abundance of humus. In standing waters such factors are revealed by the clarity or turbidity of the water. Moreover, a body of water does not remain unchanged for long periods, but can become altered in a great many ways.

"Healthy" lakes and streams

When we try to picture an ecologically sound body of water, we think first that it must be well lighted and contain an abundance of oxygen, more than is needed for the chemical and metabolic processes taking place within it. Natural bodies of water can, at least temporarily, depart widely from the optimum, even if they are quite untouched by man. A brook in the high mountains, inhabited by insect larvae, can be transiently unin-

▷
Upper left: Trash washed up on the bank of the Rhine.
Upper right: Water plants and algae on a eutrophic pond.
Lower left: Garbage swept along by the Sieg (near Herchen) after a period of high water.
Lower right: The shore of the island Reichenau in Lake Constance.

habitable if avalanches cover it so deeply that for months it flows in complete darkness under the pile of snow and debris. When the snow melts, or there is heavy rainfall, whole stream communities can be swept away. There are also bodies of water in which conditions are usually on the borderline for survival of certain organisms. Only a few specially adapted organisms can exist in the waters of caves. Hot springs are well outside the ordinary range of habitats, but some organisms live even there. Certain blue-green algae can endure water temperatures up to 70°C, and flagellates, ciliates and amoebas have been found in water at a temperature of 57–58°C.

The combination of oxygen imbalance and pollution leads to putrefaction of the water, as organic matter is broken down under partially or completely anaerobic conditions. Even this situation can occur naturally; in parts of many bodies of water the oxygen concentration is occasionally or chronically so low that only specially adapted organisms can survive. The decay of plants and animals on a muddy bottom consumes oxygen at a high rate; even in quite shallow waters this process can cause the formation of hydrogen sulfide. In brackish waters there is then an overdevelopment of green algae (*Enteromorpha intestinalis*) and *Vaucheria*. Sulfur bacteria can also develop on masses of sedge and reed leaves that sink into the water, even when no sewage is present.

In boggy ditches, particularly during cold spells in early spring, one may find a rusty brown slime of iron bacteria; they crowd out animals that ordinarily live in the ditches draining meadows, such as water beetles, insect larvae and small fish. Even drastic chemical imbalances can occur locally under natural conditions. For example, if a deer dies in a woodland pond from which no stream flows, its decay affects the chemical composition of the whole pond unless carrion-eating organisms get rid of the body very quickly. The pond falls into an oxygen-depleted state just as a brook does when the liquid from a manure pit is dumped into it.

Massive overproduction, or "blooms," of plant microorganisms also occur in lakes unaffected by man, especially in the tropics. Another example is the well-known Lake Nakuru in Kenya, with its turbid water, the black, salt-encrusted sludge on its shores, and its vast flocks of birds. Here it is evident how great the productivity and rate of food consumption can be in such a body of water. Cautious estimates indicate that in this lake, with an area of 3700 hectares, the total weight of the birds feeding on plankton and small animals (chiefly the lesser flamingo) is about a million kilograms and that of the fish-eaters (predominantly pelicans, cormorants, anhingas and herons), about 4000 kilograms. Nevertheless, food is always available for all these birds. In a number of such cases of natural, untouched waters, ecosystems have developed in conditions which in central Europe would be considered disastrous. The ecological balance of European waters can of course also be endangered by natural phenomena, but these are limited in extent and duration.

By contrast, the danger presented by man's activities far exceeds that

Upper left: Pollution of a small brook near Alost (Belgium) by refuse from a chicken slaughterhouse.
Upper right: Pollution of the Rhine near Düsseldorf by the influx of industrial wastes.
Lower left: Ground contaminated by deposits of sludge from a sewage plant.
Lower right: Pollution of the Rio Tinto (Spain) by wastes from an iron-ore mine.

of any natural disaster. These are already having direct and in some cases serious effects on human life itself. And the threat is increasing, as we persist in our traditional attitudes toward natural events and the natural resources that support our existence. During the last centuries man has caused a marked change in many inland waters. Even the ground water is at risk. A supply of ground water can be drawn upon so heavily that it is exhausted, unless care is taken to replenish it. Where the water table is near the surface, lowering it may harm the plants growing above. There are many pollutants which can enter the ground water—for example, petroleum wastes (Fig. 3-2) presents a constantly increasing danger to this subterranean water supply.

Some shallow lakes have been drained dry, and others are about to meet the same fate. On the other hand, man has created new lakes in many places, damming rivers to form reservoirs for irrigation and drinking water and, above all, to generate electricity. The immediate consequences and chain reactions that can result are illustrated by the Brokopondo Reservoir in Surinam (South America), built specifically to supply energy to the aluminum industry. To make room for it, 5000 natives of the area had to be resettled. About 9700 animals (turtles, deer, monkeys and guinea pigs) were saved by special precautions, but many drowned. The trees and shrubs submerged under the rising water decayed and caused a severe drop in its oxygen content. Soon the water was carpeted by masses of water hyacinth (*Eichhornia*), which occupied more than 52% of the surface of the lake and housed great hordes of mosquito larvae. The destruction of these larvae by insecticides has left poisons in the water, the effects of which cannot yet be predicted.

In Germany there has been particular emphasis on straightening and otherwise reshaping many small and large waterways—in the case of the rivers primarily as an aid to shipping and the generation of electricity, and in the smaller streams for the sake of making agriculture easier and increasing the harvests. When the course of a stream is straightened, it becomes shorter; the meandering of the rivers, which is a property of natural flowing waters, is prevented. The intention is to eliminate several processes: the washing away and building up of different sections of the banks; the more or less rapid displacements of deep and shallow places and of sand and gravel banks; and finally the floods which often occur in certain regions when the river must carry more water than usual.

But since the resultant course of the river is usually about one third shorter, the gradient must be steeper and the eroding force of the river greater. Because of some remaining curvature and various instabilities, the river continues to scrape away at some parts of its bed more than others, under natural conditions this process results mainly in erosion of the banks, but in the straightened waterway larger hollows are excavated in the bottom. The materials carried away by the water are deposited, even in a straightened river, at sites where the gradient is less steep—and often

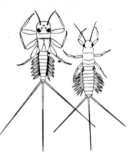

Fig. 3-1. Larvae of May-flies from clean, well-oxygenated brooks: left, *Heptagenia*; right, *Paraleptophlebia*.

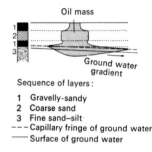

Oil mass

Ground water gradient

Sequence of layers:
1   Gravelly-sandy
2   Coarse sand
3   Fine sand–silt
- - - Capillary fringe of ground water
——— Surface of ground water

Fig. 3-2. Pollution of ground water by mineral oil. The oil penetrates the ground to depths which depend on local conditions. As it flows, ground water carries oil along with it.

where such deposits are undesirable. To prevent lateral erosion, the banks are slanted at a calculated angle and stabilized as well as possible. To avoid erosion of the bottom and control the current, piers and dams are constructed. Thus the river is divided into sections with sharp boundaries. Basins are created in which the current flows quietly, without the agitation and mixing of the water which is an important factor in natural streams. At each dam, on the other hand, there is a violent waterfall which, though it does greatly raise the oxygen concentration in the water, is detrimental to life in most other respects.

Examples of rivers divided into distinct levels by dams are the Main and the Mosel. In the canalization of the Mosel, which was done after the last war to assist shipping and create power plants, fourteen dams were built. The project was carefully planned and, at considerable extra expense, structural measures were adopted to meet all the essential criteria with respect to the towns along the river, local drainage problems, retention of muddy suspensions from the Saarland, the highway system and preservation of the landscape. But the unique character of the Mosel was lost (see Color plate, p. 577).

In the many brooks with "controlled" courses found throughout central Europe, the alterations described here—straightening, shaping and stabilizing of the banks, and damming—were carried out similarly. In Schleswig-Holstein over 90% of all the brooks were modified in this way. Since the changes were made chiefly for the sake of agriculture, the brook beds were set well below the surface of the ground, usually one to one and a half meters, so as to drain the adjacent fields. The consequences here were like those following the subdivision of the rivers. The upstream migrations of fish in the spawning season were made more difficult or even impossible; the dispersal of amphipods and other brook dwellers is also prevented. This effect is less pronounced in the case of species that live in the water only as larvae, and when sexually mature can reach other sections of the brook by flying or moving overland, and lay their eggs there—as long as the conditions in those parts of the brook are appropriate.

But other animals that choose their habitat mainly on the basis of the current itself often fail to find the necessary conditions in the "improved" streams. In a completely controlled brook the only choice is between a steady weak current and the downward plunge of the water at the dam. Among the species thus deprived of a habitat is the caddis fly *Neureclipsis*; the net its larva uses to filter food from the water is held open only by the current. It collapses limply when the current is too weak, and in the regions just downstream from a waterfall it would be torn to shreds.

Each section of a controlled brook has a uniform depth, increasing gradually toward the dam. If this depth is about 50–75 cm, and if the water is brown and turbid because of soil suspensions or sewage, the light

Fig. 3-3. Examples of organisms that can live even in poorly oxygenated, contaminated water. Above, the flagellate *Euglena*, identifiable by the spindle-shaped body with a flagellum at the anterior end, numerous green chlorophyll-containing plastids in the cytoplasm, a red eyespot (black dot in the drawing) and a pulsating vacuole near the hind end. Often masses of them can be seen as a green tint in pools of liquid manure.—Below, a group of *Euglena*, showing how much they can change their shapes and the way they normally crowd around a particle of refuse.—Right, the red larva of the midge *Chironomus*.

0.1 mm   1 mm

intensity at its bed is so low that none of the higher water plants can grow there. If in addition the inclined banks are stabilized with mats woven of strips of wood, as is currently very common, only a few scattered plants can become established even there. There is thus an accumulation of anti-biological properties in controlled brooks: the absence of places for animals to settle or hide; the lack of plants to serve as food; unfavorable changes in the stream bed because of the uniform deposition of fine sediments, which if sewage is discharged into the stream can even be a decaying sludge of dead fungi and the like; a lack of oxygen as a result of insufficient agitation of the water; the resultant absence of photosynthesizing organisms; and the high rate of oxygen consumption in the decaying sludge. The mud coating the stream bed impedes the percolation of water, so that the ground water is replenished hardly at all by leakage from the stream.

Thus a brook which once, perhaps, had the character of a trout stream, loses all its distinctive traits and all its ability to support life. As long as the water is not polluted, masses of amphipods and other animals can collect on the occasional plants that hang into the water as they would in a natural brook bed; but they must all crowd into the few such suitable places that remain. The greater part of such artificial streams is devoid of animal life. But from a limnological point of view it is even worse if the bottom is lined with cement or the water is conducted through kilometers of underground pipes. Cut off from light and air, a stream is of no use whatever as a habitat.

The danger to the inland waters of which the public is now most aware is the steady increase, practically everywhere in the world, of pollution. Pollution in the broadest sense includes all departures from a state appropriate to local conditions, whether physical or chemical in nature. It can amount to frequent or permanent clouding of the water, increase in temperature, the presence of mud with components (such as coaldust) inimical to life, and organic matter that decays—thus extracting oxygen from the water and in many cases even producing hydrogen sulfide and other toxic substances. Other pollutants are household sewage, wastes from food processing plants, water drained from agricultural land, petroleum derivatives, and poisonous compounds such as cyanide, heavy-metal salts, acids, lye, chlorine and fluorine—not to mention contamination by herbicides, pesticides and radioactive materials (see Color plates, pp. 568 and 577).

On top of all this, water is being contaminated by garbage, which some people persist in dumping anywhere in the countryside despite all the warnings against and penalties for such behavior. Even community garbage dumps, regulated in certain respects, often present a danger because they are improperly located.

Sewage used to be poured into lakes and streams with no prior processing at all, except for that fraction that was used to fertilize fields.

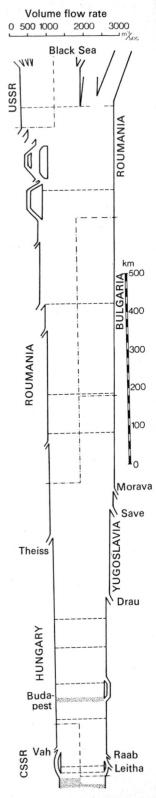

Volume flow rate

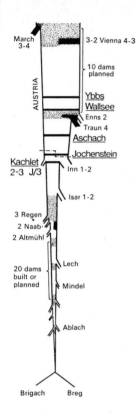

March
3-4

3-2 Vienna 4-3

10 dams
planned

Ybbs
Wallsee

Enns 2

Traun 4

Aschach

Jochenstein

AUSTRIA

Kachlet
2-3 J/3

Inn 1-2

Isar 1-2

3 Regen

2 Naab

2 Altmühl

20 dams
built or
planned

Lech

Mindel

Ablach

Brigach   Breg

---- National border
----- Planned dam
▬▬ Dam (name underlined)
☐ Pollution level 2
▒ Pollution level ~ 3
■ Pollution level ~ 4
Numbers by } = Pollution level
the names }   of water

Fig. 3-4. Man-made
changes in the Danube,
as it passes through eight
countries. In the lower
reaches (opposite page)
the changes due to dams
(46 now built or planned)
are emphasized. The
diagram above indicates
the centers of pollution by
domestic and industrial
sewage, concentrated in
the most densely populated
and heavily industrialized
upper reaches.

Even in those times this practice gave rise to severe local pollution here
and there. Such difficulties are known to have occurred in brooks which
were used as early as the 16th Century to carry away wastes from tanneries
and textile factories. Of course, the industries of a hundred to a hundred
and fifty years ago hardly produced wastes as harmful as those of today.
But even a hundred years ago certain sections of rivers—for example, the
lower Main in West Germany and the lower Thames—in England were
carrying a very heavy load of industrial wastes. Because of the smaller
population, the simpler way of life, and the lack of flush toilets, the amount
of sewage were not so great as to cause serious problems.

To gain some idea of the amounts of pollutants currently produced
in an industrialized country, let us refer to the situation in western Europe
or the U.S. The average daily amount of waste in the sewage produced
by one individual (including his share in all the necessary public utilities)
is customarily expressed by the related "biochemical oxygen demand."
Experience has shown that the sewage bacteria chiefly responsible for the
biological decomposition of this daily quantity of organic matter consume
from about fifty-four to ninety grams of oxygen during the first five
days—at the end of which most of the carbon compounds in the sewage
have been decomposed. According to a survey by Böhnke in 1971,
household sewage in West Germany accounts for 60 million of these
"individual units"; the wastes from industries of all sorts would correspond to a population of 50 million, and those from the animals kept on
farms and for other business purposes would correspond to a human
population of 300 million. Altogether, this amounts to 410 million units
or equivalent population, per day—every day of the year. For comparison,
U.S. waste generation would amount to more than 700 million similar
units. To this is added, in the last quarter of the year, wastes from the
sugar factories (80 million units) and liquids lost in the preparation of
fermented fodder for agricultural use (also 80 million units), which occurs
mainly in September and October. In these two months, then, the amount
of wastes produced in West Germany reaches a peak; it corresponds to
570 million units per day.

Different regions vary in the rate of sewage production. The amount
of household sewage is of course in direct proportion to the distribution
of the population. Other forms of sewage are localized to certain regions,
such as industrial developments, where their rates of production are
characteristically high. High concentrations of wastes occur often in the
drainage waters from fields and farms, but they enter the general water
system in occasional spurts rather than at a steady rate.

If nothing were done to prevent it, most of these water-borne wastes
would find their way into natural bodies of water by one route or another.
Usually they would be distributed far beyond their sites of origin, becoming to some extent diluted and in part decomposed by natural processes. Nevertheless, they could have injurious effects.

The manner in which sewage affects a small brook can be illustrated with the example of a dairy farm producing 2.4 million gallons (9 million kilograms) of milk annually. Of this, 1.6 million gallons (6 million kilograms) are made into cheese and 60,000 gallons (220,000 kilograms) into butter; 10,000 gallons (38,000 kilograms) are used as drinking milk. The waste matter in the sewage from this farm during the winter half-year amounts to 650, and in the summer to 930, of the above equivalent population (individual) units. It consists primarily of milky washing and rinsing water, but also contains detergents and other cleaners and probably whey from time to time. It had been hoped that the waste water could be cleaned in a pond on the premises, but this hope was ill-founded. The fermentation of organic substances (predominantly lactose and protein) in summer causes a coating of floating gray slime to form on the surface of the pond; it is so thick that birds can walk about on it catching the large numbers of alder flies there—the fly larvae thrive in this mass. The liquid flowing away from the pond is always turbid, with a milky color.

Quantitative aspects of pollution

Not until it has flowed for ten kilometers and been mixed with clean brook water does the organic matter in this water become decomposed to such an extent that amphipods, caddis-fly larvae and other animals typical of well-oxygenated water can live in the stream. Moreover, the appearance of this brook changes with the seasons. Sewage fungi develop primarily in the cool months; then their furry colonies cover the whole bed of the brook. In summer these disappear, and the stream is free for other organisms. At this time of year the water is inhabited by the nine-spined stickleback (*Pungitius pungitius*), which lives in the adjacent unpolluted bog waters; fish species that require more oxygen, such as roach, juvenile pike and eels, which under other circumstances also belong in a brook of this sort, are never found in this one.

As examples of the pollution conditions in large European rivers, we include diagrams for the Rhine (Fig. 3-5) and the Danube (Fig. 3-4). In the latter figure the volume-flow rate at the mouth is also indicated. It is clear that the input of pollutants to the Danube is concentrated particularly in the densely populated upper reaches. In the case of the Rhine, there is an additional steady input of salt along its entire course, carried by tributaries from the alkali regions of France. The situation is similar in the Werra and Weser Rivers, where the salts come from the Thuringian alkali soils. At its junction with the Weser, the Werra has a chloride content up to more than six grams per liter, almost the same salinity as the Baltic Sea.

The pollution of large rivers

It very often happens that an indirect contamination of lake water produces a set of phenomena like that mentioned above in connection with Lake Nakuru of Kenya. This overfertilization of the water called "eutrophication," (though "hypertrophication" would be better) results from an oversupply of nutrients, especially phosphate and nitrogen, from

Eutrophication

sewage, cleaning compounds and the like. The first effect is an unnaturally rapid multiplication of the microscopic algae, especially blue-green algae of the genera *Microcystis*, *Aphanizomenon*, and *Oscillatoria*, which then die off in masses. This is followed by a multiplication of bacteria, which decompose the dead algae and in the process use up the oxygen in the water. Finally the bottom is covered with decaying ooze, which gives off methane and hydrogen sulfide (see Color plate, p. 567).

So-called "blooms" of blue-green algae are at the very least annoying to man—who has himself caused them—in that they make the water unhygienic for swimming and fill the air with unpleasant smells. In some cases there may even be a danger of poisoning, by substances produced by the algal metabolism. To make such water useful for industry, agriculture, or drinking water is either difficult and expensive or actually impossible. Problems of this sort occur on a large scale in the delta region of Holland, where the people are very dependent on surface water, and there are similar difficulties developing in most of the lakes of central Europe; the same problem arises wherever valleys are dammed up to provide sources of drinking water, as is done in West Germany.

The steps to be taken

In the long run it would be disastrous for nature, as well as for mankind, if this thoughtless interference with the waters were to continue. And it is becoming harder and harder to control the situation, as people grow steadily more intent upon having all the modern "conveniences." Herein lies the chief source of the difficulty. In order to take countermeasures, people must know the cause and effects of the evil they face. To this end, the relevant research programs must be intensified, for we are still far from understanding all the implications even of the present situation, and new problems are constantly arising. Research can help us to work out methods of rescuing polluted waters as well as avoiding further damage. If this is to be achieved, we must have information about the relationships between type and amount of a given pollutant, the conditions under which it is decomposed, the possibilities for its oxidation, the amount of oxygen consumed during its decomposition, and so on.

Methods and goals in sewage treatment

Once such factors have been measured and evaluated statistically, it is up to technology to design the installations that are required. These include, for example, the least harmful forms of canalization and other engineering of bodies of water, the shape and size of the containers and the ventilation arrangements in treatment plants, and similar considerations. The technology of dealing with waste water has become an important branch of today's economy. In the years following the last World War, the cities and many rural communities of central Europe were equipped with sewage-treatment plants; in the simplest case these were simply basins in which the heavy particulate contents of the water could settle out. Now there is an increasing tendency to add biological cleaning installations, in which the dissolved organic substances are consumed and decomposed by microorganisms, primarily bacteria. Here an effort is made to provide the microscopic decomposers with the best possible environment, so that they can multiply at a great rate and do their job of cleaning most efficiently.

In the various parts of a biological treatment facility, quite characteristic microcommunities develop. For example, in the liquid phase one finds predominantly bacteria, flagellates, ciliates, annelids, nematodes and larvae of the moth-fly *Psychoda*; the higher of these forms feed in part upon the lower forms. On the other hand, small blue-green, green and siliceous algae settle on the well-lighted surface of the sediment. In the pool where sediment and water are kept in constant motion by pumping in air, small clumps of inorganic materials and bacteria form; ciliates such as the sessile, stalked *Vorticella* attach to these and feed upon them. It is quite astonishing that these animals can exist here. Under a microscope they contract cell body and stalk at the slightest vibration, but in the vigorously churning water of the clarification pool, comparable in motion to a river just beneath a waterfall, they survive and even reproduce.

Chemical precipitation methods are still used where required in sewage treatment—now particularly to rid the cleaned water of phosphates; even after all the publicity against their use in detergents, these are still too abundant. Finally, there are a number of ways to kill the germs in sewage. Effective treatment plants of all sizes have been designed, from small installations for isolated groups of houses to gigantic ones for the major metropolitan centers. A special problem in the modern approach is to keep the sewage entirely away from certain areas. For example, in an industrialized region through which streams flow, all the waste water is kept separate and collected at a suitable spot for cleaning. To protect a lake, the sewage from all the shore communities is piped around it, to a treatment plant downstream from the lake. Installations combining mechanical, biological and chemical stages are the most common; to a great extent these determine the condition of the network of waterways in the surrounding countryside.

In future it will be necessary to go beyond the installation of sewage-treatment plants and find suitable methods of keeping natural bodies of water in good condition by treating them directly. The particularly vulnerable lakes, a majority of which in today's developed countries have a profundal zone without oxygen, and decaying sediment on the bottom, can be sanitized either by scooping out the sediment or by covering it over with a claylike mineral layer. Supplementary methods might include artificial aeration, feeding in water from a clean brook, draining off the spoiled deep water, piping away the sewage from the lakeside communities, and if necessary sacrificing an isolated part of the lake for the sake of the remainder, as has been considered in the case of Lake Erie.

In conclusion, the role of the administration (in the broadest sense)

▷
Upper left: One of the dam and lock installations on the Mosel (Lehmen/ Kreis Mayen). Canalization of the Mosel for international ship traffic greatly changed the natural habitats of this river and did considerable harm to the former animal and plant communities.
Upper right: Pollution of the Rhine by wastes from the chemical industry. Because of the countless waste inflows, this river— once famous for its salmon and sturgeon—has become the "giant sewer of Europe."
Below: The North-Baltic Canal, a technical feat which benefits shipping to the detriment of the water cycle: following the construction of this canal, the water table in the surroundings fell by twenty meters.

The "catchment areas" of treatment plants

The cleaning of natural waters

◁

Upper left: A colony of sea lions (*Otaria byronia*) on the Valdés Peninsula (Argentina).
Upper right: The aftermath of the slaughter: skins of sea lions and elephant seals (*Mirounga leonina*) on the Argentina coast.
Center: The Masai breed cattle in the steppe and savanna regions on the edges of the eastern African national parks for traditional reasons of social standing; they are not aware of the consequences of overgrazing, which will affect even their own descendants.
Lower left: A Papuan in the New Guinea highland with the traditional brideprice; it consists of skins of Raggi's greater bird of paradise (*Paradisaea apoda raggiana*), the tail feathers of *Astrapia*, and the redblack wing feathers of the vulturine parrot (*Psittrichas fulgidus*).
Lower right: To dance for the tourists, today's Papuans decorate themselves lavishly with feathers. Here they display feathers of *Astrapia stephaniae*, King of Saxony's bird of paradise (*Pteridophora alberti*), and the lesser bird of paradise (*Paradisaea minor*). These species are increasingly endangered by this practice (see Chapter 4).

Biological management of water and forest, by W. Klausewitz

must be mentioned. This includes the formulation and enactment of legislation in the areas of water management, public health, conservation, municipal and rural planning, and even international law. Most developed countries today have laws directed toward problems of water management and protection, as well as professional advisory services and organizations of interested citizens. All these were first instituted in the industrial regions, which were hit hardest by the waste-disposal emergency. In these places it is impossible to reestablish natural, healthy conditions, but it is still possible to save their inhabitants from outright disaster. Besides the insight and attitudes of individuals, cost is of course a decisive factor. A few figures based on the situation in the United States are illustrative. Of 18,000 American towns and cities, only about 9000 so far have sewage systems with adequate treatment plants. About 7000 have sewage systems with only primary settling facilities, and as far as the local waters are concerned this may be worse than if there were no community sewers at all. In contrast, only about 20% of Germany's 24,000 communities have any kind of sewage treatment, and the sewer and plant construction required to bring German systems to adequacy by the year 2000 would cost—on the basis of today's prices—about 150 billion marks (about $65 billion).

Comparison with other public expenses on a per capita basis reveals that in the United States $1.50 is spent per unit time for water and sewage management for every $1.00 spent on scientific research and $1.75 on education. All of these, certainly, are major expenditures. Industry itself spends large sums of money to clean its often very harmful wastes; but this does not necessarily imply that they are sufficient to keep natural bodies of waters in even a moderately healthy state. After comparing the waste-water statistics of 1957 and 1963, the West German government in 1968 came to the pessimistic conclusion that the efforts made up to that point had not yet had "any visible success with respect to the condition of the natural bodies of water." Except for certain isolated cases cases of improvement, pollution had actually increased. In some other comparable countries the situation is no better, but in certain nations improvements have been made.

In the final analysis it will simply be necessary for every individual in prosperous countries to control his urge to have more comfort and convenience, otherwise healthy life on this planet may gradually disappear. For despite all available efforts, the natural bodies of water will be destroyed, and mankind will have lost an important and irreplaceable part of his surroundings.

One and a half billion cubic kilometers of water are in more or less close contact with the surface of the earth, as sea water in the oceans, as ice in the polar caps and glaciers, as fresh water in rivers, lakes and other surface waters, as ground water and as water vapor in the atmosphere. But less than one percent of this enormous quantity is involved, through precipitation and evaporation, in the continual circulation of water in the biosphere.

Every day more than a thousand cubic kilometers of water fall onto the surface of the globe as rain. The same amount evaporates into the atmosphere. Around 85% of this evaporates from the ocean surface, while the remaining 15% comes from the ground, the plants, and the surface of the inland waters. 75% of the precipitation falls directly back into the ocean, and 25% reaches the land. The difference between evaporation from and precipitation onto the land is made up by the rain clouds moving over the land from the ocean. 70% of the precipitation onto the land is given back to the atmosphere by evaporation. The remaining 30% flows back to the sea in rivulets, brooks, and rivers or percolates into the ground.

In the top layers of the ground a considerable fraction of the water provides the plants with moisture. The rest continues to percolate downward, eventually collecting as ground water above an impermeable layer of rock. While the water near the surface has a direct biological effect everywhere, the ground water is important to plants only where the roots reach below the water table. If the water table is lowered very much, the composition of the local plant community undergoes a marked change; for example, within a few years bog vegetation can be transformed into a steppe community.

Every raindrop ultimately finds its way back to the ocean or the atmosphere, but the length of the path and the time taken to travel it can vary within wide limits. If a raindrop falls on a vigorous mixed forest with many strata of plants, it eventually infiltrates a loose, nutrient-rich soil and may stay there for years. The plants are of course constantly taking water from the ground and transpiring it at the surfaces of the leaves, but much moisture is bound to the soil particles. Moreover, the thick cushions of moss growing on the forest floor, which suck up water like sponges and only very slowly give it up again to their surroundings, are important stores of water.

In addition, the leafy canopy of the forest protects the ground from the drying effect of the sunlight and of moving air; this "shield" within the forest ensures that the local microclimate is humid. Below such a mixed forest the water table is usually rather high, since there is only a small amount of surface runoff and a relatively large proportion of the rain percolates down to the ground water. Large natural forests are so effective in modifying the climate that, because of the relatively high humidity in the air above them, the precipitation is distinctly greater there than on an equal area of cultivated or built-up land; there is rarely a real water shortage in such a forest. Even in midsummer the soil and air of the forests are damp and rather cool.

Of course, only a stratified, mixed forest with luxuriant undergrowth has such a beneficial effect on water balance; a stand of one kind of

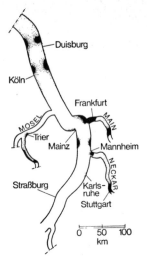

Fig. 3-5. Centers of pollution of the Rhine and its tributaries. Black: most concentrated pollution; dotted, less concentrated.

conifer is much less effective in this respect. In a coniferous forest not only the crowns of the trees, but their roots as well, spread out in single, fairly shallow layers, whereas in a mixed forest the space is filled with a dense network comprising several layers. Fallen needles cover the ground with a raw humus on which neither leafy plants nor mossy cushions can grow. For these reasons, coniferous forests hold water considerably less effectively, the surface runoff is relatively large, and the humidity is lowered; the soil tends to dry out faster and the local precipitation may be less.

As has already been mentioned (Chapter 12, Part One), a recent tendency in Germany has been to emphasize profitable timber plantations of fast-growing conifers. These collections of trees, arranged with military precision in rows and columns so that the term "forest" hardly applies to them, are devoid of undergrowth. In some places neatness used to be carried so far that the ground was swept or raked clean of all litter. That such woodland not only is extraordinarily unfavorable for water retention, but also has such an impoverished fauna that certain pests can develop to plague proportions, is a reasonable inference to anyone capable of biological or ecological thinking. The only solution, from the point of view of overall biological relationships, is a return to the mixed forests. Even though this realization has become widely accepted, it has still not been put into pratice generally.

As an historical development, the introduction of timber plantations of rapidly growing tree species (spruce in particular) is entirely understandable, as was the hurried reforestation of large logged-over areas after the last war—for example, in the Black Forest. But one wonders why those responsible for forestry, from the Ministries downward, still persist in this program by ensuring that cleared forest land is planted again with stands of spruce or, worse, that the deciduous trees in some of the remaining mixed forest are killed by sprays and later replaced by conifers. The motives here are entirely those of short-term economy, concerned with the profit shown on the annual balance sheets; the fact that overall ecological balance is thereby disrupted is ignored now as it has always been ignored.

With respect to the water cycle, deforested areas where no trees are replanted and where the vegetation is sparse are still less favorable than the tree plantations. The rain is not caught by a canopy of leaves but strikes the ground directly. This loosens the uppermost part of the topsoil, especially during cloudbursts. If the plant cover is a meager growth of grasses or grain crops, it provides no protection against desiccation by sun and wind; there is no opportunity for a local microclimate with high humidity to develop. In the ground there is no close-packed network of roots to hold the soil together; the earth is not porous enough to soak up much moisture even during heavy rains. Part of the water that falls does percolate through the soil, but most of it usually stays on or near the surface and runs off in the form of little rivulets.

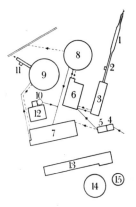

Fig. 3-6. Layout of a well-designed town sewage plant with mechanical and biological stages and an installation for phosphate precipitation and reduction. 1. Inflow with sand trap; 2. Device for measurement of inflow; 3. Mechanical cleaning of the town sewage; 4 and 5. Mechanical cleaning of dairy-farm sewage; 6. Air-agitated pool I; 7. Air-agitated pool II; 8. Secondary clearing pool I; 9. Secondary clearing pool II; 10. Mixing and storage containers for phosphate precipitation; 11. Drain into a brook, with volume-measuring device; 12. Plant office building; 13. Pump house; 14. Tower for decaying sludge; 15. Container for burnable gas released from sludge.—The arrows show the variable directions of flow of the sewage. Solid lines: combined treatment of water from town and farm. Dashed lines: separate treatment of the two inputs.

These small streams can easily carry away topsoil, especially if the land slopes. With every rain, a little of the nutrient-rich humus is lost, and the quality of the soil steadily declines. This erosion can be so pronounced. that naked rock is exposed and a barren, leached-out wasteland is formed Once the soil has been disrupted and washed away, there is no way for plant growth to turn the rock and stone that remains into new fertile soil. Altogether, there is a direct relationship between the plant community of a region and its water balance. The more dense the vegetation in an area and the more diverse its subdivisions, the greater is the retained water supply—despite the high rate of transpiration.

Only a few decades ago people thought quite differently. It was claimed that mixed or deciduous forests, because of their high transpiration rates, withdrew excessive amounts of water from the ground. It is known that a deciduous tree of normal size can transpire 200 liters of water per day, and under certain conditions twice as much. One hectare of spruce or beech forest in summer transpires as much as 50,000 liters of water a day, all of which has first been extracted from the soil. From this fact, the erroneus conclusion was drawn that a deforested region was more favorable to the general water balance, since it depleted the soil less than a forest would. This line of reasoning failed to take into account certain important facts: In a cleared area only a small fraction of the water coming to earth as precipitation is retained and stored; and a paucity of trees enhances erosion of the soil. Moreover, less precipitation falls. All things considered, the forest—or an equivalently dense, multilayered plant cover—is actually extremely effective in conserving water.

If the route of a raindrop on its way to the sea is shortened, the general water balance suffers in every case. Man can bring about such a shortening not only by interfering with the original plant cover, but by engineering changes in the natural surface-water system. As little as a century ago, Europe was significantly more moist than it is today. There were large bogs, swampy areas, and—to the sorrow of the farmers—countless "sour meadows" essentially useless for agriculture. The annual overflowing of the brooks and rivers often damaged the communities on their banks.

We have discussed earlier in this chapter the program of modifications that was followed. The intent was to drain the land so that it could be cultivated, to "improve" the sour meadows, to be able to build on land near the banks, to prevent flood damage in the villages and towns, and to make the larger waterways more readily navigable. Wet or swampy areas were drained by way of open ditches or systems of pipes. Brooks flowing through complicated bends and loops and supporting an abundant vegetation were canalized by straightening and stabilization of the banks, and similar procedures turned rivers into canals useful for shipping. These changes are still being made today, for financial reasons, although it has long since been evident that such manipulations of the watercourses in many cases bring not an improvement, but rather a deterioration, with respect to the general water balance and the total ecosystem.

When land is drained, the water table falls and the plant cover changes accordingly. Whereas earlier the soil became saturated with moisture when stream water levels were at their height and took months for the water to drain back to the ocean (years, in fact, for the part that returned via ground water). Now instead the rain water remains on the surface, runs off rapidly, and in the straightened, canalized brooks and rivers has little contact with the surrounding land or stream of ground water. Thus it requires only a few days to return to the sea.

The magnitude of these effects was emphasized as early as 1954 by Reinhard Demoll, who cited the classic mistake of the Rhine River example. In the Freisinger Plain north of Munich, West Germany, the water table fell from a depth of two meters in 1933 to eleven meters, following waterway modifications; down in the Wertach Plain south of Augsburg, Germany, it fell by ten meters, and somewhat further down, near Kembs, the fall was as great as twenty meters. In northern Germany the water table has also been lowered by twenty meters in some places—for example, in the regions of the North Baltic Canal and the Mittelland Canal—and in parts of the highly industrialized regions of Sachsen-Anhalt the depth of the water table has been changed from 1.5 meters to eighty!

The fact that such canalization does not pay in terms of the overall economy is demonstrated by its results in the case of the Danube River in Bavaria. There, too, the water table has clearly fallen; there are distinct signs that the dense woods that used to grow on damp soil along the river banks are beginning to give way to steppes. "The profit in the upper reaches, measured in millions," wrote Demoll, "is offset by a loss of billions in the plain." Although this was pointed out two decades ago, the Danube River continues to be controlled.

As populations grow and the water requirements of industry rise steadily, the consumption of drinking water is increasing at an alarming rate. The vital supply of potable water is provided in large part by ground water. But the stores of ground water are progressively decreasing as a result of forest clearing, draining large areas of land, and canalization of the surface waters. A good deal more of it is also being removed directly. The "High Plains" of Texas are becoming barren land as groundwater is rapidly exhausted. The supply is now far from adequate. In certain areas, it has already become necessary to fall back upon river or lake water contaminated by sewage for water supplies. Until recently about four million people have been drinking water from the Rhine River; soon it will be ten million. Some regions must now draw their drinking water from far away. For example, Los Angeles water now comes $400\pm$miles from northern California, Stuttgart, West Germany, is supplied by Lake Constance, more than a hundred kilometers ($70+$miles) away. Certain clever operators have now found an easy source of income, selling bottles of what is claimed to be (and may in fact be) spring water to city dwellers although it has been shown that, from some suppliers, this bottled water is by no means as sanitary as it should be.

The technologists concerned with the waterways in general believe that the building of reservoirs is the best solution both to the problem of floods and to that of replenishing the ground water. First a brook is straightened and the adjacent region drained; then it is interrupted by artificial lakes which permanently submerge large parts of the adjacent region. It is true that these reservoirs can in principle be practicable ways of raising the water table and keeping a steady influx to the ground water. Nevertheless, there are two serious reservations to be noted. A lake can stay in a healthy state, automatically cleaning its own water, only if it and the streams flowing into it are not loaded with industrial wastes and household sewage, and if artificial eutrophication—overfertilization and excess algal growth followed by the death of most of the organisms—is prevented. Neither of these is possible under current urban and rural conditions.

We have already pointed out that sewage water, even after it has passed through a treatment plant, very soon forms a layer of decaying sludge on the bottoms of lakes. This applies as well to artificial lakes and reservoirs. There the layer of sludge grows steadily deeper; the water sinking from the lake to replenish the ground water contains chemicals, substances that alter its taste, and in some cases even disease pathogens. Gradually the lake bottom becomes less permeable, as particles of sludge work their way into the pore system of the ground. The flow from the surface into the ground water slows and soon ceases altogether. When that happens, the reservoir has lost its essential function of supplying potable ground water.

All things considered, these much-praised reservoirs are by no means, at least as far as the ground water is concerned, a valid and equivalent substitute for the water stores that used to exist in the form of the large natural forests, the wet and sour meadows, bogs and swamps, and not least the natural lakes and streams. Reservoirs, especially in the mechanized and industrialized regions that make up much of Europe, are simply parts of an artificial environment, not real components of an ecosystem with its water cycle. These and many other such projects—even those claimed to be "environment-oriented"—cannot in the long run prevent extensive drying up of the land and large-scale changes of climate. The trend from lush countryside to arid steppe, which began more than a hundred years ago with man's thoughtless manipulations of land and water, has already had a much greater impact than most people suspect.

4 Animals in the Changed Environment

By Th. Schultze-
Westrum

Every animal and plant species has a right to exist on our earth. Each has earned its place by diverging from other species in the course of evolution, surviving as a biological entity in its particular environment, and becoming a member of a community and a component in an ecosystem. Communities are not static; since life began species have come and gone, and none can survive forever. When man appeared on the scene, a new destructive force was imposed upon this natural flux in the biosphere. At first the balance was maintained; man fit in as a part of the ecosystem he inhabited.

But this delicate structure began to crumble when the unprecedented dispersal and cultural development of man led to the creation of urban centers and to the predominance of technology. People that have stayed close to nature can "sense" even today what uses they can make of their environment, without overexploitation and its consequences. This sensitivity was acquired by primitive peoples gradually over long perods of time, and was passed on in the form of tradition. When the old order was dissolved their bonds with nature were broken as well; traditional wisdom was forgotten. At the same time, exploitation of the environment increased dramatically, both because of advances in methodology and because of the population growth described in Chapter One.

The ominous march of civilization

Today this fateful double effect accompanying the development of a high civilization—the loss of self-restraint in utilization of resources, which parallels the revolution of techniques—threatens our very existence. Utilization of the environment in highly-developed cultures has been equivalent to ruthless exploitation; the choice has appeared to be submission to, or battle against, the forces of nature, rather than integration into a natural system. We know now that certain peoples have destroyed themselves by such exploitation; their once blooming habitats degenerated into desert. With the procrastination characteristic of man when he must change his ways, our own culture is only now beginning gradually to take steps to preserve its environment. There is a growing tendency, however, to question the desirability of unrestricted technological progress. Research in the natural sciences is being directed toward finding methods to repair the damage that has been done, and to prevent further harm. A new awareness of the environment is finally beginning to develop.

To replace the lost self-control of the initial stages, which was followed by wanton despoiling of nature, there is gradually developing a considered, farsighted, scientifically based management of natural resources. But the alarm signals still point to the utmost danger; it is still a completely open question, whether we will really be able to take effective action at this stage—whether we will succeed in getting a grip on the reins again.

There are still places on earth where men and animals live side by side in harmony—in the regions of South America, Australia, Oceania and Africa inhabited by certain primitive tribes. Attempts have been made to explain this compatibility on the basis of the low human population density and the rather ineffectual weapons these people use in hunting. Such explanations fail to take into account that the people display a pronounced self-control in the ways they use their environment, as long as the net effect is to their own advantage. For example, the Motu, a Melanesian tribe on the south coast of New Guinea, made an annual collection of the eggs of sea birds on the offshore islands, for they were a valuable source of protein; but they never took more than 80% of the eggs, so that enough were left to maintain the bird population. When this tradition, which exemplified the bond between the tribe and their natural surroundings, was disrupted by contact with civilization, and people from other parts of the country settled in the territory of the Motu tribe, all the eggs were collected; as a result the bird colonies disappeared.

A second example: An Australian fisheries expert came to a coastal village of eastern New Guinea and tried to teach the people how to make and use a new type of large net. But the head man of the village did not want to have anything to do with it, and tried to drive the stranger away. He was afraid that these more effective nets would catch too many fish and that the stocks would be reduced to the point that no fish would be left for coming generations. A final example concerns the bird of paradise, a typical inhabitant of New Guinea. In the highlands there, and to a lesser extent in the lowlands, the most decorative feathers of the males of several species of bird of paradise are part of the traditional dance costume and are valued quite highly. The trees in which Raggi's greater bird of paradise (*Paradisaea apoda raggiana*) performed their court ship became the traditional property of certain clans. The people killed only the old males, which in a sense were "ripe for harvest." When the old social order came to an end, as a result of the importation of outside culture, this system of self-limitation also collapsed; firearms were brought in, and the country was pacified so that there was little risk of attack during hunting expeditions. Moreover, a modern monetary system was introduced, which meant that those who killed the most birds of paradise obtained the largest

Management of
natural resources

Examples of self-
regulation

▷
The jaguar (*Panthera onca*; upper left) and leopard (*Panthera pardus*; lower right), like almost all spotted cats, have been nearly doomed to extinction because of their fashionable fur. At the last minute, import restrictions have at least put a brake on the export of their pelts.
The preservation of the tiger (*Panthera tigris*; lower left) is one of the foremost concerns of the international conservation movement. Only in the Gir Forest of Indochina has a small residual population of the Persian lion (*Panthera leo persica*; upper right) been able to survive.

◁
Above, left to right:
Several species of the
monkey genus *Colobus*,
native to the mountain
and rain forests of Africa,
are endangered by fur-
hunters and logging; of
these, the Zanzibar form
C. badius kirkii has already
become very rare.

The criterion:
advantages to man

◁
The golden lion marmoset
(*Leontideus rosalia*) of the
southern Brazilian coastal
mountains is in extreme
danger because of trapping
and destruction of the
forests.
In the Philippines there
remain only about fifty
breeding pairs of the
monkey-eating eagle
(*Pithecophaga jefferyi*).
Center, left to right: To
save the very rare Arabian
oryx (*Oyrx gazella leucoryx*)
from certain extinction,
breeding groups have been
resettled in an open reserve
and in zoos. The vicuna
(*Lama vicugna*) is now
under international pro-
tection; its population in
the high Andes had declined to 2000 animals. All
marine turtles are faced
with annihilation if specific
steps are not taken to help
them.
Below: The large herds of
caribou will wander the
North American tundra
in future decades only if
conservation measures are
effective.

Political development
and the rise of
exploitation

share of the newly imported consumer goods. Finally, the gradual build-up of the tourist trade acted as an incentive to the hunting of birds of paradise; in the dances organized as "shows" the men are weighed down with decorations of feathers (see Color plate, p. 578). The result is that in the densely populated Chimbu region of the central highlands, where the males of this species of bird of paradise used to perform their courtship dances just outside the villages, Raggi's greater bird of paradise has now practically become extinct. A chain of dealers currently provides the area with birds from other parts of the country.

The tradition of self-control in using the environment can be observed only where advantages to man are associated with it. For example, the Papuans each year burn off broad expanses of land—in the course of chasing down kangaroos and cassowaries, to obtain clear land for gardens, or with no apparent reason whatsoever. The fact that populations of soil-dwelling small animals with limited ranges are endangered by this practice never occurs to the natives, for none of these animals has any practical importance to them. Other harm to the ecosystem—destruction of the original plant communities, erosion in the mountain terrain deforested by fires—also seems to have no significance for the human settlers. Evidently such damage is perceived so slowly that it never attains an important place in the system of cultural traditions; where visible deterioration has occurred, such as the change from lush woodland to steppe, no one realizes that it might be related to the burning that was done.

The situation is much the same among the African tribes of herdsmen —for example, the Masai—whose herds are allowed to grow as large as possible and cause corresponding overgrazing (see Color plate, p. 578). The damage is not perceived by the Masai themselves, within the time span an individual can comprehend; at least, they note nothing that they can associate with the activities of their herds. The Masai raise large herds not to provide meat but to increase their social standing. Such special cultural developments detrimental to the environment are also to be found in other countries, but they are rare at the primitive level of culture.

The uncontrolled depletion of natural resources did not increase until man created political systems. Examples of this effect at a relatively low level of political development were found in Hawaii, where certain small birds were killed in excessive numbers to produce feather cloaks for dignitaries; several species of honeycreepers (Drepanidae) and honeyeaters (Meliphagidae) were exterminated. In New Zealand the moas (family Dinornithidae), about nineteen species of which were distributed there, formed the basic food of the immigrating Moriori and later the Maori, who hunted these birds so intensively that the last remnants finally died out—though probably not until the 17th Century.

With the transition to more highly organized cultures, man has largely lost his awareness that natural resources are not capable of renewing themselves indefinitely. But this was not true everywhere. The peasant class in Europe retained much that had been learned by past generations of experience, until the end of the last century, when mechanization of agricultural methods won the day. It is true that the agrarian countryside in central Europe, as it was until the mid-1800's, no longer afforded a habitat for large animal species like the aurochs, wisent, wild horse, elk, brown bear, wolf and lynx, which depended on wilderness for survival, but the countryside was still in a biologically sound condition; as we now look back it seems to have been entirely suitable as a habitat for man, fully worthy of preservation. A natural wilderness is not an adequate environment for civilized humans, and must be modified if men are to live there. Our appreciation of pure wilderness as a monument to unadulterated nature could develop only after the wilderness had been driven back, so that it lost its threatening aspect.

Similarly, it has only become possible to truly regret the loss of elements of nature not directly useful to man once people had been released from their traditional bonds with nature. As a rule, the conscious elevation of landscape and animal as objects of value in themselves first arose among city-dwellers, and it was there that the conservation movement had its origins. Generations of farmers have shaped the countryside into something the best planners would never have been able to attain; but while this was going on, the farmers would have had little sympathy for our present way of viewing their achievement. The conservation movement was full of emotional overtones, aesthetically and culturally oriented; at that time no one thought of the sober, hard fact of potential self-destruction that now determines our approach to conservation.

Beginning of the conservation movement

Currently many countries are trying to place permanent conservation orders on their remnants of wilderness, with their abundance of animal species. But to actually preserve the few significant sections of virgin landscape that still remain on earth, they must win a race against time. It is still true that the people willing to act to protect nature are a minority group without power, in comparison to the representatives of resolute business and industrial concerns. Their success will depend on their ability to delay further disruption of our environment until realization of its significance to man has become so widespread that direct measures can be taken. This race is well under way, and every individual who enters on our side and takes an active part will bring victory that much closer.

Protection of the wilderness that remains

Preservation of nature for its own sake is the real goal, but little progress in this direction has occurred unless obvious advantages to people —particularly opportunities for recreation and education—were involved. Modern environmentalists gained widespread attention only when they were forced to defend the biological soundness of the human habitat and prevent exhaustion of food resources. Here the two points of view—preservation of nature for its own sake and for the sake of man— fuse in a way that also favors the protection of endangered animal species.

**Protection of
endangered species**

But the attempt to protect the animals is now encountering financial difficulties and a lack of personnel, so that the only practical approach is to work for the survival of a selected few of the endangered species. Since the scientific determination and classification of species is still far from complete, this enforced selectivity may mean that certain forms become extinct before we even find out that they existed. A study of the progress reports of the large international organizations for the protection of endangered animals will make clear just how severe these limitations have become.

The "Red Data Book" of the IUCN lists, for mammals and birds alone, no less than 600 endangered species and subspecies. Since the year 1600, an estimated 150 forms of mammals and 120 of birds have been exterminated. According to the data of N. Simon and P. Geroudet regarding the birds, prior to 1700 about ten species and subspecies disappeared, between 1700 and 1800 about twenty died out, another twenty were lost between 1800 and 1850, about fifty between 1850 and 1900, and about the same number since 1900. During the last hundred years, then, an average of one bird species or subspecies became extinct per year. The examples of exterminated species that are probably most familiar—the aurochs (*Bos primigenius*) in 1627, the dodo (*Raphus cucullatus*) and the Rodriguez solitaire (*Pezophaps solitaria*) in the 17th Century, Steller's sea cow (*Rhytina gigas*) around 1850, the quagga (*Equus quagga quagga*) in 1883, the passenger pigeon (*Ectopistes migratorius*) in 1907 and the Carolina parakeet (*Conuropus carolinensis*) at the beginning of the 20th Century—represent only a very small percentage of the species man has made extinct.

Total or local disappearance of a species can be brought about by both direct and indirect means. The event with the most serious consequences must surely have been the introduction of firearms. With modern guns available, the moderation traditionally practiced in hunting was broken down everywhere. A related factor has been the shift of the population beyond the age-old limits of their territories. Under the sway of colonial politics, settlers and hunters invaded countries where, with no traditional bonds to restrain them, they killed animals not only for food but for the pure "joy" of hunting and shooting. Competition with the previous inhabitants of the land also played a role; the animals used as food by the natives were sometimes killed in order to drive away or kill off the people themselves. The eradication of the bison in the North American prairies in the second half of the 19th Century proceeded concurrently with that of the Indians.

**Modern firearms
change the hunting
tradition**

In Europe certain animals were persecuted because they were "dangerous" to man or his property; among them were the wolf, brown bear, lynx and wildcat, otter and other mustelid species, birds of prey and other birds. There are still countries that offer a bounty for such "pests" as the wolf and eagle. Kangaroos in Australia, ungulates in Africa, and guanacos, vicunas, and deer in South America are shot, poisoned and driven out of their territories to obtain pasture for cattle and sheep, or fields for cultivation. In the end such crusades can culminate in the complete annihilation of these species.

The overexploitation of wild animals for food has a similar outcome. It can take the form of shooting or trapping the many species which reproduce too slowly to make good their losses. This is true, for example, of almost all the animals that are hunted in the Mediterranean region, including the songbirds, as well as the large game living outside the national parks in Africa. There is currently a particular threat to the caribou of North America (*Rangifer tarandus caribou*, *Rangifer tarandus arcticus* and other subspecies; see Color plate, p. 588) and to the vicuna (*Lama vicugna*; see Color plate, p. 588) of the South American Andes. The population of the latter, according to the most recent estimates, has shrunk in two decades from 50,000 to 2000. Equally endangered are the Mindoro buffalo (*Bubalus arnee mindorensis*) in the Philippines, of which at most 200 individuals are still alive, the gaur (*Bos gaurus*) in southeastern Asia, all three subspecies of which have been eliminated in certain areas, and finally a number of small and large marsupials and birds in Australia and the neighboring islands.

Whales, especially the large baleen whales, and all species of sea cows and marine turtles (see Color plate, p. 588) also offer alarming examples of unrestrained killing of animals for food. And excessive numbers of animals have been shot and trapped for other reasons: crocodiles, monitors and large snakes for their skins; large and small cats, monkeys and seals for their fur; birds of paradise, herons and other birds for their plumage; and rhinoceroses for the raw material of pseudo-medicaments for the superstitious. Hunters calling themselves "sportsmen" menace the polar bear (*Thalarctos maritimus*), various subspecies of tiger (*Panthera tigris*; see Color plate, p. 587) and the Nile crocodile (*Crocodylus niloticus*) in parts of their ranges; the Asian subspecies of the lion (*Panthera leo persica*; see Color plate, p. 587) and cheetah (*Acinonyx jubatus venaticus*) have already nearly disappeared.

Hunting for skins and furs

The capture of animals for sale to private individuals and to zoos has also been taken to such an extreme that certain species are in great danger. Among these are the mountain tapir (*Tapirus pinchaque*), the Central American tapir (*Tapirus bairdi*), the orang-utan (*Pongo pygmaeus*), lion-tailed macaque (*Macaca silenus*), woolly spider monkey (*Brachyteles arachnoides*), Goeldi's monkey (*Callimico goeldii*), golden lion marmoset (*Leontideus rosalia*; see Color plate, p. 588), monkey-eating eagle (*Pithecophaga jefferyi*; see Color plate, p. 588), and several reptile species including alligators, caimans and turtles (*Pseudemys*). Young animals of these reptile species are imported in large numbers and sold as pets, whereupon they are usually housed and fed improperly and eventually die. The spur-tailed and spur-thighed Mediterranean land tortoises (*Testudo hermanni* and

The threat from animal-lovers and zoos

Testudo graeca) have also been exported in masses from their homeland into all parts of the world, and as a result the populations have declined severely. "Hobbies" that involve the collecting of the eggs or young of birds have put many species in danger; here we shall mention only the crane, Eleonora's falcon (*Falco eleonorae*), the bearded vulture (*Gypaëtus barbatus*) and the gyrfalcon (*Falco rusticolus*).

The situation becomes extremely precarious for species that are not only persecuted directly by man but also threatened indirectly by his activities. Unfortunately, this is true of most animals. The foremost of such effects is the destruction of the natural habitat and food supply. This threat is critical for species restricted to a certain type of habitat; among these are several prosimian species in the progressively disappearing forests of Madagascar—for example, the aye-aye (*Daubentonia madagascariensis*), the indri (*Indri indri*), the sifakas (*Propithecus verreauxi* and *Propithecus diadema*), the mongoose lemur (*Lemur mongoz*) and some other lemurs. In the oak-beech forests of New Guinea the blue bird of paradise (*Paradisaea rudolphi*), the astrapias and other birds are similarly affected. Well over half of all large animals on earth are threatened, now or in the near future, both by hunting and by the shrinking and alteration of their original habitat. This is an alarming proportion, and it makes clear that only our activities can decide whether these animals will survive. Unrestrained clearing of the forests in the tropics and elsewhere, the use of arid grasslands as cattle ranges in Australia, Africa and South America, the harnessing of flowing waters and drainage of swamps and bogs are the most important of such activities. The logging operations carried out in humid tropical regions by powerful international concerns are destroying day by day, stands of forest that can never be replaced.

The danger is especially clear in certain developing countries which are themselves eager to use their natural resources for short-term profit. At the same time, their forests are being exploited by foreign timber companies with little sympathy for the long-term welfare of the country. Huge machines flatten the forest; the valuable wood is separated and the rest is turned into shavings and chipboard. Since reforestation does not even approach the magnitude of the destruction, the land deteriorates and loses much of its value as a habitat for both animals and man. In the long run this leads to serious impoverishment of the economy of such countries. An especially impressive example is the island of Madagascar, where apart from nature reserves there are hardly any original forest communities of appreciable extent. Among the direct consequences here are an increasing predominance of steppe land and twenty-three species faced with extinction among the prosimians alone. Nevertheless, logging operations there continue at an accelerated pace, as they do in southeastern Asia, South America, Africa and New Guinea.

Another case in point involves the natural streams, swamps and bogs. As ecosystems, and in the large-scale water cycle, they are of great biological significance. But all over the world the water balances of these habitats are being altered. In central Europe, for example, bogs, valleys through which streams follow their natural courses, and swampy areas of land are being destroyed one after another, even though their significance to fauna and flora, as well as to people in need of rest and quiet, has long been realized. The agricultural land thus obtained hardly yields sufficient harvests to be worth while. The taxpayer who could best use these areas as a change from his everyday routine is the one who pays the government to "clean up the countryside," putting under cultivation the last bits of unused land that are not protected by conservation laws. Millions are being spent every year quite openly, to destroy things of value that can never be replaced. Behind all this is the truly primitive notion of the struggle against nature, the taming of the wilderness—an attitude that has no place in contemporary life, and for which we will pay dearly. Working industriously toward the wrong goal, such programs in upper Bavaria, the adjacent parts of Austria, and other important recreational areas of Europe are depreciating not only what remains of the original waste land but even the traditional agrarian lands.

The disastrous "cleaning up" project

One of the main threats to the existence of other organisms is man's accelerating poisoning of the biosphere. No habitat is entirely spared. The highly toxic heavy metals cadmium and mercury, which are transported as industrial wastes to the sea, and the pesticide DDT have been detected even in Arctic regions, where they have been carried by deep-sea currents. They are found in the bodies of polar bears and Eskimos. Even the so-called pure-air zones are being invaded by poisons. A data-collecting station in Whiteface Mountain, 450 kilometers from New York, not uncommonly measures 5000–7000 particles of atmospheric pollutants per cubic centimeter where previously the count was only one to five particles per cubic centimeter. From the Puerto Rico marine trench, about 8000 meters deep, a ship brought up not only the occasional fish but also empty fruit-juice and beer cans, scraps of aluminum foil, bottles and a flashlight battery. No animal species has yet been demonstrably killed off as a direct consequence of this global contamination, but certain birds of prey and coastal birds are not far from extinction.

Poisoning of the biosphere

However, in regions with high concentrations of harmful chemicals and waste materials, populations of animals and entire communities are exterminated. Examples include the massive mortality of fish in lakes, rivers and coastal waters, the death of soil organisms as a result of the spraying of chemicals in forests, and the obliteration of bird colonies because of contamination with oil. As has already been described, the concentration of toxic substances in organisms increases ominously at higher levels in the food chain; along with the prey that each animal eats it consumes the poisons the prey has taken up. There they are stored, since the rate of decomposition in many cases (for example, that of DDT) in the body is extremely slow. Reproductive failure is a common conse-

Noxious chemicals and wastes

quence; tumor formation and even cancer, and damage to the genetic material are other long-term possibilities.

The dangers of pest control

At first, the use of chemical pesticides for the extermination of disease transmitters—for example, in the case of malaria in the tropics and subtropics—was predominantly beneficial to man. Meanwhile, however, it has turned out that the unrestricted use of DDT and stronger poisons has severely disrupted biological equilibrium. Even deep into the jungle, almost every pool of water that could be reached was sprayed to kill off the anopheles mosquito. Not only the malaria mosquitoes were killed, but many other animals as well, including the mosquitoes' natural enemies. In the jungle villages along the Sepik River in New Guinea, for example, the huts of the Papuans collapsed some time after the spraying operations carried out by the Australian government. Together with the malaria mosquitoes and flies, the natural antagonists of a wood-eating insect (*Heradia nigrivitta*) had been exterminated. The Papuans reacted unambiguously: they drove the spraying teams out of their settlements.

Introduction of alien animals upsets the ecosystem

In the age of exploration, seafarers and colonists were already beginning to bring new species to foreign lands. Domestic goats and pigs were turned loose on islands to serve as an emergency food supply, songbirds were brought to the new country to counteract homesickness, and other domestic animals such as cats, dogs, pigs, goats and cattle wandered into the wild of their own accord and were able to survive. Game animals introduced to New Zealand and South America dispersed rapidly. Most of these introduced animals proved harmful in their new homes, for the ecosystems there were not adjusted to them and the balance of nature was upset. In Chapter 19, Part One, this situation was discussed at length. Partially as a result of the devastation caused in Australia by the introduction of the rabbit and the red fox, thirty-two marsupial species are now listed in the "Red Data Book." The rivers of Australia and New Guinea were stocked with no less than nine alien fish species; in some places they disturbed the biological equilibrium so severely that people are now considering the introduction of predatory fish to keep the other imported species under control. The possible consequences of these further steps seem to be clear to no one; evidently little has been learned from the damage that has already been done.

As a countermeasure against pests in sugar-cane plantations, the South American giant toad (*Bufo marinus*) was introduced in many tropical countries; it became a disastrous menace to small vertebrates and other soil organisms. In New Zealand, stocking the land with European animals proved especially unfortunate. The government there has now established a special authority with the responsibility for limiting the mass reproduction of some of these species—not only to save rare native bird species from extinction, but also to protect inhabited sites from desolation by overgrazing.

Islands and island groups like the Galapagos, with their unique fauna, suffer from the introduction of goats, pigs, cats, dogs, and rats brought —whether intentionally or not—by man; on some of the islands they have nearly eliminated the giant tortoises, and on others certain species of birds are threatened. The brown rat and house mouse, which have been carried to almost every spot on earth by land and by ocean shipping, have become a real menace to certain animal species. Brown rats are on the point of eradicating the Auckland rail (*Rallus muelleri*), the mocking bird *Ramphocinclus brachyurus brachyurus* of Martinique, and other forms.

What possible action can we take to save endangered species from extinction? The most permanent solution is surely the preservation of sections of natural habitats in the form of national parks and nature reserves. For most land vertebrates this form of conservation is practicable, as long as sufficient virgin territory is available. According to the findings of population dynamics, animal populations must be of a certain size or larger if they are to retain enough social viability to ensure reproduction and self-maintenance. Certain species have probably already declined to such a point that a further decline can no longer be prevented. Among these are the New Zealand owl-parrot or kakapo (*Strigops habroptilus*), the total population of which now comprises less than a hundred individuals—even though large parts of its original habitat are under strict protection. It was thought that the same fate was in store for the Javan rhinoceros (*Rhinoceros sondaicus*), only twenty to twenty-five individuals of which are still living in the Ujung-Kulon nature reserve at the western tip of Java; but according to the latest reports young have recently been born in this last remaining colony.

It is more difficult to ensure the preservation of endangered species which go on long-distance migrations. These include birds which live in the reserves only during the breeding season and at other times are liable to be shot, and marine animals such as whales and their relatives. The endangered marine mammals include not only the large baleen whale, certain other whale species and all the sea cows, but also the three species of the monk seal genus *Monachus*, of which the Caribbean species is probably already extinct. The field studies of Michael and Bernhard Grzimek in the Serengeti steppe have shown how necessary it is, in establishing the boundaries of national parks, to include the regions through which the herds of steppe animals migrate.

According to the accepted definition, established by the IUCN, "national parks" are relatively large regions, containing one or more ecosystems which man has not appreciably changed by exploiting them, where the plant and animal species are of scientific, educational or recreational value or where the natural landscape is distinguished by unusual beauty. Furthermore, the existence of a "national park" in a country implies that the highest authorities there have taken steps to preserve the land along with its ecological, geomorphological and aesthetic characteristics. Visitors are allowed access, under certain conditions, for the

National parks and preserves

sake of recreation and education. In light of this definition it is clear that Germany, for example, still does not have a true national park even though a "Bayerischer Wald National Park" was dedicated in eastern Bavaria as early as 1970. Since the forest continues to be exploited for timber and the safety of the original natural community has not really been assured, the name "national park" should be withheld from such places until further steps are taken.

Monuments to human culture are not usually considered to be "protected objects" in national parks. In this respect there is a marked need to expand the definition of the "national park"; it is not at all apparent why historical structures or villages, if their presence can be reconciled with the principles of nature conservation, should not be accepted elements of national parks. On the contrary, assigning untouched countryside and man-made treasures to one and the same conservation authority, responsible for preserving an optimal blend of our natural and historical heritages, would permit the creation of real national parks in the comprehensive sense of the word. The establishment of national parks has already brought considerable financial benefit to several countries, as a result of increased tourism. In Kenya, for example, the income to the state from the foreign visitors to the large parks exceeded that from the coffee plantations, and in fact leads the list of all sources of income. In the USA, where the first national park in the world was founded in 1872, 200 million people visited the national parks in 1971. The developing countries are in the best position in this respect, since they can now set aside extensive national parks without making a large investment in them, ensuring a promising adjunct to their future economies.

Whereas the goal of a national park is to protect one or more ecosystems as large units, "animal preserves" serve to prevent the extinction of certain endangered species or associations of species within their natural environment. The area covered by such a preserve—for example, that for the Cretan wild goat (*Capra aegagrus cretica*) in Greece—is usually smaller than that of a national park, and the public is admitted only under special circumstances. Once it was believed that it sufficed to place a region under protection and thereafter to leave it alone. But under the favorable conditions prevailing within its boundaries certain species reproduced so rapidly that they began to destroy the biological equilibrium. People hesitated for a long time to control this imbalance by trapping and shooting. Not until the plants in several African national parks were severely damaged by too-dense populations of elephants and other large animals did the responsible authorities make up their minds to reduce the numbers of these animals.

Even extensive preserves are not independent of ecological disruptions taking place outside their boundaries. The pressure of immigration from outside becomes unnaturally great; furthermore, climatic changes in the surroundings of a park affect the interior of the park as well. Certain animal species, especially carnivores, were hunted excessively before such parks were established and subsequently remain too rare, in comparison with the herds of grazing animals, to contribute much to their natural selection. In North American national parks it has actually been a practice —well-intentioned, but biologically unfounded—to shoot wolves in order to protect "more valuable" species from them. As a result, the stocks of deer have in some cases grown so large that regular "crashes" have occurred when the environment could no longer sustain them. Only by regular culling to keep the populations at an optimal size can a balance be maintained. Controlled utilization of certain species within the boundaries of preserves—previously rejected—must also be recognized as permissible.

Other conservation efforts

These measures toward the preservation of natural habitats are supplemented by conservation laws forbidding the killing, capturing or other interference with protected species anywhere within a state, country or other legislative unit. Of course, they can work only where the government that enacts them also has means of enforcing them. In some countries there is a department of "hunters" or gamekeepers with the responsibility of guarding and caring for the animals in the preserves.

In a few special cases national and international bodies have decided to save a particularly endangered species by capturing a breeding group from the wild and keeping it in captivity. For example, several such groups of Arabian oryx (*Oryx gazella leucoryx*), which once was widely distributed in Arabia, have been established in Phoenix and other places in the USA, and at two places in Arabia; the only fairly large population still living free, in Oman, did not seem sufficient to ensure the survival of this subspecies. Of course, to be suitable for such an experiment, a species must be able to live and reproduce under human care. Other examples, such as that of the wisent (*Bison bonasus*) are mentioned in Chapter 24, Part One.

Conservationists have recently succeeded in resettling species that had died out in certain parts of their natural ranges. Breeding groups taken from captivity or from viable natural populations were transferred to suitable habitats. These include, for example, the Alpine ibex (*Capra ibex ibex*) in the northern Alps, and beavers (*Castor fiber*), eagle owls (*Bubo bubo*) and swamp turtles (*Emys orbicularis*) at various suitable sites in central Europe. But it should be a matter of principle to stock a habitat only with a subspecies that once lived there naturally. Similarly, it is only proper to strengthen a residual population by adding animals to it if it is on the point of extinction without such assistance.

The vigorous efforts being made by government bodies, national and international organizations, and many private individuals should not deceive us into thinking that everything possible is being done; much more help is needed, and financial contributions are urgently required for the purchase of nature preserves, if we are not to lose the race against time.

The present funds and manpower are not nearly enough

In the "Red Data Book" of the IUCN I have examined the practical steps that have been taken to protect the 295 endangered mammals. For 108 of them, despite the recognized threat, nothing at all has been done. A further eighty have been placed under protection, locally or throughout their ranges, by law. But such laws often exist only on paper, since there is no way of enforcing them in the wild. Only 107 mammal species and subspecies have so far received practical protection—for example, by the setting aside of a part of their range or another of the methods described above. In some of these cases, such protection was simply a by-product of another measure, such as the establishment of a national park. Finally, it must be kept in mind that the list of endangered animals in the "Red Data Book" is by no means complete. All things considered, it remains true today that of the mammal species on the verge of becoming extinct, one in three is receiving no aid at all.

5 The Sea in Danger

To many people, the ocean is a symbol of unadulterated purity; even today pictures of crisp, clean rolling surf are useful to the designers of detergent ads. Until very recently the words "ocean pollution" had hardly been spoken. But decades ago bathers on the beach were beginning to be annoyed by oil, and sea birds covered with oil attracted the attention of a concerned minority. In 1954 the first international agreement against oil pollution by ships was concluded. But it was not until 1959 that the first international congress concerned with questions of marine pollution was held, in Berkeley, California. Even then not all the problems involved had been recognized nor had their full implications been understood.

In recent years a store of scientific data on the pollution of the ocean has steadily accumulated and been made available to the general public. By now probably every moderately well-read person knows that the problem is not limited to certain critical sites, such as the vicinity of ports or popular bathing beaches. The view from an orbiting satellite shows us how vulnerable is the thin film of air and water that makes possible life on this planet. The condition of the entire biosphere is reflected in the atmosphere and in the oceans of the world. The very first signs of global pollution of the sea, which are becoming visible today, must call forth immediate action; failing that, noxious substances will, during our children's lifetimes, become ten to a hundred times more concentrated than they are now.

In nature whole communities of organisms, known as the "decomposers," specialize in the metabolic breakdown of traditional domestic sewage. This decomposition of organic matter also occurs in the ocean, again largely by the agency of bacteria; as in the inland waters, the bacteria use up oxygen in the process. If there is not enough oxygen available, the processes of fermentation go much more slowly; stinking decay products are released, and the balance of the aquatic ecosystem, is upset.

In general, domestic sewage is no threat to the ocean. But in secluded bays and in esturaries the problem is similar to that in fresh water: the self-

By S. A. Gerlach

Decomposition of organic matter

cleaning capacity of the water can be exceeded and there can be a shortage of oxygen. Even on the open coast, if large cities discharge all their sewage into the sea at one point, dead zones develop around the point of influx; the fauna changes, as resistant species crowd out the usual inhabitants.

In the German coastal waters there are so far only a few places where the situation has become serious; an example is the Trave River from Lübeck to its mouth in the Lübecker Bucht. It is true that the Elbe, Weser and Ems Rivers are polluted, and their oxygen content is considerably below the saturation level, but fish mortality as a result of oxygen deficiency is still a rare occurrence there. Nevertheless, if the influx of decomposable organic matter increases, it will endanger these rivers as well. The coast inhabitants, then, are justified in their objections to Dutch plans to discharge large quantities of organic waste into the estuarine region of the Ems.

Eutrophication

The eutrophication of inland waters has been described in Chapter Three. The ocean, too, if it is overfertilized, can develop an undesirable flora which crowds out the natural algal communities. In recent years dinoflagellates (for example, *Gonioaulax*) that used to be encountered only rarely have been observed at several places in the North Sea. They are unpleasant organisms, for they form toxins which are carried up the food chain; they enter the fish by way of crustaceans and clams and in man they can cause fatal poisoning. In tropical and subtropical waters mass outbreaks of such poisonous protozoans can color the water red. These "red tides" are a regularly recurring phenomenon off the Florida coast. People there are accustomed to them and know what fish should not be eaten at certain times of year. But the red tides in the North Sea are something new. There are scientists who think that eutrophication is responsible, that the red tides are enhanced by an abundant supply of nutrients.

Calculations indicate that about a seventh of the phosphorus entering the North Sea comes from rivers, and thus in part from sewage and other dissolved wastes. A further increase in this undesired fertilization of the ocean will presumably cause changes, especially since eighty per cent of the influx accumulates in the southern part of the North Sea. The situation is even more worrisome in the Baltic, where the deep water is naturally low in oxygen and is enriched only from time to time, when the weather is favorable, by masses of oxygen-rich water from the Skagerrak. A large number of cities on the Baltic Sea dump their sewage into it. When this sewage is decomposed in the upper waters nitrogen and phosphorus are liberated, which bring about a more luxuriant growth of microscopic algae. Dying algae sink; the more rapid their growth at the surface, the more abundant are the remains that accumulate at the bottom. Bacterial decomposition in the depths completely uses up the slight amounts of oxygen available there. The consequence is the release of hydrogen sulfide, and the local formation of decaying sludge, like that occurring in the fjords of the Baltic coast of Germany.

In 1960 each person in the catchment area of the Baltic Sea contributed on average 1.5 grams per day of phosphorus to the sewage; in 1970 this figure had risen to four grams. The reason for this increase is the excessive fertilization of agricultural areas; a considerable fraction of the fertilizer is washed into the ocean by streams. Another factor is the use of detergents: the modern highly effective detergents contain up to 40% phosphate salts. The chemical industry can obtain unlimited quantities of nitrogen from the air, but phosphorus that enters the water is lost to human use. The reserves of phosphorus-containing ores are limited. If one considers the welfare of coming generations, the current unrestrained use of this element for the sake of dazzling-white laundry is quite irresponsible.

In unprocessed domestic sewage there are masses of bacteria and viruses, including those excreted by men and domestic animals. Most of them are harmless, but where people have contagious diseases, the disease pathogens also enter the sewage. As an indicator of the microbial pollution of water, it is customary to use a bacterium regularly found in considerable numbers in all samples of excrement: *Escherichia coli*. If a swimming spot in a river or lake regularly shows a concentration of 100–1000 coliform bacteria in 100 ml water, then the public health authorities consider prohibiting swimming there. In the USA similar limits are set for bathing beaches at the coasts. But in other countries people seem to be less worried; in Great Britain health officials even doubt whether evidence of the presence of these fecal bacteria implies any danger at all to the health of swimmers.

In fact, it cannot incontestably be demonstrated that the notorious gastro-intestinal sicknesses suffered by seaside vacationers are associated with swimming in water loaded with sewage. The gathering of large numbers of people from different places, the overcrowding in the holiday months, and the not infrequent inadequacy of hygiene in resorts would encourage such epidemics in any case. Ocean waters actually have a bacteriocidal effect. Moreover, because there is more water available, dilution is usually greater than in fresh water; pathogens in small numbers are often not capable of starting an infection. These factors, fortunately, act to prevent infection from disease pathogens in the ocean. Nevertheless, there is reason to suspect that some viruses are less affected by the inhibitory factors than are bacteria. It is absolutely necessary that even cities on the ocean, which have so far dumped raw sewage into estuaries and coastal waters, install treatment plants. Cleanliness commands this, for apart from direct danger to health, no one much likes the idea of swimming in feces.

There is a more effective way to acquire disease pathogens from sea water than by swimming in it; that is, to eat them along with seafood— expecially oysters, which are often eaten raw. Clams, mussels and oysters are all filter-feeders, which sweep bacteria into their digestive tracts along with other food particles; consequently there is in many cases an accumulation of pathogens within the animal. Unless special precautions are taken

Germs in the ocean

Pathogens in seafood

one can easily become infected by eating raw oysters. It is quite right that the sites where oysters are grown are subject to strict hygienic regulations. In many cases the industry is required to disinfect bivalves before they are sold, or to keep them in pure water so that they release the germs they have taken in.

Industrial wastes

One cannot discuss domestic sewage and industrial wastes entirely separately. On one hand, the waste products of many branches of industry behave like sewage, in that they are biologically degraded to the level of carbon dioxide. On the other, many factories discharge their wastes into public sewage systems; what is eventually poured into the coastal waters is a mixture of household and industrial wastes. Not uncommonly toxic substances are mixed in as well, which hamper the biological decomposition of the sewage in the treatment plants.

In Cuxhaven and Bremerhaven, the fish-processing industries discharge their waste water, together with that from the houses there, into the Elbe and the Weser, respectively; the only prior treatment is removal of some of the fats. Bacterial decomposition of this industrial sewage, which consists chiefly of protein, presents no difficulty in the coastal waters as long as enough oxygen is available. But it has recently been demonstrated that there is already a distinct reduction in the oxygen content of the Weser, so that the construction of biological treatment centers has become necessary. The sewage from the Bremerhaven fish industry, after all, corresponds to the domestic output of at least a hundred thousand people. More difficult problems arise in other cases—for example, with paper and cellulose factories, for lignin and cellulose are decomposed very slowly. Deposits of these substances create lifeless districts on the ocean floor.

Sewage sludge

At many places along the coasts other methods have been tried; either the sewage is piped far out into the ocean, or the sludge from the sewage plants is periodically hauled out to sea and dumped. This sludge contains not only domestic wastes but all sorts of components from industry, in varying proportions. It has been estimated that along with such sludge about a metric ton of polychlorinated biphenyls per year is dumped in the estuaries of the Thames, the Clyde, and the Mersey (near Manchester). A million tons of sludge from the city of Glasgow is sunk in the Firth of Clyde each year; most of this is organic refuse from domestic sources, which is definitely a nutritious substrate for the marine organisms. Correspondingly, the fauna of the sea floor near the dump site is larger in biomass, if not in number of species, than that in the surrounding areas. But at the same time copper, lead and zinc have become considerably more concentrated in the organisms and the substances on the bottom, as has the poisonous mercury. This is a matter for concern, if the animals that have consumed these metals are to serve as food for people. Finally, domestic sewage also carries considerable amounts of oil and oil residues into the sea—more than is spilled in accidents to tankers.

It has long been known that the capacity of inland waters to absorb harmful materials is limited. But when draining wastes into the ocean, people have comfortably accepted the delusion that it was infinitely large and therefore could dilute enormous amounts of garbage and sewage to unnoticeable levels. In recent years the evidence has accumulated that the capacity of the sea has been overestimated. A little later we shall give some examples of this situation. But I should like to begin by describing a large-scale experiment in which the disposal of industrial wastes in the ocean has not thus far produced any detrimental effects.

The incentive for a thorough scientific examination of ocean pollution in the coastal region of Germany was provided in 1966 by a plan to set up a titanium works on the Blexer Groden near Nordenham on the lower Weser. To produce titanium dioxide, a valuable dye, titanium ore was to be treated with sulfuric acid. Wastes generated by this procedure are iron sulfate and more dilute sulfuric acid at a concentration of about 18%. Since there is no worthwhile use to which these can be put, the titanium company wanted to carry them out into the North Sea with tankers; there it was proposed to release them into the water—stirred up by the ship's propellers—as has been done for several years in the Atlantic off New York and off the coast of Holland.

Sulfuric acid and iron sulfate

But even then it could be foreseen that the freedom of the seas would have to be restricted for the sake of public welfare, so government officials and research institutes were called upon to judge whether disposal in this way could cause damage. The answer turned out to be rather vague: The experts could not be certain that damage would result, nor could they guarantee that it would not. An area of 2.5 by 5 nautical miles, about eleven nautical miles northwest of Heligoland, was designated as the dumping grounds. Since May, 1969, a daily average of 1750 metric tons of wastes from the titanium industry are being put into the North Sea at this site. This waste contains 14% iron sulfate, 10% sulfuric acid, and about 3% mineral impurities. The effects of this waste disposal have been studied, as a sort of massive experiment, by a number of scientific research institutes in Bremerhaven, Heligoland, Hamburg. So far the various results are contradictory. Whereas in the laboratory it has been demonstrated that the wastes from the titanium plant damage organisms even when greatly diluted, in the open ocean no detrimental effect has yet become apparent.

Before the dumping began the bottom fauna in the area concerned had been investigated. After four years of exposure to the wastes no changes could be observed that were ascribable to this exposure. If the titanium wastes had been injurious, the more sensitive species should have died out, or at least no further colonization by young animals should have occurred. But till now there is no evidence that either has happened. Numerous experiments with the original liquid waste, on the other hand, have shown that even at a dilution of 1:50,000 it harms planktonic algae, fish eggs and fish larvae. Apparently such concentrations are reached in the North Sea only in the immediate vicinity of the tanker, and damage to the organisms there makes no appreciable difference when the area as a whole is considered. In any case, one may conclude from the experiments that the dumping of even relatively harmless wastes, like those from the titanium works, cannot be done on a very large scale without harm to the marine communities.

Mercury in industrial discharges

Minamata is a town of 50,000 inhabitants on the Shiranui Sea, on the eastern side of the Japanese island Kyushu. Many of these people are engaged in fishery, but apart from that the town is economically dependent upon the Shin-Nihon Chisso Hiryo factory, which along with other products produces large amounts of vinyl chloride and acetaldehyde. It was in 1953 that a puzzling syndrome first appeared among the people of Minamata. Three years later the disease took on epidemic proportions; a contagious form of meningitis was suspected, and the patients were isolated. A study commission under Dr. Hosokawa, the director of the Minamata factory's hospital, discovered that all the patients had similar symptoms: first numbness of the lips and limbs, and after two weeks impairment of tactile sense, speech and hearing. Their gait became irregular; they walked as though drunk, incapable of stopping suddenly or turning around. The most striking symptom in all the patients was a narrowing of the field of vision. Of 116 officially recorded patients, forty-three died; of those who survived only a few recovered completely, whereas most of them sustained permanent disabilities.

From these symptoms Professor Shimanosuke Katsuki of Kumamoto University inferred heavy-metal poisoning. It was determined that all the patients had eaten a great deal of fish. Moreover, cats were also observed to show symptoms of the Minamata disease; when it was discovered that feeding fish from the Minamata bay to healthy cats produced the symptoms, it was clear that the disease was a form of food poisoning. At the beginning of 1957 further fishing in the bay was forbidden. In that year no one contracted the disease, and in the following year there were only three cases.

The search for the poison took three years and was plagued by dissension. There were many heavy metals in the water discharged by the chemical factory. The factory impeded the investigation, and was even successful in its attempts to discredit the findings that were presented. Not until 1969 was it possible to demonstrate that mercury in organic compounds must have caused the poisoning. Indeed, in 1960 the discharge from the factory was shown to include methyl mercury, but the Japanese chemical lobby succeeded in preventing official recognition of these findings. Then, in 1965, the same sickness broke out at the mouth of the Agano River in the district of Niigato; thirty people fell ill, and five of them died. This time the source of the poison was the mercury-containing wastes from the Kanose factory of Showa Denko, which again had found their way into the people along with the fish they ate. The government had still not taken a clear stance by 1968. For the first time in Japanese history, suits were then brought by the victims against the chemical companies, charging pollution of the environment; since then damages have been paid.

Now we know that in nature, probably with the assistance of microorganisms, very short-lived organic mercury compounds can form from metallic mercury and inorganic mercury salts. Metallic mercury itself is so slightly poisonous that in the last century it was still being recommended as a medication to treat bowel disorders. On the other hand, the methyl mercury discharged by the factory in Minamata is so toxic that thirty milligrams will kill a cat. If mercury is taken up by an organism, moreover, it takes a long time until organic mercury compounds are excreted; they accumulate in the musculature and other parts of the body. Inorganic mercury compounds, on the other hand, accumulate only in blood and liver, and are quickly removed from the body.

In other countries, too, industrial wastes have produced considerable concentrations of mercury in food fish, though usually without unpleasant consequences to the population. But in Sweden forty regions, some of them along the coasts, had to be barred to fishing; there are five such closed regions in Finland, and others in Norway, Canada, and in at least seventeen states of the USA. It will be a long time before the mercury in these regions has deposited out sufficiently to be removed from biological circulation.

In 1972 a factory for alkali-chloride electrolysis was started in Wilhelmshaven; now one can only hope that the use of such new procedures will not result in loading of the coastal waters with mercury. Otherwise, the situation in the German coastal region is still good; but it has been claimed that the Rhine each year carries to the North Sea sixty metric tons of mercury, a considerable part of which originates in German industry.

How much mercury can a person consume without harm? Mercury is a toxic substance, of no importance for any bodily function; however, water, air, rock and thus all kinds of food contain traces of it. All that can be done is to try to keep the uptake of mercury in food as low as possible. To achieve this, it would really be necessary to give up eating fish altogether, for fish contains more mercury than any other food. In some respects, though, the flesh of fish is superior to other sources of protein; marine fish accumulate in their bodies other trace elements like iodine and bromine which the human body urgently requires. The question should be formulated differently: How much mercury can a fish contain, in order that the benefit to the health of the person who eats it outweighs the possibility of harm? An answer to this question depends upon the amount of fish that is eaten.

It is extraordinarily difficult to set a limit on the tolerable mercury content of ocean fish. In Japan and Norway, where fish is a major part of the diet, the limit would have to be lower than, for example, in Germany, Sweden and Great Britain. When the events in Japan revealed that fish in the Minamata bay contained 50 mg mercury per kilogram, the Swedish

Ministry of Health recommended a safety limit of 0.5 mg/kg. Then it was discovered that in Lake Vänern many fish exceeded this limit, so it was raised to 1 mg/kg. Since then this has remained the criterion. It had been overlooked that the Japanese data referred to dry weight and not, as in Sweden and most other countries, to the fresh weight of the fish. This fact did not become known in Sweden until a public hearing was held in February, 1968; it means that, among people who eat a lot of fish, mercury poisoning appears when the fish contain about 10 mg/kg fresh weight. Currently the debate about the proper limit is still going on in Sweden; in the USA and Canada 0.5 mg/kg is considered a maximal concentration. In Great Britain no limit has been prescribed, since people have calmly concluded that there has been no increased danger in recent times; fish has not harmed anyone yet, the reasoning goes, so there is no cause for excitement. In Germany, too, there is at present no rule governing the maximum allowable mercury in animals to be used as food.

Little is known so far about the distribution and effects of other heavy metals and trace elements. Cadmium and zinc appear in the waste water from galvanizing works and metal foundries, together with lead and copper. Other suspect elements are selenium, arsenic, antimony and bismuth. Cadmium, for example, is harmful to organisms even in extremely dilute solutions, possibly as low as 0.6 millionths of a gram per liter; this level is only five times higher than the natural concentration. It is also stored in organisms, and cadmium poisoning has also caused human deaths following the eating of fish.

Radioactive materials Nuclear reactors, in their normal operation, produce small but measurable quantities of radioactive isotopes of zinc, cobalt and other elements. If the reactors are cooled by sea water, these substances make their way into the ocean. Experts of the International Atomic Energy Commission have calculated that even with storage of radioisotopes in organisms used by man as food, the danger from this source is insignificant compared with the natural radioactivity of our environment. But in each case it must be tested which radioisotope is concentrated the most strongly. Radioactive zinc from a nuclear power plant on the Blackwater Estuary in Great Britain is stored by oysters; near the nuclear-fuel reprocessing plant at Windscale on the Irish Sea radioactive rubidium was recovered in large amounts from red algae, which are eaten as a local delicacy by the people living on the coast there.

Warm effluents Organisms living in the open ocean are adapted to a very narrow range of temperatures. Inhabitants of the coastal regions, on the other hand, must cope with seasonal and smaller daily temperature fluctuations, and with sudden changes that depend on the weather; they are therefore capable of withstanding some artificial change of the water temperature. It should be possible to calculate how much warm cooling-water one can safely pump into a coastal region. In Biscayne Bay (Florida) the power station at Turkey Point pours an average of thirty-six cubic meters per second of water at 35–37°C into the shallow coastal waters; the normal average temperature of these waters in winter falls to 17°C and in summer rises to 31°C. Over an area of almost twenty hectares around the outlet a warming by 5°C above these average temperatures has been measured; seaweed, the usual algae and the larger animals have disappeared, while blue-green algae adapted to warm conditions have become established. A region of 120 hectares showed warming by more than 3°C; here the rise in temperature had only a slight effect on the summer population of algae. Animals were common in this region, and fish gathered there in winter, though they avoided it in summer. In general, therefore, it probably holds for such waters that warming by more than 3°C should not be permitted.

For decades polychlorinated biphenyls have been used in large amounts because of a number of important properties; they are very stable, keeping their oily consistency even at a temperature of 800°C. This makes them useful as coolant fluids and in heat exchangers. Polychlorinated biphenyls (abbreviated PCB) serve as transformer oil and as components of paints and lacquers, agricultural chemicals and plastics.

Polychlorinated biphenyls

The biological effects of PCB in many ways resemble those of DDT and other agricultural chemicals of the chlorinated-hydrocarbon group; they are very resistant to biological degradation in the environment, are taken up and stored by organisms and probably passed up the food chain, act as poisons and like DDT impair the reproductive ability of birds. In a chicken farm in the USA, when there was a sudden marked deterioration in the ability of chicks to hatch, the food of the laying hens was checked; considerable amounts of PCB were found in the fish meal. The reason was not that PCB had been in the living fish, but that there was a leaky pipe in the fish-meal factory; PCB had dripped onto the meal as it was being produced. There have been other disturbing reports, where PCB has found its way into the ocean, either through improperly sealed pipes or with sludge from sewage plants.

When chemists began to find chlorinated hydrocarbons in marine animals, in the early 1960's, they often made no attempt to separate PCB from DDT. Meanwhile techniques have been improved, and there are a number of investigations showing that PCB damage is also widespread. Particularly glaring examples are offered by the pelicans off the California coast, which were already in great danger from DDT. In a hundred birds, an average of 200 mg PCB per kilogram was measured. The fat in the pectoral muscles of white-tailed sea eagles in the vicinity of Stockholm is said to have contained 14,000 mg/kg PCB. In the eggs of the terns of Long Island Sound 100–200 mg/kg PCB have been found; presumably the impaired development and crippling of embryos and young in this colony are the consequences of the high PCB content. Sea birds on the British coasts, the populations of which declined sharply in 1969, also proved to contain large amounts of PCB; analysis of the English marine plankton revealed 0.03 kg/mg PCB, and herring had as much as 2.6 mg/kg. Under the circumstances it is not surprising that PCB is found in humans as well: in the vicinity of Münster, human fat was shown to contain 5.7 kg/mg, and in mothers' milk there was 3.5 mg per kilogram of fat.

We still have no good explanation of how PCB is spread through the environment. Since these materials burn only at temperatures above 800°C, lower-temperature combustion processes send them into the atmosphere unchanged. It is possible that some of the factors involved in the global distribution of PCB are the same as those for DDT (see Chapter 6). It is thus right that the few producers of PCB limit their production. Regulations must be demanded so that PCB can be used only where it cannot escape into the environment and where a guarantee is given that the PCB no longer required is effectively burned in special installations.

Pesticides in waste water

In 1961 on the coast of Jutland, north of Limfjord, a chemical factory increased its production of the pesticide parathion. The wastes from this factory were piped into the North Sea. In 1964 it became known that fish near the outlet of the pipe, and lobsters up to sixty kilometers away along the coast, were dying. Investigations revealed that the waste water from the factory was lethal to lobsters even when diluted by a factor of 1:50,000; the wastes were more poisonous than parathion itself. The factory was made to clean its waste water so well that guppies—the aquarium fish *Lebistes reticulatus*—could survive in it at a dilution of 1:50.

In 1965, the colony of Sandwich terns on the island of Griend off the coast of Holland was severely reduced. Of the more than 20,000 breeding pairs only about 1000 remained alive; the dying birds showed clear signs of poisoning. The fish upon which the terns fed had been affected by the water drained from a chemical factory near Rotterdam which produced telodrin, dieldrin and endrin. Since then ways have been found to ensure that this sort of poisonous waste no longer leaves the factory.

Near Los Angeles is the factory of the largest DDT producer in the USA. In 1971 it was still dumping between 150 and 250 kilograms of DDT-like substances, some of them unsuccessful batches of DDT itself, into Santa Monica Bay, and it had presumably been doing so at the same rate for years. Fish caught near the discharge point had a concentration of up to 57 mg/kg DDT in the muscles and 1026 mg/kg in the liver. Like mercury and some radioactive trace elements, DDT accumulates in organisms; the rate of accumulation is increased, of course, if the animals eat food containing DDT. Long-lived animals at the end of the food chain therefore display the highest concentrations of DDT and other persistent pesticides.

This is why the sea birds, fish-eaters that terminate that food chain, are in particular danger. Hardly any effects are noticeable in the adult birds themselves, but the eggs have thinner shells than those laid by birds in unpolluted parts of the sea, and they are easily crushed during brooding, so that few young hatch. The colony of brown pelicans on an island off Los Angeles in 1969 comprised 550 breeding adults. Only five young hatched;

most of the eggs had broken. In them were found DDT compounds at concentrations as high as 2600 mg/kg. The pelican populations in South Carolina have also been declining for the last twelve years, even though no more than 4 mg/kg DDT, on the average, has so far been found in their eggs.

Experiments have shown that DDT affects calcium metabolism. Thinning of the eggshells and breaking of the eggs during brooding can be produced experimentally in American black ducks (*Anas rubripes*) by feeding them fodder containing 30 mg/kg (dry weight) DDT compounds. The DDT accumulates in the eggs, reaching a concentration of 144 mg/kg; the eggshells are 32% thinner, and 21% of the eggs break during brooding as compared with 2% of those of control animals not fed DDT. There is also thought to be an effect of DDT upon the sexual hormones. High DDT poisoning is not limited to pelicans; near Monterey, analyses showed 805 mg DDT compounds per kg of liver in the ring-billed gull, 412 mg/kg in Leach's storm petrel, and 192–192 mg/kg in the western grebe. California sea lions had 911 mg/kg in the fat, and 12 mg/kg in the brain.

Pesticides enter the ocean not only as waste products from chemical factories, but also after they have been used. Dangerous waste water was produced in Great Britain at sites where sheep were bathed in dieldrin. Pesticides also are dissolved in the sewage from factories that process wool or make carpets; in the process they soak the wool in a solution to protect it against moths. These pollutants harm not only fish but also bivalves, shrimp and sensitive planktonic algae. Similarly, coastal regions adjacent to agricultural and forested land where insecticides are used in large quantities are exposed to severe pollution. When the water is high in the Colorado River, and much sediment is transported to the mouth of the river, the pesticides adhering to sediment particles cause a noticeable rise in concentration even in the ocean. At such times the fish there have 3–8 mg/kg DDT in their bodies. In Southern California, when the flies that were annoying visitors on the beach were sprayed with DDT, the pesticide accumulated in mackerels at concentrations of 2–17 mg/kg, so that sale of those fish had to be prohibited. In general, it can be said that a considerable part of the DDT used in programs for insect control eventually reaches the ocean.

For a long time, there have been ordinances and laws in Germany to prevent excessive pollution of the inland waters. In 1967 the coastal waters were also legally protected; the terms of the legislation concerning water within the country were extended to the coastal waters out to the three-mile limit. Cities in the coastal regions are required to treat their sewage wherever untreated sewage could be detrimental to public welfare.

Detrimental effects can be of several kinds: water pollution can cause the prohibition of swimming, lack of oxygen can lead to the death of marine organisms, and poisons can contaminate food taken from the sea.

Protection of coastal waters

On the other hand, the ocean is quite capable of dissipating waste materials that would be disastrous to the inland waters. Rock-salt and potassium salts are dangerous pollutants in lakes and streams; they are threatening the viability of the upper Weser and its tributaries. Coastal waters, however, can take up large quantities of such drainage water and not suffer at all.

The Thames is an example of the fact that decisive action can produce success. By 1957 practically all life had vanished from the Thames estuary. Twelve years of well-planned, thorough sewage treatment resulted in the reappearance, in 1969, of fifty species of organisms; now birds again winter on the tide flats of Thamesmead, where they find an abundance of worms and molluscs.

Oil pollution

A considerable part of the 2.2 billion metric tons of petroleum transported over the earth every year goes by ship. 0.44 billion tons come from undersea wells, and 1.5 billion tons are carried across the oceans by tankers. This level represents a tenfold increase over that of thirty years ago, and a further increase in petroleum production is expected in the future. It is not surprising, then, that in 1970 alone a total of five to ten million tons of oil were spilled into the ocean—as a result of shipwrecks, cleaning the oil tanks of the tankers, pumping the bilges of about 45,000 ocean-going ships, accidents in submarine drilling and leaks in pipes, and the dumping of domestic sewage.

The intensive efforts to reduce these effects of shipping upon pollution of the ocean with oil cannot appreciably reduce marine pollution; but a great deal will have been gained if, despite increased production, increased spillage is prevented. The tanks in which petroleum is transported must be cleaned of the tarry residues that settle out on their walls. This is done while the tankers are carrying ballast back to the regions of oil production. Because of the international agreement to prevent pollution of the sea by oil, the terms of which have several times been made more strict, 70% of the tanker tonnage has now adopted the new "load on top" procedure, in which dirtying of the ocean with oily wash water is slight. Large parts of the world's oceans have been declared off-limits for the cleaning of tanks. In addition, freighters over a certain size must be equipped with oil extractors, so that oil that gets into the bilge water during lubrication and oil changes is not pumped overboard.

Despite these improvements in safety measures, there is still no way to prevent accidents like the wreck of the *Torrey Canyon*. On March 18, 1967, in broad daylight with good weather, this tanker ran up onto the Seven Stones Reef northeast of the Scilly Isles at a speed of seventeen knots. The ship was loaded with 117,000 metric tons of crude oil from the Persian Gulf. Six of the eighteen tanks were slit open; 30,000 tons of oil ran out, and covering an area twenty nautical miles across drifted toward the English Channel. Part of this mass of oil, about 15,000 tons, reached Brittany between Les Heaut and the bay of Lannion on April 11. Because of the stormy seas during the days after the wreck, a further 18,000 tons of oil flowed out of the ship. A strong west wind drove this oil onto the coast of Cornwall between the 24th and 26th of March. On March 26 the wreck broke up in a heavy sea, so that another 40,000 to 50,000 tons of oil were released and eventually driven by the wind into the Bay of Biscay.

A similar tanker catastrophe in the southern North Sea is actually over-due, for according to world statistics 50% of all collisions of ships of over 500 gross registered tons occur between Dover and the mouth of the Elbe. Since the sizes of tankers are steadily increasing, and loads of 250,000 tons have become routine, the magnitude of the possible disaster is enormous.

Until a few years ago, the words "oil pollution" simply suggested two unpleasant consequences: people's enjoyment of the bathing beaches was spoiled, and sea birds were smeared with oil and died. In Great Britain, at the beginning of the 1950's, it was concluded, from finds of oil-covered sea birds on the beaches, that in the British Isles alone 50,000 to 250,000 birds were killed per year. 500 tons of oil spilled in the Hohwachter Bucht in 1953 cost the lives of 10,000 birds, and in 1955 near Scharhörn 8000 tons killed 50,000 sea birds.

Until fairly recently, the main action taken against oil spills was treat-ment with detergents, which created an oil-in-water emulsion. This was tried when the *Torrey Canyon* was wrecked, both in the open ocean and to clean the slimy coasts of Cornwall for the coming summer season. Alto-gether, 10,000 tons of detergents were used, as a countermeasure against about 14,000 tons of oil. More biological damage was done by the deter-gents than the oil could have caused. In contrast, the French used pulver-ized chalk to sink the already altered oil drifting on the surface of the ocean. This method was very successful; only 3000 tons of chalk were needed to sink about 30,000 tons of oil.

The detergents used in the *Torrey Canyon* disaster were relatively poisonous; such substances are more effective against oil, the more aro-matic components they contain. In the meantime, much less poisonous detergents have been developed, which can be used when a strip of coast is threatened directly by drifting oil, or to clean already dirtied beaches. Moreover, quite a number of other oil-binding substances are available, and experiments have been done to find suitable treatments after which fields of oil on the ocean surface can be set on fire. Wherever it is prac-ticable, the preferred method today is mechanical removal by scoops and suction. But in particular, experts are seriously reconsidering the necessity of doing anything at all about floating oil; the surface of the ocean is in the long run the best place for it, as long as coasts are not threatened. Unfortunately, one must accept the fact that sea birds contacting the oil will die; but neither emulsification of the oil with detergents nor binding it so that it sinks to the bottom really removes the oil. On the contrary, emulsified oil acts as a poison at any depth.

Crude oil consists of thousands of different components, in which the molecules are either arranged as simple or branched chains or as saturated or unsaturated rings. Oil from various sources differs in composition, depending on the conditions under which it was formed in geological history. When crude oil flows onto the ocean, the components with a low boiling point evaporate into the atmosphere, while other—in many cases very poisonous—components dissolve in the sea water. A quarter of the oil can disappear rapidly in these ways; little is known about the biological effects of these components. The remainder, left floating on the water, is to a great extent decomposed, more rapidly in warm seas than in cold regions. Decomposition involves the activities of bacteria and yeasts which feed on oil and burn up oxygen in the process. This decomposition is most rapid on the surface of the ocean; the light at the surface enhances oxidation. After a few weeks or months most of the oil disappears from the water surface, even without special treatment by man.

But there do remain tarry substances that strongly resist attack by microorganisms and in some cases are entirely unaltered. Among them are aromatic components with benzene rings, the carcinogenic effect of which has been proven. In the future, research will have to be especially concerned with these in order to find out what quantities are carried unchanged through the food chain. It also remains to be shown how much the marine vegetation itself contributes to the formation of carcinogens, and the relative rates of artificial and natural production of these substances. If petroleum reaches the sediments at the bottom, it remains effective for a long time. In Buzzards Bay 600 metric tons of diesel oil entered the ocean. One and a half years later, the sediments in the area were still poisonous to organisms; they contained 70 kg of hydrocarbons per kilogram.

Dumping rubbish at sea

It is expensive to haul refuse out to sea in ships and sink it. This method is chosen only if the refuse cannot be stored harmlessly or decomposed or burned—that is, chiefly in the cases of munitions, poison gas, radioactive materials and certain residues of the plastics industry. Since the ocean outside the three-mile zone is in general "free," it has not so far been possible to prevent anyone from dumping whatever he liked. While oil pollution angers bathers and calls bird conservationists into action, for decades—unnoticed by the public—many thousand barrels of chemical residues have been dumped into the ocean by various European industrial nations. Great Britain alone, between 1963 and 1969, disposed of about 30,000 barrels of cyanides, arsenic and other poisons in the North Atlantic, as well as 38,000 barrels of chlorinated hydrocarbons.

In 1970 Scandinavian scientists succeeded in demonstrating the presence of aliphatic chlorinated hydrocarbons in the open Atlantic and in the coastal waters of Norway. These were toxic wastes from the manufacture of PVC or polyvinyl chloride, a plastic. If chemical analysis can reveal these in the open ocean, there is indeed great danger to the marine organisms, especially since they are persistent substances that accumulate in the food chain. In barrels found by fishermen, an enormous variety of such substances have been found; many barrels were fished up not in the open ocean but just off the coasts of Holland and Germany. There is thus reason to suspect that many a ship's captain is increasing his profits by dumping barrels of poison not on the high seas, but shortly after leaving the harbor.

In July of 1971 the coastal freighter *Stella maris* sailed out from Rotterdam, loaded with 600 metric tons of wastes from the Dutch AKZO vinyl chloride factory. Its instructions were to sink its cargo near Halten Bank, sixty nautical miles west of Norway. When this became known, the Scandinavian governments raised objections, since the proposed dumpsite was close to an important fishing ground. The *Stella maris* was thereupon redirected to a position south of Iceland; on the way, it planned to coal at Thorshavn in the Faroes. This was emphatically prevented by the fishermen of Thorshavn; a proposal to coal at Stornoway in the Hebrides encountered opposition from the British government, and in case the freighter had any intention of entering Irish waters, Ireland threatened it with a warship. On the 26th of July the ship returned to Rotterdam with its mission unaccomplished; the barrels are being stored there until an installation for burning special refuse has been completed.

This case set the countries on the northeastern Atlantic into action. Government representatives met in Oslo in October, 1971, and worked out a protective agreement forbidding the dumping of persistent chlorinated hydrocarbons, mercury, cadmium, carcinogens and floating plastics in the high seas. For many other substances there were special provisions, and any sinking of materials in the sea had to be authorized by the governments concerned. This agreement, signed on February 15, 1972, by the participating countries, is an important step toward keeping the oceans in a sound condition.

The sinking of radioactive wastes, not controlled by the Oslo pact, is already governed by international agreements. The USA regularly deposited such materials in the Pacific between 1946 and 1957, and Great Britain did the same in the Atlantic. Countries belonging to the organization for European economic cooperation sank experimental barrels of radioactive waste in the depths of the ocean off the Iberian peninsula and studied the results. The barrels are supposed to be so sturdy that they should not corrode away until some of the radioactivity has decayed. For very long-lived poisons, however, packing them in barrels does not prevent their eventual dispersal; it can at best ensure that the substances really do sink to great depths, and do not mix directly with the surface water.

Meanwhile, oceanographic research with sensitive measuring devices has shown that even on the deep sea floor there are appreciable currents amounting to some centimeters per second. This means that the benthic regions are probably more closely linked to the large-scale circulation of water in the ocean than was formerly thought. Persistent poisons will therefore eventually return to the surface. An intriguing notion being entertained at the moment is to drop rubbish into the depths at points where tectonic movements of the earth's crust are thought to suck the superficial part of the ocean floor into the planet's interior.

Indirect marine pollution

In most of the cases discussed so far, pollutants have been discharged or dumped directly into the sea. But it should be remembered that everything that enters a river reaches the ocean eventually, unless it is biologically decomposed beforehand or sediments out. Moreover, contaminants can enter the ocean by way of the air. Prior to 1970 increased radioactivity of sea water had been observed as a consequence of the explosion of atomic bombs and of radioactive fallout, and in that year it became clear that other air-borne substances can also pollute the sea. Air pollution, after all, is not limited to large cities and concentrations of industry, but is a global phenomenon (see Chapter 9); the air over the open ocean shows minute concentrations of harmful materials produced by human civilization: dust, chemicals, and trace gases. Precipitation washes these substances out of the atmosphere and, since a large fraction of the precipitation fall over the ocean, many of them accumulate there.

Mercury on the high seas

We have heard above of several cases of mass mercury poisoning, in which a specific source could be traced. Since 1970, widespread testing has indicated the possibility of a more general pollution. Mercury has been found in the livers of fur seals on the Pribiloff Islands in the northern Pacific in canned tuna, in the flesh of sharks from the Indian Ocean, in the livers of northern pilot whales (*Globicephala melaena*) stranded on the California coast, in swordfish, in the muscles of Norwegian gulls, and so on. In general it can be said that fish from unpolluted habitats may contain up to 0.155 mg/kg mercury, but in the animals listed above this value was far exceeded.

When higher concentrations of mercury are found in tuna and swordfish, seals and whales, it may occur naturally; these are long-lived fish-eaters, terminal consumers in the food chain, which during their lifetime must accumulate a certain amount of mercury. But this does not change the fact that the margin between the mercury concentration in tuna and that possibly harmful to human health is small. In eating sea mammals and birds, also terminal consumers feeding exclusively on fish, one should be especially cautious. In Finland a woman fell ill with mercury poisoning; she had eaten a great many eggs of a goosander, on an isolated rocky island far from any sewage discharge point. Whereas whitefish in Finland's Saima Lake contained 0.2 mg/kg mercury, the fat of three ringed seals in the lake, which eat chiefly whitefish, was found to contain 74, 130 and 210 mg/kg mercury.

Recently it has become clear that mercury not only drains from industrial sites into the coastal regions, but also enters the atmosphere. It is liberated in the combustion of coal and petroleum, in the processing of iron ore and in the production of cement. Altogether, the amount of mercury entering the ocean for which man is directly responsible is at most

15,000 tons per year. When this figure is compared with the total mercury in all the world's oceans—100 to 200 million tons—it does not seem particularly large. However, estimates of the natural input of mercury to the oceans indicate a magnitude comparable to that from human sources: 2500 to 44,000 tons come from rock and 2500 to 15,000 tons are leached out by rain water. The degree to which polluted air and other human activities affect the overall mercury concentration in our environment has not yet been determined. In any case, we must make every effort to prevent either the coastal regions or the open seas from receiving larger amounts of mercury in future. Even at very low concentrations, it can be toxic to marine organisms. In complex organic compounds such as those used against mold, it impairs photosynthesis in sensitive marine algae—for example, the siliceous alga *Nitzschia delicatissima*—in a concentration of 0.1 $\mu g/1$.

A person who lives in a large city today is thought to consume forty times as much lead per day, in his food and drinking water, in cigarette smoke and in the air he breathes, as someone in the pre-industrial era. The lead content in the blood of many city dwellers is already approaching concentrations that cause symptoms of poisoning. It is thus a matter for real concern when the lead content of even sea water rises. In pre-industrial times about 11,000 tons of lead per year reached the ocean, freed by natural weathering. At present, the estimate is 430,000 tons per year, obviously a vast increase over the natural rate of influx.

Lead in the ocean

All the evidence indicates that the oceans are afflicted with lead pollution, originating chiefly in the extensive use since 1940, of tetra-ethyl lead as an anti-knock agent in gasoline. About 350,000 tons of lead per year are released into the atmosphere with automobile exhausts in the northern hemisphere; about 250,000 tons of this are carried by precipitation into the ocean. Marine biology has not yet paid enough attention to the question of the damage lead can do in the sea. In the Institute of Oceanography in Bremerhaven, mussels subjected experimentally to high concentrations of lead showed no reaction during the first forty days. Later animals died which had been living in water with more than 0.5 mg/1 dissolved lead salts. This is a much higher concentration than we can expect to find in the ocean. But the degree to which lead at very low concentrations is accumulated by organisms and passed on in the food chain is still not known. In the livers of bass caught near Los Angeles lead was found at a concentration of 22 mg/kg, whereas fish caught off Peru had only 9 mg/kg.

We have mentioned above that DDT and other chlorinated hydrocarbons used in agriculture contaminate sewage and sometimes accumulate in worrisome amounts in food fish, and even more commonly in sea birds. Today this chemical is distributed throughout the world. In the fat of antarctic Weddell's seals (*Leptonychotes weddelli*) and crab-eating seals (*Lobodon carcinophagus*) 0.12 to 0.4 mg/kg DDT were found, and in penguins 0.05 mg/kg. The fat of Wilson's storm petrel (*Oceanites oceanicus*),

Global ocean pollution by DDT

which breeds on the antarctic islands, contained 420 mg/kg DDT, and the eggs of a hook-billed petrel (*Pterodroma hasitata cahow*), 6.4 mg/kg.

If this posion is demonstrable in these animals, which live far from any site of production or application of DDT, we should not be surprised that fish samples from all coastal waters and the high sea contain DDT, even though the concentrations are not yet serious as far as human health is concerned. The values are above average in the herring—because of its high fat content—and in the livers of fish, the eggs of sea birds, and the fat of marine mammals. International expeditions are currently studying the oceans of the world, to obtain a reliable picture of the distribution of DDT and similar chlorinated hydrocarbons.

When DDT is sprayed from planes over forests, fields, or the swamps where mosquitoes breed, some of it remains as fine droplets in the air. Of the poison that does fall onto plants and the soil, much of it remains there for years. On the average it takes ten years until these residues have fallen to 5% of the amounts immediately after application. We do not yet know enough about where the other 95% has gone. Like other chlorinated hydrocarbons, DDT is quite resistant to bacterial or chemical decomposition under natural circumstances. It is known that DDT is converted to DDD by some bacteria, and to DDE by many organisms, but these compounds are also chlorinated hydrocarbons, some of which are even more poisonous than the original DDT. Similar transformations are known for other pesticides, but so far there are only a few examples of such substances actually being converted to carbon dioxide. The soil fungus *Trichoderma koningi* can perform such a conversion of dieldrin; it remains to be shown whether this process is significant in nature. And scientists are still investigating the degree to which chlorinated hydrocarbons are destroyed by light.

DDT hardly evaporates at all, but it is carried into the atmosphere by evaporating soil water. Precipitation washes it out of the atmosphere and it eventually reaches the ocean. This route is more important than transport by the rivers. We do not yet know at what rate decomposition of DDT and similar compounds occurs in the ocean. DDT is evidently fairly resistant even there, to account for its worldwide occurrence. Nor do we know how rapidly DDT is removed from the biosphere into deposits in lifeless strata of the earth. After a hurricane, oysters of Tres Palacios Bay (USA) contained five to seven times as much DDT as previously; possibly it had been liberated from sediments stirred up by the hurricane. Since DDT has a strong chemical affinity for living tissue, it tends to be retained in the upper sediment layers, those inhabited by organisms, and only gradually is transported to the depths as sediments accumulate. The DDT now to be found in the oceans will thus retain its effectiveness for years or decades.

Currently it is thought that about a quarter of the DDT produced is carried into the ocean by precipitation. In 1970, that would have been about 25,000 metric tons. Until better estimates are available, we can assume that at present about half a million tons of DDT are affecting the biosphere on our planet. Of course, this amount is not evenly distributed. But on the average it corresponds to a milligram per square meter, a millionth of a gram in every liter of the top meter of ocean water, or 0.01 millionth of a gram in every liter of the productive water layer down to a depth of 100 meters. Its affinity for fats and tissues is such that it can be taken up even from such low concentrations and accumulated in plants and animals.

Experiments with DDT in which one of the carbon atoms has been replaced by the radioactive isotope C^{14} permit relatively easy demonstration of the amounts of DDT that accumulate in living organisms. Such studies have been done at the Institute of Oceanography in Bremerhaven. Marine worms of the genus *Lanice* kept in water with a DDT concentration of 0.01 $\mu g/l$ extract so much within three days that the DDT concentration in their tissues becomes two hundred times as great. The amount taken up is correspondingly greater when the concentration in the surroundings is higher: with 2 $\mu g/l$ in the water, the concentration in the worms is 84 $\mu g/kg$ after two days and 5120 $\mu g/kg$ after a month. Similar results have been obtained with other organisms. Some scientists go so far as to say that there is essentially no free DDT in natural waters, since almost all of it either sticks to the surfaces of organisms or is collected in their tissues.

Fish also take DDT directly from the water, by way of the gills and secondarily with their food. When a worm experimentally loaded with 5.4 μg DDT is fed to a sole, only six hours later the concentration in the brain of the fish is 260 $\mu g/kg$, and in the liver as much as 80 $\mu g/kg$. When flounders were given 15 μg DDT, administered with their food over a period of fourteen days, after a month 5% of the DDT consumed was still in the brain, kidney and gut, while 13% remained in the musculature; the rest had probably been excreted.

Such experiments confirm that DDT content does increase gradually from traces in the phytoplankton to measurable quantities in planktonic animals, values of about 0.1 mg/kg in fish, and considerably higher concentrations in sea birds and mammals that feed exclusively upon fish. There is convincing documentation of a global distribution of DDT through the atmosphere, and of the capacity of organisms to store DDT when they are exposed to only minute concentrations and to pass it on up the food chain. Given this situation, what consequences are to be expected?

Sensitive organisms are harmed when exposed to a DDT concentration of only 1 $\mu g/l$; at present such concentrations would only be.likely to occur in the vicinity of waste-discharge points. Even so, this justifies the demand that chlorinated hydrocarbons no longer be allowed to enter the ocean. Since we do not know whether there is a mutual enhancement of the effects of several of these substances in combination, there is reason for concern in any case—especially since damage, once it is noted, cannot soon be repaired. Given the persistence of these compounds, we must accept that their effects will continue for years or decades to come, even if production were stopped today.

If the fish eaten by sea birds contain more than 0.1–1 mg/kg DDT, the extinction of the birds is imminent; as mentioned above, DDT then accumulates in the birds to such an extent that the shells of their eggs become thin and some of the brood is lost before hatching. Whereas the DDT content of fish taken from the high seas is less than this value, many of the measurements from coastal regions, including the North Sea, are so high as to arouse concern for the immediate future of the birds. The eggs of English sea birds contain about 9 mg/kg and those of Baltic Sea murres, up to 40 mg/kg. Sea birds are particularly important "test objects" because of their sensitivity to chlorinated hydrocarbons. If they should die out, this would be a warning we could not ignore; further poisoning of the ocean with chlorinated hydrocarbons would have to be prevented.

Man himself is not at present menaced by the DDT in the ocean; only in rare instances, when more than 5 mg/kg DDT has been found in food fish, have limited regions on the coast of the USA had to be closed to fishing. Indeed, the very reason DDT is so popular as an insecticide is that it is highly poisonous to insects while having relatively little effect on warm-blooded animals, including man. Infants, however, are particularly vulnerable; they have the highest DDT concentrations in the population because they take in with their mother's milk relatively more, per kg body weight, than do adults. The organizations of the UN concerned with nutrition and health have determined that a human being can take in $10 \mu g$ DDT per kilogram body weight every day with no fear of injury. For a man weighing seventy kilograms, that would be 0.7 mg per day—ten times as much as is in his food currently. Even heavily contaminated fish, containing 5 mg/kg DDT, could thus be eaten at a rate of 125 grams per day without exceeding the tolerance limits, and that is four times the present average consumption of thirty grams daily. The low DDT content in marine fish caught on the high seas is therefore insignificant by this measure.

However, it is necessary to consider not only fish eaten as such, but fish meal and fish oil. Certain oil compounds from herring, originally containing 0.1 mg/kg DDT, become more concentrated during processing, so that they eventually contain 1.75 mg/kg. When such products are fed to domestic animals, a further concentration of DDT is to be expected as it accumulates in their flesh. Investigations of the effects of chlorinated hydrocarbons upon metabolism, tumor formation and the genetic material are in progress. Presumably more refined methods will reveal the effects of even small concentrations of DDT; and it is hardly likely that the tolerance limit of 5 mg/kg that now holds for fish in the USA will be raised. If ocean fishery is to provide wholesome food in the future, and if we hope to make even more use of the ocean as a source of food than before, these arguments alone make it urgent that chlorinated hydrocarbons no longer be put into the sea.

The North Sea is a shallow body of water at the edge of the Atlantic. Large parts of it are less than fifty meters deep, the total volume of water is only 54,000 cubic kilometers, and the exchange of water with the Bay of Biscay and the North Atlantic is so slight that sea water on the average remains in the North Sea for more than two years before mixing again with that of the Atlantic. The North Sea is surrounded by industrial nations, including Great Britain, the Benelux countries, and Germany; France also sends wastes into it by way of the Rhine and the eastward-flowing current in the English Channel. Moreover, the industries in countries on the Baltic Sea are in communication with the North Sea by way of the Skagerrak. The stretch from Dover to the mouth of the Elbe is the most heavily travelled shipping lane on earth, and shipwrecks and collisions are correspondingly common there.

Pollution of the North Sea

One would expect, then, that the North Sea should have been greatly altered by the influx of wastes over the past hundred and fifty years; nevertheless, it remains one of the regions of the world most abundantly populated by fish. Even now there is no evidence suggesting that the stocks of fish are declining as a result of waste disposal there. The bottom fauna in Helgoländer Bucht in 1968 was made up of the same species found there forty years previously.

At the same time, it should be said that the coastal regions in northern Germany themselves are still relatively unaffected by modern technology; industry is concentrated further inland, and there are only a few large cities in the immediate vicinity of the coast. But since the mid-1960's there has been an unmistakeable trend for industry to become established on the coast. In addition to the advantage of such a location for transport, a decisive consideration has been that controls on air and water pollution here would probably not be so strict as in densely populated regions. This attitude has led to the construction of industrial centers and nuclear reactors on the lower reaches of the Elbe, between Stade and Cuxhaven, on the lower Weser between Brake and Blexen, and on the Jade bay seaward from Wilhelmshaven; further projects are under discussion which would involve the Ems, the coast of Butjadingen between Jade and the Weser, and the region of Scharhörn-Neuwerk seaward from Cuxhaven. In parallel with these developments, tourism has undergone a considerable increase in the last decade on all the German coasts; in the Baltic region, especially, the usually uncleaned sewage from the holiday resorts and camping places pollutes the coastal waters.

At one time the supposedly inexhaustible masses of ocean water were regarded as a bottomless cesspit for sewage and refuse of every kind. The motto of the time might well have been, "Dilution is the solution to pollution." But in the last ten years, from 1962 to 1972, it has become clear that even the self-cleaning capacity of the ocean is finite and can be

The sea—a cesspool

overtaxed. Today we can see how fortunate we are that despite one and a half centuries of the development of civilization and economic growth in Europe, the North Sea is still in a sound condition; we know from experience with the inland waters how easily a lake or stream can become unbalanced and how difficult—if not impossible—it is to restore it to health. In the inland waters there have been many cases of such great accumulation of noxious substances in organisms that they are useless as food.

In a few years, researchers will be able to predict just when disaster can be expected, if use of the North Sea as a cesspool continues to increase at the current rate. At least the danger has now been recognized and is known to the general public. Industrial installations being set up on the coast are subject to the same requirements as those further inland. Communities must build treatment facilities for their domestic sewage. It will take years to put these measures into effect, but there is hope that the North Sea will be kept alive and will provide food for European tables for a long time to come.

But it must be understood that regional industrialization and an economy based on seaports are not reconcilable with modern methods or intensive fishery, including the husbandry or "aquaculture" of marine animals. Legal injunctions and safety precautions cannot prevent occasional accidents; further harm can easily occur. In 1971, for example, there were complaints from the Dutch purchasers of mussels from the Mellum region in the outer part of the Jade bay, because they tasted of oil.

In exchange for the industrial and population centers still to be built, we must count on losing more of the natural landscape and its flora and fauna. Hence there is every reason to support attempts to protect the regions that are left—the North Frisian Islands up to the Danish border, the East Frisian Islands between Wangerooge and Borkum, and the shallow sea between these islands and the coast. Here, as along the beach areas of the Baltic Sea, there is an ideal opportunity to preserve the countryside while paying due regard to the needs of people for rest and recreation.

In the long term, of course, the North Sea, like other small seas fortunate enough to have escaped thus far, must share the fate of the global system which underlies all oceans. From all that has been said above, we are quite certain that industrialized man is capable of causing global pollution with persistent substances that accumulate in the environment, and that if the present tendency continues, the concentrations of noxious substances will steadily increase in all of the ocean systems. It is not yet possible to set up a "schedule of ocean pollution" and predict the amounts of pollutants mankind will encounter in ten, forty or seventy years unless the present trend is terminated. On the open ocean it is much more difficult than in coastal waters to identify the culprit, to say nothing of changing his ways. The person responsible for the pollution may live thousands of miles away, and have no idea of the consequences of his actions.

6 Biological Equilibrium

The more biologists have studied living organisms, the clearer has been their recognition of the intimate reciprocal relationships among plants, animals, and their abiotic environment. Wherever plants and animals are found, they are of types specially adapted to the local environmental conditions, and the physical and chemical factors in any habitat are responsible for the size and composition of the communities typically living there.

This dependence of community upon its environment (its biotope), by its very nature, produces fluctuations in population density, course of development and generation time of the different species; a parallelism between these fluctuations and the changes in the biotope is almost always discernible. Natural communities, then, are not rigid structures. But the changes they undergo are subject to a degree of control, and under ordinary circumstances they fluctuate about an equilibrium level.

Such systems of individuals and communities, together with their environment, are called ecosystems; they may be as enormous as the ocean or as tiny as the puddle left by a rainstorm. Ecosystems appear superficially to be independent entities, comparable perhaps to a manned spaceship in orbit. But ultimately all of them depend upon one environmental factor—light. From light comes the energy that supports life, just as the solar cells in a spaceship provide electricity.

As earlier chapters have shown, this energy is converted by photosynthesis, the process in which green plants change water, carbon dioxide and nutrient salts to organic matter. Animals are incapable of transforming sunlight metabolically into usable energy, and so must rely upon their food, either eating the plants directly or using the more indirect approach of the carnivores. Thus the solar energy taken up by the plants circulates through the entire ecosystem in the form of organic matter. At last it reaches the "decomposers," microorganisms that feed upon dead plants and animals and in so doing reconvert them to their original components—water, carbon dioxide, and mineral salts. In this very complicated cyclic process man, too, has his place.

By W. Tobias

Light and ecosystems

Ecocatastrophes

Under natural conditions, these processes approach an equilibrated state. When the factors controlling an ecological system suddenly depart from their ordinary ranges, this balance can be seriously upset, and in extreme cases a collapse of the system may result. But under natural circumstances such "ecocatastrophes" are very rare. Populations of many species, reduced when conditions are unfavorable, almost always return to their original equilibrium levels when the environment returns to its previous state.

Temperature and food supply

Often climatic factors, especially temperature, are decisive in regulating animal populations. Prolonged cold periods in the winter can indirectly reduce the stocks of fish-eating birds, since the ice covering the water prevents them from finding food. In England, the density of common heron (*Ardea cinerea*) nests on two large rivers was monitored from 1934 to 1963. Each harsh winter brought about a sharp reduction in the heron colony. But in mild winters the deficit was quickly made up; the number of occupied nests, and thus of individual birds, increased.

Similar fluctuations in the population density of a species can be caused by differences in the availability of food. Mule deer (*Odocoileus hemionus*) in Arizona had been hunted so extensively that they nearly became extinct, but at the beginning of the century a protected reservation was established in the Kaibab Plateau area. The natural predators of the deer, pumas and wolves, were hunted until extinct in the area. At first the stocks of mule deer increased slowly, but then, because of the food available and the freedom from predation, the rate accelerated so that by the end of the first two decades there were twenty-five times the original number of deer. This overpopulation led to severe overgrazing. The consequence was a food shortage that caused starvation of many young deer, and the population "crashed." After some time this marked reduction in the numbers of deer resulted in renewal of the range land. Eventually an equilibrium was established between the size of the deer population and that of the food supply. Replacement of predation by hunting was necessary to keep the deer population within limits.

Self-regulation

Some animal populations can also regulate their densities autonomously, uninfluenced by environmental factors. For example, the tadpoles of many anurans—tree toads, grass frogs, fire-bellied toads, British toads, and others—eat both the spawn of their own species and that of the other species sharing their habitat. This behavior prevents the overpopulation that would otherwise develop, for these anurans often lay many thousand eggs at a time. As another example, there are nutrient-poor ponds and lakes in northern Scandinavia where the fish population consists entirely of perch of approximately the same age and size. The explanation is that the young fish are hunted and eaten by the older ones, and can grow to maturity only when the number of old perch decreases.

Trout lay their eggs on the sandy or gravelly bottoms of bodies of water rich in oxygen; many of these eggs fall below the surface, into gaps between the sand grains and stones. Since the oxygen supply at these deeper levels is reduced, it often happens that large numbers of these embryos suffocate and die. They decay, and this process uses up even more of the oxygen in the immediate surroundings; moreover, they are sources of infection for other eggs which are still developing. In the face of these cumulative effects, one would expect each generation to suffer severe losses. But the larvae of certain species of stone fly reduce this threat. They feed on the dead embryos, thus removing decay products harmful to the trout spawn; at the same time, they are unable to bite through the hard shells of healthy eggs. In this example, then, one species helps maintain the population of another.

There are countless cases of predator-prey relationships in the animal kingdom which act to balance biological conditions. The predatory species and the prey species are in a state of dynamic equilibrium with one another; if the prey species should become particularly abundant, the population density of the predator rises until the number of prey has been reduced to a certain minimum. The large predator population creates a food shortage for itself and must in turn decline—which allows the prey to multiply again. Many years of observations of the snowy owl (*Nyctea scandiaca*) and its prey, the collared lemming (*Dicrostonyx greenlandicus*), revealed that every "lemming year" was followed by an upward jump in the number of snowy owls; on the other hand, after years in which there were few lemmings almost no owls were sighted.

Predator-prey relationships

These examples illustrate the kinds of factors which tend, under natural circumstances, to equilibrate biological systems. In a complete system, of course, the meshing of countless other factors makes the situation much more complicated, so that a detailed analysis must often be limited to subsystems.

Since man has been exerting an ever increasing influence upon nature, many natural habitats have vanished and many more have been reduced. Even the polar regions and the tundra, the sea islands and the deserts are beginning to lose much of their virgin quality in the atomic age. In the search for wealth from the soil, airplanes, automobiles, modern ships and bulldozers combine to open them up for exploitation; in the arms race between the nations they are occupied as military outposts and proving grounds for nuclear weapons. In most of the rest of the world, wherever nature has managed to survive in some form, the original habitats have given way to landscapes marked by man and capable of only a limited amount of self-regulation. Further human intervention can further upset the balance of such artificial ecosystems.

The "pseudo-ecosystems" created by man

The course of past human intervention, described earlier in the book, can be summarized as follows. When Neolithic agriculture and animal husbandry turned nomads into settlers, human influence was small. The growth of the earth's population and the onset of the age of technology brought about truly profound changes. Today these changes have become so vast—amounting to the total destruction of natural surroundings in parts of the world—that the sphere of human life, so intimately interrelated with nature as a whole, is seriously restricted. Almost any mistake man makes in tampering with the complex machinery of nature brings a magnified revenge; many of the early attempts to repair the damage have failed because of ecological ignorance.

Monocultures and pests

When people lived by gathering wild plants, they were in a natural equilibrium with plant-eating insects. But when they began to cultivate high-yield types of plants in monocultures, these insects throve and became pests that could destroy entire harvests. As agriculture was progressively extended, the pest insects moved with it, into regions where they had never lived before. For example, the potato beetle of the southwestern USA spread rapidly as far as southeastern Europe.

In the age of industry, chemicals came into use as a means of preventing outbreaks of pests. At first these methods were successful, but as their use was intensified new problems became apparent. Many insects developed a hereditary resistance to pesticides (a well-known example of this is the resistance to DDT); new pest species appeared where their natural enemies had been annihilated by poisons. Moreover, pesticides have accumulated in the bodies of warm-blooded animals, including man himself, and affected their health (see Chapter 7). Equilibrium was no longer maintained, for the newly created artificial monocultures were incapable of self-regulation.

It was quite reasonable then to try keeping the pest population down with biological methods—for example, by taking advantage of the predator-prey system or the parasite-host system—but failures were common, and in some cases there were unsuspected effects upon the native animals. To overcome the plague of rats in the sugar-cane plantations of Jamaica, the mongoose (*Herpestes edwardsi*) was introduced there in the second half of the last century. The mongoose did in fact dominate the rats in a short time, but then multiplied so rapidly that it in turn became a pest, attacking domestic animals and almost exterminating many native island species of amphibians, snakes, lizards, birds and small mammals.

The integrated approach to agriculture

Such efforts to control ecological balance in monocultures by purely biological or chemical means have been frustrated time and again. Today people are gradually coming to realize that nature cannot be so readily manipulated, and that the only way out of the dilemma is to adopt methods based on fundamental ecological principles. An integrated approach to agriculture—a synthesis of chemical and biological pest control, new methods of crop rotation, artificial fertilization and cultivation, and breeding programs based on recent research—should eventually succeed in restoring the lost ecological balance and bringing the agrarian regions more nearly into line with natural habitats. Such programs of course depend upon a vital environmental factor that has long been ignored—water (see Chapter 3). Wherever the water balance has been upset, the consequences for the ecosystem are disastrous.

Forests and water balance

The thoughtless levelling of large forests has reduced the retention of water in the regions concerned. In historical times clear-cut areas have often been used as grazing land; the result was not only destruction of the closed plant cover, but packing of the soil by the trampling animals, which decreased its storage capacity and eventually culminated in erosion, leaching or periodic floods. Later attempts to restore a normal biological and hydrological situation, by reforestation of former mixed-forest regions with pure conifer plantations, have been ineffective. Modification of the watercourses, with the aim of preventing floods by more rapid drainage, is just as mistaken.

The impoverishment of species in plantations of conifers, and the deterioration of water balance resulting from canalization and land drainage, have been mentioned in other chapters. In undisturbed natural regions one "hydrological engineer" has solved the technical problems associated with the rapid removal of rain water in an admirable way. This is the beaver (*Castor fiber*). His dams of wood, built across the courses of rivers, raise the local water table, encouraging plant growth along the riverbanks. For this reason many regions in North America where beaver once lived are now being restocked with these animals.

Collapse of aquatic ecosystems

The greatest menace to water today, as described in the chapter on the inland waters (Chapter 3), is pollution. In the densely populated centers of industry, raw sewage and industrial wastes have led almost everywhere to the collapse of aquatic plant and animal communities. The river and lake organisms that have not yet been killed will not long be able to bear the burden of pollutants. The self-cleaning capacity of bodies of water is overloaded. Instead of a balanced relationship between producers, consumers and decomposers, the scale has been tipped toward the decomposers —chiefly bacteria and other microorganisms. In breaking down the excessive quantities of human wastes they deplete the water of oxygen, so that oxygen-breathing animals can no longer survive. A surplus of nutrient salts, primarily detergent phosphates, in sewage encourages an overproduction of aquatic plants. This too is followed by oxygen depletion and decay, and the end result is the collapse of the whole intricate system. Even in the ocean comparable processes can now be discerned (see Chapter 5). The only remedy is to clean all sewage and other waste-carrying water, so that biological equilibrium is restored.

The destructive effect of civilization on naturally controlled biological processes is especially clear in these examples concerning water, but it is also evident in every biological system on every continent. Only an understanding of biological interactions can help man to correct past errors and to prevent, by careful planning, further disruption of the biological equilibrium.

7 Pesticides and Fertilizers

By W. Schuphan

The man in the street is most aware of the damage to the environment done by industry. It is obvious in the state of the poisoned plants he sees, the smog he breathes, and the corroded buildings that surround him. Out in the country, on the other hand, deterioration is not so evident. Where farming and forestry are concerned, even an expert cannot always perceive immediately the consequences of the intensive use of inorganic fertilizers, pesticides, and herbicides. But these dangers are no less real. Indeed, since the damage is so little apparent it is more insidious; it is overlooked and its influence on the health of man and animal is underestimated. To detect these poisons scientists must use the most sensitive biological and chemical tests, and large- and small-scale experiments are necessary to assess the threat and recommend countermeasures.

The contamination of the environment with toxic materials is a complex phenomenon; no single source of pollution should be considered alone. Many of the pollutants originating with man can interact in such a way that their toxicity is mutually enhanced. The severity of illness can be greatly increased with exposure to certain combinations of pesticides or of pesticides and medicines.

Not long ago the group of polychlorinated biphenyls (PCB) was discovered to be a persistent (not easily decomposed) pollutant on a global scale, like DDT. PCB resembles DDT in chemical and physical characteristics, although it is not a pesticide. Its identification and effects in marine animals, birds of prey and sea birds, mothers' milk and human fat have been described in Chapter 5. According to Japanese studies, PCB in humans can cause liver damage, impairment of vision, alterations in pigmentation and deterioration of the nervous system. PCB and DDT in combination are more toxic than either alone.

It is useful in this connection to take up the notion of "stress." A stress syndrome can be produced by one's life style in general, and in particular by diet, environmental influences and by the tensions associated with working in the modern industrial society. Stress involves extreme demands on the heart and circulatory system, as well as the nervous system; in highly developed industrialized countries especially, the contribution of stress to the death rate is considerable.

The diagram in Figure 7-1 illustrates one category of the environmental contributions to stress—the "external" pollution of air, soil and water outside the enclosed spaces occupied by man. Here we include any sort of contamination that has a negative effect upon health. The chief purpose of this diagram is to show how the potential dangers from field and forest fit into the total picture of environmental pollution.

"External" pollution

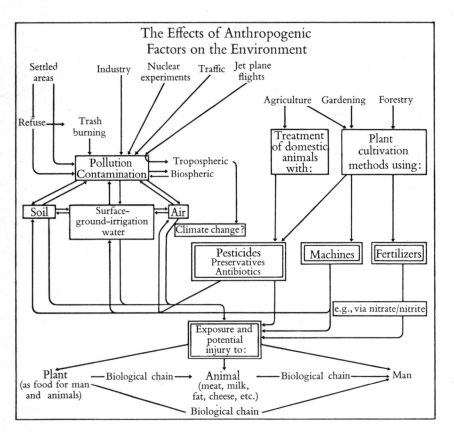

Fig. 7-1. The pollution problem is a complex of many factors, some of which are diagrammed here.

Of course, it must be mentioned that the "green sector" of the environment, as opposed to the "built-up sector," is still in a much sounder condition, if only because of the production of oxygen by the plants. But this comparison must not mislead us into ignoring the hidden dangers to health in the "green sector." Exploitation of the soil with the aim of achieving the greatest possible harvest at any price is no longer defensible from a biological standpoint. However one may wish it were otherwise, one cannot agree with dealers in agricultural chemicals, or their spokesmen in science and the applied areas, when they call agriculture a peaceful island in the ominous flood of contemporary environmental pollution.

Figure 7-1 does not treat "internal" pollution within transport facilities and enclosed dwelling and working areas. An analogy in the "green sector" is the "forcing" of vegetables and fruit in greenhouses. The residues of pesticides are usually found in higher concentrations in greenhouse crops than in those grown in the open; this could well be due to the failure of vaporized pesticides to escape, so that they recondense on the plants.

One crop, tobacco, plays an extraordinarily important role in "internal" pollution, presenting two dangers to health. The tobacco smoke itself bears poisons such as nicotine, carbon monoxide and carcinogens. The second danger comes from the fact that pesticide residues (dithiocarbamates) remain on the growing tobacco leaves after drying and fermentation. The greatest permissible content of the dithiocarbamates maneb and zineb, used to protect leafy vegetables and fruit (including wine grapes), is 3 ppm (parts per million, or mg/kg); the dithiocarbamate content of European and Oriental cigarettes, for comparison, ranges from 52 to 206 ppm.

The problems raised by tobacco smoke in the "internal" environment, with its extreme threat to health, have received relatively little attention at the official level. Babies, children and adult nonsmokers in confined vehicles, waiting rooms and public buildings are forced to breathe the air dirtied by smokers. They may be affected as much as people breathing the worst smog produced by "external" industrial sources. The disparity in attitudes to these two sorts of pollution, appalling to many of us, is evidence of how environmentalists are affected by different kinds of self-interest.

Pollution from agricultural sources

Businesslike attitudes and rational actions, along with scientific and technological research, are responsible for the prosperity and wealth of consumer goods made available by the industrial revolution. But no one has given much thought to the fact that for every such development, unaccompanied by effective measures to protect soil, water and air, the price will eventually have to be paid. The industrial environment, which ought to provide a habitat and wholesome food, was largely ignored in the hectic race for technological progress and economic advantage. Only as pollution reached frightening levels have those in responsible positions begun to take notice. Since 1970 the governments in many countries have suddenly started to apply intensive countermeasures. In the "green sector" the course of events has been like that in industry, but with a certain delay, since mass production and the business ethic have necessarily been tempered by the laws of biology and biochemistry.

The problems of environmental pollution in the "green sector" are now becoming apparent. These have arisen in part from the tendency toward mass production of plants and animals, at ever lower "per-unit" prices. Agrarian economists demanded that intensive use should be made of every means—especially inorganic fertilizers and pesticides—to achieve the highest possible yields of commercially attractive produce, with as much urgency as if it were a matter of winning a war; but this approach has often backfired. In the European countries, for example, it has often happened that surplus fruit and vegetables, overproduced by extreme application of fertilizers and pesticides, have had to be destroyed.

But other consequences are far worse than such purely financial disasters. If cultivation of crops were based on the principles of agrarian biology, nutritious, wholesome plants could be marketed without so much emphasis on the attraction of customers by appearance alone. The diagram in Figure 7-2 shows agricultural procedures which lead to an increase, and others which lead to a decrease, of crop disease and infestation by pests.

Thoughtlessly intensive agriculture, designed to produce the highest yields with the greatest possible immediate profits, encourages disease and pests. As a result, in order that the produce be immaculate in appearance, further treatment with poisons is required, leaving more poisonous residues on and in both crops and soil.

On the other hand, if one is willing to forego the goal of the "highest yields at any risk," there are alternatives. If producers apply the results of research in agrarian biology and plant physiology, it is possible to reduce plant disease and pest infestation. A wider range of disease-resistant varieties of high nutritional value is produced, and less poisoning of the soil and food crops is required.

Farming and forestry, as already mentioned, do relatively little harm

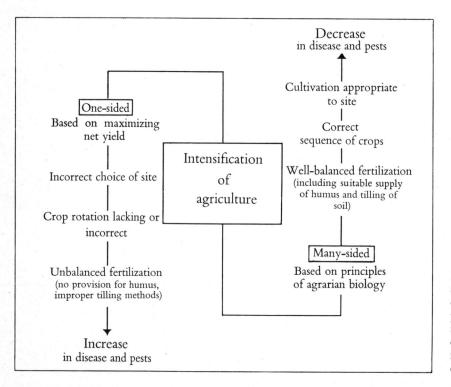

Fig. 7-2. Two methods of agriculture producing different results; intensive profit-minded procedures result in an increase of disease and pests, while a more diversified approach can lead to a decrease.

Causes of eutrophication

to the environment in Europe. When the eutrophication of lakes and streams became an issue, the blame was at first laid on phosphate-containing fertilizers. But now it is accepted that the phosphates in detergents and fecal materials reaching the watercourses by way of sewage bear the chief responsibility.

To be sure, soluble nitrates from fertilizer may contribute to eutrophication of these waters. They are washed out of the soil by rain, or carried in the drainage channels from irrigated fields. These nitrates are not all of inorganic origin; some come from organic sources such as the urine and dung of domestic animals, compost, and even human excreta (in some countries, the liquid component of such sewage is cleaned by watering fields with it).

Nitrogen is a component of vital tissues in plants and animals. It occurs in the amino acids, which combine to form proteins, in enzymes, in pigments such as chlorophyll and hemoglobin, and in vitamins of the B group. Nitrogen compounds are taken up directly by plants, and by animals and ultimately man when they eat the plants.

There is not nearly enough manure and compost to perform even their main agricultural job—the physical and microbiological improvement of the soil—to say nothing of the fact that they offer a very inadequate supply of nitrogen. Therefore modern farmers feed their crops almost exclusively with commercial fertilizers containing inorganic nitrogen. But these lack an important property of organic fertilizers; the latter liberate their nutrients at different rates, depending on the prevailing conditions, so that on the whole they become available to the plants when they are most needed. Plants fed with inorganic nitrogen tend to be overfed, and as a result nitrate is stored in their vascular systems. Furthermore, because of the lack of humus in the soil, the nitrates can be washed out into the ground water. Another undesirable effect of heavy application of inorganic nitrogen is the accumulation of free amino acids (i.e., not incorporated into proteins) and a decrease in the vital amino acid methionine. Excessive nitrogen fertilization also leads to a decline in plant quality in terms of taste, to reduced storability, and to an increase of disease and attack by pests, which in turn forces the farmer to apply more pesticides. Again, one is then faced with the serious problem of toxic residues in the crops. Other dangers associated with overfertilization with nitrogen, involving the health of people and dairy cattle, will be discussed later in this chapter.

Nitrogen is a gaseous element comprising about 78% of the atmosphere. Plants cannot take it up directly in this form, but there are certain bacteria and blue-green algae that can do so; some of them live free in the soil and some bacteria are symbiotic in the roots of leguminous plants. As an inorganic fertilizer, nitrogen is applied to crops in various forms, particularly as nitrates and as salts of the ammonium cation. Nitrates (salts containing the NO_3 ion) have proved not to be entirely harmless, especially when converted to nitrites (salts containing the NO_2 ion), which can be poisonous.

Because the nitrate problem is so central to environmental pollution, since 1953 we have carried on experiments with spinach (*Spinacia oleracea*) and a close relative of the red beet, the sugar or fodder beet (*Beta vulgaris*). These have been grown in the field, in cement frames, and in climate-controlled rooms. In the climate-chambers all factors affecting growth, including light and temperature, were controlled. The object was to examine the mechanisms by which nitrate and nitrite (formed from ammonia in the soil by certain bacteria) appear in food and fodder plants under various ecological conditions. We were concerned both with the natural environment—climate and soil—and with agricultural procedures which can critically affect them. The climatic factors of interest were the variations in duration of sunshine, temperature, and precipitation over many years; the relationship of the time of sowing and of germination to ecological conditions and to fertilization was observed. On the basis of our experiments and the research of others, the following can be said:

1. Depending on its physiological constitution, the plant takes up nitrogen as either the nitrate or the ammonium ion, and from these it forms amino acids and high-molecular-weight proteins.

2. This process is carried almost to completion, so that no appreciable nitrate remains in the plant, only if all the factors affecting growth—espec-

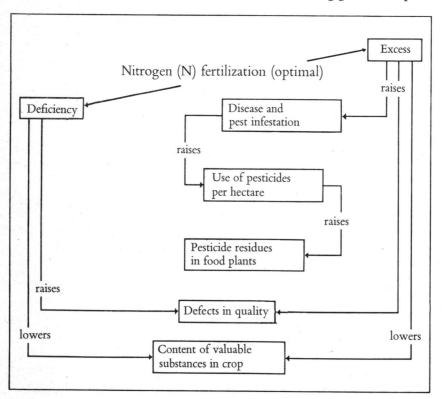

Fig. 7-3. Schematic representation of the negative consequences of inadequate fertilization, and of excessive fertilization, with nitrogen. There are a few exceptions: for example, nitrogen application suppresses the pathogens that cause the bases of wheat stalks to turn black.

Fig. 7-4. Some of the results of experiments on the "model plant" spinach. The differences between the curves for the various years reflect the differing amounts of sunshine in the growing seasons (cf. Fig. 7-6).

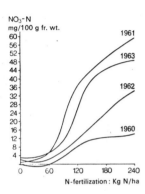

NO₃-N
mg/100 g fr. wt.

Effect of nitrogenous fertilizer applications with the spring spinach variety Matador, harvested in mid–May of each year.

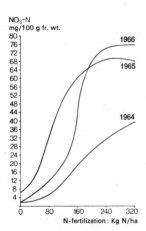

NO₃-N
mg/100 g fr. wt.

Effect of nitrogenous fertilizer applications with the varieties Matador (1964 and 1965) and Früremona-R (1966). Harvests in mid–May each year.

ially the water supply from the soil, the light intensity, and under some conditions the temperature—are very favorable.

3. During prolonged drought, the concentration of nitrate in the plant is high even though the nitrogen supply is kept constant. Correspondingly, during the 1950 drought in Missouri the high nitrate content in the fodder was responsible for considerable mortality among the cattle.

4. When other factors, especially the water supply, are favorable to growth, high light intensity enhances photosynthesis and thus the formation of protein; associated with this is a fall of the nitrate level in the plant, even though the provision of nitrogen from the soil and from fertilizer is increased.

5. In addition to the availability of light and water, agricultural procedures also have clear effects. Heavy applications of nitrogen fertilizer, as would be expected, result in high nitrate concentrations in the plants. If additional trace elements (copper, zinc, boron, molybdenum and cobalt) are supplied along with this extra nitrogen, they normally have no effect upon a soil-grown plant's nitrate concentration—in contrast to the observed effects in experiments with plants grown on an artificial substrate. After application of the herbicide 2,4-D the nitrate content of the plants rises as it does after heavy application of nitrogen.

6. For nitrite concentrations dangerous to health to develop, there must first be high nitrate concentrations. In spinach, dangerous levels of nitrite can be brought about by a high nitrogen content of the soil or by excessive nitrogen fertilization (more than 80–90 kg nitrogen per hectare), or of course by a combination of the two. When harvested spinach plants are shaken about for a long time during transport and then stored at high temperature, internal heating processes occur and there is a bacterial breakdown of nitrate to nitrite in the tissues. Bacterial reduction to nitrite is possible even in nitrate-rich deep-frozen spinach, as well as in cooked spinach that has been stored and reheated.

7. Nitrate is stored in quite large amounts by Chenopodiaceae like spinach and beets, by large forms of *Brassica* such as cabbage and kohlrabi, by radishes and by lettuce. On the other hand, the nitrate content of carrots is particularly low, even after heavy applications of nitrogen fertilizer; according to our investigations, then, there is no danger of nitrite poisoning from carrots.

Figure 7-6 shows the results of experiments in different years which demonstrate that spinach, as a "model plant," has a lower nitrate content when the light intensity is high than when there is less light (except for 1960, when the harvest was too early). The effects of different applications of nitrogenous fertilizer to the same plot of land during these years are shown in Fig. 7-4.

Our seven-year experiments on the minerals found in spinach under different conditions of fertilization are summarized in Figure 7-5. Since potassium occurs in relatively large amounts in spinach, it is shown on a

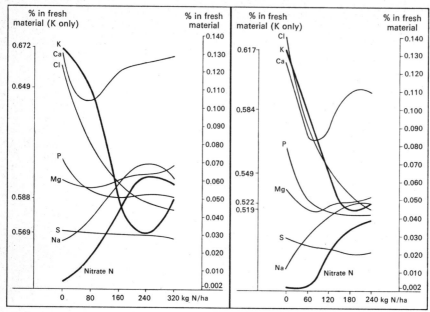

Fig. 7-5. The results of seven years' experiments on the mineral content of spinach as a function of fertilization. A spring variety was used. Curves in the left graph show average results for three years (1964–1966) and those on the right, for four years (1960–1963). Ca, calcium; Cl, chlorine; K, potassium; Mg, magnesium; Na, sodium; P, phosphorus; S, sulfur.

separate scale. As the application of nitrogen is increased, the potassium concentration declines sharply, whereas sodium, already present in abundance in the salted food we eat, rises relatively rapidly. One may well ask why we have devoted so much space here to the discussion and illustration of the phenomena underlying the nitrate problem. The reason is that well-financed efforts have been made by interested parties to play down the whole question—in fact to deny the significance of nitrogenous fertilizers as a potential environmental threat.

Our attention was first drawn to the effects of nitrogen fertilization upon spinach by a number of cases, from 1963 on, of the poisoning of infants in Hamburg, Kiel and Berlin who had eaten spinach prepared from fresh or deep-frozen produce. In samples of the spinach they had been fed, unusually high amounts of toxic nitrite were discovered. In an infant, especially during its first three months of life, nitrite can cause collapse of the circulatory system and the dangerous condition called methemoglobinemia, the external sign of which is a bluish skin tint (cyanosis). Unless methylene blue is injected in time, nitrite poisoning can be fatal. If cooking water containing nitrate is used, the danger is considerably increased.

The extent of this latter threat is indicated by measurements from a well sunk in the vineyard and orchard region of the Rheingau; the water it produced had a nitrate content of 120–150 mg/1 (see the recommended limit of 50 mg/1 discussed below). This water can be drunk only if it is mixed with pure water from the higher-altitude forests. F. Schwille, of the government hydrological institute in Koblenz, found high to very high nitrate contents in the water under vineyard soils in the Mosel valley and

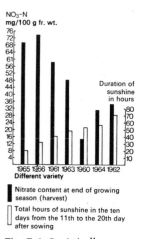

Fig. 7-6. Statistically significant inverse relationship between amount of sunshine and nitrate in spring spinach, varieties Matador (1960–65) and Früremona (1966).

the Rhine lowlands, but not under forested areas. This provides further evidence that the nitrate in the ground water of these regions comes from fertilizers.

In Figure 7-7 we illustrate the potential harm associated with different stages in the cycle of nitrogen as it is transported through the biotic and abiotic components of the ecosystem. The diagram also indicates certain disease symptoms seen in adults and brought about by nitrate or nitrite; these do not involve cyanosis, as does nitrite poisoning in infants.

Particularly drastic effects are observed when fertilization (for example, with easily leached nitrogenous materials) is carried out over a long period with plants grown under glass, if the greenhouses are situated on soils where the water table is high. This is the case in the Netherlands,

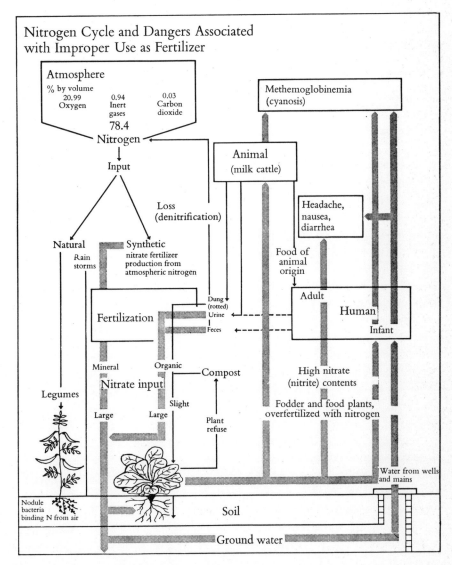

Fig. 7-7. Nitrogen cycle, through biotic and abiotic parts of an ecosystem, indicating possible damage due to improper use of nitrogen as fertilizer.

where many acres of land are covered with greenhouses for vegetables, around Naaldwijk near the Hague. The three crops of lettuce grown there during the winter, when the light is weak, must be started off with a small amount of nitrogen, until the roots of the plants grow down to the ground water, which is rich in nitrate because of long-term fertilization practices. The nitrate content of such produce is always appreciable.

Swedish scientists, in fact, found by far the highest values in imported Dutch lettuce; the nitrate content averaged 244 mg per 100 grams fresh weight, and ranged from 48 to 538 mg/100 g. On February 1, 1972, we found 186 mg of nitrate in 100 g of Dutch lettuce. Although the toxicologists have taken no clear stand on the tolerable limit of nitrate (for water they have set a provisory limit of 50 mg/1), one must bear in mind that lettuce, in contrast to spinach, is eaten uncooked. This means that the entire content of nitrate—precursor of the poisonous nitrite—is consumed. Such high nitrate contents can be brought about only by heavy applications of nitrogenous fertilizer.

Canned goods also present problems if the nitrate content of the food is high. High nitrate concentrations can cause corrosion of the tin lining of the cans; the tin content of the food in the can rises, and nitrous oxide gas (N_2O) is formed.

Opponents of chemical pesticides still occasionally maintain that the use of highly poisonous compounds is a recent development, a consequence of the general prosperity following the Second World War. But this view is mistaken. In the early 1920's apple orchards, for example, were already being treated with Bordeaux mixture to prevent fungus diseases, and with very poisonous arsenic- and nicotine-containing substances to destroy insect pests. Where cabbage was grown on a large scale, the highly toxic sublimate of mercury chloride was used against cabbage fly. In the "good old days" people were just as willing to use chemical pesticides of great, though usually only direct, toxicity. Even then, especially with monocultures in orchards and vineyards, it seemed impossible to manage without chemicals to protect the plants.

Pesticides

Truck farmers, however, long before the war, had discovered that other procedures besides the use of pesticides can prevent pests and disease in annual crops. These included careful selection of the planting sites for each type of vegetable and suitable choice of times for sowing and transplanting, proper succession of crops within a given year and from one year to the next, and a mixture of organic and inorganic fertilizers designed and measured out according to the needs of the different plants. As long as these practices were followed, it was not necessary for vegetable-growers to apply massive doses of the pesticides known at that time. The problem of chemical residues became acute only after the last war, when systemic and persistent pesticides were introduced.

With regard to terminology, most "pesticides" do not kill all kinds of insect pests. For example, DDT, carbaryl and methylparathion are effective against aphids, but not against spider mites; in fact, they clearly enhance the reproduction of spider mites. "Systemic" pesticides are those taken into the plant by way of the roots and leaf surfaces and transported through the plant's vascular system. "Persistent" pesticides are not readily decomposed and remain for a long time in the soil, in plants, and in the fatty tissues of humans.

Arsenic poisoning in vineyards

We have emphasized acute (immediate) toxicity as a characteristic of the pesticides formerly in use, but this is not true of one chemical used extensively and lavishly in vineyards until the 1940's—arsenic. Even at that time, arsenic contaminated vineyard soil, but not until 1942 was its insidious chronic toxicity—to man when consumed with wine—realized. Slow poisoning of this sort was something new among pesticides; but as new types were developed and came into wide use after the Second World War, especially DDT and other organochlorides, chronic toxicity practically became the rule.

In 1942, after arsenic sprays had been used by German vine-growers for decades, they were prohibited. It had been recognized that considerable residues of arsenic remained in the wine, particularly in the so-called "house drink" of the vintagers, the wine made from the skins. A chemical laboratory in Speyer studied 336 samples of wine bottled for sale in 1938 and found as much as 14.4 mg arsenic per liter; earlier vintages contained as much as 24 mg/1. In older wine-growers and vineyard workers of the Mosel and Kaiserstuhl regions, the regular consumption of the house wine, with its higher arsenic concentration, induced cancer after a latent period of twelve to twenty years, with cancer of the liver predominating. This had not been suspected, since no test results were made available before arsenicals were recommended for vineyard use.

In 1972 vintagers of the two regions and their employees were still falling ill and dying of chronic arsenic poisoning, though application of the pesticide was stopped in 1942. In a single German vineyard region thirty-three such cases of illness or death were reported in 1959, and in the four years that followed the reported cases numbered twenty-seven, thirty-four, thirty and fifty-one. In another vineyard region, each year between 1964 and 1972—thirty years after the arsenicals had been used— brought forth three or four new officially recognized (and thus eligible for compensation) cases of arsenic poisoning. Similar consequences of insufficient testing prior to the recommendation of chemicals for general use can be cited for other pesticides and growth-regulators.

Here we shall focus in particular on DDT (dichlor-diphenyl-trichlorethane), which brought the Nobel Prize in 1948 to the man who discovered its use as a pesticide, the Swiss researcher Paul Müller. In the first years of the Second World War people were advised to use it without reservation on food and fodder plants, since it was said to be entirely harmless to warm-blooded animals. Ten years later we learned from the U.S. Department of Agriculture that fodder treated with DDT, while doing no damage to the cows themselves, when transferred to the calves in the milk could seriously impair their health. These findings were confirmed in 1953 by experiments sponsored jointly by university institutes and Swiss pesticide manufacturers. The Swiss experimenters recognized that when a pesticide dust is spread by plane to control May beetles, a tenth of the amount lands on the surface of the grass. Cows were fed with this grass and, just as in the USA, were found to suffer no visible harm. But the health of calves raised on their milk deteriorated severely; the damage included the nervous system, and in some cases proved fatal. In 1972 German scientists discovered that a conversion product of DDT, DDD—like the widely used fungicide captan and the multipurpose dibromethane, used against soil nematodes, fungi and insects—has "certainly . . . a mutagenic effect."

These cases of long-term loading of the environment with pesticides transformable into metabolites of varying toxicity (for example, DDT is converted to DDE or DDD) are not isolated instances. Without making any claim to completeness, we shall now list briefly a number of other disturbing research results.

Both man and his animals accumulate in their fat deposits the unsaturated chlorinated hydrocarbons in the plants they eat; and man stores even more of such substances because he also eats fowl, milk-fat and cheese. In the fatty tissues of fowl Ehrenstorfer found the pesticides DDT, BHC, lindane and dieldrin. Danish analysts searching for residues confirmed the earlier reports of American and British investigators that such storage also occurs in milk, butter and animal fodder. Seven hundred and fifty Danish milk and butter samples were found to contain residues of one or more pesticide ingredients (for example, DDT, dieldrin, α-BHC and lindane were present in concentrations of 0.02–0.10 mg/kg), although fodder of vegetable origin in Denmark has few or no residues. The chief cause of the contamination was considered to be the oil cakes imported from the tropics and subtropics to be fed to the cows; these displayed fairly large amounts of pesticide residues. But pesticide dust carried on the wind and washed down with rain may also contribute.

The extraordinarily long persistence of aldrin and dieldrin has also been clearly demonstrated in carrots, an important baby food. We discovered that carrots store these fat-soluble pesticides in aromatic oils in the cortical tissues, where they are protected from enzymatic breakdown and retained in unacceptable amounts for as long as six months. After treatment with aldrin carrots proved to contain a great deal less carotene (7–21%) than normal. According to Engst's findings, the same considerations apply to the use of lindane in East Germany. And carrots not only store such insecticides; they also take up herbicides from the soil.

In 1968 Engst reported his investigations on the degree of contamination of the East German population by DDT. He found an average of 13.1 mg DDT plus DDE per kilogram of body fat, and even in infants

Findings in East Germany

the value was 7.5 mg/kg. In the body fat of sixty adult West Germans, Maier-Bode found an average of 2.18 mg/kg DDT plus DDE, which he justifiably considers a low value as compared with the 15.4 mg/kg found in the USA. The warnings I have been giving repeatedly since 1953, against DDT and other persistent chlorinated hydrocarbons, may thus have done some good in Germany.

As reported by Heeschen and his coworkers in 1971, human milk contains ten times more chlorinated insecticides than cows' milk. Acker and Schulte in Münster/Westfalen found mothers' milk to contain both DDT and its metabolites, as well as β-benzenehexachloride (β-BHC), hexachlorbenzol (HCB), and polychlorinated biphenyls (PCB). The chlorinated biphenyls are not pesticides; they are used on a large scale in industry and are a component of paints. But they are similar to DDT in being persistent environment pollutants, damaging health. The finding of these chemicals in human tissues is just as alarming as another finding— that pesticides of the organochloride group, because of their persistence, are already accumulating seriously in the general environment. The damage caused by some of these chemicals extends far beyond that associated with their actual use as insecticides, according to R. Wegler. For example, only the pure γ-isomer of BHC, lindane, is now used as a pesticide, because it has a relatively small effect on the taste of the produce. The rest of the BHC produced, at least 80% of the end product, cannot be used in insecticides and must somehow be disposed of. According to Wilfried Ebing and Ingolf Schuphan, there is no way to detoxify the particularly dangerous and persistent β-BHC by industrial processes.

Accumulation in food chains

The situation is further complicated by the fact that insecticides vary not only in chemical composition and in acute and chronic toxicity, but also in the pattern of environmental contamination, especially with respect to biological accumulation. Among those that are acutely toxic, we have chosen typical examples from two large groups of insecticides for which research results are available, and compared them with the natural product pyrethrum, also used against insects. Most of the insecticides in the organochloride group have a high acute toxicity. However, in some of them, of which DDT is an example, the acute toxicity is relatively low. These are in marked contrast to the extraordinarily great toxic effect of the organo-phosphate parathion (E 605). Like all organo-phosphates, though, parathion displays relatively little chronic toxicity—a claim which cannot be made for DDT and most of the other organo-chlorides.

Moreover, it has been established beyond doubt that the organo-chlorides, because of their persistence and their widespread distribution by water and wind, are also involved in an insidious sequence of accumulation along the food chain. They affect plant metabolism so as to alter plants biochemically and physiologically—as, for example, in the above-mentioned change in the carotene content of carrots. Organo-phosphates can behave similarly; parathion (E 605) has been shown to affect assimilation and respiration in plants, as well as their content of vitamin C and sugar.

Once again, in connection with the governmental approval of pesticides, it is necessary to emphasize the folly of trying to minimize such problems. In future, toxicological tests to determine whether new active ingredients, and the commercial products including them, are to be approved must extend to the level at which the consumer encounters them—the produce sold in the market as food. Up till now such tests, whether by the manufacturers themselves or by government agencies, have been unrealistic in this sense, depending upon animal experiments with either the active ingredient alone or the commercial pesticide. For about a decade we have been demanding tests on a more practical basis, in which animals are fed plants that have been treated with the pesticide in question as well as with all the other chemicals to which they might normally be exposed during their growing season, so that any additive or potentiating effects are taken into account.

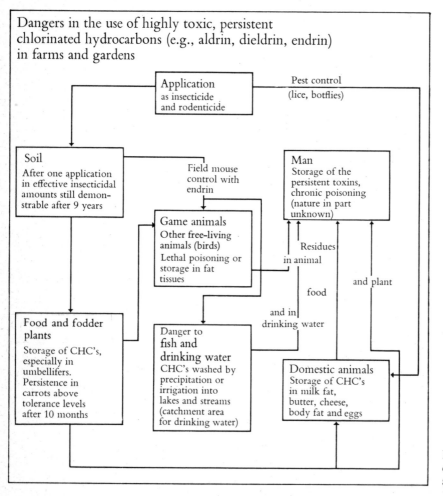

Fig. 7-8. "Biological chains" involving chlorinated hydrocarbons.

During the time an apple is developing, its surface is contacted by at least six, and usually more, sprays or dusts of chemicals to kill fungi, insects and mites, to control the rate of growth, and to intensify the color of the fruit. And we speak here only of the fruit of a single season; where the whole apple tree is concerned, the number of chemical applications is considerably greater. Experiments have shown that chemical interactions can occur under such conditions, both among the applied substances and with the natural plant chemicals. There is a distinct possibility that new substances are formed in the plant, which may be more or less poisonous, and that the content of important nutrients is altered.

That indirect effects are difficult to detect has already been illustrated with the example of the DDT on grass eaten by cows, which first has an obvious effect on the calves that drink their milk. When DDT is fed to American robins (*Turdus migratorius*), it has practically no effect. But if DDT moves through the bodies of earthworms, it becomes a deadly poison to the robins that eat the worms. In this case, the way the toxicity is enhanced is unknown. We do know that DDE, a derivative of DDT, causes thinning of the shells in eggs of the Old World kestrel, so that fewer young hatch alive. Another derivative, DDD, also impairs eggshell formation and reduces the number of successful hatchings in mallards. It is evident from these examples and the summary in Fig. 7-8 that toxic pesticide residues in the environment constitute a great danger to the animals as well as to man.

The danger to wild animals

There have been alarming reports from Sweden about poisoning of animals in the wild by agricultural insecticides, especially mercury-based compounds used to disinfect grain seed. The Swedish author of these reports commented that Swedish farmers were among Europe's heaviest users of agricultural chemicals, particularly those used to treat seed and to kill weeds. As more poisonous chemicals are used in agriculture, he continued, the bird populations decline; those most seriously affected have been owls and diurnal birds of prey (the peregrine falcon, Old World kestrel, hen harrier, common buzzard, white-tailed sea eagle, eagle-owl, tawny owl, long-eared owl), gallinaceous birds and pigeons (partridge, pheasant, ring-necked dove), rooks and songbirds such as sky and wood lark, ortolan and corn bunting, and yellowhammer. Unusually high mortality among the nestlings has also been caused in the starling, pied flycatcher, and oyege-tit by insecticides, and in the whinchat by herbicides. Thousands of chaffinches died in the autumn in a region where poisons (monochloracetic acid plus dinitro compounds) had been sprayed to make the tops of the potato plants die off more quickly.

In southwestern Germany, in 1957, there was a mass outbreak of field mice in the flat meadows formerly flooded by a now-canalized river; to get rid of them, the whole area was sprayed with endrin, without the knowledge of the government officials concerned. The area poisoned covered 1600 hectares. Mammals and birds had no opportunity to escape to unpoisoned fields. The dead animals found after the operation included twenty-nine hares, two roe deer, four weasels, three polecats, seven barn owls, three long-eared owls, one Old World kestrel and one buzzard. The fact that hares and game birds are not given enough chance to flee when pesticides are sprayed over vineyards by helicopter, in the opinion of foresters and the people who hunt there, is the reason for the catastrophic decline of these animals in the Rheingau.

Statistically significant results obtained by French scientists studying the toxic effect of the herbicide 2,4-D upon pheasants and certain partridges were published in 1970. The experiments were stimulated by the "spectacular disappearance" of these birds, not only in France. 2,4-D proved to be extremely toxic, especially to partridge eggs. After birds experimentally treated with this substance had brooded for nineteen days, about 76% of the pheasant embryos were dead; the corresponding result for red partridge was 43% and for grey partridges, 77%. Of the surviving young, which hatched after twenty-four days, most were crippled or deformed to various degrees, and their body size was smaller than that of the untreated control birds.

We know that contamination of surface water by the misuse of chlorinated hydrocarbons can kill fish and water birds. It is now also known that some chemicals in this group—for example, DDT—can accumulate in the plankton of these waters. Fish and water birds that feed on plankton accumulate these poisons in their bodies and pass them on to man if they are eaten. It has been reported that DDT and other chlorinated hydrocarbons, as well as parathion, have been found in ground water and in the water from wells. In view of this, the large-scale spraying of endrin mentioned above was an instance of gross negligence. Indeed, the producers of endrin preparations published a brochure on September 1, 1959, with the warning: "Because of the close juxtaposition of cultivated and wooded areas to water catchment areas, which due to the crisis in the drinking water supply are having to be continually expanded, and considering the fact that there is essentially no brook, river, lake or reservoir that may not be required for the same purpose, large-area applications of endrin to control field mice must be considered inadmissible."

Even experts are often uncertain about the toxicity of newly developed insecticides, no doubt in part because of the design (as discussed above) of the experiments to test them. The resultant "credibility gap" has led to a healthy mistrust of the modern use of pesticides on the part of consumers. 1964 was the year of the thirty-fourth conference on agricultural chemicals sponsored by a government biological institute in Wiesbaden, Germany. On this occasion a well-known investigator of residues, who earlier had recommended the use of "dimethoate," a toxic insecticide, against the fruit flies that attack cherries, expressed the opinion that it could also be used against carrot flies. Seven years later, however, the same researcher reported that, according to results obtained by American scientists,

Uncertainty among experts

dimethoate is decomposed to form metabolites eight times more toxic than the original chemical. Almost every day the world literature in the field presents new results of the same kind, in particular concerning the enhancement of toxicity when different pesticides are used simultaneously. For example, mice were much more seriously affected when two or three different substances were used; such combinations included endrin plus aldrin, endrin plus chlordane, methoxychlor plus chlordane, methoxychlor plus dieldrin, and chlordane plus two phosphoric-acid esters (parathiion and malathion). In other cases toxicity was unchanged or even diminished.

Having considered all these findings, which for laymen especially present a baffling but alarming array of difficulties, we are faced with the question: "What is to be done?" Some of the necessary steps have already been hinted at in the preceding discussion. The search for "integrated" methods of plant protection and fertilization, which combine chemical and other techniques so as to do the least harm in the long run, must receive generous financial support, so that procedures guaranteeing wholesomeness of all food and fodder plants can soon be put into general practice. It is also possible to determine the metabolic derivatives of pesticides; we already know of some that are ten times as poisonous as the substance from which they were formed.

Internal controls, however, are not enough. We know, for example, from the Danish investigations mentioned above, that contaminated produce can be imported from abroad. As long as this is possible, efforts to ensure the purity of domestic food may be partially negated. One possible solution was suggested in the German parliament in 1972: the requirement of an importation certificate.

Food-purity control

Germany already has official machinery for checking the quality of human food, but it is overtaxed, depending on random samples of goods, and without more stringent laws cannot fulfill its task. The suggestion is that it be obligatory for any foreign exporter of vegetable or animal food to accompany his shipments to Germany by a certificate attesting to the type and amount of pesticides and fertilizers with which the food was treated. Falsehoods and omissions should be punishable by severe penalties, such as confiscation and destruction of the goods at the sender's expense. Checks could be made at the borders, and the indicated laboratory analyses carried out more efficiently than with random samples of goods already on the market.

Enforced certification of food shipments can also serve an educational function in the exporting countries. The notion of such certification, which we first suggested in a publication in 1968, has been successful at an international level for decades, in the case of importation of living plants. The certificate required for this is a warranty of the health of the plants, stating that the plants to be imported or exported are free of disease and pests.

Fertilizer and pesticide industries have recently begun to contribute to efforts in these directions. This is gratifying, for the consequences of continued neglect of these threats to humanity, and to all the organisms of the earth, are frightening indeed.

▷
The ocean in danger. Above: Since 1969, every day 1750 tons of iron-containing sulfuric acid are poured from ships into the North Sea northwest of Helgoland.
Lower left: The off-shore drilling facility "Mr. Louie" in the North Sea near Juist. As a result of the drilling operation, there was an escape of petroleum into the sea.
Lower right: Until 1972 the raw sewage from the large city Kiel was discharged into the Baltic Sea near Bülk. The sewage fans out over a wide area as it drifts into the Eckernförder Bucht.

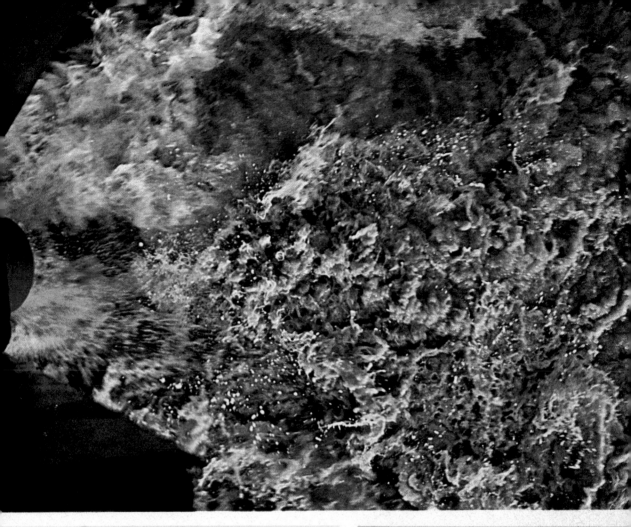

8   The Waste Explosion

By J. Krebs

The population growth and economic development that followed the Second World War was accompanied by an increasing emphasis on technology and city life, as well as a rise in general prosperity. There was a change in life style; consumption increased and production kept pace with it, largely as a result of automation. The goods produced were shorter-lived and more subject to the whims of fashion, and packaging became a science in itself. Finally, we have the current trend toward using disposable items for many everyday functions. All this has generated an avalanche of refuse, which in German is popularly called the "Müllflut" (rubbish flood), in America, the "solid wastes stream."

At the same time, dwellings and work areas have become more crowded. In the United States the concentration of people in cities is such that almost 75% of the population occupies only 10% of the area of the country. The disposal of refuse in such centers creates obvious problems, which extend to the surrounding countryside. Such crowding, of course, tends to make people migrate back out of the cities. Firms that formerly chose sites chiefly on the basis of the transport situation are beginning to take into account the desirability of a region as a place to live, and the recreational opportunities it offers. At the same time, this means that such desirable regions face the danger of rapid deterioration, as the population— and the refuse it produces—increases.

Industry itself, with the great diversity of production processes and of raw materials, is responsible for a variety of wastes. Gases, liquids and solids are produced which poison the air, the water and the soil. Whereas expert attention has long been paid to the pollution of air and water, and more or less useful ways of preventing or minimizing it have been suggested, the problem of getting rid of the solid waste is still unsolved. It is true that machinery for garbage collection and removal has been developed to such an extent that it can eliminate about 60–75% of the rubbish produced. But by no means is all such equipment up to modern standards, and it often cannot be adapted to meet the requirements of

◁
Above: As the mountains of garbage and rubbish are piled higher and higher, they make evident a problem of the consumer society, the extent and significance of which has still not been adequately appreciated.
Lower left: Uncontrolled rubbish deposits, like this burning heap near Dahlhausen on the Ruhr, destroy the landscape. Poisons and other substances leached out of the rubbish can cause the ground water to deteriorate and even become undrinkable.
Lower right: A correlate of prosperity: abandoned cars in a Munich park.

newly proposed improved methods of disposal. This is made evident by the many haphazard dump sites where huge mounds of trash accumulate with no provision for protection of the surroundings. These dumps do not just spoil the landscape aesthetically; they are sometimes a threat to health and to the longterm state of the environment.

To consider the problem of waste disposal in detail, we shall take as an example the situation in West Germany. There, waste is categorized with respect to collection and disposal in the following manner 1. Household garbage, which includes all the domestic wastes that are put into garbage cans. 2. Household waste too large to fit into a garbage can, such as old mattresses, crates, electrical appliances and so on; these are collected on fixed days several times a year. 3. Street sweepings, including dust, dead leaves, market wastes, and the like. 4. The solid wastes from factories and businesses, which are collected in cans. 5. Special wastes from industrial plants, which because of toxicity or other properties require special treatment or precautions. 6. Industrial rubble produced in amounts so large that it cannot be removed routinely; examples are slag from mines and the waste from sand and gravel pits. 7. Discarded or wrecked automobiles and tires. 8. Refuse from livestock and slaughterhouses, which for reasons of hygiene cannot be included in the regular garbage collection. 9. Hospital refuse, also separated from other garbage on hygienic grounds, which must be incinerated or otherwise disinfected on the premises under the supervision of health officials. 10. Radioactive wastes, including all solid refuse which is radioactive or contaminated by radioactive materials. These categories are pertinent also to Great Britain, United States, and many other countries.

Table 8-1.   Rubbish collected in the U.S. in 1968

	Weight in millions of tons	Volume in millions of cubic yards
Household garbage, special household rubbish, and street sweepings	80–100	320–400
Industrial wastes of the garbage type	150–200	540–600
Special industrial wastes	120–150	120–150
Rubble from mines, steel processing, etc.	1,500	750
Automobiles (10 million vehicles)	1	——

Table 8–1 (continued)

	Weight in millions of tons	Volume in millions of cubic yards
Discarded tires	1.5–1.8	7–9
Wastes from livestock farms	1,400	1,400
Slaughterhouse refuse and wastes from animal farms	3	
Total approx.	3,300	3200

Recent studies have predicted that by 1975 rubbish in the first three categories, which can be grouped as waste derived from individuals, would amount to 0.2–0.35 metric tons (440–770 lbs.) per person per year; with Germany's 61.6 million inhabitants, that would amount to between twelve and twenty-two million tons in a year. For the year 1980 the prediction is 0.3–0.5 tons per person or, with 61.8 million inhabitants, nineteen to thirty-one million tons of trash. Americans are richer in rubbish as compared to Germans; the average solid waste per individual in the U.S. was about 0.9 metric tons (2000 lbs.) in 1975, and the total for the country around 200 million tons for categories 1 to 3 above.

The garbage explosion raises even more of a problem if one considers not weight but the volume that will be occupied. In the United States, for individual-derived rubbish alone, each inhabitant will require 3.0–4.0 cubic yards (4–5 cubic meters) for the year's output in 1975 and 5.5–7.0 cubic yards (7–9 cubic meters) in 1980. Comparable figures for Germany would be 0.8–1.2 cubic yards (1–1.6 cubic meters) and 1.4–1.9 cubic yards (1.8–2.5 cubic meters), respectively.

Household refuse in the U.S. is composed of various kinds of materials, including about 12–15% garbage (food wastes) and 40–50% paper; plastics account for 7–9%; metals, glass and inerts make up the remainder. The contribution of ashes from domestic furnaces has fallen as people switched from coal-fired systems to more modern sources of heat. By 1980, the domestic burning of solid fuel may become negligible unless increasing costs of oil and gas turn the trend back toward greater use of coal. An important group of materials, amounting to 40–50% of the total, is paper and cardboard. The amounts of such waste will increase with less burning in the home, and greater use of packaging.

Packaging materials, especially those of plastic, deserve special consideration. The rate of growth in this category is far greater than that of the traditional packaging materials—paper, wood, cardboard, glass and metal. At present plastics amount to about 3–4% of European household refuse, but 7–9% of American refuse. Some predictions suggest that by 1980 the proportion of plastic in the total rubbish will rise about 75%, based upon the assumption that plastic production will double. The following figures give the current and predicted proportions of such substances (in %) in packaging materials in Germany and the U.S:

| | 1975 | | 1980 | |
	Germany	U.S.	Germany	U.S.
Plastics	7.5	5	9	7
Glass	22.5	18	20	16
Paper	50	57	51	60
Wood	10	7	10	5
Metal	10	13	10	12

Waste made up of the particularly problematic PVC (polyvinyl chloride) products have been predicted to increase from 100,000 metric tons in 1970 to 200,000 tons in 1980, but this still amounts to only about one percent by weight of the total world refuse. In comparison with the other plastic products of polystryrene and polyolefines, the production of PVC products should decrease because of mounting concern for hazards in PVC manufacture and incineration.

The increased proportions of paper and plastics in rubbish cause the weight for a given volume to decrease, but the total volume required is greatly increased. Calculations indicate, for example, that the introduction of nonreturnable plastic bottles will raise the amount of plastic in household refuse in Germany from the present fifty liters per person per year to 190 liters.

Industrial wastes can be estimated only roughly. Each day, industry in the U.S. produces about 600,000 tons of refuse similar to household wastes (category 4) and about 500,000 tons of special refuse (category 5); rubble from mines, steel foundries and so on amounts to around 1.5 billion tons a year. The total weight of refuse specifically associated with industrial production has so far been increasing by about 3–4% each year, largely because production itself has increased. Moreover, it is to be expected that wherever disposal of this rubbish becomes more expensive, new techniques will be developed to make use of such materials as by-products.

On the basis of various predictions, it can be assumed that in Germany in 1975 1.36 million, and in 1980 1.62 million, automobile bodies will require disposal. These figures correspond to 0.68 and 0.81 million tons, respectively, of scrap metal. According to recent data, about thirty million old tires are thrown out in Germany each year. Considering the increasing number of cars and the declining popularity of retreads, 330,000 tons of discarded tires are expected in 1975. In the U.S.A. about 10 million cars and 180 million tires are discarded each year.

As part of the restructuring of agriculture in the Common Market, there is to be a further increase in concentrated animal husbandry, and the associated refuse will increase in proportion. At present the wastes from German slaughterhouses amount to more than 800,000 tons per year and those from animal farms (cadavers of cattle, pigs and fowl) to about 100,000 tons a year. In comparison, U.S. figures amount to more than 3,000,000 tons of slaughterhouse wastes and 400,000 tons of farm animal wastes, with more than 1 billion tons of manure.

Category 9, summarized as "hospital refuse," includes the refuse from doctors', dentists' and veterinarians' consulting rooms and from the educational institutions in these fields. Its amount and composition is largely unknown, since it is difficult to obtain data for all these separate sources. However, use of disposable sheets, utensils, etc., in medical care has greatly increased waste generation in hospitals.

Rubbish disposal

The real starting point in tackling the problem of rubbish disposal is knowledge of the composition of the rubbish. The methods of disposal practiced so far degrade the organic matter or combust burnables and drive off the water it contains; the mineral components remain essentially unchanged and require storage space. The goal of all disposal methods is to make the rubbish "hygienically unobjectionable" and to compress it to the smallest possible volume for storage. The methods can be listed (in increasing order of rate of volume reduction) as follows: 1. orderly deposition of the smallest fragments obtainable by mechanical means; 2. composting, with the aim of obtaining a product for soil enrichment; 3. combustion, with or without utilization of the heat released.

Organized depots

At present, the rubbish from about 85% of the U.S. population is stored in dumps, but only a tenth of this goes to sanitary landfills, of which there are about 1800 in the country. "Sanitary landfills" are storage places where no open burning is permitted, refuse is covered with soil daily, and water pollution is prevented. The main problem in siting such fills is the lack of suitable areas that are both large enough and convenient to the centers of rubbish production. The rubbish is compacted by earth-moving machinery and/or in special compactors where it is crushed or broken; the volume reduction achieved amounts to about 30%–50%. Several systems are used for refuse deposition in Europe. The fragmented rubbish may first be set out for a few months in uncompressed layers to rot, so that the oxygen supply is optimized and decay processes are accelerated. Another method is to mix the rubbish with soil, so as to get decomposition off to a good start with the help of soil bacteria. German experience has shown that with a layer two meters deep, compressed after about five years, almost complete stabilization can be achieved. When the site has been filled, the terrain is suitable for planting and support of recreational facilities.

Composting

Composting is based on the idea of using a large part of the rubbish for soil improvement. To this end, the organic components of household refuse and garden refuse are combined with sewage sludge, and occasionally with manure. In Germany there are currently sixteen such compost works, where the rubbish from about two percent of the population is converted to compost. In the Netherlands, four plants serve about 15% of the people. The production of satisfactory compost is made more difficult by the increasing amounts of undesirable components in refuse—for example, plastic—since complicated procedures are necessary to remove these. By a combination of composting, sale of the compost product and organized deposition of the residual rubbish, the volume can be reduced to about 40%. However, there are limits to the value of the compost. Possibilities for its use exist in vineyards, orchards and truck farms as well as in landscape and garden architecture and public park maintenance; but people seem to have certain reservations about the use of this "garbage compost."

In the U.S. now there are about 120 installations designed to burn the rubbish from around 20% of the population. The chief advantages of this treatment are the maximal degree of volume reduction—to about 15%—and the mineralization of the organic components. Of course, the combustion of plastics, especially PVC, presents a special problem. The liberated hydrogen chloride gas, if it occurs in the exhaust gas at certain concentrations, can alter or destroy metal equipment. At present it is still not possible to tell the extent of the air-pollution danger associated with rubbish-burning installations. However, refuse is a low-sulfur fuel, and till now the corrosion due to the hydrochloric acid released from PVC was relatively limited. As petroleum becomes more expensive, refuse may find significant use as a renewable substitute fuel for space heating or electricity production.

Combustion

In the effort to stem the flood of rubbish, people have entertained a number of possibilities, some of them bizarre. These range from the idea of shooting refuse into outer space to plans for converting it to gas or alcohol; it has been proposed that refuse be transported by the kind of system in which messages in cylinders are sent through tubes by compressed air. So far, however, all of these notions remain financially unrealistic. A more practicable goal is that of "recycling" certain types of rubbish. Composting is not the only way to include our wastes in the natural cycle of matter; some industrialists are considering putting formerly discarded by-products to use. It has proved economically feasible, taking into account processing and transport costs, to shred old autos and reuse the metal.

How to stem the flood

In the long term, an effort must be made to reuse, or use in a new way, all the "special rubbish" from industrial plants; at present, some materials are wasted which could be used again without any further processing. The development of new techniques and reorganization of the production process toward this end must be actively encouraged.

A general solution to the rubbish problem appears to be impossible, for any form of disposal involves the three factors space, air and water;

in eliminating the disadvantages associated with one of these factors, one makes things worse with respect to another. But what can be achieved is the change from a "discarding economy" to a "cycling economy." We shall have to find the point at which a tolerable restriction of the freedom of industrial expansion to meet consumer demand is balanced against the right of humans to protect themselves and their environment.

9 Air Pollution

For millennia man has been polluting the air, but for almost as long this pollution has been insignificant, a minor consequence of the use of fire. The advantages of fire were so great that people were willing to put up with the deterioration of the air they breathed and the dirtying of roof and walls by soot. Warmth was preferable to pure air and a clean cave. This early pollution had only very local effects, for man lived in small groups in an immense natural habitat.

Even large aggregations of men within communities such as existed in classical antiquity probably had few problems of this kind. The climate in many of these regions was so mild that heating was hardly necessary, and the industry of the time required so little energy that air pollution —except for unpleasant smells—remained within bounds. This was true of all municipalities throughout the Middle Ages and up to the beginning of the 19th Century. The effects of the process of industrialization, culminating in the situation we have today, have been described adequately in earlier chapters. Until recently, people have acquiesced to certain levels of pollution as the price of "boundless progress" They have tried to compensate in some ways—for example, by building the cities on a more open plan, or separating residential and industrial districts. But they have not demanded that technology and industry accept responsibility for the cleanliness of the environment, and the purity of the air.

The air, the mixture of gases that envelopes the earth, circulates so vigorously that its composition is practically uniform up to an altitude of about a hundred kilometers—78% nitrogen, 21% oxygen, 0.9% inert gases, and 0.03% carbon dioxide. It also contains varying amounts of water vapor, dust, and nitrogen and sulfur compounds. Changes in the composition of the air are produced by both natural processes, such as respiration and biological decomposition, and human activities. Air pollution is primarily a consequence of the burning of wood, coal and petroleum.

The 30% rise in carbon dioxide concentration which is predicted to

▷

Above: The pall over the city of Munich is formed by emissions from domestic furnaces and vehicles. In densely settled areas automobile exhausts, fumes from heating systems, and dust can be a real danger to health, especially in the winter.

By A. V. Hesler

▷

Below: Currents of cold air in a valley of the Taunus Mountains. For the air quality in a city to be improved, certain areas must be kept free of buildings, so that they can produce or channel fresh air. In these pictures, cold air currents are indicated by recordings of the soil temperature (warm = yellow; cold = dark blue) made from an airplane at certain times (here, over a three hour period). This idea (A. V. Hesler) was put into practice for the first time in 1972, by the regional planning authority for the lower Main in Frankfurt.

What is air?

occur by the year 2000 (above the level existing at the beginning of industrialization) would cause a global temperature increase of 1°C, because of the heat-storing capacity of carbon dioxide. This change could bring about the melting of large amounts of polar ice, and a consequent loss of land area. Presumably, though, such warming will not occur, because of a compensating factor; the dust in the air, a small but steadily increasing amount, reflects some of the sun's radiation back into space, so that the earth is heated less.

Conversely, however, the climate over limited areas does have a marked effect upon the degree of air pollution. Climate, the most important aspects of which are temperature, air pressure, wind and humidity, depends upon latitude, altitude, the nature of the earth's surface and the vegetation in a given region. The factor that most affects air pollution is the wind. Whereas well-ventilated regions can still have relatively wholesome air even though the rate of pollution is high, the air in poorly ventilated areas deteriorates with only moderate rates of pollution.

Ventilation of a region is hampered primarily by the terrain. Settlements in river valleys or surrounded by hills suffer especially from poor air circulation. They must depend upon small-scale wind systems brought about by local temperature gradients. Over a built-up area, which stores and radiates heat, warmed air rises because of its lower density, spreads out, and sinks again over the cooler land or water. There it is further cooled and sucked back into the city to complete the circulation pattern. Depending on the geographical situation of a city, the predominant wind patterns may involve sea-land winds, mountain-valley winds, or plains winds. Local wind systems are also affected by the vegetation and the arrangement of building complexes.

Poorly ventilated areas are particularly vulnerable to "inversions." These are patterns of air layering within which, in contrast to the usual decrease in temperature by about 6°C for every thousand meters altitude, the temperature actually increases with altitude. When this happens, the layer of warm air lies over the cold mass like the lid of a coffin, preventing exchange with the still higher layers, so that after a short time the layer near the ground becomes heavily loaded with dust and gaseous wastes. Persistence and depth of the inversion layers depend on the time of year. In summer the thickness is less, so that high chimneys may even bypass the inversion layer; moreover, inversions tend to be disrupted by strong sunshine. In winter inversions can be more massive, and be maintained for days. Phenomena of this sort cause the well-known smog disasters, the worst of which occurred in London in December, 1952, and cost the lives of four thousand people.

Different kinds of vegetation also radiate heat to different degrees, and thus contribute to the establishment of local air-circulation patterns. There is also a mechanical effect, since grass, taller herbs, and woodland offer differing resistances to the horizontal flow of air. Dense rows of

Climate

◁
Industrial facilities emit a great variety of air pollutants.
Above: Waste gases and dust (the red-brown cloud of smoke) discharged from a steel plant with a converter; Ruhr region.
Below: The emissions from a few factories can affect the countryside for miles around if the weather is unfavorable; the photograph was taken during an invasion in the Turin Basin.

trees or hedges, just like embankments or trenches, can deflect the entire air current if they are appropriately oriented. This effect can be turned to advantage whenever it is desired to divert air currents in particular directions.

The nature of the plant cover has yet another effect upon local circulation, in that it can alter the humidity. Humidity, in turn, affects the degree and type of air pollution. High humidity enhances the conversion of waste gases into more poisonous compounds, but on the other hand it facilitates gas exchange in plants and hence oxygen production. The latter effect is extremely important in view of the fact that the oxygen consumption of a city is twenty times as great as the oxygen production, even if there is three hundred square meters of greenery per inhabitant.

Vegetation

Even more significant is the cleaning action of vegetation covering an appreciable area. The greatest filtering effect is exerted by trees and shrubs in combination. Plants lower the wind velocity and contribute to the formation of eddies; in addition, dust particles tend to accumulate on leaves and needles. Dust settles most readily on conifers, presumably because of the more abundant secretion of terpenes (organic compounds, the chief components of which are aromatic oils) by the needles. Rain washes the dust deposits into the soil, where they can assist the formation of humus and thus actually have a beneficial effect.

Over the past hundred years, the people lured into the cities by the factories have had to be provided with housing. In deciding how this was to be done, the principles of "city planning" were rarely applied—decisions were based simply on availability of land. In many cases, unfortunately, this is still true. As a result, we have cities without adequate ventilation, with insufficient green areas to help clean and cool the air, and with no clear zones left to act as ducts to the outside, which could channel fresh air from the surrounding countryside into the city center. Even now little attention is paid to factors that could affect the climate in a city. In fact, each new area taken over for building not only loses its original function of climate improvement but actually adds to the pollution; in some cases, new construction cuts off or constricts a passage through which fresh air might have entered the rest of the city.

The structure of towns and cities

The extent and position of the green areas in cities have in the past usually been determined by aesthetic considerations, or simply left to chance. Only recently has planning been based on considerations of local climate. Gradually people are becoming aware that it is possible and important to preserve the natural climate or even to create a new local climate by the design and placement of the buildings. Areas capable of producing fresh air or cleaning the air must in future be protected as strictly as those that assist movement of the air into the center of the city.

Basically, three kinds of polluters or "emitters" are involved: industry, household furnaces, and motor vehicles. The contribution of each of these groups to the overall air pollution varies widely from one region to another. In general it is assumed that industry is the chief culprit. But that is not always the case. It is certainly true near large-scale industrial complexes, but not necessarily so where individual factories are scattered among residential areas. Under such circumstances industry stands out only in terms of the number of different waste gases produced, whereas furnace smoke and vehicle exhaust, especially in an inversion situation, bear a far greater share of the responsibility. Most of the industrial fumes are given out through high chimneys, which may expel them above the inversion layer into air where they are rapidly dissipated. But the emission from houses and cars enters the air near the ground, so that noxious gases inevitably accumulate there. Of course, houses are not generally heated all the year round, but it is precisely in the cold part of the year that inversions are most severe. Moreover, with automatic heating systems there is a tendency to heat buildings for a larger fraction of the year. Central-heating systems that supply hot water contribute to pollution throughout the year.

Harmful gases and
their effects

Population centers vary greatly with respect to degree of industrialization, type of industry, fuel burned, and density of motorized traffic. The figures for Los Angeles, for example, are quite different from those for Ankara or the Ruhr district. But a number of noxious gases are given off by almost all the polluters mentioned; they are formed during the various combustion or production processes. Among them are the following:

Sulfur dioxide is produced by the burning of fluid fuels in sulfuric acid factories by the refining of ore, and in the burning of coal and petroleum products. The sulfur content in these fuels is quite variable. Like hydrogen sulfide, sulfur dioxide causes corrosion of metals, discoloration, etching and cracking of cement, limestone, sandstone and tiles, and discoloration and softening of painted surfaces.

Carbon monoxide is the chief component of automobile exhaust. But it is also formed when coal is burned and thus is a component of both industrial and household smoke. This odorless and colorless gas is a deadly respiratory poison. The binding of carbon monoxide to hemoglobin makes red corpuscles incapable of transporting oxygen.

Hydrocarbons are also produced by the operation of gasoline and diesel engines, and in smaller amounts by the burning of coal. This group includes benzopyrene, which arises when organic compounds are burned; its sources include the coal, gas and crude oil heating systems of industry. Like other hydrocarbons, benzopyrene is carcinogenic; it adheres to fine dust particles and enters the respiratory system, but also can attack the skin.

Oxides of nitrogen result from the burning of both oil and coal and automobile exhausts are a major source of nitrogen oxides as pollutants. They are also among the chief components of industrial emissions, especially from heating plants and chemical factories. Nitrogen oxides cause blood congestion, lung edema and dilation of the arteries; even slight concentrations of nitrogen oxides bring about irritation, coughing, damage to the bronchi and similar symptoms.

Fluorides are generated primarily in the production of artificial fertilizers, ceramics, stoneware and aluminum, and with certain methods of steel production; chlorides are given off by chemical factories and when plastics are burned. In fairly large quantities, fluoride disturbs the normal process of calcium carbonate deposition, and thus the growth of bones. At higher concentrations they irritate the skin and mucous membranes. Even in small amounts they are toxic to plants—three times as toxic as sulfur dioxide. Animals that have eaten fluorine-containing fodder become ill. Hydrogen fluoride gives a matte finish to glass and ceramics; hydrogen chloride is of course also corrosive.

Aldehydes are produced in small quantities by the burning of engine fuels, coals and furnace oil. Phenols come mainly from the production of artificial resin, explosives, insecticides, and in petrochemistry, refineries and shellac factories. Formaldehyde damages the gastrointestinal system and the lungs; phenols affect the spleen, liver, kidneys and lungs.

Lead pollutes the air as a result of certain industrial processes, but it is chiefly notorious as a residue of combustion in motors. The extent of lead contamination from vehicle traffic is still largely unknown. With a "normal" daily per capita lead intake of 300 millionths of a gram in food and about fifty millionths of a gram in the air that is breathed, no effects have as yet been observed. Acute lead poisoning, though, impairs the synthesis of hemoglobin and the activity of the kidneys, and in small children can cause permanent brain damage.

Other pollutants, primarily associated with automobile exhaust, are formed from hydrocarbons and nitrogen oxides in the presence of sunlight. They cause eye irritation and respiratory difficulty, and they damage plants. Ozone irritates the respiratory passages and penetrates far into the lungs.

Excessive dust is also an air pollutant. Dust can be formed by the burning of solid fuels with large residues of ash and by the processing of minerals. In comparison to the relatively dust-free air over the ocean, country air can contain ten times as much, town air thirty-five times as much, and the air of large cities a hundred and fifty times as much dust. These concentrations of dust can filter out as much as fifty percent of the sunlight, and almost all the ultraviolet light. On fine dust particles, those with diameters of five microns or less, there is a tendency for sulfur dioxide molecules and carcinogenic hydrocarbons to accumulate.

Finally, the psychological stress associated with air pollution deserves mention. Its effects include lowered performance and difficulty in concentrating, disturbance of sleep, and so on. It is also distressing to note that the destructive action of corrosive gases has exposed countless irreplaceable works of art to decay, and many are already lost forever.

In addition to the noxious gases, pollution by odors will become more   Pollution by odors prevalent in the future. These come particularly from the chemical, petroleum-processing and food industries, as well as from the intensified animal farming and automotive traffic. And we can certainly expect new sources of odors to be added to those we already have.

The effects of harmful gases have not yet been completely determined, and in general they are referred to particular components of the gases. Almost nothing is known about the extent to which the observed effects are enhanced by the combined action of different gases. Thus there may be danger to man even though the individual pollutants are present in concentrations below the toxic levels determined for each substance in isolation.

The amounts of gases discharged

Air pollutant emission rates in highly industrialized countries are staggering. In the United States, in 1970, about 147 million tons of carbon monoxide, 25 million tons of dust, 34 million tons of sulfur dioxide, 23 million tons of nitrogen oxides, and 35 million tons of hydrocarbons were emitted into the air. These data provide only a starting point for evaluation of the real situation. Geographic factors, weather, the concentration of industry, the number of automobiles, and the structure of residential regions all vary so widely that each definable space must be considered separately.

Nor is it any easier to make reliable predictions on the basis of developments thus far. There is no doubt that the consumption of energy and industrial production will increase; but this does not necessarily mean a parallel increase in harmful gases. We do not even know whether those gases we are trying to control today will still be the crucial ones in the future.

Legislation

The legal framework for the control of air pollution was first set up in the U.S. in 1963, after weak laws passed in 1955 and 1960 accomplished little. Amendments to the 1963 Clean Air Act were enacted in 1967 and in 1970. Also, the 1965 Motor Vehicle Air Pollution Control Act established emission levels for new motor vehicles.

The 1963 and 1967 air pollution control laws were ineffectual in the United States because enforcement of the law entailed development of regional air quality zones, establishment of air quality criteria and provision of technical air pollution abatement assistance by the Department of Health Education and Welfare. To enforce maintenance of air quality in a given region, the regulatory agency was compelled to follow a slow, cumbersome "enforcement conference" procedure. Between 1963 and 1970, only one case of air quality violation was processed through a Federal court, with inconsequential results.

The 1970 Amendments to the Clean Air Act gave the Environmental Protection Agency (EPA) the power to establish national ambient air quality standards based upon "primary" and "secondary" effects on living segments of the environment; i.e. "primary" is equivalent to "direct" and "secondary" is equivalent to "indirect." This law also empowered the EPA to establish emissions levels for sources of pollutants, such as motor vehicles and power plants. National ambient air quality standards are shown below:

Pollutant	Primary	Secondary
Particulate Matter		
Annual geometric mean	75	60
Maximum 24-hr. concentration★	260	150
Sulphur oxides		
Annual arithmetic mean	80	60
Maximum 24-hr. concentration★	365	260
Carbon Monoxide		
Maximum 8-hr. concentration★	10	10
Maximum 1-hr. concentration★	40	40
Photochemical oxidants		
Maximum 1-hr. concentration★	160	160
Hydrocarbons		
Maximum 3-hr. (6–9AM) concentration★	160	160
Nitrogen oxides		
Annual arithmetic mean	100	100

★ Not to be exceeded more than once each year. (All concentrations in micrograms/cubic meter except for CO which is in milligrams/cubic meter.)

Since polluted air does not stop at national borders, several international agreements have been concluded in recent years. In Europe in 1969, Germany and Holland began to exchange views toward establishing common criteria for the evaluation of noxious gases and other air pollution. In May of 1971, France and Germany agreed to collaborate closely in the area of environment protection. Agreements with England were concluded in July of 1971, concerning the formation of bilateral working groups with the same goal. The Economic Commission for Europe is also involved in international cooperation; its work consists primarily of information exchange, including that between east and west, and putting forward recommendations. NATO has also formed a committee devoted to problems of the environment. In the working group of the Committee for Challenges of Modern Society the "pilot system" is being applied. One country serves as the "pilot country" while other countries act as "co-pilots" in the same undertaking. This group seeks practical solutions to environmental problems which require only presently available technology and can thus be carried out immediately.

One example of such collaborative effort is the "air-purity/meteorological study in the lower Main region" (the area of Frankfurt, Offenbach

International cooperation

and Hanau), the results of which are being compared with similar studies in St. Louis (USA) and Ankara (Turkey). Recommendations are also being worked out for harmonizing national control measures on legal and administrative fronts. Finally, the Organization for Economic Cooperation and Development (the members of which include the western European countries, Canada, Japan and the USA) is also investigating the economic effects of the measures taken for environment protection and the negative consequences of pollution for economic development. The European communities intend to work out an overall plan, based on the following considerations:

1. Research concerned with protection of the environment must be coordinated and performed jointly.

2. Common organs must be empowered to carry out political decisions made in common.

3. When tax law is harmonized within the European Economic Community, advantage must be taken of the opportunity to introduce taxation in the area of environmental pollution.

4. The member countries, the regions or provinces, and the cities or rural districts are to retain extensive powers with respect to environment protection. At this level the Community can act only in an advisory capacity.

The United Nations too, for several years, has been occupied with the problem of preserving the quality of the air, through its sub-organizations the World Meterorological Organization (which is responsible for atmospheric observations, giving warning of hurricanes, and weather prediction) and the World Health Organization.

Measures to be taken

In the United States, the following steps are planned to reduce air pollution in the future: Levels of contamination with noxious gases are to be determined, their further development estimated, and suggestions made for the maintenance of air purity within air quality regions. Monitoring stations are to be set up by operators of stationary sources so that air impurities can be continually checked. Air quality criteria, concentration levels at which adverse biological effects occur, are to be established for humans and animals. These criteria, constantly re-examined, will form the bases for ambient air quality standard revisions. For mobile sources, the intent is to lower, step by step, the content of pollutants in vehicle exhaust, until by 1975 the hydrocarbon value is 2.5% of that for 1968; the CO content is to be reduced to 3.4 grams per mile starting by 1975, and NO emissions are to be cut to 0.4 grams per mile by 1975.

While these steps forward are gratifying, it must be emphasized that continued attentiveness is absolutely required, if air pollution is to be minimized and the polluters properly controlled. If people's awareness of their deteriorating environment had been awakened earlier, and if questions of the environment had been ranked as highly as economic growth, it is very unlikely that the present state of pollution would even have come about. And even now one cannot be optimistic. It is remarkably difficult for the officials concerned to convert popular slogans into action; this becomes evident wherever the banning of private cars from the worst-polluted zones is under discussion. Not even during catastrophic smog situations can people force themselves to draw the logical conclusions and act accordingly.

10   The "Peaceful Atom"

By P. Weish and
E. Gruber

Ten years after the first atomic bomb was detonated, a program with the motto "Atoms For Peace" was begun. It was to emphasize the use of nuclear fission to generate electrical power, as contrasted with its well-known military uses. Today many countries generate a small, but growing, fraction of their domestic electricity with nuclear reactors. One of the most important aspects of this development is that all such installations create radioactive waste products.

Radioactivity involves the spontaneous disintegration of unstable atomic nuclei, accompanied by the emission of radiation in some form. The customary unit of activity, the curie, is defined as a disintegration rate of thirty-seven billion disintegrations per second; this rate corresponds roughly to the activity of a gram of radium-226. The half-life of a given radioactive material is the time required for the activity to decline to half of the original value.

Some radioactive nuclei (radioisotopes) have half-lives greater than a billion years. These still retain an appreciable part of the activity present at the time the earth came into being. Such isotopes contribute to the natural radiation in the environment. The radioactive isotope potassium-40 (half-life 1.3 billion years), which comprises 0.012% of natural potassium, is found in rock such as granite, in sea water and in organisms themselves. The components of the radiation measured in nature are summarized in Fig. 10-1.

Radiation from the soil varies relatively widely, depending on its mineral composition. Extreme values are found in part of the Indian province Kerala, where about three quarters of the world's thorium deposits are located. Thorium is the long-lived parent substance of one of the natural radioactive-decay series.

The intensity of radiation from outer space—"cosmic rays"—increases with altitude, because of the shielding effect of the atmosphere. The shielding effect of water is even greater; at a depth of a hundred meters below the surface the intensity has fallen to less than a percent of the

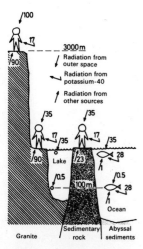

Fig. 10-1. The distribution of ionizing radiation from natural sources in millirad per year (1 rad corresponds to an energy uptake of 100 erg per gram tissue).

incident radiation. In the atmosphere, radiation from outer space induces the formation of certain radioisotopes—for example, radioactive carbon and tritium—so that equilibrium levels of these substances are maintained.

With the testing of nuclear weapons and the spread of nuclear technology, increasing amounts of radioisotopes are penetrating all regions of the biosphere. All approaches to nuclear-fission technology begin with the mining of uranium. There are a number of uranium ores from which this metal can be obtained; for example, pitchblende (U_3O_8) was mined very early in Joachimsthal (Czechoslovakia). With uranium are found its natural decay products, in a radiochemical equilibrium; some of these are gases, which have not escaped from the dense rock. But the ground water can wash out small amounts of these products. In those rare cases in which ground water flows through uranium-containing rock and immediately thereafter through coal deposits, radioactive materials collect in the coal. The major European coal deposits are free of such radioactive impurities. Since uranium ore usually lies quite deep, its radiation is of no significance to the biosphere. But if the occasionally occurring radioactively contaminated coal is burned, the natural radioisotopes (for example, radium) remain bound to the ashes.

The use of fossil fuels such as coal, petroleum and natural gas has liberated rather large amounts of carbon dioxide. Since the carbon in these fuels has been separated from the carbon cycle for so long, its radioactive atoms have long since become inactive. Thus the proportion of radioactive carbon in the biosphere had been reduced; it had fallen by 4% in 1950. The decay of radioactive carbon is accompanied by the emission of "soft" beta rays (low-energy electrons); the product of this decay is nitrogen. Radiation and the conversion of elements have the most profound consequences when carbon-14 has been incorporated into the DNA of the cell nucleus. In this case the actual conversion of carbon to nitrogen, apart from the radiation emitted, can bring about a mutation. The large-scale testing of atomic bombs, spurred on by the arms race, has liberated at least twenty metric tons of radioactive fission products and caused a new, massive increase in the radiocarbon content of the biosphere. Since the half-life of radioactive carbon is 5600 years, the biological effects will last for many generations.

The raw ore brought up from the uranium mines is broken up mechanically; the uranium is then leached out and transported for further processing. The sandlike waste that remains, the so-called "tailings," contain the radioactive products of the natural decay of uranium. So far about a hundred million tons of these tailings have accumulated in the USA. They are kept in enormous piles, some of them near rivers. The preceding chemical treatment of the ore and the large surface area of the heaps facilitate the weathering process, so that there is erosion and washing of the natural radioisotopes into the surface and ground water. Radium-226 is particularly dangerous; it is taken up by organisms and accumulated

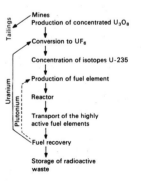

Fig. 10-2. The atomic-fuel cycle.

in the skeleton like calcium. In vertebrates the chief damage is done to the blood-producing cells in the bone marrow. The eventual consequences of this radiation can include bone cancer and leukemia.

In considering the effects of radium, one must include those of its radioactive decay products. The direct product, the radioactive inert gas radon-222, can escape from the tailings. Often the tailings are used as a cheap structural material, with the result that the inhabitants of these buildings may be exposed to stronger radiation than the miners in the uranium pits. Radon is a cause of the lung cancer that is considered the characteristic disease of uranium miners. Smokers are particularly susceptible, because the damage already done to their lungs may enhance the effect of the radiation.

The generation of electricity—the main goal of "peaceful" nuclear technology

Even before the uranium has been used to generate electricity, for every metric ton of uranium-235 in the reactor fuel one hundred grams of radium-226, with its radioactive decay products, have been set free in the environment with the tailings. But such quantities of radium in the biosphere, in themselves cause for anxiety, become insignificant when one considers the radioactivity generated artificially in the reactors. The fission of one gram of uranium or plutonium gives rise to products which after decaying for a hundred days are about a thousand times as radioactive as radium. The long-lasting radioactivity produced during one year of operation of a 1000-megawatt nuclear power plant corresponds to that of a thousand Hiroshima bombs; this of course does not imply that the reactor has the same explosive force. The actual radiation level in the reactor during its operation is considerably higher, both because of the fission neutrons and the short-lived isotopes being produced there.

Great technical effort has been expended to make accidents in such plants impossible or improbable. Still, human error and technical inadequacy can never be entirely excluded. Since there has so far been little practical experience with commercial reactors for major power plants, study of the possibilities of occurrence of accidents must rely upon estimates and limiting assumptions. An accident due to loss of coolant or supercritical chain reactions, in which radioactive fission products are released into the biosphere, could have grievous effects.

Even under normal conditions, radioactive substances are continually being released into the environment with the gaseous and liquid wastes from such reactors. Moreover, the maintained heat stress, the high internal pressure, and the corrosive effects of ionizing radiation have been known to cause leaks in the uranium-containing fuel elements and thus an increase in the rate of release of fission products. Thus the best possible operating conditions—without such leaks—are not the proper basis for estimates of effects of such plants on the environment.

Most nuclear power plants require large quantities of cooling water to transfer heat from the reactor to steam turbines; for this reason they tend to be built next to rivers or coasts. For technical reasons, the efficiency of nuclear power plants is about 30% less than that of ordinary thermal plants. A corresponding amount of additional waste heat must be conducted away by the cooling system. The river water warmed in the heat exchangers and then discharged causes long-term disturbances in the river communities, even though the rise in temperature may not appear very great. Two main factors are responsible: first, the solubility of oxygen in water falls as the temperature rises, so that the oxygen content decreases; second, the metabolic rates of organisms rise with temperature, and their oxygen requirements increase markedly. In the power plant itself conditions are favorable for the multiplication of bacteria, whereas the ciliates, rotifers and other organisms that feed on bacteria die. The toxins from the bacteria and the blue-green algae, which also thrive at higher temperatures, along with the depletion of oxygen, cause fish mortality and decay. Since there is no practical way to remove the toxins, it is questionable whether such rivers can be used for drinking water. But even without conspicuous fish mortality the populations of some species are annihilated, since the temperatures are too high for them to reproduce.

Financial considerations dictate the construction of larger and larger power plants, so that the local heat stress is intensified. In the winter months the situation is especially critical, since the low water level in the rivers coincides with an increase in electrical consumption for lighting and heating. A special problem is presented by the warming of lakes that have a seasonal stratification pattern. In summer the cold deeper zone is separated by the thermocline from the layer above, and at this time there is no exchange of oxygen between the two layers. The temperature differences are reduced in the fall, so that there is mixing of the water and the oxygen in the deeper water is replenished. When large power plants on the shore discharge warm water into the upper layer of such a lake, the seasonal overturn of the water is delayed and may be prevented altogether. Considerable damage to the lake communities can result.

Both the artificial heating of lakes and streams and the presence of cooling towers enhance the formation of dense fog, particularly in the cold season, and change the local climate. These, especially in industrial regions, can combine with the pollution of air and water to exacerbate an already critical situation.

The real problem of nuclear technology, though, is the radioactivity produced in the reactor by nuclear fission itself. The formation of neutron-absorbing fission products, and the associated degrading of the fuel, make it necessary to change the fuel elements when only about 60% of the uranium has been consumed. The exhausted elements are stored for several months, and then transported in refrigerated and appropriately shielded containers to the reprocessing facilities. There the material covering the fuel elements, until that point nearly intact, is removed and the contents are dissolved in acids. The uranium and the plutonium (formed

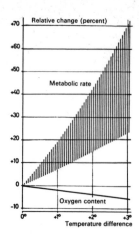

Fig. 10-3. Variation with temperature of the oxygen supply and oxygen consumption in fresh water.

from uranium-238 by neutron capture) are separated from the highly radioactive fission products by complicated chemical procedures, to be used as fuel again.

This phase of nuclear technology, the reprocessing of the fuel elements, is inseparably associated with the operation of reactors; the waste gases and water from this process are much more radioactive than those from a nuclear reactor in normal operation. For example, the radioactive inert gas krypton-85 is released into the atmosphere in its entirety; since inert gases dissolve in body fluids, it enters organisms and becomes a biologically effective agent. Should the predictions of the growth of the nuclear industry actually be fulfilled, it is to be expected that by the year 2000 krypton-85 will be produced at the rate of 250 million curies per year, so that within two to three generations the radiation to which people are exposed will have doubled because of this isotope alone. In addition to the gaseous wastes, considerable radioactivity is released with the waste water, passing either into the surface inland waters or directly into the ocean.

Fluid radioactive waste

The highly radioactive fission products present other special problems. At present these are kept, in the form of dissolved nitrates of the fission products, in stainless steel containers in large storage facilities; each container, with a volume of 100,000 liters, holds radioactivity amounting to about 100 million curies. As a result of the absorption of beta and gamma rays, the tanks heat up. The fluids are at the boiling point for years, and must be cooled. To prevent local overheating on the bottom of the container and explosive vaporization, the hot solids present are kept from settling out by stirring with compressed air. Corrosion by acid and radiation gradually destroys the container, so that the waste liquids must be moved to new tanks at intervals of about five years.

In about this time span, radioactivity and heat generation have declined to the point that an attempt could be made to move the waste to permanent storage. But in spite of extensive investigations, no method of performing this operation on a large scale has been found that does not involve critical disadvantages. During the centuries of storage, the material must be checked and guarded constantly, since for lack of experience there can be no guarantee of safety. A glance into history, however, reveals that no human social system has endured for such a long time as the control of radioactive wastes will require. The necessary perfection of waste storage lies in the limbo between technocratic ideals and a real world in which people make mistakes. Even the acts of fanatics—or natural phenomena—could bring about nuclear disasters. If only a minute fraction of the radioactivity artificially produced by nuclear technology were liberated, which seems unavoidable over the centuries, there would be a considerable radioactive contamination of the biosphere, particularly by the long-lived fission products.

If we are to understand the biological consequences of this line of development, it is essential to know the distribution of the radioisotopes in animal and plant communities and the effect of low radiation doses upon the organisms themselves. The effects of high doses are apparent a relatively short time after exposure; they take the form of skin burns, the falling out of hair, damage to the blood-forming organs and similar symptoms. By contrast, the consequences of low doses of radiation can be seen only after long periods during which the irradiated organisms appear unharmed. There is a basic distinction between somatic and genetic effects. The somatic effect is limited to the irradiated individual, whereas modifications of the genetic material appear only in the offspring of such an individual.

In 1927 Hermann J. Müller demonstrated that ionizing radiation produces mutations. A strict proportionality could be detected between the radiation dose and the number of mutations produced. Once it has occurred, a mutation is not reversible; thus the genetic material summates the effects of even low radiation doses throughout an individual's life. The notion that there is a threshold for radiation effects—that is, a dose so low that it has no effect at all—has neither experimental support nor theoretical justification. Because of their discrete nature, the biological effects of ionizing radiation, as radiation intensity is reduced, become not weaker, but less frequent. Since each such molecular interaction is capable of producing a mutation, genetic changes can be expected to occur no matter how low the radiation dose. The natural mutation rate, at least in part, is ascribable to the natural radiation in the environment.

The diversity of life on earth has been developing for billions of years. Changes in genes increased the range of variation of morphology and behavior, which is one of the prerequisites for the evolution of organisms. The great majority of mutations decrease the likelihood that an animal will reproduce successfully; the selection pressure operating under natural conditions thus acts primarily against mutation. The interplay of mutation and selection, together with isolating mechanisms, can explain the continual evolution of living beings and the origin of species. With increasing levels of organization and differentiation of organisms, the probability becomes smaller that mutations, random and undirected alterations, will bestow a selective advantage upon the organism affected. As a rule, they tend rather to disrupt a system that is in delicate balance within itself and with its environment.

A well-known example is the reduction of the wings of flying insects. In special ecological circumstances—for example, on small islands from which insects in flight could easily be swept away by the wind—stumpy wings have a selective advantage. But in ordinary conditions this mutation is not propagated, since flies with stumpy wings die before they are able to reproduce. In organisms with a double complement of chromosomes, there can be "recessive" mutations which do not become apparent as long as they are limited to one chromosome; they are thus not

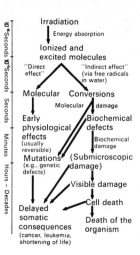

Fig. 10-4. The effects of radiation in biological systems (diagrammatic).

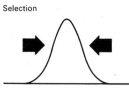

Fig. 10-5. Mutation broadens the range of variation of heritable characteristics; selection weeds out a narrow part of the range.

weeded out, but remain as variations of the genotype. The many possibilities for recombinations of genes during sexual reproductions also increase variation. In the long term, the significance of these differently developed capacities and characteristics within a reproducing community lies in the opportunity for more rapid and appropriate adaptation to changed environmental conditions. For species with a short generation time and the ability to produce large numbers of offspring, an increase in the rate of mutation because of radiation would not necessarily be a disadvantage; their adaptability to alterations in the environment can even be improved.

Man, the most endangered organism

In contrast, humans have few offspring, long generations, complex genetic makeup and, in particular, are somewhat protected from natural selection as a result of civilization. They are thus the organisms most seriously endangered by an increase in radiation. The ways in which regional differences in the radiation to which people are exposed are reflected in the effects on human genes are hard to discern from direct observations. In regions of extremely high natural radioactivity such as Kerala there is effective selection because of the high infant mortality in the local population; for this reason alone no striking accumulation of defective genes is to be expected there. Really informative statistics could be obtained only with large populations, initially related but then genetically isolated and exposed for generations to differing amounts of radiation —and then only if their life styles, diets, level of medical care and other important factors were comparable. Of course, no such statistics are available; but the lack of such information must not be equated with an absence of radiation damage.

Genetic injury to humans covers a broad spectrum of more or less abnormal conditions. Enzyme defects, allergies, intolerance of medicines and other unspecific types of damage become apparent only under special circumstances. An increasing number of special metabolic diseases are being recognized, along with or as the cause of psychological and behavioral changes. With these, it sometimes happens that the symptoms can be alleviated while the causes, which are associated with genetic alterations, of course cannot.

Since most genetic alterations become apparent only if both parents are carriers of the same mutation, the genetic consequences of ionizing radiation become progressively more visible after generations have passed. Therefore only a rough estimate of the extent of damage resulting from recent changes in radiation exposure can be made at present. It is also understandable that the geneticists in particular are unanimous in warning against the slightest additional exposure.

It was once thought that the main delayed somatic effect of radiation was the pathological multiplication of white blood corpuscles (leukemia). In the early years of X-ray and isotope research this was the most commonly observed form of delayed damage. Not until recently has it become

generally recognized, in part as a result of studies of the survivors of
Hiroshima and Nagasaki, that essentially all kinds of cancer can be induced
by ionizing radiation, though as a rule they appear later than leukemia.
This implies that the incidence of cancer to be expected as a result of
radiation must be raised. That is, since leukemia accounts for 5–10% of
all cases of cancer, the total risk of radiation cancer may be ten to twenty
times higher than the risk of leukemia, which has been used as a basis for
many calculations regarding radiation safeguards.

Radiation-induced
cancer

As in the case of genetic damage, no threshold (i.e., no harmless radiation dose) can be established for the carcinogenic effect. The mechanism
by which radiation induces cancer is not yet understood, but it seems
appropriate to seek the cause in mutations of somatic cells.

Radioisotopes are especially dangerous if incorporated in the body,
for they can then affect cells and tissues directly. Alpha and beta rays
interact strongly with matter and produce marked biological effects.
Atomic tests in the atmosphere gave rise to large quantities of radioactive
particles which are kept suspended in the air by various mechanisms and
carried all over the world by the air currents. Particles in inhaled air
having diameters of about one micron are especially likely to attach to
the alveoli, so that nearby cells can be exposed to high radiation doses for
long periods of time. These radioactive particles remain a problem of
current concern, even though testing in the atmosphere has been stopped.
The use of atomic bombs for "peaceful" purposes such as those considered
in the Plowshare Program would present essentially the same dangers,
since these too involve the uncontrollable liberation of fission products.

In view of the expansion of nuclear technology, the plutonium question is becoming increasingly critical. As the fuel of the "breeder" reactors
that are now being developed, this metal will in future be produced and
processed in large amounts. The isotope plutonium-239 is a hard-alpha-
particle emitter with a half-life of 24,000 years. Like uranium, plutonium
ignites spontaneously in contact with air and as it burns forms a fine
aerosol of the oxide. Furthermore, plutonium is extremely poisonous;
only a few millionths of a gram are lethal to humans, and far smaller
amounts can be carcinogenic. For every ten thousand aerosol particles
breathed in, one case of lung cancer is to be expected—regardless of the
number of people among whom they are distributed. In the complex
technical realm of nuclear industry, as past experience has shown, it is
practically impossible to avoid incidents that lead to radioactive contamination of the environment. The long half-life, in particular, makes it more
than questionable whether future industrial energy production should be
based on plutonium.

But life on earth is endangered not only by way of the atmosphere,
with its fission-derived radioactive gases and aerosols. Far more momentous is the contamination of the water that envelopes the planet. This occurs
when rain washes radioactive substances out of the air.

The plants—the base of our food chain—are contaminated by radio-isotopes not only on their surfaces but from the soil, through their roots. Animals that feed on them consume the radioactive substances as well; these are distributed differently in the body according to their chemical properties. Whereas strontium-90, an element similar to calcium, is incorporated primarily into bone, radioiodide accumulates in the thyroid gland and cesium-137 in the musculature. For humans, especially infants, an important source of radioactive contamination by strontium-90 is cow's milk. The potential biological effect of this isotope is enhanced by the fact that its decay product, yttrium-90, a high-energy beta emitter, accumulates—among other places—in the gonads. Moreover, it must be emphasized that in all organisms the sensitivity of the young to radiation is considerably higher than that of adults. Accumulation of radioactivity is clearly discernible in slowly growing plants—for example, the lichens eaten by reindeer. Consuming the milk and meat from these animals, the herdsmen of Lappland are exposed to forty times as much radioactive cesium as the Finns that live further south.

Artificial radioactivity enters the surface waters with precipitation and the waste water from nuclear installations. The radioisotopes are taken up by organisms, concentrated in certain organs, and stored. The strontium-90 content of various inhabitants of a fresh-water habitat near one such installation has recently been measured. As expected, it had become most concentrated in the skeletons of the fish and land mammals of this community. The calcium content of fresh water plays an important role here: in waters low in calcium the accumulation of strontium is greatest. Because of the wide fluctuations in the chemical composition of inland waters, there may be great variation in the capacity for such contamination. The situation is even more alarming with regard to radio-phosphorus, which has been found to accumulate in the eggs of water birds to a concentration more than one and a half million times that in the river water.

The oceans, too, are increasingly threatened by the effects of fission. Although the authorities are turning away from the practice of dumping highly radioactive materials into the ocean, the quantity of waste water of low to medium activity which is discharged into rivers and seas is steadily mounting. In addition, atomic submarines, even in normal operation, pollute the ocean with certain wastes; when they are wrecked, and once the reactor has been destroyed by corrosion, the entire contents of fission products enter the sea. As an example, to dilute the fission products of the atomic submarine *Thresher*, which sank in 1963, to the currently permissible (but still not harmless) concentrations, water would be needed in an amount roughly equivalent to twice the contents of the Black Sea.

Both water currents and marine organisms affect the distribution of radioactive materials in the ocean. Euphausid shrimp travel about six

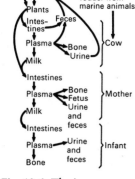

Fig. 10-6. The incorporation of strontium-90 via cow's milk.

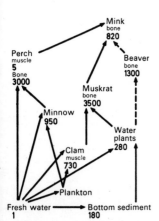

Fig. 10-7. Progressive concentration of strontium-90 in the food chain of a fresh-water biotope.

hundred meters a day in their vertical cycle of migration; they are an effective biological "elevator" to bring radioisotopes from the depths, into the food webs of the upper levels. The global distribution of many substances—for example, the stable insecticides—illustrates clearly the extent to which matter is exchanged in the biosphere. Similar distribution of artificial radioactivity, and especially of the long-lived and biologically significant components, is also bound to occur eventually.

Marine organisms not only assist the distribution of such radioactivity; they are themselves affected. Here again the young stages are the most subject to damage. Pelagic fish eggs, for example, accumulate radio-yttrium strongly in their membranes. Even at isotope concentrations considered permissible in drinking water, the fish larvae are damaged. In some parts of the ocean, such as the Irish Sea, artificial radioactivity has already reached a level causing visible damage to the fish eggs. Extensive radio-contamination of the oceans will reduce the food that man can harvest in the world's fisheries; which yield, it is worth noting, decreased for the first time in 1969.

Whereas it once appeared that nuclear energy production could contribute to a solution of our environmental crises, it is becoming clear that it is part of the problem as well. As far as reduction of environmental pollution is concerned, experience so far indicates that nuclear technology has failed within its own province. The oceans and continents are threatened increasingly by the conseuqences of exposure to radiation. It is little consolation that much of this contamination is being caused by the "peaceful" applications of atomic energy.

11 The Consequences of Excessive Noise

By G. Jacobs

The world is full of sounds, made by living beings and their inanimate surroundings. The constant motion of molecules would stimulate our ears continuously if our ears were more sensitive. We are also restricted in the range of frequencies we hear; 16 hz (1 hz = 1 oscillation per second) is about the lowest frequency detectable, and 20,000 hz the highest. Natural sounds—howling wind, roaring surf, or thunder—can inspire awe and terror, or joy and well-being, depending on the circumstances. That is, sounds of abiotic origin elicit sensations and reactions in organisms; still stronger effects are produced by the signals and calls of animals, and especially—in humans—by speech.

As organisms have evolved, the variety of sounds on earth has increased as well. Since man has begun to master nature with the help of technology, the diversity and intensity of sounds have increased even more rapidly. The average noise level in a city street rose fourfold between the turn of the century and the Second World War, and since then it has doubled again. The levels of noise commonly experienced by people today are severely troublesome and can even cause actual injury. Sound can transport considerable amounts of energy. This is evident, for example, in the way that window panes are shaken by thunder and airplane noises.

The nature of sound

Before discussing the subjective aspects of noise, we shall consider the properties of sound objectively. Sound is a sequence of periodic pressure waves that propagate through any medium, such as air or water. Without such a medium there can be no sound; in outer space there is no noise. Sound waves propagate at different speeds in different media—about 330 meters per second in air, 1468 m/sec in water, and even faster in solids. With appropriate devices, one can measure the pressure waves.

It is most uncommon for noise to consist of a single tone. Usually it is a "broad-band" sound, a combination of many different rates of oscillation. Noise can be analyzed and described in terms of the frequencies and amplitudes of the component oscillations. These and other measures enable one to evaluate the physical aspects of noise, but it is more difficult to judge the physical and psychological effects it will have upon people. We tend to think of noise primarily as a problem affecting mankind, and only as an afterthought consider its consequences for other living organisms.

The fact that the English language distinguishes between "noise" and "sound" offers a starting point for a discussion of the complex human responses involved. The word "sound" is more objective and comprehensive. It denotes a variety of perceptual experiences (in its psychological definition) or oscillatory patterns (in its physical definition), ranging from an almost inaudible whisper to an explosion or the scream of a siren. "Noise" usually has a negative connotation, implying the lack of a pleasant, musical quality or a disagreeable loudness. These attributes have both absolute and relative aspects; they can be measured objectively or described subjectively. Just as the absolute silence of outer space might be unbearable for man, sounds can affect us to the point of physical and mental damage. Where is the border line? What is endurable and what injurious?

Sound and noise

The World Health Organization defines "health" as the "state of bodily, mental and social well-being." In considering the effects of noise on people, anything that impairs this state must be taken into account. It is common knowledge that physical pain, mental distress and social tension affect a person's sense of well-being, and each of these can be induced by noise.

Damage to health

Often it is difficult to establish uniform criteria regarding annoyance and injury, because of variations in sensitivity among people. Depending upon one's background, profession, age, and origin, one may react to noise in very different ways. According to certain American studies, the inhabitants of economically developing countries are significantly less sensitive to noise than those of the highly developed industrial nations; and within the latter, it is the poorer people who are the less sensitive to noise.

Sociological research must be combined with physical measurements if a useful basis for noise evaluation is to be achieved. Sound intensity is the simplest measurable factor, both for determining nuisance levels and for predictions of the medical effects to be expected. But the degree of disturbance of course depends upon the character of the noise and the physical and mental characteristics of the person affected.

The sick are usually very sensitive to noise; it can impede and prolong the process of recovery. Noise is particularly disturbing, as F. von Tischendorf has reported, to patients who have recently undergone surgery, those suffering from nervous and mental disease or heart and circulatory illness, and people who are exhausted or under severe mental strain. According to Lüderitz, patients with hypothyroidism are awakened by quieter sounds than are healthy people. This also seems to be true of patients with exophthalmic goiter. On the other hand, chronically underweight people are less easily aroused than healthy ones.

High frequencies are considered to be more annoying than lower frequencies. Low-frequency sounds must have a 20–40% greater phon value (the phon scale is a logarithmic measure of perceived sound loudness) than higher-frequency sounds to achieve the same effect; this amounts to at least a doubling of the intensity. A sound pressure level of 120 decibels is generally considered to represent the pain threshold, and an increase of 6 decibels indicates a doubling of sound pressure level. Above this level permanent damage is done to the auditory system. As G. Jansen has noted, in animal experiments sounds in this range of intensities cause skin burns, paralysis and other injury.

Levels of response

The Max Planck Institute of Occupational Psychology has categorized some of the effects upon humans, in terms of the approximate perceived intensity at which they are elicited, as follows:

Noise level I
30–60 phon   Annoyance: psychological effects
Noise level II
60–90 phon   Danger to health: psychological and autonomic-nervous-system effects

Noise level III
90–120 phon   Damage to health: psychological and autonomic effects, influence upon auditory organs
Noise level IV
over 120 phon   Immediate occurrence of pain and permanent damage

A "phon" is a measure of loudness; the Sound Pressure Level at 1,000 cycles per second (cps) which is equally noisy as the perceived sound pressure level at another frequency. A sound pressure level of 92 dB at 20 cps has a "loudness" of 40 phons.

In 1969 the committee of the German Ministry of the Interior was charged with making recommendations about the effects of noise, and adopted the above values. For comparison, below is a list of common sounds and their intensities, published by Effenberger and Koch in 1957:

Whispering	10–20 dB
Normal conversation	60 dB
Inside bedroom	30 dB
Inside private office	40 dB
Inside general office	50 dB
Inside auto at high speed	80 dB
Full symphony	90 dB
Inside propellor plane	100 dB
Near elevated train	110 dB
Threshold of pain	130–140 dB
Jet airplane	140 dB

Many people are exposed all day to noise well above the level of annoyance—that is, noise having a purely psychological effect. Everyday work in factories, occupation of offices and stores on main streets, travel to and from these places of work, and even life at home in some areas can endanger health, with both psychological and autonomic effects. In particular, injury is done to the inhabitants of some densely populated areas simply because the layout of the city is inappropriate. It would in fact be possible to make such noisy areas unobjectionable in this regard. However, the conflict between financial interests on the one side and human needs on the other is especially apparant when it comes to such aspects of city planning.

When the real situation existing in many places is viewed in the light of the limits in the regulations of the Swiss Anti-Noise Commission it becomes clear how far we are from a "tolerable" environment with respect to noise. At present, there are no standards like this in the U.S. These limits are as follows:

SWISS NOISE CODE
(dB–A scale*)

Situation	Background Noise		Frequent Peaks		Infrequent Peaks	
	Night	*Day*	*Night*	*Day*	*Night*	*Day*
Hospital, Resort	35	45	45	50	55	55
Quiet Residential	45	55	55	65	65	70
Mixed	45	60	55	70	65	75
Commercial	50	60	60	70	65	75
Industrial	55	65	60	75	70	80
Traffic Arteries	60	70	70	80	80	90

* "dB–A scale" indicates sound pressure level measured with a meter designed to simulate the response of the human ear (A scale).

An important factor in exposure to noise is that the ear, with which we detect sounds, is not protected by nature—as is the eye—with a shield to shut off its input entirely from time to time. Even ear plugs are not completely effective, since sounds are also conducted to the inner ear through bone. Ordinarily, we are forced to hear noise. When we do so, the body may respond by expending energy, which involves a certain strain, whether or not the disturbed person is conscious of the fact. Symptoms of tiredness are one consequence, and in people doing mental work there can be a considerable deterioration in efficiency, or even a complete loss of the ability to work. The performance of other demanding activities can also be impaired. Even quite simple jobs are affected, and the error rate rises. Athletes know how greatly their performance depends upon extreme concentration, which can be broken by the slightest disturbance.

Increased stimulation of the autonomic nervous system can eventually bring about disturbances of organ function. Scientists ascribe to this cause a change in the activity of stomach and gall bladder, muscular tension, increased intestinal activity and higher metabolic rates. Similarly, W. Lejeune observed a transient impairment of vision amounting to as much as 26%. In addition to these kinds of damage, there may be increased pressure of the cerebrospinal fluid, and strain to the circulatory system. Disease of the heart and vascular system, acceleration of the heartbeat and high blood pressure are in any case counted among the unfortunate consequences of civilization. To a person already suffering from heart and circulatory disease, noise can be fatal.

W. Bürck has shown graphically how, during prolonged exposure to noise, an early phase of unconscious energy expenditure can produce diminished efficiency at work. The second phase is characterized by undesirable changes in heart activity, respiration, circulation of blood in the skin (see Fig. 11-2), skin temperature, blood pressure and gastrointestinal activity, as well as by nervous irritability, depression and a loss of enthusiasm for work. In the third phase, the consequences of noise are injury to the auditory system, impairment of equilibrium, buzzing in the ears, insomnia and nausea.

Noise also interferes with conversation. The consequences are often ill temper, bickering, and even enmity. F. J. Meister determined that when speech and noise are equal in intensity only about 30% of the syllables are understood.

The amount of exposure to noise, and the time the body has to recover between exposures, are also important factors. A person reacts to a prolonged sound differently than to sounds that recur, whether or not pitch and intensity are the same each time. A mathematical expression for such interrupted noise has been formulated to reflect the physical and mental effects of as many aspects as possible—duration of exposure, maximum intensity, time to reach maximum intensity, and duration of interruptions. The resulting measure of noncontinuous noise, called the "equivalent prolonged-sound level," of course does not reflect all elements of noise that affects humans. Nevertheless, this so-called "$\overline{Q}$ (Q-bar) procedure" has been employed in legislation in Germany, despite its equivocal legal status, to determine the equivalent prolonged-sound level for aircraft noise. A similar procedure is used in the United States, by requirement of the Occupational Safety and Health Act, to assess the cumulative effects of exposure to noises of varying intensities. Special meters have been made, called dosimeters, which contain integrating electronic circuits to yield a value of cumulative "noise dose."

Leppman has described an "expectation effect," which is a truly exhausting form of noise disturbance; this is associated with sound that gradually grows in intensity as a prelude to a very loud sustained noise or detonation. Several processes in factories produce such noises, as do vehicles; an approaching train or airplane becomes slowly louder and finally passes with a roar. With city vehicles, the expectation effect is particularly evident at a traffic light, where the red light causes a pause which is terminated by a sudden burst of engine noise.

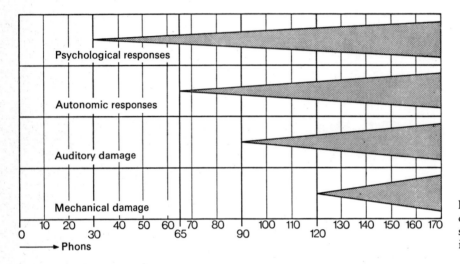

Fig. 11-1. Successive stages of the human response to sound, as intensity is increased.

Studies have shown that sounds are more disturbing, the greater their information content. Direction, character, intensity, pitch and other aspects can all convey information. Traffic sounds, for example contain a great deal of information; trucks, cars, streetcars and motorcycles can be distinguished on the basis of the sounds them make. Even particular makes of car can be identified, as well as the direction in which they are moving.

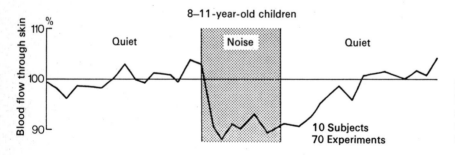

Fig. 11-2. Changes in blood circulation in the skin of children in response to noise (broad-band noise, 91 ± 2 phon).

It would be easier to evaluate noise if its effects were not so dependent on the individual peculiarities of people. Southern Europeans tend to be more temperamental, and northerners more placid. Children are lively and less sensitive than older people, even though the range of sounds they hear is greater. A person can tolerate the noise he produces himself better

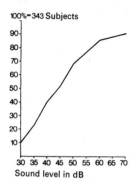

Fig. 11-3. The effects of noise on sleep. The graph shows the amount of noise needed to awaken various fractions of sleeping people (343 subjects of different ages and sexes). dB = decibel, a unit of the logarithmic scale of sound intensity.

than noise from other—possibly inimical—people. A pop band playing at an intensity corresponding to the noise of heavy industry gives pleasure to some people, whereas others prefer the industrial noise to the band, because they associate it with the idea of economic growth and a secure existence. The noise of an evening party in a friend's next-door garden hardly bothers us at all, but we are annoyed by the far quieter sound of a neighbor we dislike listening to music at night with the windows open. The degree of disturbance, then, depends on one's attitude. This subjective element can be so pronounced that people will deny hearing a certain sound in some cases and in others find it extraordinarily irritating.

From the fact that some people become accustomed to noise we should not conclude that they are immune to harm. According to Lehmann and Tamm, there is no complete adaptation to noise. Personal insensitivity gives no protection from the physical consequences of noise exposure, since it is impossible to block the autonomic reactions. The result may be an illness, the cause of which is not recognized.

So far we have described only the effects of noise upon awake, responsive people. But since the ear responds to sound even during sleep, the nervous system is excited even then. The quality of sleep of course affects both general health and mood. For example, we speak of a refreshing, deep sleep or a light sleep. When sleep is interrupted, its recuperative effect is diminished. The amount of noise needed to wake a person varies, but it has been shown that the quality of sleep can be impaired by noise even if the sleeper is not awakened.

For undisturbed sleep to be ensured, the noise level in the room must be no higher than 25 phon. As F. von Tischendorf writes, it is not a matter of indifference whether children must sleep in the presence of traffic noise, radio music and other sounds. In such situations the sleep is of poor quality; the inevitable effects are "increasing nervousness, inability to concentrate and a general decline in performance." Experiments by Lehmann and Tamm showed that the disturbances during sleep cause a rise in peripheral resistance to blood flow and a reduction of the blood-pressure fluctuations; the result is an impairment of circulation and heart activity. For this reason it is dangerous to take sleeping pills in order to sleep in spite of noise. These drugs simply raise the awakening threshold, while the nervous system remains unprotected. Where disturbance due to noise threatens to impair a person's health, the doctor must sometimes prescribe moving to a quieter residence. In this connection we should also mention the interruption of sleep by the noise of nighttime traffic and airplanes; these are often loud enough to disrupt sleep.

To summarize, the progressive series of effects described by Lehmann can be extended somewhat to include the following: Difficulty in understanding, disturbances, weakening of concentration, annoyance, disruption of sleep, irritability, decline in performance, dissatisfaction, strained family relationships, difficulties on the job, open conflict, psychological illness. In some cases, noise stress can be associated with organic illness and injury to the auditory system.

In short, people overexposed to noise find it difficult to live together in harmony. The harm done to the individual spills over into the socio-logical sphere. One reason that the dangers inherent in noise are so little recognized is the difficulty, when damage is done, of pinning down the precise cause. This is also one of the reasons that noise-abatement legisla-tion is so difficult to formulate.

A devastating phenomenon of our times, and one that can even do considerable mechanical damage, is the sonic boom. Its destructive effects are difficult to measure. It strikes sleeping and waking people alike with no warning whatever. The demand that sonic booms be prevented over in-habited areas will—it is to be hoped—gradually be put into practice widely. In densely-populated Europe this would amount to a general pro-hibition, though of course this does not hold for the rest of the world. In any event, it must be urged that flight at supersonic speeds be limited to the military, and that such practice flights be made only over uninhabited areas.

The sonic boom

Concern about the enormous increase in noise should extend to its effects upon other animals, besides man. Psychological disturbance may not play a role, but animals can be affected in quite different ways. Only recently, for example, it has been realized that fish are not mute. Like bats, they emit sounds which humans do not hear. The same is true of other groups of mammals, such as shrews and dolphins. Dogs also perceive fre-quencies which we cannot hear. We still have no idea what harm our noisy inventions may eventually do to every sensitive living being.

Supplementary Readings

These references of books and articles published in scientific journals deal with animals and topics that are covered in this volume. Some of these were the original sources on which the content of this book is based. These titles are intended as an aid to readers who are interested in additional information and more detailed coverage of the subjects contained in this book.

General References

Geiler, H.: *Ökologie der Land- und Süßwassertiere.* Braunschweig (*Vieweg*) 1971.
Grzimek, B. eds. in chief: *Grzimeks Animal Life Encyclopedia*, 13 Vols., Van Nostrand Reinhold, 1976.
Illies, J.: *Introduction to Zoogeography*, Verry, 1975.
Kühnelt, W: *Grundriß der Ökologie.* Jena (G. Fischer) 1965.
Odum, E. P.: *Ecology*, New York, Holt, Rinehart, and Winston, 1975.
Schwertfeger, F.: *Ökologie der Tiere.* 2 Bde., Berlin (Parey) 1964–1968.
Thienemann, A.: *Leben und Umwelt, Vom Gesamthaushalt der Natur.* Hamburg (Rowohlt) 1956 (Rowohlts deutsche Enzyklopädie, 22).
Tischler, W.: *Synökologie der Landtiere.* Stuttgart (G. Fischer) 1955.
Uexküll, J. v.: *Streifzüge durch die Umwelten von Tieren und Menschen. Bedeutungslehre.* Frankfurt/M. (S. Fischer) 1970 (1. Auflage 1934 und 1940).

Adaptations to the Abiotic Environment

Ambühl, H.: *Die Bedeutung der Strömung als ökologischer Faktor.* In: Schweiz. Zeitschr. f. Hydrol. 21, 1959, S. 133–264.
Caspers, H.: *Rhythmische Erscheinungen in der Fortpflanzung von Clunio marinus und das Problem der lunaren Periodizität bei Organismen.* In: Archiv f. Hydrobiol. Suppl. 18, 1951.
— : *Neue Beobachtungen über den Palolowurm auf Samoa.* In: VII. Conf. internat. Soc. Stud. ritmi biologici, Siena 1961.
Grote, A.: *Der Sauerstoffgehalt der Seen.* In: Die Binnengewässer, Bd. 14, Stuttgart (Schweizerbart) 1934.
Hynes, H. B. N.: *The Ecology of Running Waters.* Liverpool Univ. Press 1970.
Jens, G.: *Über den lunaren Rhythmus der Blankaalwanderung.* In: Archiv f. Fischerei 4, 1952.
Macan, T. T.: *Freshwater Ecology.* London (Longmans) 1963.
Ohle, .W.: *Kalksystematik unserer Binnengewässer und der Kalkgehalt Rügener Bäche.* In: Geologie der Meere und der Binnengewässer 1, 1937.
Remane, A. u. Schlieper, C.: *Die Biologie des Brackwassers.* In: Die Binnengewässer, Bd. 22, Stuttgart (Schweizerbart) 1958.
Schaller, F.: *Die Unterwelt des Tierreichs.* Berlin (Springer) 1962.
Schlieper, C.: *Physiologie des Brackwassers.* In: Die Binnengewässer, Bd. 22, Stuttgart (Schweizerbart) 1958.

Adaptations to the Biotic Environment

Food

Hesse, R., u. Doflein, F.: *Tierbau und Tierleben in ihrem Zusammenhang betrachtet.* Bd. 2: *Das Tier als Teil des Naturganzen.* Jena (G. Fischer) 1943.
Blumen und Insekten:
Bänziger, H.: *Bloodsucking Moths of Malaya.* In: Fauna 1, 1971.
Daumer, K.: *Blumenfarben wie sie die Bienen sehen.* In: Zeitschr. f. vergl. Physiol. 41, 1958.
Faegri, K., u. van der Pijl, L.: *The Principles of Pollination Ecology.* New York (Pergamon) 1966.
Frisch, K. v.: *Tanzsprache und Orientierung der Bienen.* Berlin u. a. (Springer) 1965.
Knoll, F.: *Die Biologie der Blüte.* Berlin u. a. (Springer) 1956 (Verständl. Wissenschaft, 57).
Kugler, H.: *Blütenökologie.* Stuttgart (G. Fischer) ²1970.

Kullenberg, B.: *Studies in Ophrys Pollination.* In: Zoolog. Bidrag van Uppsala 34, 1961.
Loew, E.: *Das Leben der Blüten.* Berlin 1895.
Meeuse, B. J. D.: *The Story of Pollination.* New York 1961.
Pijl. L. van der, u. Dodson, C. H.: *Orchid Flowers, their Pollination and Evolution.* Univ. of Miami Press 1966.
Porsch, O.: *Der Vogel als Blumenbestäuber.* In: Biologia gen. 9, 1933.
— : *Ein neuer Typus Fledermausblumen.* In: Biologia gen. 15, 1942.
Schremmer, F.: *Über normalen Blumenbesuch und das Lernvermögen blütenbesuchender Insekten.* In: Österr. Bot. Zeitschr. 102, 1955.
— : *Morphologische Anpassungen von Tieren—insbesondere Insekten—an die Gewinnung von Blumennahrung.* In: Verh. Deutsche Zool. Ges. Saarbrücken, 1961.
—: *»Geborgte Beweglichkeit« bei der Bestäubung von Blütenpflanzen.* In: Umschau 1969.
Sprengel, Ch. K.: *Das entdeckte Geheimnis der Natur in Bau und Befruchtung der Blumen.* Berlin 1793.
Vogel, S.: *Blütenbiologische Typen als Elemente der Sippengliederung.* In: Bot. Studien, 1954.
— :*Ölproduzierende Blumen, die durch ölsammelnde Bienen bestäubt,* In: Naturwissenschaften 58, 1971.
Werth, E.: *Bau und Leben der Blumen.* Stuttgart 1956.

Animal-Plant Interaction

Becher, E.: *Die fremddienliche Zweckmäßigkeit der Pflanzengallen.* Leipzig 1917.
Buhr, H.: *Bestimmungstabellen der Gallen (Zoo- und Phyto-Cecidien) an Pflanzen Mittel- und Nordeuropas.* 2 Bde., Jena (G. Fischer) 1964/65.
Janzen, D. H.: *Interaction of the Bull's-horn Acacia with an Ant Inhabitant in Eastern Mexico.* In: Univ. Kansas Science Bulletin 47, 1967.
Kerner v. Marilaun: *Pflanzenleben.* 2 Bde., Leipzig und Wien 1898.
Küster, E.: *Die Gallen der Pflanzen. Ein Lehrbuch der Botaniker und Entomologen.* Leipzig 1911.
Mani, M. S.: *The Ecology of Plant Galls.* Den Haag 1964 (Monographiae Biologicae 12).
Müller-Schneider, P.: *Beiträge zur Kenntnis der Samenverbreitung durch Ameisen.* In: Ber. d. Schweizer. Bot. Ges. 80, 1970.
Zweigelt, F.: *Problematik der Gallenforschung.* In: Mikroskopie 1, 1947, H. 5/6, S.159–173.
Nachahmung, Tarnung, Täuschung:
Curio, E.: *Die Schutzanpassungen dreier Raupen eines Schwärmers (Lepidopt., Sphingidae) auf Galapagos.* In: Zool. Jb. Syst. 92, 1965.
Kloft, W.: *Versuch einer Analyse der Trophobiotischen Beziehungen von Ameisen zu Aphiden.* In: Biol. Zentralbl. 78, 1959.
Kullenberg, B.: *Studies in Ophrys Pollination.* In: Zool. Bidrag Uppsala 34, 1961.
Lloyd, J. E.: *Aggressive Mimicry in Photuris: Firefly femmes fatales.* In: Science 149, 1956.
Mertens, R.: *Das Problem der Mimikry bei Korallenschlangen.* In: Zool. Jb. Syst. 84, 1956.
Owen, D. F.: *Industrial Melanism in North American Moths.* In: Amer. Nat. 95, 1961.
Ruiter, L. de: *Some Remarks on Problems of the Ecology and Evolution of Mimicry.* In: Arch. Néerl. Zool. 13, Suppl. 1, 1958.
Schwanitz, F.: *Die Entstehung der Nutzpflanzen.* In: G. Heberer (Hg): Die Evolution der Organismen, Stuttgart (G. Fischer) 1959.
Shelford, L.: *Observations on some mimetic Insects and Spiders from Borneo and Singapore.* In: Proceedings Zool. Soc. London, 1902.
Wasman, E.: *Die Ameisenmimikry.* In: Abhandl. zur Theoret. Biol. H. 19, 1925.
Wickler, W.: *Socio-sexual Signals and their intraspecific Imitation among Primates.* In: D. Morris (Hg.): Primate Ethology, London 1967.

On Population Biology

Krebs, Charles J.: *Ecology*: the Experimental Analysis of Distribution and Abundance. New York, Harper & Row, 1972.
Rickleffs, Robert E.: *Ecology*. Newton Mass., Chiron Press, 1973.
May, Robert M.: *Stability and Complexity in Model Ecosystems*. Princeton Univ. 1973.

On Community Ecology

Whittaker, Robert H.: Communities and Ecosystems, 2nd ed. New York: Macmillan, 1975
Kendeigh, S. Charles.: Ecology, with Special Reference to Animals and Man. Englewood Cliffs, N.J., Prentice-Hall, 1974.
Eyre, S. R.: Vegetation and Soils: a World Picture. Chicago, Aldine, 1963.
Walter, Heinrich.: Vegetation of the Earth, in Relation to Climate and the Eco-Physiological Conditions. New York, Springer-Verlag, 1973.

On Animal Adaptations (and communities)

Hesse, Richard, W. C. Allee, and Karl P. Schmidt.: Ecological Animal Geography. 2nd ed. New York, Wiley, 1951.
Allee, W. C., Orlando Park, Alfred E. Emerson, Thomas Park, and Karl P. Schmidt.: Principle of Animal Ecology. Philadelphia, Saunders, 1949.
Schmidt-Nielsen, Knut.: Desert Animals: *Physiological Problems of Heat and Water*. Oxford, Clarendon, 1964
Smith, Robert Leo.: *Ecology and Field Biology*. New York, Harper & Row, 1966.

On Niches

Whittaker, Robert H. and Simon A. Levin, eds.: *Niche: Theory and Application*. Stroudsburg, Pa., Dowden, Hutchinson & Ross, 1975.
Hardin, G.: The competitive exclusion principle. Science 131: 1292–1297, 1960.
Whittaker, R. H., S. A. Levin, & R. B. Root.: Niche, habitat, and ecotope. American Naturalist 107: 321–338, 1973.

Habitats

Cold Latitudes and High Mountains

Baker, P. T.: *Human Adaptation to High Altitude*. In: Science 163, 1969.
Bolschakow, W. N.: *Zur Anpassung der Kleinsäugetiere an die Gebirgsverhältnisse*. In: Zoolog. Anz. 180, 1968.
Deschwander, J. S., u. a. (Hg.): *Der Mensch im Klima Zentral- und Ost-Nepals*. In: Khumbu Himal, Bd. 2, Innsbruck/München 1968.
Gaussen, H., u. Barruel, P.: *Montagnes. La vie aux hautes altitudes*. Paris 1955.
Handschin, E.: *Über die Collembolenfauna der Nivalstufe*. In: Revue Suisse Zool. 27, 1919.
Irving, L.: *Adaptations to Cold*. In: Sci. Amer. 214, 1966.
Janetschek, H.: *Tierische Successionen auf hochalpinem Neuland*. Innsbruck 1949.
–: *Das Problem der inneralpinen Eiszeitüberdauerung durch Tiere. Ein Beitrag zur Geschichte des Nivalfauna*. In: Österr. Zool. Zeitschr. 6, 1956.
– : *Arthropod Ecology of South Victoria Land*. In: Antarctic Research Ser. 10, 1967.
Holdgate, M. W. (Hg): *Antarctic Ecology*. London/New York 1970.
Ökologie der alpinen Waldgrenze. Symposion Innsbruck 1966. In: Mitt. der Forstl. Bundesversuchsanst. Wien, 75, 1967.
Reisigl, H.: *Zur Systematik und Ökologie alpines Bodenalgen*. In: Österr. Bot. Zeitschr. 111, 1964.
– : *Die Pflanzenwelt der Alpen*. In: Die Welt der Alpen. Innsbruck/Frankfurt 1970.

Schmölzer, K.: *Die Kartierung von Tiergemeinschaften in der Biozoenotik*. In: Österr. Zool Zeitschr. 4, 1953.
– : *Die Kleintierwelt der Nunatakker als Zeugen einer Eiszeitüberdauerung*. In: Mitt. Zool, Mus. Berlin 38, 1962.
Swan, L. W.: *The Ecology of the High Himalayas*. In: Sci. Amer. 205, 1961.
– : *Ecology of the Heights*. In: Nat. History, Apr. 1963.
Troll, C.: *Studien zur vergleichenden Geographie des Hochgebirge der Erde*. In: Bericht der 23. Hauptversamml. Ges. v. Freunden u. Förderern d. Univ. Bonn, 1941.
– : *Über das Wesen der Hochgebirgsnatur*. In: Jahrb. des Dt. Alpenvereins 80, 1955.
Udvardy, M. D. F.: *Dynamics Zoogeography, with Special Reference to Land Animals*. New York, Van Nostrand Reinhold, 1969.
Walter, H.: *Vegetationszonen und Klima*. Stuttgart 1970.
Zschokke, F.: *Die Tierwelt der Hochgebirgsseen*. Zurich 1900.

Soil

Brauns, A.: *Terricole Dipterenlarven: Puppen terricoler, Dipterenlarven Untersuchungen zur angewandten Bodenbiologie*, 2 Bde., Göttingen u.a. (Musterschmidt) 1954.
– : *Waldinsekten und Streubewohner*. Taschenbuchführer. Braunschweig (Naturhist Museum) ²1966.
– : *Praktische Bodenbiologie*, Stuttgart (G. Fischer) 1968.
– : *Taschenbuch der Waldinsekten*. 2 Bde., Stuttgart (G. Fischer). ²1970.
Dunger, W.: *Unbekanntes Leben im Boden*. Leipzig u. a. (Urania) 1970.
Franz, H.: *Bodenleben und Bodenfruchtbarkeit*. Wien (Hollinek) 1949.
Kás, V.: *Mikroorganismen im Boden*. Wittenberg (Ziemsen) 1966.
Kühnelt, W.: *Bodenbiologie*. Wien (Herold) 1950.
Pallissa, A.: *Bodenzoologie*. Berlin (Akademie-Verlag) 1964.
Schaller, F.: *Die Unterwelt des Tierreiches*. Berlin u. a. (Springer) 1962.
Trolldenier, G.: *Bodenbiologie*. Stuttgart (Franckh) 1971.

Steppes and Savannas

Brown, L.: *Afrika*. München/Zurich (Droemer) 1966.
Harthoorn, A.: *Elefanten als Landschaftsgärtner schwer ersetzbar*. In: Das Tier 12, 1972.
Hendrichs, H.: *Schätzungen der Huftierbiomasse in der Dornbuschsavanne nördlich und westlich der Serengetisteppe in Ostafrika nach einem neuen Verfahren und Bemerkungen zur Biomasse der anderen pflanzenfressenden Tierarten*. In: Säugetierkundl Mitt. 18, 1970.
– : *Beobachtungen und Untersuchungen zur Ökologie und Ethologie, insbesondere zur sozialen Organisation ostafrikanischer Säugetiere*. In: Zeitschr. f. Tierpsychologie 30, 1972.
Kulzer, E.: *Die afrikanische Savanne als Lebensraum*. In: Natur 70, 1962.
Leppik, E.: *Evolutionary Correlation between Plants. Insects, Animals and Soils*. In: Am Societ. Litt. Estonicae in America (Yearbook of the Estonian Learned Society in America) 3, 1959–1963.
Lindsay, G.: *The East African Savannas*. In: Pacific Discovery 23, 1970.
Neill, W.: *The Geography of Life*. New York/London, Columbia Univ. Press 1969.
Peus, F.: *Die ökologische und geographische Determination des Hochmoores als »Steppe«*. In: Veröff. des Naturwiss. Vereins Osnabruck 25, 1950.
Pfeffer, P.: *Asien*. München/Zürich (Droemer) 1969 (Knaurs Kontinente in Farben).
Sanderson, I.: *Nordamerika*. München/Zürich (Droemer) 1962.
Tyler, J.: *Vertebrates in a Prairie Dog Town*. In.: Proceed. Oklahoma Acad. Sci. 50, 1971.
Walter, H.: *Die Bedeutung des Großwildes für die Ausbildung der Pflanzendecke*. In: Stuttgarter Beiträge zur Naturkunde 69, 1961.
– : *Die Vegetation der Erde in ökophysiologischer Betrachtung*. 2 Bde., Jena (G. Fischer) 1964–1968.
Vorontsov, N.: *The Ways of Food Specialization and Evolution of the Alimentary System in Muroidea*. In: Symp. Theriologicum, Prag 1962.

Deserts

Dekeyser, P. L., u. Derivot, J.: *La vie animale au Sahara*. Paris (Colin) 1959.

Dorst, J.: *Südamerika und Mittelamerika.* München/Zürich (Droemer) 1968.
Findlay, R.: *Great American Deserts.* National Geographic Soc., 1972.
Lavauden, L.: *Les vertébrés du Sahara.* Tunis (Guénard) 1926.
Leopold, A. S.: *Die Wüste.* Time-Life International 1970.
Schiffers, H. (Hg.): *Die Sahara und ihre Randgebiete. Darstellung eines Naturgroßraumes.* 3 Bde., München (Weltforum) 1971–1973.
Die Welt in der leben. München/Zürich (Droemer) 1952.

Tropical Rainforests

Bünning, E.: *Der tropische Regenwald.* Berlin u. a. (Springer) 1956.
Fittkau, E. J., u. Klinge, H.: *On Biomass and Trophic Structure of the Central Amazonian Rain Forest Ecosystem.* In: Biotropica, Washington, 1973.
Hueck, K.: *Die Wälder Südamerikas.* Stuttgart (G. Fischer) 1966.
Mertens, R.: *Die Tierwelt des tropischen Regenwaldes.* Frankfurt (W. Kramer) 1948.
Odum, H. T., u. Pigeon, R. I. (Hg.): *A tropical Rainforest. A Study of Irradiation and Ecology at El Verde.* Oak Ridge 1970.
alder der Erde. Stuttgart (Vig. Das Beste) 1969.
Die Wunder des Lebens. München/Zürich (Droemer) 1961.

The Oceans

Deacon, G. E. R.: *Die Meere der Welt. Ihre Eroberung, ihre Geheimnisse.* Stuttgart (Belser) 1963.
—: *Seas, Man and Men. An Atlas-History of Man's Exploration of the Oceans.* Garden City/N.Y., Doubleday 1962.
Dietrich, G., u. Ullrich, J.: *Atlas zur Ozeanographie.* Mannheim (Bibliogr. Institut) 1968.
Fricke, H. W., u. Eibl-Eibesfeldt, I.: *Korallenmeer.* Stuttgart (Belser) 1972.
Günther, K., u. Deckert, K.: *Wunderwelt der Tiefsee.* Berlin (Herbig) 1950.
Heezen, B. C., u. Hollister, C.: *The Face of the Deep.* London (Oxford Univ. Press) 1971.
Hentschel, E.: *Das Leben des Weltmeeres.* Berlin u. a. (Springer) 1929.
—: *Ozeanische Lebensgemeinschaften.* Berlin (Mittler) 1932.
Marshall, N. B.: *Tiefseebiologie.* Jena (G. Fischer) 1961.
— (Hg.): *Aspects of marine Zoology.* London (Acad. Press) 1967.
Miller, R. C.: *Das Meer.* München/Zürich (Droemer) 1969.
Tait, V. R.: *Das Meer als Lebensraum. Meeresökologie.* München (dtv) 1971.
Thorson, G.: *Erforschung des Meeres. Eine Bestandsaufnahme.* München (Kindler) 1972.

Inland Waters

Illies, J.: *Die Lebensgemeinschaft des Bergbachs.* Wittenberg (Ziemsen) 1961 (Neue Brehm-Bücherei, 289).
Lenz, F.: *Biologie der Süßwasserseen.* Berlin (Springer) 1928.
Ruttner, F.: *Grundriß der Limnologie.* Berlin (de Gruyter) 1958.
Schwoerbel, J.: *Einführung in die Limnologie.* Stuttgart (G. Fischer) 1971 (Univ. Taschenb., 31).
Thienemann, A.: *Die Binnengewässer Mitteleuropas.* Stuttgart (Schweizerbart) 1925.
—: *Die Binnengewässer in Natur und Kultur.* Berlin (Springer) 1955.
Welch, P.: *Limnology.* New York, McGraw Hill 1952.
Wesenberg-Lund, C.: *Biologie der Süßwassertiere.* Wien (Springer) 1939.
—: *Biologie der Süßwasserinsekten.* Berlin (Springer) 1943.

Distribution of Animals

Brundin, L.: *Transantarctic Relationships and their Significance, as evidenced by Chironomid Midges.* In: Kungl. Svenska Vetensk. Akad. Handl. 11 (1), 1966.
Illies, J.: *Limnofauna Europaea,* Stuttgart (G. Fischer) 1971.
—: *Einführung in die Tiergeographie.* Stuttgart (G. Fischer) 1971 (Univ. Taschenb., 2).

Keast, A.: *Bird Speciation on the Australian Continent.* In: Bull. Mus. Comp. Zool. 123 (8), 1961.
Kraus, O.: *Taxonomische und tiergeographische Studien an Myriapoden und Araneen aus Zentralamerika.* Diss. Frankfurt/M. 1955.
Lattin, G. de: *Grundriß der Zoogeographie.* Jena (G. Fischer) 1967.
Macarthur, R. H.: *Geographical Ecology. Patterns in the Distribution of Species.* New York 1972.
—, u. Wilson, E. O.: *The Theory of Island Biogeography.* Princeton Univ. Press 1967.
Moreau, R. E.: *The Bird Faunas of Africa and its Islands.* London/New York 1966.
Müller, P.: *The Distribution Centres oᶜ Terrestrial Vertebrates in the Neotropical Region.* Den Haag (Junk) 1973 (Biogeographica, 3).
Reinig, W. F.: *Die Holarktis.* Jena (G. Fischer) 1937.

Man as Environment

Hunter and Gatherer

Bandi, H. G.: *Die Steinzeit. 40 000 Jahre Felsbilder.* Baden-Baden (Holle) 1960.
—, Breuil u. a.: *Die Steinzeit.* Baden-Baden (Holle) 1964.
—, u. Maringer, J.: *Die Kunst der Eiszeit.* Basel (Holbein) 1952.
Graziosi, P.: *Die Kunst der Altsteinzeit.* Stuttgart (Kohlhammer) 1955.
Kühn, H.: *Eiszeitkunst. Die Geschichte ihrer Erforschung.* Göttingen (Musterschmidt) 1965.
— : *Eiszeitmalerei.* München 1956.
— *Die Felsbilder Europas.* Stuttgart (Kohlhammer) 1956.

Domestic Animals

Engelmann, C.: *So leben Hühner, Tauben, Gänse.* Radebeul (Neumann) 1972.
Herre, W.: *Das Ren als Haustier.* Leipzig (Akademie Vlg.) 1955.
— : *Das Tier als Gefährte des Großstadtmenschen.* In: Hochschultage 1967 in Lübeck, 1967.
Herre, W.: *Haustiere—zoologisch gesehen.* Stuttgart (G. Fischer) 1973.
Klein D. R.: *Food Selection by North American Deer and their Response to Over-utilization to prefered Plant Species.* Blackwell Scientific Publications, Oxford/Edinburgh 1970.
Leedsu . Vajda (Hg.): *Man, Culture and Animals.* Washington 1965 (Publ. No. 78 of the American Association for the Advancement of Science).
Otremba, E., u. Kessler, M.: *Die Stellung der Viehwirtschaft im Agrarraum der Erde.* Wiesbaden 1965.
Schinkel, H.-G.: *Haltung, Zucht und Pflege des Viehs bei den Nomaden Ost- und Nordostafrikas.* Berlin (Akademie Verlag) 1970.
Zimen, E.: *Wölfe und Königspudel, vergleichende Verhaltensbeobachtungen.* München (Piper) 1971.

Animals as Food

Harrison, R.: *Tiermaschinen.* München (Biederstein) 1965.
Hornung, E.: *Der Eine und die Vielen.* Darmstadt (Wiss. Buchgesellschaft) 1971.
Illies, J.: *Anthropologie des Tieres.* München (Piper) 1973.
Morus: *Eine Geschichte der Tiere.* Hamburg (Rowohlt) 1952.
Skriver, C. A.: *Der Verrat der Kirchen an den Tieren.* München (Starczewski) 1967.

Animals in the Zoo

Curtis, L.: *Zoological Park Fundamentals.* Washington 1968.
Fisher, J.: *Zoos of the World,* New York 1967.
Grzimek, B.: *Was Zoologische Gärten waren und sind.* In: Hundertjähriger Zoo in Frankfurt a. M., Frankfurt 1958.
Hahn, E.: *Zoos.* London 1968.
Hediger, H.: *Wild Animals in Captivity.* London 1950.
— : *Tierpsychologie im Zoo und im Zirkus.* Basel 1961.

— : *Mensch und Tier im Zoo. Eine Tiergarten-Biologie.* Rüschlikon 1965.

Kirchshofer, R. (H.g): *Zoologische Gärten der Welt—Die Welt des Zoo.* Innsbruck/Frankfurt 1966.

— : *Von Tieren im Zoo.* Innsbruck/Frankfurt 1971.

The Environment of Man

General References:

Bacq, Z. M., u. Alexander, P.: *Fundamentals of Radiobiology.* Oxford, Pergamon Press 1951.

Bodenheimer, F. S.: *Problems of Animal Ecology.* Oxford Univ. Press, 1938.

Buchwald, K., u. Engelhard, W.: *Handbuch fur Landschaftspflege u. Naturschutz.* München (BLV) 1968 ff.

Carr-Saunders, A. M.: *World Population. Past Growth and Present Trends.* Oxford, Clarendon Press 1936.

Carson, R.: *Der stumme Frühling.* München (Biederstein) 1962.

Coenen, Fehrenbach, Fritsch u. a.: *Alternativen zur Umweltkrise. Raubbau oder Partnerschaft?* München (Hanser) 1972.

Commoner, B.: *Science and Survival.* New York Ballantine 1970.

Demoll, R.: *Bändigt den Menschen. Gegen die Natur oder mit ihr?* München (Bruckmann) 1960

Dreyhaupt, F. J.: *Luftreinhaltung als Faktor der Stadtund Regionalplanung.* Köln 1971 (Schriftenr. Umweltschutz, 1).

Ehrlich, P. R. u. A. R.: *Bevölkerungswachstum und Umweltkrise. Die Ökologie des Menschen.* Frankfurt/M. (S. Fischer) 1972.

Franz, J. M., u. Krieg, A.: *Biologische Schädlingsbekämpfung.* Berlin/Hamburg (Parey) 1972.

Galbraith, J. K.: *Gesellschaft im Überfluß.* München/Zürich (Droemer) 1959.

Hayek, F. A.: *Der Weg zur Knechtschaft.* Erlenbach/Zürich 1952.

Kade, G.: *Ökonomische und gesellschaftliche Aspekte des Umweltschutzes.* In: Gewerkschaftl. Monatshefte 22, 1970.

Klein, W.: *Immissionsschutzrecht.* München 1968.

Krawczynski, S. J. B.: *Radioaktive Abfälle. Aufbereitung—Lagerung—Beseitigung.* München (Thiemig) 1967.

Kurzrock, R.: *Probleme der Umweltforschung.* Berlin (Colloquium) 1973.

Leibundgut, H. (Hg.): *Schutz unseres Lebensraumes.* Symposium an der ETH in Zürich. München (BLV) 1971.

Lützenkirchen, W. H.: *Verbrechen ohne Richter. Mord an der Umwelt in der Bundesrepublik.* Köln/Berlin (Kiepenheuer u. Witsch) 1972.

Medizin und Städtebau. 2 Bde., Munchen u. a. 1957.

Müller, W., u. Renger, R.: *Wer verteidigtunsere Umwelt? Grundlagen und Organisation des Umweltschutzes in der Bundesrepublik.* Köln (Wissensch. u. Politik) 1972.

Olschowy, G. (Hg.): *Belastete Landschaft—Gefährdete Umwelt.* München (Goldmann) 1972.

Pauling, L.: *Leben oder Tod im Atomzeitalter.* Wien (Sensen) 1960.

Polikarpov, G. G.: *Radioecology of Aquatic Organisms. The Accumulation and Biological Effect of Radioactive Substances.* Amsterdam, North Holland Publ. 1966.

Samuelson, P. A.: *Volkswirtschaftslehre.* Bd. 1, Köln 1970.

Schultze, H. (Hg.): *Umwelt-Report. Unser verschmutzter Planet.* Frankfurt/M. (Umschau) 1973.

Schuphan, W.: *Lebensform und Landwirtschaft in ihren Wechselbeziehungen* In: Gesundes Land—Gesundes Leben. München (Pflaum) 1953.

— : *Zur Qualität der Nahrungspflanzen.* München u. a. (BLV) 1961.

Sioli, H. (Hg.): *Ökologie und Lebensschutz in internationaler Sicht.* Freiburg i. B. (Rombach) 1973.

Sternglass, E. J.: *Low Level Radiation.* New York, Ballantine 1972.

Tamplin, A. R., u. Gofman, J. W.: *»Population Control« through Nuclear Pollution.* Chicago, Nelson Hall 1970.

Umweltschutz. *Das Umweltprogramm der Bundesregierung.* Einf. D Genscher. Stuttgart (Kohlhammer) 1972.

Vester, F.: *Das Überlebensprogramm.* München (Kindler) 1972.

Wagner, F.: *Die Wissenschaft und die gefährdete Welt. Eine Wissenschaftssoziologie der Atomphysik.* München (Beck) 1969.

Weish, P., u. Gruber, E,: *Atomwirtschaft und Umweltsituation. Die Radiointoxikation der Biosphäre.* Frankfurt/M. 1973.

Weizsäcker, E. v.: *Humanökologie und Umweltschutz.* München (Kösel) 1972.

On Environmental Problems

Cook, E.: *Energy for millenium three.* Technology Review 75(2): 16–23 1972.

Hardin, G.: *The tragedy of the commons.* Science 162: 1243–1248, 1968.

Miles, Rufus E.: *Man's population predicament.* Popul. Bulletin 27(2): 1–39, 1971.

Murdoch, William W., ed.: *Environment, Resources, Pollution, and Society.* 1971.

Hinkley, Alden D.: *Applied Ecology: a Nontechnical Approach.* New York: Macmillan 1975.

Wagner, Richard H.: *Environment and Man.* New York: Norton 1971

Picture Credits

Photographs: Dr. Altenkirch, Göttingen (p. 155 right, p. 156 upper left). Dr. Ant, Hamm (p. 558 lower left and right, p. 577 bottom). ARDEA, London (p. 137 top, p. 341 lower middle, p. 512 first row right). Prof. Ax, Göttingen (p. 327, 328, 333, 334). Barrenberger/ZEFA, Düsseldorf (p. 568 upper left). Bavaria, Munich (p. 258 above). Bertram-Luftbild, Munich (Riem) (p. 655 above; perm. government of Upper Bavaria G 4/26 614). Biedermann/ZEFA (p. 182 lower left, p. 384 upper left). Big Mike/ZEFA (p. 646 above). Bisserot/Photo Researchers, England (p. 138 upper right). Bonath/ZEFA (p. 182 upper right). Bonnacker/Mauritius, Mittenwald (p. 192 bottom). Dr. Bracht, Amberg (p. 240 upper right). Prof. Brauns, Braunschweig (p. 221, 222, 227, 228). Dr. Brehm, Schlitz (p. 64). Breninger, Munich (p. 210 lower right). Burton/Photo Researchers (p. 54 right, p. 343 lower left, p. 357 top, second row middle). Prof. Caspers, Hamburg (p. 63). Collignon, Munich (p. 182, second picture right, p. 239 lower left). Colorphoto Hinz, Basel (p. 449). Deutsche Luftbild KG, Hamburg (p. 548 bottom, p. 645 lower left). dpa, Frankfurt (p. 512, second row left). Everts/ZEFA (p. 568 lower right). Dr. Felten, Frankfurt (p. 341 top). Dr. Fittkau, Plön (p. 268 lower middle, p. 286 top, middle left and bottom, p. 295 all pictures except lower left, p. 384 upper right, p. 393 bottom, p. 394 upper left) Friedmann/Mauritius (p. 393 top). Geeserer/Bavarian Ministry of Development and the Environment, Munich (p. 646 lower right). Dr. Geisler, Gundelfingen (p. 394 middle left and right, bottom right). George, Hamburg (p. 258 lower left, p. 267 upper left and middle, p. 268 upper left and middle, middle, lower left and right). Prof. Gerlach, Bremerhaven (p. 645 top). Grøndal, Vienna (p. 181 top and bottom). Gruhl, Farchant (p. 341 lower left, p. 343 second row from top left). Hackenberg/ZEFA (p. 568 lower left). Dr. Haefelfinger, Basel (p. 357 upper left, middle and right). Harz, Gröbenzell (p. 156 upper right). Heilmann/ZEFA (p. 547 upper left). Dr. von Hesler, Frankfurt (p. 655 all three pictures bottom, p. 656 bottom). Prof. Illies, Schlitz (p. 257 top, p. 384 all four pictures bottom). Interholc, Vienna (p. 89 top). Prof. Janetschek, Innsbruck (p. 191, second picture left). Kanus/Bavaria (p. 239 lower right, p. 258 lower right). Dr. Kinzer, Kiel (p. 357, top second row left and bottom). Dr. Kirchshofer, Frankfurt (p. 505, first row left and right, second and fourth row right, p. 506 first row left and right, p. 511 first and third row left, p. 512 first row left, third and fourth row left and right). Köster, Munich (p. 342 lower right, p. 343 upper left). Kramann/Mauritius (p. 182 lower right). Landesbildstelle Rheinland-Pfalz, Koblenz (p. 577 upper right). Landesbildstelle Württemberg, Stuttgart (p. 567 lower right). Layer, Mannheim (p. 383 upper middle). Leidmann/Bavaria (p. 240 lower right). Lummer/ZEFA (p. 512 second row right, p. 588 second row middle).

Magnussen/Mauritius (p. 567 upper right). Man/ZEFA (p. 258 lower middle). Marcuse, Munich (p. 143 bottom). Prof. Matthes, Erlangen (p. 89 middle and bottom). Dr. Meijering, Schlitz (p. 54 left from top to bottom). Moog, Kettwig (p. 557 and p. 558 top, p. 577 upper left, p. 656 top). Mosauer, Altenmarkt (p. 557 bottom). Dr. Mühlenberg, (p. 118 upper left). Müller/roebild, Frankfurt (p. 156 bottom). Müller/ZEFA (p. 547 upper right). Müller-Schwarze/Okapia (p. 191 bottom). Dr. Muuß, Altenholz/Kiel (p. 547 lower left, p. 645 lower right, p. 548 upper left and right). Muschenetz/Bavaria (p. 267 lower middle and right). Nieuwenhuizen, Holland (p. 394 lower left). Okapia, Frankfurt (p. 143 upper right, p. 240 lower left, p. 296 lower left and right, p. 505 second and fourth row left, third row left and right, p. 511 all pictures except first and third row left, p. 578 upper left and right, p. 587 upper left and lower right, p. 588 first row right and second row left). Ott/Photo Researchers (p. 182 upper left, p. 588 bottom). Oxford Scientific Films Ltd./Photo Researchers (p. 383, second row, first, second and third picture). Paysan, Stuttgart (p. 312 top, p. 383 upper left). Pfletschinger/Bavaria (p. 90 right, p. 137 lower left and right). Power/Photo Researchers (p. 342 top, p. 343 lower right). Quedens, Amrum (p. 309). Rastl, Bad Aussee (p. 192 top, p. 210 all pictures except lower right). Reimer/Mauritius (p. 343, second row from bottom left and right). Reiserer/Bavaria (p. 588, second row right). Revers-Widauer/ZEFA (p. 578 middle). roebild, Frankfurt (p. 209). Dr. Roer, Bonn (p. 267 upper right). Root/Okapia (p. 240 upper left, p. 588 first row left). Dr. Rüppell, Erlangen (p. 191 upper left and right, p. 312 lower right, p. 394 upper right). Sankhala/Okapia (p. 587 upper right). Dr. Sauer, Munich (p. 138 upper right and bottom). Dr. Sauer/Bavaria (p. 90 lower left, p. 383 second row right edge, lower right and left). Dr. Sauer/ZEFA (p. 90 upper left). Scharf/roebild (p. 267 lower left). Schmida, Braunschweig (p. 239 top, p. 312 lower left). Scholz/Bavaria (p. 296 top). Schulze/Bavaria (p. 450 top). Prof. Schremmer, Heidelberg (p. 90 middle left, p. 117, p. 118 all pictures except left top, p. 123, p. 124 all pictures except lower left, p. 295 lower left). Schrempp, Oberrimsingen (p. 155 left from top to bottom). Dr. Schultze-Westrum, Assenhausen (p. 144 right, p. 285, p. 286 middle right, p. 450 bottom, p. 578 lower left and right). Siewert/Mauritius (p. 267 middle). Sillner, Großschwarzenlohe (p. 341 lower right, p. 342 lower left, p. 343 upper right). Skobe/Mauritius (p. 343 second row from top, right). Sommer/ZEFA (p. 568 upper right). Suominen/Anthony, Starnberg (p. 383 upper right). Strass/ZEFA (p. 257 bottom). Teasy/ZEFA (p. 646 lower left). Thau/Bavaria (p. 588 first row middle). Dr. Thiel, Hamburg (p. 358 left and right). Vetter/ZEFA (p. 547 lower left). Wachsmann/ZEFA (p. 567 upper left). Dr. Wickler, Seewiesen (p. 143

upper left, p. 144 all pictures left, p. 567 lower left). ZEFA, Düsseldorf (p. 53, p. 587 lower left).

Color plates: painted by K. Großmann, Frankfurt (pp. 310/311; p. 344; all plates in Chapter 19; Prof. P. Müller, Saarbrücken, consultant).

Black-and-white drawings: E. Diller, Munich (pp. 245 bottom, to 255, 260, 262 top, 265, 280 bottom). K. Großmann (pp. 126, 127, 130, Chapter 12, pp. 262/263 bottom, 324/325 bottom). H. Huber, Munich (pp. 69, 72/73, 175, 178, 179, 184, 185, 200 bottom, 270, 271, 273, 277, 278/279, 280 top, Chapter 20). K. Steffel, Munich (Chapters 1, 2 and 3, pp. 70, 71, 72, 73, 74, 75, Chapter 5, pp. 93, 98 top, Chapter 9, pp. 172, 173, 180, 188, 189, 198, 199, 242, 243, 244, 245 top, 259, 272, 275, 276, 281, 302, 306, 308, 314, 317, 319, 321, 323, 324 top, 325 top, 331, 336, 337, 345, 347, 362, 387-389, 391-406, 412, 415, 422, 425, 427, 432, 435, 438, Chapter 21, Chapter 22; Part II: Chapter 1, pp. 550, 551, 554, Chapters 3 and 11). G. Thiele, Munich (pp. 363-370, 552). R. Thiele, Munich (pp. 300/301, Chapter 24). G. Wankmüller, Munich (Chapter 13, pp. 315, 330, 372; Part II: Chapter 7). Original drawings from the authors: W. Altenkirch (Chapter 10). P. Ax (pp. 330, 331 and 346). H.-P. Bulnheim, (pp. 320, 321). E. J. Fittkau (pp. 288/289, 290, 291, 303, 304). S. Husmann (pp. 372 bottom, 373 to 381). J. Illies (pp. 390, 398). H. Janetschek (pp. 196, 197, 200 top). D. Matthes (pp. 86, 91 to 93, 97 to100). P. Rietschel (Chapter 23). F. Schremmer (Chapter 7, pp. 131 to 133). J. Schwoerbel (pp. 382-386). P. Weish and E. Gruber (Part II: Chapter 10). Photo layout: G. Wankmüller, Munich

Conversion Tables of Metric to U.S. and British Systems

U.S. Customary to Metric		Metric to U.S. Customary	

—— Length ——

To convert	Multiply by	To convert	Multiply by
in. to mm.	25.4	mm. to in.	0.039
in. to cm.	2.54	cm. to in.	0.394
ft. to m.	0.305	m. to ft.	3.281
yd. to m.	0.914	m. to yd.	1.094
mi. to km.	1.609	km. to mi.	0.621

—— Area ——

sq. in. to sq. cm.	6.452	sq. cm. to sq. in.	0.155
sq. ft. to sq. mi.	0.093	sq. m. to sq. ft.	10.764
sq. yd. to sq. m.	0.836	sq. m. to sq. yd.	1.196
sq. mi. to ha.	258.999	ha. to sq. mi.	0.004

—— Volume ——

cu. in. to cc.	16.387	cc. to cu. in.	0.061
cu. ft. to cu. m.	0.028	cu. m. to cu. ft.	35.315
cu. yd. to cu. m.	0.765	cu. m. to cu. yd.	1.308

—— Capacity (liquid) ——

fl. oz. to liter	0.03	liter to fl. oz.	33.815
qt. to liter	0.946	liter to qt.	1.057
gal. to liter	3.785	liter to gal.	0.264

—— Mass (weight) ——

oz. avdp. to g.	28.35	g. to oz. avdp.	0.035
lb. avdp. to kg.	0.454	kg. to lb. avdp.	2.205
ton to t.	0.907	t. to ton	1.102
l. t. to t.	1.016	t. to l. t.	0.984

Abbreviations

U.S. Customary	Metric
avdp.—avoirdupois	cc.—cubic centimeter(s)
ft.—foot, feet	cm.—centimeter(s)
gal.—gallon(s)	cu.—cubic
in.—inch(es)	g.—gram(s)
lb.—pound(s)	ha.—hectare(s)
l. t.—long ton(s)	kg.—kilogram(s)
mi.—mile(s)	m.—meter(s)
oz.—ounce(s)	mm.—millimeter(s)
qt.—quart(s)	t.—metric ton(s)
sq.—square	
yd.—yard(s)	

By kind permission of Walker: Mammals of the World
©1968 Johns Hopkins Press, Baltimore, Md., U.S.A.

TEMPERATURE

AREA

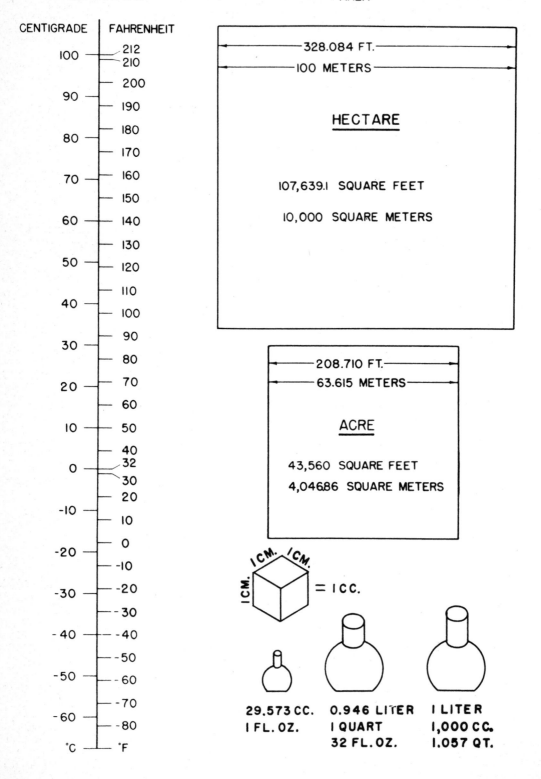

CENTIGRADE **FAHRENHEIT**

CENTIGRADE	FAHRENHEIT
100	212 / 210
90	200 / 190
80	180 / 170
70	160 / 150
60	140 / 130
50	120 / 110
40	100 / 90
30	80 / 70
20	60 / 50
10	40 / 32 / 30 / 20
0	10 / 0
-10	-10
-20	-20 / -30
-30	-40
-40	-50 / -60
-50	-70
-60	-80
°C	°F

HECTARE

328.084 FT.

100 METERS

107,639.1 SQUARE FEET

10,000 SQUARE METERS

ACRE

208.710 FT.

63.615 METERS

43,560 SQUARE FEET

4,046.86 SQUARE METERS

I CM. I CM. I CM. = I CC.

29.573 CC.
I FL. OZ.

0.946 LITER
I QUART
32 FL. OZ.

I LITER
1,000 CC.
1.057 QT.

WEIGHT

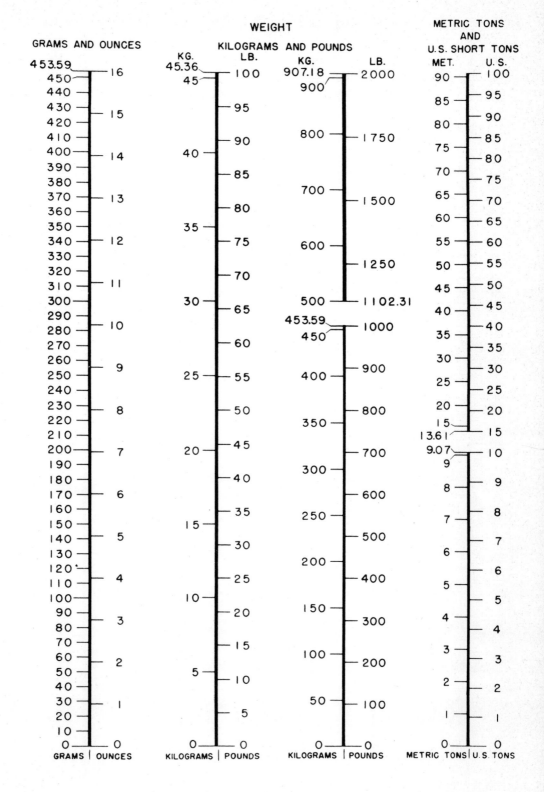

GRAMS AND OUNCES

KILOGRAMS AND POUNDS

METRIC TONS AND U.S. SHORT TONS

LENGTH: MILLIMETERS AND INCHES

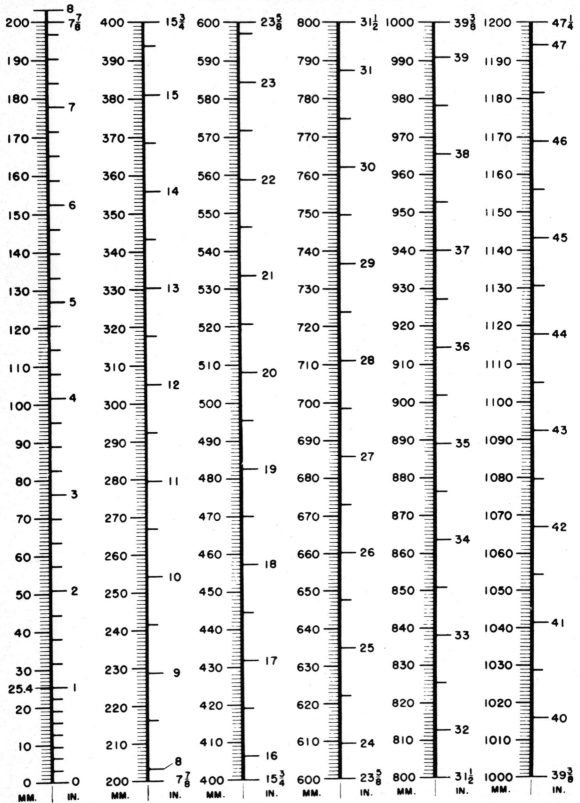

LENGTH

METERS AND FEET

KILOMETERS AND MILES

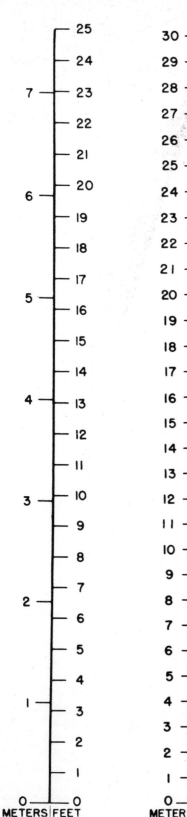

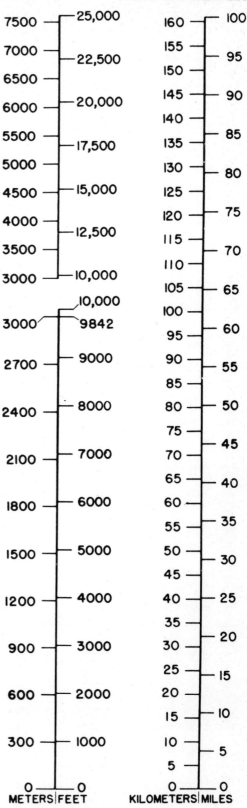

Index